$5.45

READINGS|FROM
**SCIENTIFIC
AMERICAN**

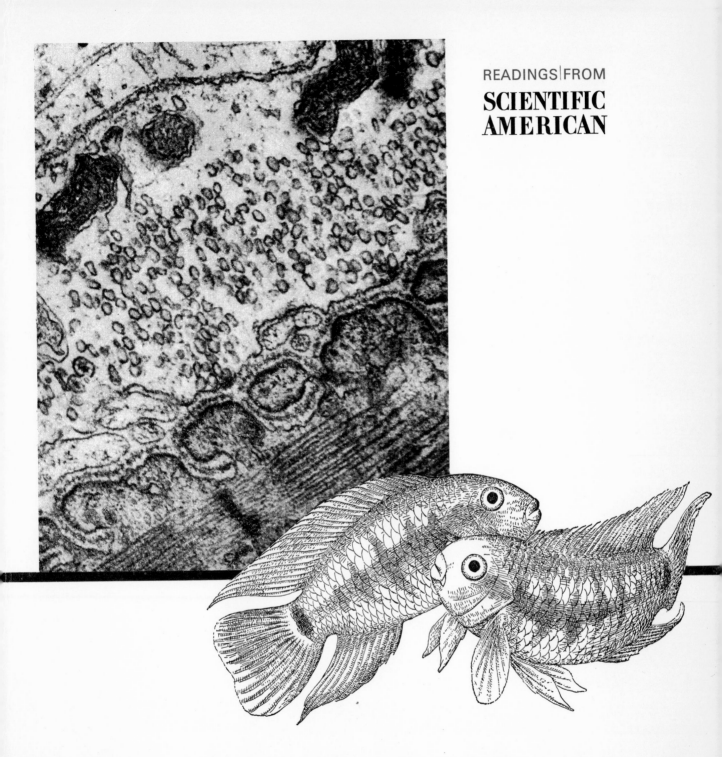

# PSYCHOBIOLOGY
## The Biological Bases of Behavior

*Introductions by James L. McGaugh · Norman M. Weinberger · Richard E. Whalen*

Readings from
## SCIENTIFIC AMERICAN

# PSYCHOBIOLOGY
## The Biological Bases of Behavior

WITH INTRODUCTIONS BY *James L. McGaugh, Norman M. Weinberger,*
*Richard E. Whalen* UNIVERSITY OF CALIFORNIA, IRVINE

 W. H. Freeman and Company SAN FRANCISCO AND LONDON

Each of the SCIENTIFIC AMERICAN articles in *Psychobiology* is available as a separate Offprint at twenty cents each. For a complete listing of approximately 550 articles now available as Offprints, write to W. H. Freeman and Company, 660 Market Street, San Francisco, California 94104.

Printed in the United States of America.     (*B2*)
Library of Congress Catalog Card Number: 67-12182.

# PREFACE

Our understanding of the biological bases of behavior has been aided by research in numerous disciplines. Ethology, psychology, neurology, neurophysiology, biochemistry, endocrinology, pharmacology, psychiatry, and anthropology have all contributed significantly to man's endeavors to understand the mechanisms responsible for behavior. Over the past two decades, many of these research findings have appeared in summarizing articles in SCIENTIFIC AMERICAN. These articles, written by leading scientists, provide highly readable accounts of research progress in each area.

This volume brings together 45 articles that are concerned with the biological bases of behavior. Not all areas of psychobiology are covered, but the present collection does provide representative views of some of the exciting findings of recent psychobiological research. The book is organized into ten sections. The first three introduce the problems of animal behavior and discuss some of the physiological mechanisms involved. The next sections (IV, V, and VI) deal with problems of learning, memory, motivation, and emotion. Sections VII, VIII, and IX are concerned with perceptual processes and brain mechanisms. The final section concerns psychopharmacology—that is, the effects of drugs on behavior.

The contents and organization of the present volume reflect our attempts to provide material that will both pique the interest of the reader and introduce him to some of the basic problem areas of psychobiology. We have successfully utilized a preliminary edition of this collection in an introductory course in the biological sciences, where systematic treatment of the biological bases of behavior is often neglected. It is our hope that the availability of the following articles as a bound collection will help stimulate instruction in psychobiology in similar courses in both psychology and biology.

September, 1966

JAMES L. MCGAUGH
NORMAN M. WEINBERGER
RICHARD E. WHALEN

# CONTENTS

---

*Note on cross-references:* References to articles included in this book are noted by the title of the article and the page on which it begins; references to articles that are available as offprints but are not included here are noted by the article's title and offprint number; references to articles published by SCIENTIFIC AMERICAN but which are not available as offprints are noted by the title of the article and the month and year of its publication.

# Part I

## ANIMAL BEHAVIOR

# I

## ANIMAL BEHAVIOR

*Introduction*   If organisms are to survive, they must be adapted to their environments. Some of the adaptations are of a morphological nature, such as the structural characteristics of the lung in air-breathing animals; some of the adaptations are of a physiological nature, such as the regulation of body temperature by shivering; and some of the adaptations are of a behavioral nature, such as the nest-building activities of birds. Each type of adaptation helps the animal to survive, to reproduce, and thereby to maintain his species.

In the United States, the study of behavioral adaptations has been pursued by psychologists and biologists who have been predominantly concerned with mechanisms of adaptation, such as sensory and perceptual processes, motivational states, and the nature of learning. In Europe, behavior has been studied predominantly by a group of biologists, known as ethologists, who have examined the instincts and behavioral adaptations as they occur in the field. Psychologists and biologists have both made important contributions to our understanding of how animals behave and of the mechanisms that control behavior. The present section illustrates the problems studied by these workers and the physical and conceptual tools they use in behavior analysis.

The first step in the analysis of a behavior pattern must be a thorough description of the behavior. However, a scientist cannot proceed to analyze behavior effectively if he does not understand the dimensions and variability of the behavior. In "The Curious Behavior of the Stickleback" (page 5) N. Tinbergen, one of the leading contemporary ethologists, provides a description of the fascinating reproductive behavior of stickleback fish. The behavior of these animals is quite complex, yet it is stereotyped in the sense that all male sticklebacks show the same components in the reproductive behavior sequence: nest building, courtship, egg laying and fertilization, and care of the eggs and young. As Tinbergen points out, each step in the sequence is under the control of specific external "sign" stimuli and internal drive states.

At a quite different evolutionary level, S. L. Washburn and I. DeVore describe "The Social Life of Baboons" (page 10). The authors' naturalistic studies provide the basis for analyses of troop cohesion and self-preservation. Washburn and DeVore note that troops are "organized" in such a way that the more powerful members of the group are so distributed as to be able to protect the more vulnerable members from predators. Of particular interest is their finding of the symbiotic relationship that baboons form with impalas to maximize the safety of each group.

The interaction of the baboon and impala is dependent upon the keen eyesight of the baboon and the fine sense of smell of the impala. This "dominance" of a particular sensory system is fairly typical in animals. Each species usually has one sense system that mediates most of the social interactions between members of the species, as well as between it and other species. In the salmon, the sense of smell plays an important role in the life cycle. Salmon are hatched in fresh river waters, migrate to the sea, where they spend several years maturing, and then return to the rivers to spawn. The surprising thing is that, more often than one would expect, for their own spawning activities the salmon return to the very tributary where they were hatched. A. D. Hasler and J. A. Larsen, in "The Homing Salmon" (page 20), describe their experiments, which suggest that this navigational feat is accomplished by the salmons' ability to smell the chemicals in the water.

Although the special sensory capabilities of animals help to determine their behavior and aid their survival, these special capacities present problems to the investigator. In many instances, years of careful research are needed to reveal the nature of the physical energies to which animals respond. The mechanisms that control foraging in bees is a good case in point. It is well known that when foraging bees find food they return to the hive and communicate to their hivemates the direction and distance of the food source. The classic work of Karl von Frisch showed that part of this process depends upon the bee's ability to perceive polarized light. In "Sound Communication in Honeybees" (page 24) A. Wenner reveals that the communication process also depends upon sound transmission between members of the hive. Again we see that an understanding of an animal's sensory system is necessary for an understanding of its behavior.

The differences between species in their sensory capacities and behavior are the result of the different evolutionary pressures that species have experienced. As has often been pointed out by Konrad Lorenz, the "father" of modern ethology, behavior, as much as structure, has evolved. This, of course, means that in some sense the behavior of the animal is "coded in his genes." By this phrase, some theorists mean that miniature control systems exist in the brain, which determine how the animal will behave. Thus, frequent references are made in the scientific literature to "hunger centers," "aggression centers," and "sex centers," located in particular regions of the brain. These centers are thought to be formed by gene action. This notion of how genes influence behavior does have some validity, but it has led to great controversies about the nature of "inherited behavior."

Contemporary research on how genes influence behavior does not maintain that genes control specific behavior centers, but stresses the investigation of how individual differences in genetic makeup lead to individual differences in behavior. This concept of "individual differences" has led scientists away from comparing the behavior patterns of a variety of phylogenetically very different animals to the comparison of the behavior of individuals with very similar gene patterns. For this work, some scientists have developed highly inbred strains of animals; others have worked with naturally occurring, related species of animals. The latter technique is used by both Lorenz, in "The Evolution of Behavior (page 33), and W. C. Dilger, "The Behavior of Lovebirds" (page 45).

Lorenz outlines the use and value of the comparative approach in the analysis of the display behavior. Important points which Lorenz makes are that behavior can be a valuable taxonomic characteristic for distinguishing closely related species, and that behavior characteristics are highly resistant to evolutionary change. Dilger's work also reveals the fruitfulness of the study of comparative behavior. Using lovebirds of different but closely related species, Dilger is able to define a phylogenetic hierarchy, in which recently evolved patterns of behavior are distinguished from phylogenetically old patterns.

Dilger also described his important crossbreeding experiments, which show that with much experience lovebirds can compensate for maladaptive behavior patterns that are inherited. This clear demonstration of the interaction between what is inherited and what is learned is important because it provides a model for the analysis of all behavior. It is almost certainly true that all behavior, even the so-called instincts, are the result of both genetic and experiential influences.

# 1

# THE CURIOUS BEHAVIOR OF THE STICKLEBACK

N. TINBERGEN                                    December 1952

WHEN I was a young lecturer in zoology at the University of Leyden 20 years ago, I was asked to organize a laboratory course in animal behavior for undergraduates. In my quest for animals that could be used for such a purpose, I remembered the sticklebacks I had been accustomed as a boy to catch in the ditches near my home and to raise in a backyard aquarium. It seemed that they might be ideal laboratory animals. They could be hauled in numbers out of almost every ditch; they were tame and hardy and small enough to thrive in a tank no larger than a hatbox.

I soon discovered that in choosing these former pets I had struck oil. They are so tame that they submit unfrightened to laboratory experiments, for the stickleback, like the hedgehog, depends on its spines for protection and is little disturbed by handling. Furthermore, the stickleback turned out to be an excellent subject for studying innate behavior, which it displays in some remarkably dramatic and intriguing ways. We found it to be the most reliable of various experimental animals that we worked with (including newts, bees, water insects and birds), and it became the focus of a program of research in which we now use hundreds of sticklebacks each year. The stickleback today is also a popular subject in various other zoological laboratories in Europe, notably at the universities in Groningen and Oxford. To us this little fish is what the rat is to many American psychologists.

My collaborator J. van Iersel and I have concentrated on the stickleback's courtship and reproductive behavior. The sex life of the three-spined stickleback (*Gasterosteus aculeatus*) is a complicated pattern, purely instinctive and automatic, which can be observed and manipulated almost at will.

In nature sticklebacks mate in early spring in shallow fresh waters. The mating cycle follows an unvarying ritual, which can be seen equally well in the natural habitat or in our tanks. First each male leaves the school of fish and stakes out a territory for itself, from which it will drive any intruder, male or female. Then it builds a nest. It digs a shallow pit in the sand bottom, carrying the sand away mouthful by mouthful. When this depression is about two inches square, it piles in a heap of weeds, preferably thread algae, coats the material with a sticky substance from its kidneys and shapes the weedy mass into a mound with its snout. It then bores a tunnel in the mound by wriggling through it. The tunnel, slightly shorter than an adult fish, is the nest.

Having finished the nest, the male suddenly changes color. Its normally inconspicuous gray coloring had already begun to show a faint pink blush on the chin and a greenish gloss on the back and in the eyes. Now the pink becomes a bright red and the back turns a bluish white.

IN THIS colorful, conspicuous dress the male at once begins to court females. They, in the meantime, have also become ready to mate: their bodies have grown shiny and bulky with 50 to 100 large eggs. Whenever a female enters the male's territory, he swims toward her in a series of zigzags—first a sideways turn away from her, then a quick movement toward her. After each advance the male stops for an instant and then performs another zigzag. This dance continues until the female takes notice and swims toward the male in a curious head-up posture. He then turns and swims rapidly toward the nest, and she follows. At the nest the male makes a series of rapid thrusts with his snout into the entrance. He turns on his side

as he does so and raises his dorsal spines toward his mate. Thereupon, with a few strong tail beats, she enters the nest and rests there, her head sticking out from one end and her tail from the other. The male now prods her tail base with rhythmic thrusts, and this causes her to lay her eggs. The whole courtship and egg-laying ritual takes only about one minute. As soon as she has laid her eggs, the female slips out of the nest. The male then glides in quickly to fertilize the clutch. After that he chases the female away and goes looking for another partner.

One male may escort three, four or even five females through the nest, fertilizing each patch of eggs in turn. Then his mating impulse subsides, his color darkens and he grows increasingly hostile to females. Now he guards the nest from predators and "fans" water over the eggs with his breast fins to enrich their supply of oxygen and help them to hatch. Each day the eggs need more oxygen and the fish spends more time ventilating them. The ventilating reaches a climax just before the eggs hatch. For a day or so after the young emerge the father keeps the brood together, pursuing each straggler and bringing it back in his mouth. Soon the young sticklebacks become independent and associate with the young of other broods.

TO GET light on the behavior of man, particularly his innate drives and conflicts, it is often helpful to study the elements of behavior in a simple animal. Here is a little fish that exhibits a complicated pattern of activities, all dependent on simple stimuli and drives. We have studied and analyzed its behavior by a large number of experiments, and have learned a good deal about why the stickleback behaves as it does.

Let us begin with the stimulus that

causes one stickleback to attack another. Early in our work we noticed that a male patrolling its territory would attack a red-colored intruder much more aggressively than a fish of some other color. Even a red mail van passing our windows at a distance of 100 yards could make the males in the tank charge its glass side in that direction. To investigate the reactions to colors we made a number of rough models of sticklebacks and painted some of the dummies red, some pale silver, some green. We rigged them up on thin wires and presented them one by one to the males in the tank. We found that the red models were always more provoking than the others, though even the silvery or green intruders caused some hostility.

In much the same way we tested the influence of shape, size, type of body movement and other stimuli, relating them to specific behavior in nest building, courting, attack, zigzag, fanning and so on. We discovered, for example, that a male swollen with food was courted as if it were a female.

As our work proceeded, we saw that the effective stimuli differed from one reaction to another, even when two reactions were caused by the same object. Thus a female will follow a red model wherever it leads; she will even make frantic efforts to enter a non-existent nest wherever the model is poked into the sand. Once she is in a real nest, she can be induced to spawn merely by prodding the base of her tail with a glass rod, even after she has seen the red fish that led her there removed. At one moment the male must give the visual signal of red; at the next, this stimulus is of no importance and only the tactile sensation counts. This observation led us to conclude that the stickleback responds simply to "sign stimuli," i.e., to a few characteristics of an object rather than to the object as a whole. A red fish or a red mail truck, a thrusting snout or a glass rod—it is the signal, not the object, that counts. A similar dependence on sign stimuli, which indicates the existence of special central nervous mechanisms, has been found in other species. It seems to be typical of innate behavior, and many social relationships in animals apparently are based on a system of signs.

Sticklebacks will respond to our stimuli only when they are in breeding condition. At other seasons they ignore the signs. This fact led us to investigate the internal factors that govern the fish. The obvious way to study such fluctuations is to measure the frequency and intensity of a response under standard stimulation. For some of these tests we used either uniform models or live fish confined in glass tubes so that we could control their movement. To measure the parental drive we adopted the standard of the number of seconds spent in fan-

**MALE STICKLEBACK** (*Gasterosteus aculeatus*) is photographed in full sexual markings. Its underside is a bright vermilion; its eyes, blue.

**MALE STICKLEBACK DIGS** in the sand after it has perceived its image in a mirror. This is one aspect of its behavior during a fight with another male.

**IN FIRST STAGE** of courtship the male stickleback (*left*) zigzags toward the female (*right*). The female then swims toward him with her head up. The abdomen of the female bulges with from 50 to 100 eggs.

**IN SECOND STAGE,** seen from above, the male stickleback swims toward the nest he has built and makes a series of thrusts into it with his snout. He also turns on his side and raises his dorsal spines toward the female.

ning a given number of eggs per time unit.

The stickleback's drives in the breeding sequence wax and wane in a series of cycles. Each drive runs its course in regular succession: first the male gets the urge to fight, then to build a nest, then to court a female, then to develop the brood. He will not start to build, even though material is available, until he has defended his territory for a while. Nor will he court until he has built the nest; females that approach him before the nest is finished are driven off or at best are greeted with a few zigzags. Within each cycle also there is a fixed rhythm and sequence; for example, if you fill up the pit the male has dug, he will dig one again before collecting nest material. After the pit has been filled

several times, however, the fish will build the nest without completing the pit. The development of his inner drive overcomes outside interference.

It seems likely that the rise and fall of inner drives is controlled by hormonal changes, and we are now studying the effects on these drives of castrating and giving hormones to the males. One interesting finding so far is that castration abolishes the first phases of mating, but has no effect on the parental drive. A eunuch stickleback, when given a nest of eggs, ventilates it with abandon.

I N ANY animal the innate drives themselves are only the elementary forces of behavior. It is the interaction among those drives, giving rise to conflicts, that shapes the animal's actual be-

havior, and we have devoted a major part of our work with the stickleback to this subject. It struck us, as it has often struck observers of other animals, that the belligerent male sticklebacks spent little time in actual fighting. Much of their hostility consists of display. The threat display of male sticklebacks is of two types. When two males meet at the border of their territories, they begin a series of attacks and retreats. Each takes the offensive in his own territory, and the duel seesaws back and forth across the border. Neither fish touches the other; the two dart back and forth as though attached by an invisible thread. This behavior demonstrates that the tendency to attack and the tendency to retreat are both aroused in each fish.

When the fight grows in vigor, how-

**IN THIRD STAGE,** also seen from above, the female swims into the nest. The male then prods the base of her tail and causes her to lay her eggs. When the female leaves the nest, the male enters and fertilizes the eggs.

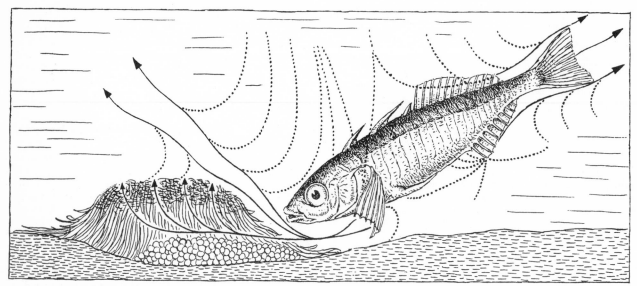

**IN FOURTH STAGE** the male "fans" water over the eggs to enrich their oxygen supply. The dotted lines show the movement of a colored solution placed in the tank; the solid lines, the direction of the water currents.

ever, the seesaw maneuver may suddenly change into something quite different. Each fish adopts an almost vertical head-down posture, turns its side to its opponent, raises its ventral spines and makes jerky movements with the whole body. Under crowded conditions, when territories are small and the fighting tendency is intense, both fish begin to dig into the sand, as if they were starting to build a nest! This observation at first astonished us. Digging is so irrelevant to the fighting stimulus that it seemed to overthrow all our ideas about the specific connection between sign and response. But it became less mysterious when we considered similar instances of incongruous behavior by other animals. Fighting starlings always preen themselves between bouts; in the midst

of a fight roosters often peck at the ground as though feeding, and wading-birds assume a sleeping posture. Even a man, in situations of embarrassment, conflict or stress, will scratch himself behind the ear.

So it appears that the stickleback does not start digging because its nest-building drive is suddenly activated. Rather, the fish is engaging in what a psychologist would call a "displacement activity." Alternating between the urge to attack and to escape, neither of which it can carry out, it finally is driven by its tension to find an outlet in an irrelevant action.

THE THEORY of displacement activity has been tested by the following experiment. We place a red model

in a male's territory and, when the fish attacks, beat it as hard as we can with its supposed antagonist. This unexpected behavior causes the fish to flee and hide in the weeds. From that shelter it glares at the intruder. Its flight impulse gradually subsides and its attack drive rises. After a few minutes the fish emerges from shelter and cautiously approaches the model. Then, just at the moment when attack and retreat are evenly balanced, it suddenly adopts the head-down posture.

A similar interaction of drives seems to motivate the male when he is courting. In the zigzag dance the movement away from the female is the purely sexual movement of leading; the movement toward her is an incipient attack. This duality can be proved by measur-

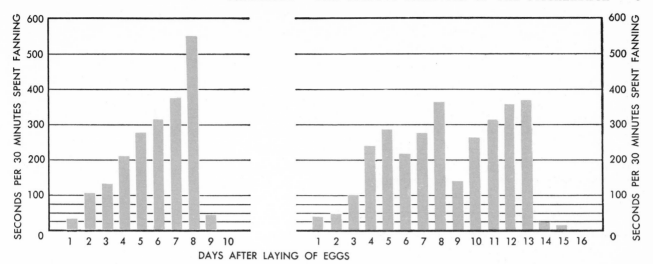

**FANNING OF EGGS** by the male stickleback follows a predictable pattern, as shown by the graph at the left. The fish spends more and more time fanning from the first day until the eighth. By the tenth day it has stopped fanning altogether. The graph at the right shows what happened when the eggs were removed on the sixth day and replaced with a fresh batch. The fanning pattern began anew, but the fanning time on the sixth day was still longer than that on the first. This suggested that fanning is controlled by internal as well as external factors.

ing the comparative intensity of the two drives in an individual male and relating it to his dance. Thus when the sex drive is strong (as measured by willingness to lead a standard female model) the zig component of the dance is pronounced and may shift to complete leading. When the fighting drive is strong (as measured by the number of bites aimed at a standard male model) the zag is more emphatic and may become a straightforward attack. A female evokes the double response because she provides sign stimuli for both aggression and sexuality. Every fish entering a male's territory evokes some degree of attack, and therefore even a big-bellied female must produce a hostile as well as a sexual response.

This complexity of drives continues when the fish have arrived at the nest. A close study of the movement by which the male indicates the entrance shows that it is very similar to fanning, at that moment an entirely irrelevant response. This fanning motion, we conclude, must be a displacement activity, caused by the fact that the male is not yet able to release his sex drive; he can ejaculate his sperm only after the female has laid her eggs. Even when the female has entered the nest, the male's drive is still frustrated. Before he can release it, he must stimulate her to spawn. The "quivering" motion with which he prods her is much like fanning. It, too, is a displacement activity and stops at the moment when the eggs are laid and the male can fertilize them. It is probable that the male's sex drive is frustrated not only by the absence of eggs but also by a strong conflict with the attack drive, which must be intense when a strange fish is so near the nest. This hostility is evident from the fact that the male raises his dorsal spines

while exhibiting the nest to the female.

The ideas briefly outlined here seem to throw considerable light on the complicated and "irrelevant" activities typical of innate behavior in various animals. Of course these ideas have to be checked in more cases. This is now being done, particularly with fish and birds, and the results are encouraging.

I AM often asked whether it is worth while to stick to one animal species for so long a time as we have been studying the stickleback. The question has two answers. I believe that one should not confine one's work entirely to a single species. No one who does can wholly avoid thinking that his animal is The Animal, the perfect representative of the whole animal kingdom. Yet the many years of work on the stickleback, tedious as much of it has been, has been highly rewarding. Without such prolonged study we could not have gained a general understanding of its entire behavior pattern. That, in turn, is essential for an insight into a number of important problems. For instance, the aggressive component in courtship could never have been detected by a study of courtship alone, but only by the simultaneous study of fighting and courtship. Displacement activities are important for an understanding of an animal's motivation. To recognize them, one must have studied the parts of the behavior from which they are "borrowed" as well as the drives which, when blocked, use them as outlets. Furthermore, the mere observation and description of the stickleback's movements has benefited from our long study. Observation improves remarkably when the same thing is seen again and again.

Concentration on the stickleback has

also been instructive to us because it meant turning away for a while from the traditional laboratory animals. A stickleback is different from a rat. Its behavior is much more purely innate and much more rigid. Because of its relative simplicity, it shows some phenomena more clearly than the behavior of any mammal can. The dependence on sign stimuli, the specificity of motivation, the interaction between two types of motivation with the resulting displacement activities are some of these phenomena.

Yet we also study other animals, because only by comparison can we find out what is of general significance and what is a special case. One result that is now beginning to emerge from the stickleback experiments is the realization that mammals are in many ways a rather exceptional group, specializing in "plastic" behavior. The simpler and more rigid behavior found in our fish seems to be the rule in most of the animal kingdom. Once one is aware of this, and aware also of the affinity of mammals to the lower vertebrates, one expects to find an innate base beneath the plastic behavior of mammals.

Thus the study of conflicting drives in so low an animal as the stickleback may throw light on human conflicts and the nature of neuroses. The part played by hostility in courtship, a phenomenon found not only in sticklebacks but in several birds, may well have a real bearing on human sex life. Even those who measure the value of a science by its immediate application to human affairs can learn some important lessons from the study of this insignificant little fish.

◆

# 2

# THE SOCIAL LIFE
# OF BABOONS

S. L. WASHBURN AND IRVEN DE VORE       June 1961

The behavior of monkeys and apes has always held great fascination for men. In recent years plain curiosity about their behavior has been reinforced by the desire to understand human behavior. Anthropologists have come to understand that the evolution of man's behavior, particularly his social behavior, has played an integral role in his biological evolution. In the attempt to reconstruct the life of man as it was shaped through the ages, many studies of primate behavior are now under way in the laboratory and in the field. As the contrasts and similarities between the behavior of primates and man—especially preagricultural, primitive man—become clearer, they should give useful insights into the kind of social behavior that characterized the ancestors of man a million years ago.

With these objectives in mind we decided to undertake a study of the baboon. We chose this animal because it is a ground-living primate and as such is confronted with the same kind of problem that faced our ancestors when they left the trees. Our observations of some 30 troops of baboons, ranging in average membership from 40 to 80 individuals, in their natural setting in Africa show that the social behavior of the baboon is one of the species' principal adaptations for survival. Most of a baboon's life is spent within a few feet of other baboons. The troop affords protection from predators and an intimate group knowledge of the territory it occupies. Viewed from the inside, the troop is composed not of neutral creatures but of strongly emotional, highly motivated members. Our data offer little support for the theory that sexuality provides the primary bond of the primate troop. It is the intensely social nature of the baboon, expressed in a diversity of inter-

individual relationships, that keeps the troop together. This conclusion calls for further observation and experimental investigation of the different social bonds. It is clear, however, that these bonds are essential to compact group living and that for a baboon life in the troop is the only way of life that is feasible.

Many game reserves in Africa support baboon populations but not all were suited to our purpose. We had to be able to locate and recognize particular troops and their individual members

GROOMING to remove dirt and parasites from the hair is a major social activity among baboons. Here one adult female grooms another while the second suckles a year-old infant.

and to follow them in their peregrinations day after day. In some reserves the brush is so thick that such systematic observation is impossible. A small park near Nairobi, in Kenya, offered most of the conditions we needed. Here 12 troops of baboons, consisting of more than 450 members, ranged the open savanna. The animals were quite tame; they clambered onto our car and even allowed us to walk beside them. In only 10 months of study, one of us (DeVore) was able to recognize most of the members of four troops and to become moderately familiar with many more. The Nairobi park, however, is small and so close to the city that the pattern of baboon life is somewhat altered. To carry on our work in an area less disturbed by humans and large enough to contain elephants, rhinoceroses, buffaloes and other ungulates as well as larger and less tame troops of baboons, we went to the Amboseli game reserve and spent two months camped at the foot of Mount Kilimanjaro. In the small part of Am-

boseli that we studied intensively there were 15 troops with a total of 1,200 members, the troops ranging in size from 13 to 185 members. The fact that the average size of the troops in Amboseli (80) is twice that of the troops in Nairobi shows the need to study the animals in several localities before generalizing.

A baboon troop may range an area of three to six square miles but it utilizes only parts of its range intensively. When water and food are widely distributed, troops rarely come within sight of each other. The ranges of neighboring troops overlap nonetheless, often extensively. This could be seen best in Amboseli at the end of the dry season. Water was concentrated in certain areas, and several troops often came to the same water hole, both to drink and to eat the lush vegetation near the water. We spent many days near these water holes, watching the baboons and the numerous other animals that came there. On one occasion we counted more

than 400 baboons around a single water hole at one time. To the casual observer they would have appeared to be one troop, but actually three large troops were feeding side by side. The troops came and went without mixing, even though members of different troops sat or foraged within a few feet of each other. Once we saw a juvenile baboon cross over to the next troop, play briefly and return to his own troop. But such behavior is rare, even in troops that come together at the same water hole day after day. At the water hole we saw no fighting between troops, but small troops slowly gave way before large ones. Troops that did not see each other frequently showed great interest in each other.

When one first sees a troop of baboons, it appears to have little order, but this is a superficial impression. The basic structure of the troop is most apparent when a large troop moves away from the safety of trees and out onto open plains. As the troop moves the less dominant

**MARCHING** baboon troop has a definite structure, with females and their young protected by dominant males in the center of the formation. This group in the Amboseli reserve in Kenya includes a female (*left*), followed by two males and a female with juvenile.

BABOON EATS A POTATO tossed to him by a member of the authors' party. Baboons are primarily herbivores but occasionally they will eat birds' eggs and even other animals.

INFANT BABOON rides on its mother's back through a park outside Nairobi. A newborn infant first travels by clinging to its mother's chest, but soon learns to ride pickaback.

adult males and perhaps a large juvenile or two occupy the van. Females and more of the older juveniles follow, and in the center of the troop are the females with infants, the young juveniles and the most dominant males. The back of the troop is a mirror image of its front, with less dominant males at the rear. Thus, without any fixed or formal order, the arrangement of the troop is such that the females and young are protected at the center. No matter from what direction a predator approaches the troop, it must first encounter the adult males.

When a predator is sighted, the adult males play an even more active role in defense of the troop. One day we saw two dogs run barking at a troop. The females and juveniles hurried, but the males continued to walk slowly. In a moment an irregular group of some 20 adult males was interposed between the dogs and the rest of the troop. When a male turned on the dogs, they ran off. We saw baboons close to hyenas, cheetahs and jackals, and usually the baboons seemed unconcerned—the other animals kept their distance. Lions were the only animals we saw putting a troop of baboons to flight. Twice we saw lions near baboons, whereupon the baboons climbed trees. From the safety of the trees the baboons barked and threatened the lions, but they offered no resistance to them on the ground.

With nonpredators the baboons' relations are largely neutral. It is common to see baboons walking among topi, eland, sable and roan antelopes, gazelles, zebras, hartebeests, gnus, giraffes and buffaloes, depending on which ungulates are common locally. When elephants or rhinoceroses walk through an area where the baboons are feeding, the baboons move out of the way at the last moment. We have seen wart hogs chasing each other, and a running rhinoceros go right through a troop, with the baboons merely stepping out of the way. We have seen male impalas fighting while baboons fed beside them. Once we saw a baboon chase a giraffe, but it seemed to be more in play than aggression.

Only rarely did we see baboons engage in hostilities against other species. On one occasion, however, we saw a baboon kill a small vervet monkey and eat it. The vervets frequented the same water holes as the baboons and usually they moved near them or even among them without incident. But one troop of baboons we observed at Victoria Falls pursued vervets on sight and attempted, without success, to keep

**LIONESS LEAPS AT A THORN TREE** into which a group of baboons has fled for safety. Lions appear to be among the few animals that successfully prey on baboons. The car in the background drove up as the authors' party was observing the scene.

them out of certain fruit trees. The vervets easily escaped in the small branches of the trees.

The baboons' food is almost entirely vegetable, although they do eat meat on rare occasions. We saw dominant males kill and eat two newborn Thomson's gazelles. Baboons are said to be fond of fledglings and birds' eggs and have even been reported digging up crocodile eggs. They also eat insects. But their diet consists principally of grass, fruit, buds and plant shoots of many kinds; in the Nairobi area alone they consume more than 50 species of plant.

For baboons, as for many herbivores, association with other species on the range often provides mutual protection. In open country their closest relations are with impalas, while in forest areas the bushbucks play a similar role. The ungulates have a keen sense of smell, and baboons have keen eyesight. Baboons are visually alert, constantly looking in all directions as they feed. If they see predators, they utter warning barks that alert not only the other baboons but also any other animals that may be in the vicinity. Similarly, a warning bark by a bushbuck or an impala will put a baboon troop to flight. A mixed herd of impalas and baboons is almost impossible to take by surprise.

Impalas are a favorite prey of cheetahs. Yet once we saw impalas, grazing in the company of baboons, make no effort to escape from a trio of approaching cheetahs. The impalas just watched as an adult male baboon stepped toward the cheetahs, uttered a cry of defiance and sent them trotting away.

The interdependence of the different species is plainly evident at a water hole, particularly where the bush is thick and visibility poor. If giraffes are drinking, zebras will run to the water. But the first animals to arrive at the water hole approach with extreme caution. In the Wankie reserve, where we also observed baboons, there are large water holes surrounded by wide areas of open sand between the water and the bushes. The baboons approached the water with great care, often resting and playing for some time in the bushes before making a hurried trip for a drink. Clearly, many animals know each other's behavior and alarm signals.

A baboon troop finds its ultimate safety, however, in the trees. It is no exaggeration to say that trees limit the distribution of baboons as much as the availability of food and water. We observed an area by a marsh in Amboseli where there was water and plenty of food. But there were lions and no trees and so there were no baboons. Only a quarter of a mile away, where lions were seen even more frequently, there were trees. Here baboons were numerous; three large troops frequented the area.

At night, when the carnivores and snakes are most active, baboons sleep high up in big trees. This is one of the baboon's primary behavioral adaptations. Diurnal living, together with an

BABOONS AND THREE OTHER SPECIES gather near a water hole (*out of picture to right*). Water holes and the relatively lush vegetation that surrounds them are common meeting places for a wide variety of herbivores. In this scene of the open savanna of

arboreal refuge at night, is an extremely effective way for them to avoid danger. The callused areas on a baboon's haunches allow it to sleep sitting up, even on small branches; a large troop can thus find sleeping places in a few trees. It is known that Colobus monkeys have a cycle of sleeping and waking throughout the night; baboons probably have a similar pattern. In any case, baboons are terrified of the dark. They arrive at the trees before night falls and stay in the branches until it is fully light. Fear of the dark, fear of falling and fear of snakes seem to be basic parts of the primate heritage.

Whether by day or night, individual

baboons do not wander away from the troop, even for a few hours. The importance of the troop in ensuring the survival of its members is dramatized by the fate of those that are badly injured or too sick to keep up with their fellows. Each day the troop travels on a circuit of two to four miles; it moves from the sleeping trees to a feeding area, feeds, rests and moves again. The pace is not rapid, but the troop does not wait for sick or injured members. A baby baboon rides its mother, but all other members of the troop must keep up on their own. Once an animal is separated from the troop the chances of death are high. Sickness and injuries severe enough to

be easily seen are frequent. For example, we saw a baboon with a broken forearm. The hand swung uselessly, and blood showed that the injury was recent. This baboon was gone the next morning and was not seen again. A sickness was widespread in the Amboseli troops, and we saw individuals dragging themselves along, making tremendous efforts to stay with the troop but falling behind. Some of these may have rejoined their troops; we are sure that at least five did not. One sick little juvenile lagged for four days and then apparently recovered. In the somewhat less natural setting of Nairobi park we saw some baboons that had lost a leg. So even severe injury does

the Amboseli reserve there are baboons in the foreground and middle distance. An impala moves across the foreground just left of center. A number of zebras are present; groups of gnus graze together at right center and move off toward the water hole (*right*).

not mean inevitable death. Nonetheless, it must greatly decrease the chance of survival.

Thus, viewed from the outside, the troop is seen to be an effective way of life and one that is essential to the survival of its individual members. What do the internal events of troop life reveal about the drives and motivations that cause individual baboons to "seek safety in numbers"? One of the best ways to approach an understanding of the behavior patterns within the troop is to watch the baboons when they are resting and feeding quietly.

Most of the troop will be gathered in small groups, grooming each other's fur or simply sitting. A typical group will contain two females with their young offspring, or an adult male with one or more females and juveniles grooming him. Many of these groups tend to persist, with the same animals that have been grooming each other walking together when the troop moves. The nucleus of such a "grooming cluster" is most often a dominant male or a mother with a very young infant. The most powerful males are highly attractive to the other troop members and are actively sought by them. In marked contrast, the males in many ungulate species, such as impalas, must constantly herd the members of their group together. But baboon males

have no need to force the other troop members to stay with them. On the contrary, their presence alone ensures that the troop will stay with them at all times.

Young infants are equally important in the formation of grooming clusters. The newborn infant is the center of social attraction. The most dominant adult males sit by the mother and walk close beside her. When the troop is resting, adult females and juveniles come to the mother, groom her and attempt to groom the infant. Other members of the troop are drawn toward the center thus formed, both by the presence of the pro-

**BABOONS AND IMPALAS** cluster together around a water hole. The two species form a mutual alarm system. The baboons have keen eyesight and the impalas a good sense of smell. Between them they quickly sense the presence of predators and take flight.

tective adult males and by their intense interest in the young infants.

In addition, many baboons, especially adult females, form preference pairs, and juvenile baboons come together in play groups that persist for several years. The general desire to stay in the troop is strengthened by these "friendships," which express themselves in the daily pattern of troop activity.

Our field observations, which so strongly suggest a high social motivation, are backed up by controlled experiment in the laboratory. Robert A. Butler of Walter Reed Army Hospital has shown that an isolated monkey will work hard when the only reward for his labor is the sight of another monkey [see "Curiosity in Monkeys," by Robert A. Butler, page 173, for the report of his experiment. In the troop this social drive is expressed in strong individual preferences, by "friendship," by interest in the infant members of the troop and by the attraction of the dominant males. Field studies show the adaptive value of these social ties. Solitary animals are far more likely to be killed, and over the generations natural selection must have favored all those factors which make learning to be sociable easy.

The learning that brings the individual baboon into full identity and participation in the baboon social system begins with the mother-child relationship. The newborn baboon rides by clinging to the hair on its mother's chest. The mother may scoop the infant on with her hand, but the infant must cling to its mother, even when she runs, from the day it is born. There is no time for this behavior to be learned. Harry F. Harlow of the University of Wisconsin has shown that an infant monkey will automatically cling to an object and much prefers objects with texture more like that of a real mother [for further details see "Love in Infant Monkeys," by Harry F. Harlow, on page 100]. Experimental studies demonstrate this clinging reflex; field observations show why it is so important.

In the beginning the baboon mother and infant are in contact 24 hours a day. The attractiveness of the young infant, moreover, assures that he and his mother will always be surrounded by attentive troop members. Experiments show that an isolated infant brought up in a laboratory does not develop normal social patterns. Beyond the first reflexive clinging, the development of social behavior requires learning. Behavior characteristic of the species depends therefore both on the baboon's biology and on the social situations that are present in the troop.

BABOONS AND ELEPHANTS have a relationship that is neutral rather than co-operative, as in the case of baboons and impalas. If an elephant or another large herbivore such as a rhinoceros moves through a troop, the baboons merely step out of the way.

As the infant matures it learns to ride on its mother's back, first clinging and then sitting upright. It begins to eat solid foods and to leave the mother for longer and longer periods to play with other infants. Eventually it plays with the other juveniles many hours a day, and its orientation shifts from the mother to this play group. It is in these play groups that the skills and behavior patterns of adult life are learned and practiced. Adult gestures, such as mounting, are frequent, but most play is a mixture of chasing, tail-pulling and mock fighting. If a juvenile is hurt and cries out, adults come running and stop the play. The presence of an adult male prevents small juveniles from being hurt. In the protected atmosphere of the play group the social bonds of the infant are widely extended.

Grooming, a significant biological function in itself, helps greatly to establish social bonds. The mother begins grooming her infant the day it is born, and the infant will be occupied with grooming for several hours a day for the rest of its life. All the older baboons do a certain amount of grooming, but it is the adult females who do most. They groom the infants, juveniles, adult males and other females. The baboons go to each other and "present" themselves for grooming. The grooming animal picks through the hair, parting it with its hands, removing dirt and parasites, usually by nibbling. Grooming is most often reciprocal, with one animal doing it for a while and then presenting itself for grooming. The animal being groomed relaxes, closes its eyes and gives every indication of complete pleasure. In addition to being pleasurable, grooming serves the important function of keeping the fur clean. Ticks are common in this area and can be seen on many animals such as dogs and lions; a baboon's skin, however, is free of them. Seen in this light, the enormous amount of time baboons spend in grooming each other is understandable. Grooming is pleasurable to the individual, it is the most important expression of close social bonds and it is biologically adaptive.

The adults in a troop are arranged in a dominance hierarchy, explicitly revealed in their relations with other members of the troop. The most dominant males will be more frequently groomed and they occupy feeding and resting positions of their choice. When a dominant animal approaches a subordinate one, the lesser animal moves out of the way. The observer can determine the order of dominance simply by watching the reactions of the baboons as they move past each other. In the tamer troops these observations can be tested by feeding. If food is tossed between two baboons, the more dominant one will take it, whereas the other may not even look at it directly.

The status of a baboon male in the dominance hierarchy depends not only on his physical condition and fighting ability but also on his relationships with other males. Some adult males in every large troop stay together much of the time, and if one of them is threatened, the others are likely to back him up. A group of such males outranks any individual, even though another male outside the group might be able to defeat any member of it separately. The hierarchy has considerable stability and this is due in large part to its dependence on clusters of males rather than the fighting ability of individuals. In troops where the rank order is clearly defined, fighting is rare. We observed frequent bickering or severe fighting in only about 15 per cent of the troops. The usual effect of the hierarchy, once relations among the males are settled, is to decrease disruptions in the troop. The dominant animals, the males in particular, will not let others fight. When bickering breaks out, they usually run to the scene and stop it. Dominant males thus protect the weaker animals against harm from inside as well as outside. Females

and juveniles come to the males to groom them or just to sit beside them. So although dominance depends ultimately on force, it leads to peace, order and popularity.

Much has been written about the importance of sex in uniting the troop, it has been said, for example, that "the powerful social magnet of sex was the major impetus to subhuman primate sociability" [this viewpoint is presented in "The Origin of Society," by Marshall D. Sahlins, Offprint #602]. Our observations lead us to assign to sexuality a much lesser, and even at times a contrary, role. The sexual behavior of baboons depends on the biological cycle of the female. She is receptive for approximately one week out of every month, when she is in estrus. When first receptive, she leaves her infant and her friendship group and goes to the males, mating first with the subordinate males and older juveniles. Later in the period of receptivity she goes to the dominant males and "presents." If a male is not interested, the female is likely to groom him and then present again. Near the end of estrus the dominant males become very interested, and the female and a male form a consort pair. They may stay together for as little as an hour or for as long as several days. Estrus disrupts all other social relationships, and consort pairs usually move to the edge of

the troop. It is at this time that fighting may take place, if the dominance order is not clearly established among the males. Normally there is no fighting over females, and a male, no matter how dominant, does not monopolize a female for long. No male is ever associated with more than one estrus female; there is nothing resembling a family or a harem among baboons.

Much the same seems to be true of other species of monkey. Sexual behavior appears to contribute little to the cohesion of the troop. Some monkeys have breeding seasons, with all mating taking place within less than half the year. But even in these species the troop continues its normal existence during the months when there is no mating. It must be remembered that among baboons a female is not sexually receptive for most of her life. She is juvenile, pregnant or lactating; estrus is a rare event in her life. Yet she does not leave the troop even for a few minutes. In baboon troops, particularly small ones, many months may pass when no female member comes into estrus; yet no animals leave the troop, and the highly structured relationships within it continue without disorganization.

The sociableness of baboons is expressed in a wide variety of behavior patterns that reinforce each other and give the troop cohesion. As the infant matures the nature of the social bonds

| | | ECOLOGY | | | ECONOMIC SYSTEM | |
| --- | --- | --- | --- | --- | --- | --- |
| | | GROUP SIZE, DENSITY AND RANGE | HOME BASE | POPULATION STRUCTURE | FOOD HABITS | ECONOMIC DEPENDENCE |
| | | GROUPS OF 50–60 COMMON BUT VARY WIDELY. ONE INDIVIDUAL PER 5–10 SQUARE MILES. RANGE 200–600 SQUARE MILES. TERRITORIAL RIGHTS; DEFEND BOUNDARIES AGAINST STRANGERS. | OCCUPY IMPROVED SITES FOR VARIABLE TIMES WHERE SICK ARE CARED FOR AND STORES KEPT. | TRIBAL ORGANIZATION OF LOCAL, EXOGAMOUS GROUPS. | OMNIVOROUS. FOOD SHARING. MEN SPECIALIZE IN HUNTING, WOMEN AND CHILDREN IN GATHERING. | INFANTS ARE DEPENDENT ON ADULTS FOR MANY YEARS. MATURITY OF MALE DELAYED BIOLOGICALLY AND CULTURALLY. HUNTING, STORAGE AND SHARING OF FOOD. |
| | | 10–200 IN GROUP. 10 INDIVIDUALS PER SQUARE MILE. RANGE 3–6 SQUARE MILES; NO TERRITORIAL DEFENSE. | NONE; SICK AND INJURED MUST KEEP UP WITH TROOP. | SMALL, INBREEDING GROUPS. | ALMOST ENTIRELY VEGETARIAN. NO FOOD SHARING, NO DIVISION OF LABOR. | INFANT ECONOMICALLY INDEPENDENT AFTER WEANING. FULL MATURITY BIOLOGICALLY DELAYED. NO HUNTING, STORAGE OR SHARING OF FOOD. |

APES AND MEN are contrasted in this chart, which indicates that although apes often seem remarkably "human," there are fundamental differences in behavior. Baboon characteristics, which may be taken as representative of ape and monkey behavior in

changes continually, but the bonds are always strong. The ties between mother and infant, between a juvenile and its peers in a play group, and between a mother and an adult male are quite different from one another. Similarly, the bond between two females in a friendship group, between the male and female in a consort pair or among the members of a cluster of males in the dominance hierarchy is based on diverse biological and behavioral factors, which offer a rich field for experimental investigation.

In addition, the troop shares a considerable social tradition. Each troop has its own range and a secure familiarity with the food and water sources, escape routes, safe refuges and sleeping places inside it. The counterpart of the intensely social life within the troop is the coordination of the activities of all the troop's members throughout their lives. Seen against the background of evolution, it is clear that in the long run only the social baboons have survived.

When comparing the social behavior of baboons with that of man, there is little to be gained from laboring the obvious differences between modern civilization and the society of baboons. The comparison must be drawn against the fundamental social behavior patterns that lie behind the vast variety of human ways of life. For this purpose we have

charted the salient features of baboon life in a native habitat alongside those of human life in preagricultural society [see chart below]. Cursory inspection shows that the differences are more numerous and significant than are the similarities.

The size of the local group is the only category in which there is not a major contrast. The degree to which these contrasts are helpful in understanding the evolution of human behavior depends, of course, on the degree to which baboon behavior is characteristic of monkeys and apes in general and therefore probably characteristic of the apes that evolved into men. Different kinds of monkey do behave differently, and many more field studies will have to be made before the precise degree of difference can be understood.

For example, many arboreal monkeys have a much smaller geographical range than baboons do. In fact, there are important differences between the size and type of range for many monkey species. But there is no suggestion that a troop of any species of monkey or ape occupies the hundreds of square miles ordinarily occupied by preagricultural human societies. Some kinds of monkey may resent intruders in their range more than baboons do, but there is no evidence that any species fights for complete control of a territory. Baboons are certainly less vocal than some other monkeys, but no

nonhuman primate has even the most rudimentary language. We believe that the fundamental contrasts in our chart would hold for the vast majority of monkeys and apes as compared with the ancestors of man. Further study of primate behavior will sharpen these contrasts and define more clearly the gap that had to be traversed from ape to human behavior. But already we can see that man is as unique in his sharing, cooperation and play patterns as he is in his locomotion, brain and language.

The basis for most of these differences may lie in hunting. Certainly the hunting of large animals must have involved co-operation among the hunters and sharing of the food within the tribe. Similarly, hunting requires an enormous extension of range and the protection of a hunting territory. If this speculation proves to be correct, much of the evolution of human behavior can be reconstructed, because the men of 500,000 years ago were skilled hunters. In locations such as Choukoutien in China and Olduvai Gorge in Africa there is evidence of both the hunters and their campsites [see "Olduvai Gorge," by L. S. B. Leakey; SCIENTIFIC AMERICAN, January, 1954]. We are confident that the study of the living primates, together with the archaeological record, will eventually make possible a much richer understanding of the evolution of human behavior.

| | SOCIAL SYSTEM | | | | | COMMUNICATION |
|---|---|---|---|---|---|---|
| ORGANIZATION | SOCIAL CONTROL | SEXUAL BEHAVIOR | MOTHER-CHILD RELATIONSHIP | PLAY | | |
| ...ANDS ARE DEPENDENT ON AND AFFILIATED WITH ONE ANOTHER IN A ...EMIOPEN SYSTEM. ...UBGROUPS BASED ON ...INSHIP. | BASED ON CUSTOM. | FEMALE CONTINUOUSLY RECEPTIVE. FAMILY BASED ON PROLONGED MALE-FEMALE RELATIONSHIP AND INCEST TABOOS. | PROLONGED; INFANT HELPLESS AND ENTIRELY DEPENDENT ON ADULTS. | INTERPERSONAL BUT ALSO CONSIDERABLE USE OF INANIMATE OBJECTS. | | LINGUISTIC COMMUNITY. LANGUAGE CRUCIAL IN THE EVOLUTION OF RELIGION, ART, TECHNOLOGY AND THE CO-OPERATION OF MANY INDIVIDUALS. |
| ...ROOP SELF-SUFFICIENT, ...LOSED TO OUTSIDERS. ...EMPORARY SUBGROUPS ...RE FORMED BASED ON ...GE AND INDIVIDUAL ...REFERENCES. | BASED ON PHYSICAL DOMINANCE. | FEMALE ESTRUS. MULTIPLE MATES. NO PROLONGED MALE-FEMALE RELATIONSHIP. | INTENSE BUT BRIEF; INFANT WELL DEVELOPED AND IN PARTIAL CONTROL. | MAINLY INTERPERSONAL AND EXPLORATORY. | | SPECIES-SPECIFIC, LARGELY GESTURAL AND CONCERNED WITH IMMEDIATE SITUATIONS. |

general, are based on laboratory and field studies; human characteristics are what is known of preagricultural Homo sapiens. The

chart suggests that there was a considerable gap between primate behavior and the behavior of the most primitive men known.

# 3

# THE HOMING SALMON

ARTHUR D. HASLER AND JAMES A. LARSEN

August 1955

A learned naturalist once remarked that among the many riddles of nature, not the least mysterious is the migration of fishes. The homing of salmon is a particularly dramatic example. The Chinook salmon of the U. S. Northwest is born in a small stream, migrates downriver to the Pacific Ocean as a young smolt and, after living in the sea for as long as five years, swims back unerringly to the stream of its birth to spawn. Its determination to return to its birthplace is legendary. No one who has seen a 100-pound Chinook salmon fling itself into the air again and again until it is exhausted in a vain effort to sur-mount a waterfall can fail to marvel at the strength of the instinct that draws the salmon upriver to the stream where it was born.

How do salmon remember their birthplace, and how do they find their way back, sometimes from 800 or 900 miles away? This enigma, which has fascinated naturalists for many years, is the subject of the research to be reported here. The question has an economic as well as a scientific interest, because new dams which stand in the salmon's way have cut heavily into salmon fishing along the Pacific Coast. Before long nearly every stream of any appreciable size in the West will be blocked by dams. It is true that the dams have fish lifts and ladders designed to help salmon to hurdle them. Unfortunately, and for reasons which are different for nearly every dam so far designed, salmon are lost in tremendous numbers.

There are six common species of salmon. One, called the Atlantic salmon, is of the same genus as the steelhead trout. These two fish go to sea and come back upstream to spawn year after year. The other five salmon species, all on the Pacific Coast, are the Chinook (also called the king salmon), the sockeye, the silver, the humpback and the chum. The

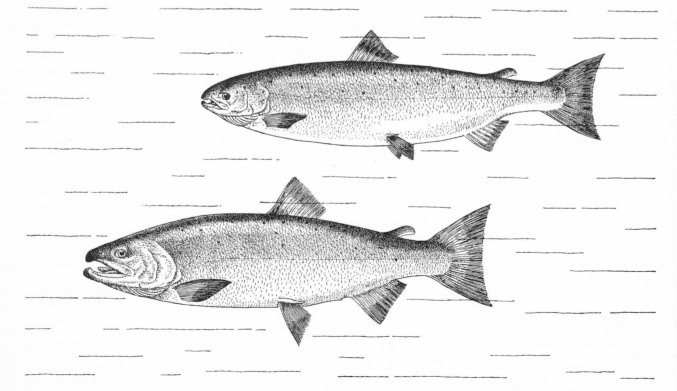

TWO COMMON SPECIES of salmon are (*top*) the Atlantic salmon (*Salmo salar*) and (*bottom*) the silver salmon (*Oncorhynchus kisutch*). The Atlantic salmon goes upstream to spawn year after year; the silver salmon, like other Pacific species, spawns only once.

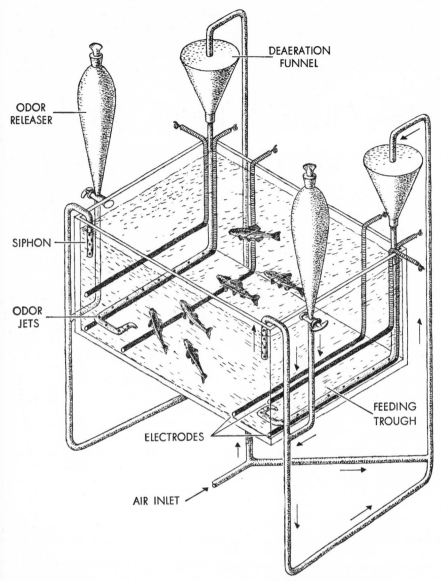

ODOR
RELEASER

DEAERATION
FUNNEL

SIPHON

ODOR
JETS

FEEDING
TROUGH

ELECTRODES

AIR INLET

**EXPERIMENTAL TANK** was built in the Wisconsin Lake Laboratory to train fish to discriminate between two odors. In this isometric drawing the vessel at the left above the tank contains water of one odor. The vessel at the right contains water of another odor. When the valve below one of the vessels was opened, the water in it was mixed with water siphoned out of the tank. The mixed water was then pumped into the tank by air. When the fish (minnows or salmon) moved toward one of the odors, they were rewarded with food. When they moved toward the other odor, they were punished with a mild electric shock from the electrodes mounted inside the tank. Each of the fish was blinded to make sure that it would not associate reward and punishment with the movements of the experimenters.

Pacific salmon home only once: after spawning they die.

A young salmon first sees the light of day when it hatches and wriggles up through the pebbles of the stream where the egg was laid and fertilized. For a few weeks the fingerling feeds on insects and small aquatic animals. Then it answers its first migratory call and swims downstream to the sea. It must survive many hazards to mature: an estimated 15 per cent of the young salmon are lost at every large dam, such as Bonneville, on the downstream trip; others die in polluted streams; many are swallowed up by bigger fish in the ocean. When, after several years in the sea, the salmon is ready to spawn, it responds to the second great migratory call. It finds the mouth of the river by which it entered the ocean and then swims steadily upstream, unerringly choosing the correct turn at each tributary fork, until it arrives at the stream where it was hatched. Generation after generation, families of salmon return to the same rivulet so consistently that populations in streams not far apart follow distinctly separate lines of evolution.

The homing behavior of the salmon

has been convincingly documented by many studies since the turn of the century. One of the most elaborate was made by Andrew L. Pritchard, Wilbert A. Clemens and Russell E. Foerster in Canada. They marked 469,326 young sockeye salmon born in a tributary of the Fraser River, and they recovered nearly 11,000 of these in the same parent stream after the fishes' migration to the ocean and back. What is more, not one of the marked fish was ever found to have strayed to another stream. This remarkable demonstration of the salmon's precision in homing has presented an exciting challenge to investigators.

At the Wisconsin Lake Laboratory during the past decade we have been studying the sense of smell in fish, beginning with minnows and going on to salmon. Our findings suggest that the salmon identifies the stream of its birth by odor and literally smells its way home from the sea.

Fish have an extremely sensitive sense of smell. This has often been observed by students of fish behavior. Karl von Frisch showed that odors from the injured skin of a fish produce a fright reaction among its schoolmates. He once noticed that when a bird dropped an injured fish in the water, the school of fish from which it had been seized quickly dispersed and later avoided the area. It is well known that sharks and tuna are drawn to a vessel by the odor of bait in the water. Indeed, the time-honored custom of spitting on bait may be founded on something more than superstition; laboratory studies have proved that human saliva is quite stimulating to the taste buds of a bullhead. The sense of taste of course is closely allied to the sense of smell. The bullhead has taste buds all over the surface of its body; they are especially numerous on its whiskers. It will quickly grab for a piece of meat that touches any part of its skin. But it becomes insensitive to taste and will not respond in this way if a nerve serving the skin buds is cut.

The smelling organs of fish have evolved in a great variety of forms. In the bony fishes the nose pits have two separate openings. The fish takes water into the front opening as it swims or breathes (sometimes assisting the intake with cilia), and then the water passes out through the second opening, which may be opened and closed rhythmically by the fish's breathing. Any odorous substances in the water stimulate the nasal receptors chemically, perhaps by an effect on enzyme reactions, and the re-

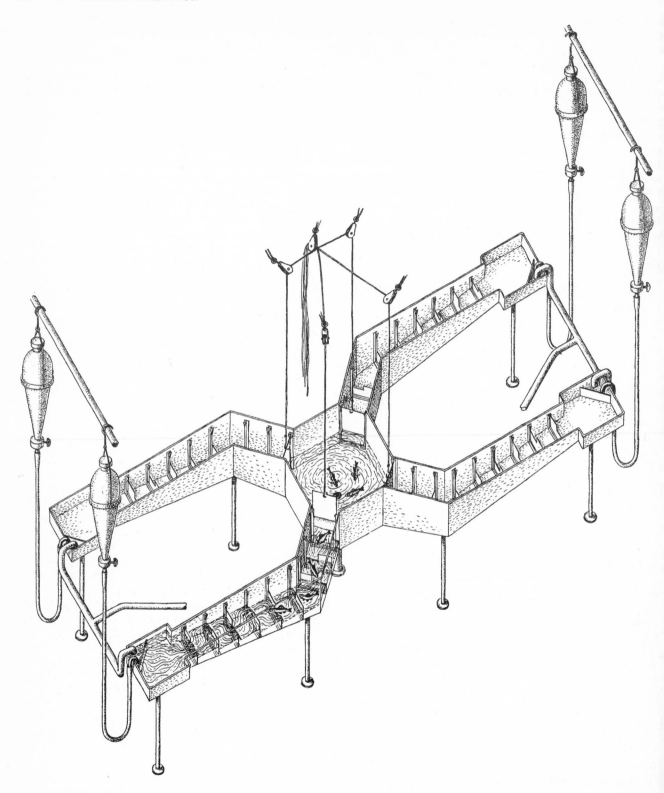

**FOUR RUNWAYS** are used to test the reaction of untrained salmon fingerlings to various odors. Water is introduced at the outer end of each runway and flows down a series of steps into a central compartment, where it drains. In the runway at the lower left the water cascades down to the central compartment in a series of miniature waterfalls; in the other runways the water is omitted to show the construction of the apparatus. Odors may be introduced into the apparatus from the vessels suspended above the runways. In an experiment salmon fingerlings are placed in the central compartment and an odor is introduced into one of the runways. When the four doors to the central compartment are opened, the fingerlings tend to enter the arms, proceeding upstream by jumping the waterfalls. Whether an odor attracts them, repels or has no effect is judged by the observed distribution of the fish in the runways.

sulting electrical impulses are relayed to the central nervous system by the olfactory nerve.

The human nose, and that of other land vertebrates, can smell a substance only if it is volatile and soluble in fat solvents. But in the final analysis smell is always aquatic, for a substance is not smelled until it passes into solution in the mucous film of the nasal passages. For fishes, of course, the odors are already in solution in their watery environment. Like any other animal, they can follow an odor to its source, as a hunting dog follows the scent of an animal. The quality or effect of a scent changes as the concentration changes; everyone knows that an odor may be pleasant at one concentration and unpleasant at another.

When we began our experiments, we first undertook to find out whether fish could distinguish the odors of different water plants. We used a specially developed aquarium with jets which could inject odors into the water. For responding to one odor (by moving toward the jet), the fish were rewarded with food; for responding to another odor, they were punished with a mild electric shock. After the fish were trained to make choices between odors, they were tested on dilute rinses from 14 different aquatic plants. They proved able to distinguish the odors of all these plants from one another.

Plants must play an important role in the life of many freshwater fish. Their odors may guide fish to feeding grounds when visibility is poor, as in muddy water or at night, and they may hold young fish from straying from protective cover. Odors may also warn fish away from poisons. In fact, we discovered that fish could be put to use to assay industrial pollutants: our trained minnows were able to detect phenol, a common pollutant, at concentrations far below those detectable by man.

All this suggested a clear-cut working hypothesis for investigating the mystery of the homing of salmon. We can suppose that every little stream has its own characteristic odor, which stays the same year after year; that young salmon become conditioned to this odor before they go to sea; that they remember the odor as they grow to maturity, and that they are able to find it and follow it to its source when they come back upstream to spawn.

Plainly there are quite a few ifs in this theory. The first one we tested was the question: Does each stream have its own odor? We took water from two creeks in Wisconsin and investigated whether fish could learn to discriminate between them. Our subjects, first minnows and then salmon, were indeed able to detect a difference. If, however, we destroyed a fish's nose tissue, it was no longer able to distinguish between the two water samples.

Chemical analysis indicated that the only major difference between the two waters lay in the organic material. By testing the fish with various fractions of the water separated by distillation, we confirmed that the identifying material was some volatile organic substance.

The idea that fish are guided by odors in their migrations was further supported by a field test. From each of two different branches of the Issaquah River in the State of Washington we took a number of sexually ripe silver salmon which had come home to spawn. We then plugged with cotton the noses of half the fish in each group and placed all the salmon in the river below the fork to make the upstream run again. Most of the fish with unplugged noses swam back to the stream they had selected the first time. But the "odor-blinded" fish migrated back in random fashion, picking the wrong stream as often as the right one.

In 1949 eggs from salmon of the Horsefly River in British Columbia were hatched and reared in a hatchery in a tributary called the Little Horsefly. Then they were flown a considerable distance and released in the main Horsefly River, from which they migrated to the sea. Three years later 13 of them had returned to their rearing place in the Little Horsefly, according to the report of the Canadian experimenters.

In our own laboratory experiments we tested the memory of fish for odors and found that they retained the ability to differentiate between odors for a long period after their training. Young fish remembered odors better than the old. That animals "remember" conditioning to which they have been exposed in their youth, and act accordingly, has been demonstrated in other fields. For instance, there is a fly which normally lays its eggs on the larvae of the flour moth, where the fly larvae then hatch and develop. But if larvae of this fly are raised on another host, the beeswax moth, when the flies mature they will seek out beeswax moth larvae on which to lay their eggs, in preference to the traditional host.

With respect to the homing of salmon we have shown, then, that different streams have different odors, that salmon respond to these odors and that they remember odors to which they have been conditioned. The next question is: Is a salmon's homeward migration guided solely by its sense of smell? If we could decoy homing salmon to a stream other than their birthplace, by means of an odor to which they were conditioned artificially, we might have not only a solution to the riddle that has puzzled scientists but also a practical means of saving the salmon—guiding them to breeding streams not obstructed by dams.

We set out to find a suitable substance to which salmon could be conditioned. A student, W. J. Wisby, and I [Arthur Hasler] designed an apparatus to test the reactions of salmon to various organic odors. It consists of a compartment from which radiate four runways, each with several steps which the fish must jump to climb the runway. Water cascades down each of the arms. An odorous substance is introduced into one of the arms, and its effect on the fish is judged by whether the odor appears to attract fish into that arm, to repel them or to be indifferent to them.

We needed a substance which initially would not be either attractive or repellent to salmon but to which they could be conditioned so that it would attract them. After testing several score organic odors, we found that dilute solutions of morpholine neither attracted nor repelled salmon but were detectable by them in extremely low concentrations— as low as one part per million. It appears that morpholine fits the requirements for the substance needed: it is soluble in water; it is detectable in extremely low concentrations; it is chemically stable under stream conditions. It is neither an attractant nor a repellent to unconditioned salmon, and would have meaning only to those conditioned to it.

Federal collaborators of ours are now conducting field tests on the Pacific Coast to learn whether salmon fry and fingerlings which have been conditioned to morpholine can be decoyed to a stream other than that of their birth when they return from the sea to spawn. Unfortunately this type of experiment may not be decisive. If the salmon are not decoyed to the new stream, it may simply mean that they cannot be drawn by a single substance but will react only to a combination of subtle odors in their parent stream. Perhaps adding morpholine to the water is like adding the whistle of a freight train to the quiet strains of a violin, cello and flute. The salmon may still seek out the subtle harmonies of an odor combination to which they have been reacting by instinct for centuries. But there is still hope that they may respond to the call of the whistle.

# 4

# SOUND COMMUNICATION IN HONEYBEES

ADRIAN M. WENNER                           April 1964

Can we ever fully understand how the members of another species communicate with one another? The question has been given a new implication by the recent proposals that we listen for messages from the planets of other stars. Whether we ever detect such messages or not, we can investigate the question here on earth. We now know of many forms of communication in other species. None is subtler or more interesting than the "language" of the honeybee.

It is no accident that Karl von Frisch of the University of Munich chose the bee for his now famous investigations of animal communication. A honeybee colony is a marvelously compact community of some 50,000 individuals; it takes care of itself and usually ignores its human investigator; its members are highly social and could not survive without constant intercommunication, and the more one looks into their methods of conversation, the more remarkable they are found to be.

The obvious features of honeybee communication have been reported widely and are now a familiar story. When a foraging bee finds a source of food, it flies back to the hive and conveys to its fellows the distance and direction of the source. In the course of doing so it performs on the vertical surface of the comb a waggling "dance" in which its abdomen traces a figure eight. The orientation and rate of the dance, it has been supposed, tells the location of the food source. This hypothesis runs into an awkward difficulty: the interior of most hives is so dark that the bees probably cannot see the dance. Investigators of the phenomenon have found, however, that the bees follow the dance by means of their antennae, which touch the dancer's body.

Robert C. King of Servomechanisms,

Inc., and I, working in my laboratory at the University of California at Santa Barbara, looked into the question further. The dancing bee traces the figure eight with the tip of its abdomen. That is not, however, the part of the body on which the observing bees usually concentrate their attention: their antennae tend to rest on the dancer's thorax. Does the thorax also describe a figure eight during the dance? We marked foraging bees with a spot of white paint on the thorax and later photographed its movement during the course of the dance in the hive by means of a series of rapid-flash exposures. The pictures showed that the thorax did not describe a figure-eight pattern [see lower illustration on page 27].

The dance pattern itself, then, can hardly convey an unequivocal message. What can? Using a tape recorder, I had discovered that during the dance the bee emitted a peculiar sound at the low frequency of 250 cycles per second. This sound was made while the bee was waggling along in the straight run of its dance. It suggested a surprising new outlook on the whole problem. Perhaps the honeybee communicated with its fellows not only by the dance movement but also by sound signals!

To test this possibility I made tape recordings of the sounds made by dancing bees after they had visited dishes of sugar syrup placed at different distances from the hive. Would the sound patterns show a relation to the distance traveled? In other words, did the foraging bee tell its hivemates the distance by means of a sound language?

Analyzed with the sound spectrograph, the sounds proved to be made up of trains, each train being further broken into pulses with a frequency of about 32 per second [see top illustration

on page 29]. The bee emitted a train of sound during each straight run of its waggling dance. A careful analysis showed that the average length of the sound trains during a given dance (and also the average number of pulses in a train) was directly proportional to the distance the bee had traveled to the food source [see bottom illustration on page 29]. The correlation was so good that it seems altogether likely—certainly as likely as any other proposed mechanism—that the bee reports the distance by means of this sound language.

How is the sound produced? The first and most obvious guess was that the bee might create the pulses of sound with the waggling of its abdomen. To resolve this question I attached a small piece of cellophane to a microphone and placed the microphone so that with each waggle the dancing bee would tap the cellophane. The sound pulses proved to be about two and a half times more frequent than the waggling taps, so it became clear that the sound could not be arising from the waggling. Harald Esch, now at the University of Munich, who independently had discovered the honeybee's dance sound at about the same time as I had, also demonstrated that it was not produced by the waggling. Instead of a cellophane-and-microphone device, he used the ingenious method of attaching a small magnet to the bee's abdomen; as the bee moved the magnet it generated a fluctuating electric voltage that was recorded simultaneously with the pulsed sound, so that the waggle and pulse rates could be compared.

The function of the sound train was illuminated by considering the question of whether or not the bee's judgment of distances is affected by the wind. Analysis of the sound-train records showed that it is to some extent. When

**EFFECT OF SOUND** on bees in a hive is illustrated by these photographs made by the author. Bees are normally in constant motion, but they quiet down at the sound of "piping," a beeping tone produced by workers. The normal motion is shown by the blurred images in the top photograph, which was made at a fifth of a second. When piping was simulated and transmitted to the hive wall by a vibrator, the bees became almost motionless, as shown by bottom photograph, made at the same aperture and speed.

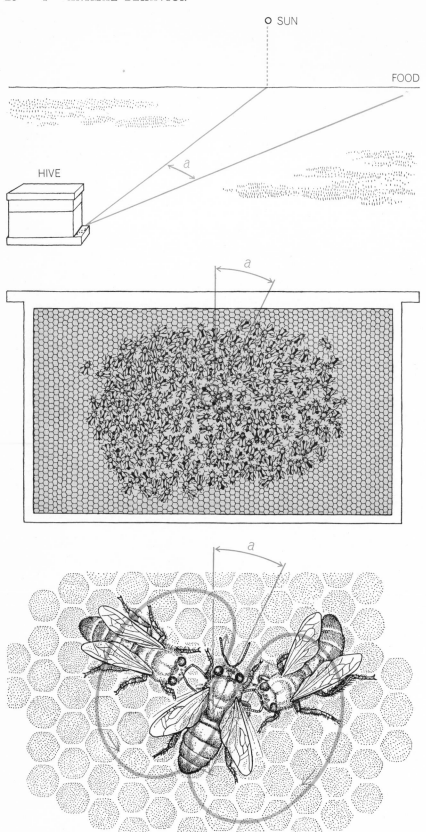

**FORAGING BEE** must transmit to its hivemates information about the distance from the hive to the food source (*top drawing*) and the angle (*a*) between the direction of the source and the direction of the sun. It does a dance on the honeycomb in which its abdomen describes a kind of figure eight (*middle*). The "straight run" (*A*) of the dance (*bottom*) has a duration proportional to the distance to the food, and it is oriented at an angle from the vertical equal to angle *a*. "Recruit" bees track the dancer's side with their antennae.

a bee flies to a source of food against the wind, the sound trains indicating the distance tend to be a little longer than when it does not buck a wind. The deviation from the true distance is not nearly so much, however, as one might expect on the basis of the wind velocity. A possible explanation is that the bee adjusts its flying efforts to the wind so that it always flies at about the same ground speed; thus, whatever the wind velocity, it can still use the elapsed time of travel to a goal as the measure of its distance. I measured the flight speed of bees under various wind conditions and found that they do tend to fly at a constant ground speed. For example, flying against a wind of five meters per second (about 11 miles per hour) bees are slowed by only about a fourth of that amount. They minimize the wind effect by flying closer to the ground. When the wind is too strong (more than 13 miles per hour), the bees simply stay in the hive.

We may conclude, then, that the foraging bee's communication to its fellows in the hive is made up of two elements: the dance and the accompanying sounds. The angle of the dance from the vertical is correlated with the angle between the food source and the overhead sun, and the length of the train of sound during the straight run of the dance tells the distance. This may not be the whole story, however. Some current experiments indicate, for instance, a strong correlation between the rate of pulse production and the strength of the sugar concentration in a food source. It may conceivably turn out that the foraging bee's entire message is carried by sound signals.

The sound spectrograph's indication of regularity and precision in the bee's dance sounds naturally drew attention to other forms of bee "talk." As everyone knows, the bee is a rather noisy animal. Even its buzz in flight, however, is not just noise. The buzz has modulations and variations. When bees begin to swarm, an experienced beekeeper can detect the event by the sound alone, even though he may be surrounded by other buzzing bees from hundreds of hives. When an individual bee is aroused to attack, its buzz rises in pitch and fluctuates in intensity. And recordings within the hive show that bees in the hive make at least 10 distinctly different sounds, some of which have already been related to specific activities.

Two of these sounds are particularly

noticeable. One, known as the characteristic hum of a beehive, is produced by the "ventilating" worker bees: bees that stand anchored on the comb or some other structure in the hive and create currents of air by beating their wings. This sound, varying in intensity, has a basic frequency of 250 cycles per second and often has strong overtones. It is usually much louder than the buzz of a flying bee, undoubtedly because the sound emitted by the ventilating bee is enhanced by the resonant vibration of the structure on which it is standing.

The other type of loud sound in the hive is heard when the hive is disturbed. When an intruder—for example an ant—approaches, the bees guarding the hive rock forward on their legs and issue a short burst of sound; they may go on repeating these warning bursts every two or three seconds for 10 minutes or more. When the hive is jarred, the collective reaction of hundreds of guarding bees is heard as a sharp, loud buzz. This is followed shortly by a "piping" of workers throughout the hive, which consists of faint beeps at half-second intervals, the sound being a complex one with a fundamental frequency of 500 cycles per second. The piping goes on for several minutes. Apparently it serves to soothe the hive; it has been found that a recording of such piping, played to the hive, will quickly quiet the disturbed bees.

The most interesting of all the hive sounds, however, is the piping of the

DANCING BEES and recruits are seen in this photograph. There are three dancers, or foragers (blurred images), heading to the right in a diagonal line starting near the upper left corner. The dancer nearest the left has a recruit on each side, the center one has two recruits on its right and the bee at the right, apparently nearing the end of its straight run, has a recruit at its right rear.

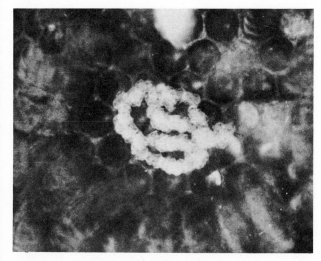

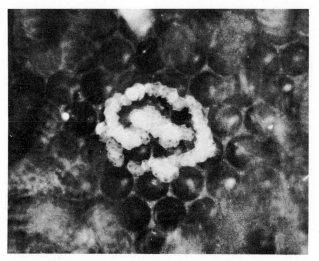

DANCE PATTERN described by the bee's thorax is not a well-defined figure eight with a distinctive straight run. This suggests that recruits would have difficulty gaining information by following the dance movements alone. To make these pictures Robert C. King and the author put a spot of white paint on the thorax of foragers and then photographed their dances by repetitive flash.

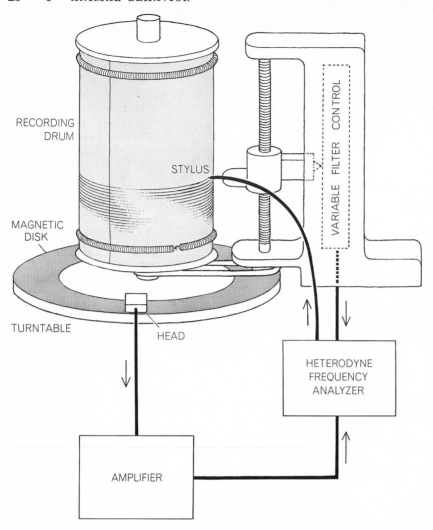

RECORDING DRUM

STYLUS

VARIABLE FILTER CONTROL

MAGNETIC DISK

TURNTABLE

HEAD

HETERODYNE FREQUENCY ANALYZER

AMPLIFIER

**BEE SOUNDS** are analyzed by a sound spectrograph. A short segment of a bee sound, recorded in the field, is transferred to the magnetic disk and then repeatedly sampled as the disk rotates with the recording drum. The stylus is a wire from which an electric spark passes to the drum, etching the recording paper. As the stylus rises, its position regulates the filter control so that the frequency analyzer extracts the proper frequency from the total sound, which is broken into a frequency "spectrum" changing with time.

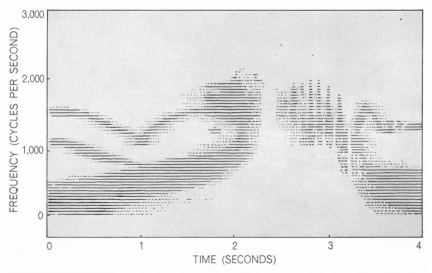

**SOUND SPECTROGRAM** displays frequency against time as shown in this schematic tracing. The amplitude of the signal components is indicated by the darkness of the trace.

queen. Naturalists have long known that queens inside the hive emit two kinds of sound, called "tooting" and "quacking." A close analysis of these sounds and the circumstances of their emission now provides the strongest evidence that bees use sound to convey specific messages.

Tooting is the regal identification of a virgin queen soon after she has emerged from the cell in which she developed. A hive cannot tolerate more than one queen at a time. In a hive that lacks a queen several queen-bearing cells develop simultaneously in a comb, but one matures earlier than the others. Once this queen has emerged, has hardened and has become steady on her legs, she proceeds to visit other queen cells, tear them open and sting to death their potential but not yet mature queens. Often, however, the worker bees do not allow her to dispose of all her potential rivals in this way; they bar her from some of the cells. She then begins to toot and continues to do so day and night, perhaps for a week or more. Her tooting rises in intensity and sometimes can be heard more than 10 feet from the hive.

Meanwhile the maturing queen bees still in cells try to get out in their turn. The worker bees hold them back, however; as fast as one of them opens the cap of her cell the workers push it back in place and glue it shut. Thereupon the imprisoned queens also start to pipe, but in a different pattern and at a lower tone than the free queen. The workers let out some of these quackers, but only one at a time. The reigning queen and the newly released rival then battle until one is killed. Sometimes the series of fights between the survivor and the new rivals goes on until only one queen is left. This survivor, still a virgin, then flies away from the hive to mate successively with several drones (on the wing) and returns to begin laying eggs.

All this has been studied in hives set up for detailed observation. The tooting and the quacking have also been recorded and analyzed spectrographically. The pattern of the first turns out to be a long toot (lasting one second) followed by several shorter toots. Its fundamental frequency is 500 cycles per second, and this is overlaid with overtones that are varied considerably in emphasis, just as they are in human speech [for human patterns see "Attention and the Perception of Speech," by Donald E. Broadbent; Offprint #467]. The quack differs from the toot in two ways: it has a lower fundamental frequency and it begins with short sounds instead of a drawn-out one.

Do the tooting and the quacking say different things to the bees? We investigated this question with a set of controlled experiments. First we recorded the tooting of a free, reigning queen in its hive. Analysis with the sound spectrograph showed that this tooting put the major emphasis on the third harmonic. We therefore mimicked this harmonic with an oscillator and played it in the same tooting pattern (a long toot followed by several short ones) in a second hive that contained a free queen and a caged one. To each sounding of the artificial toots the caged queen almost invariably responded by quacking [*see upper two illustrations on page 31*]. We then tried varying the frequency of the tone, while keeping the long-toot-short-toot pattern constant. Within a wide frequency range (600 to 2,000 cycles per second) the change in frequency seemed to make little difference: the queen still responded with quacks as long as the typical pattern of toots was the same. On the other hand, when we played the quacking pattern, the caged queen did not respond at all.

There is not much doubt that the tooting and the quacking represent certain messages. What do the messages say, and what functions do they serve? A reasonable working hypothesis is that (1) the tooting announces the presence of a free queen in the hive, (2) the quacking reports the presence of challengers ready and yearning to be freed from their cells and (3) all this information guides the worker bees. One queen tooting and others quacking means that there is just one free queen, and a quacker (but not more than one) may be released to challenge her. This procedure will result in the rapid killing off of all but one of the contenders, but that may be to the good; it will enable the hive to settle down quickly to a peaceful regime. Occasionally, however, particularly in the spring, a virgin queen or an older egg-laying queen may leave the hive permanently, taking along half of the adult bees, in the phenomenon called swarming. In the swarming season, therefore, it is essential to have a queen in reserve when the free queen departs; a quacking queen may represent survival for the hive and is not to be released until the swarm has left.

We must come back now to the important questions: How does the bee produce sounds, and how does it

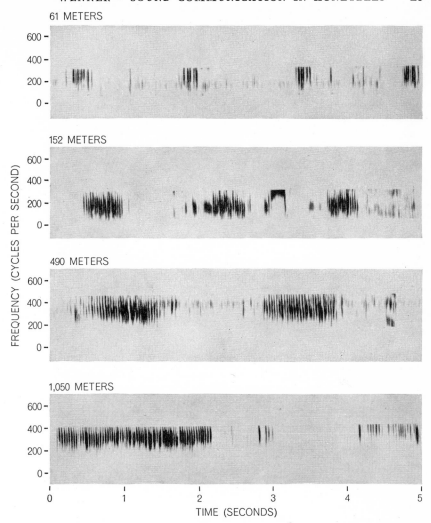

**SPECTROGRAMS** analyze the sound produced by forager bees during the dance. Sound trains are produced during the straight run; blank or light areas mark remainder of figure eight. The length of the sound train increases with the distance to the source of nectar.

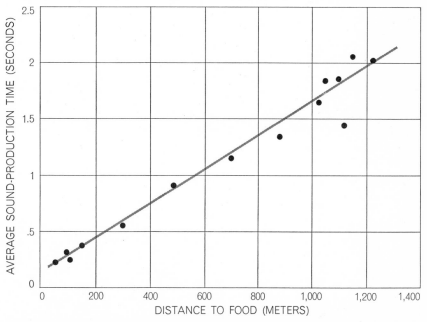

**DIRECT CORRELATION** is shown between the sound-production time and the distance the bee had just traveled to obtain food. Each point is an average for several dancing bees.

perceive them? As to the production of sound, four hypotheses have been put forward, and the answer is still not clear.

The most interesting suggestion is that the bee makes its sounds by ejecting air through its spiracles: the breathing openings in the side of its body. On purely theoretical grounds it is quite plausible that the insect could produce the observed sounds by a whistling or a bagpipe effect. But recent experiments in our laboratory and also by other investigators generally negate this theory. For one thing, if helium is substituted for nitrogen in the air in which the bee produces its sounds, this does not change the frequency of the sound; if the spiracle theory is correct, it should, because the density of a gas affects the frequency of the sound produced by vibrating a column of the gas. For another thing, it has been found that the

sounds of a piping queen do not always coincide with accordion-like movements of its abdomen, so that its abdominal spiracles cannot be producing the sound. Finally, James Simpson of the Rothamsted Experimental Station in England has shown by delicate spiracle-blocking experiments that the bee's thoracic spiracles play no part in sound production.

The other possibilities are that the bee produces sound by vibrating its wings or the sclerites (hard plates) at the base of its wings or the entire surface of the upper part of its body. Simpson and I and others have been investigating these possibilities. At the moment the wing-vibration theory seems to be the most promising.

Until recently this idea was rejected on two grounds: that a bee's wings are too small to produce sounds of the fre-

quencies and intensities heard, and that experimenters who have clipped the wings have not found that this changed the intensity of the bee's piping. The second idea is simply wrong; careful experiments show that clipping the wings does affect the bee's sound-making. It raises the frequency and reduces the intensity of the sound, and the change is proportional to the amount of wing removed [see bottom illustration on page 31]. It appears, therefore, that wing vibration is responsible at least for amplification, and probably for production, of the bee's sounds. It is hoped that experiments now under way will answer the question more definitely.

Other recent studies have shed some light on how bees "hear" sound. In the experiments in which artificial tooting was played to a caged queen it was found that the queen responded only when the sound was transmitted via a vibrator attached to the hive; when it was transmitted through the air, even with the vibrator suspended close to the bee, she did not respond at all [see second illustration from top on page 31]. Similarly, worker bees show no reaction to piping when it is airborne. On the other hand, a disturbed hive can be quickly quieted by drawing a wet finger along the observation window, which causes a squeaking sound that arises from vibration of the glass. All these observations indicate that the bees receive sound through their legs from the vibrating structure on which they stand. Quite possibly they have receiving organs for sound on their legs below the knee.

There is also evidence that they receive sound through their antennae. Eleanor H. Slifer of the University of Iowa has found that each bee antenna has thousands of "plate organs" that are remarkably like the larger tympanic (eardrum-like) organs of other insects. She has established that these plate organs are not permeable to chemicals that might be used for communication. Although this finding does not eliminate the possibility that these organs are chemoreceptors, there is now good reason to entertain the notion that they do respond to mechanical stimuli. Charles Walcott of Harvard University has made some experimental findings that support this view: he discovered that vibrations transmitted to a bee's antennae caused electrical impulses to be generated in the antennal nerves.

Conceivably the honeybee receives sound both through its legs and through its antennae. Thus it may receive a

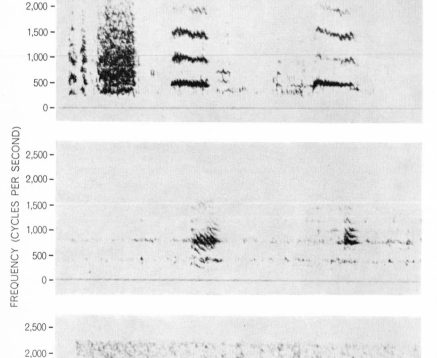

WORKER SOUNDS are shown in these spectrograms. The top tracing illustrates two sounds produced when a hive is disturbed: the sharp burst of a disturbed worker (left), followed by two faint beeps, or worker piping. The middle and bottom tracings show "croaking" and "bipping," two sounds that have yet to be related to any specific activity.

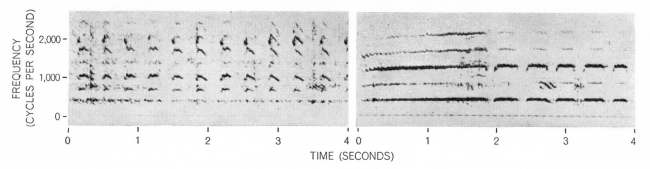

QUEEN PIPING includes "quacking" and "tooting." A queen in her cell produces quacking (*left*), a series of short pulses with emphasis on several harmonics. Once free in the hive a queen produces tooting (*right*), which begins with a long wail, has a somewhat higher fundamental frequency and usually emphasizes frequencies not simultaneously emphasized by quacking queens.

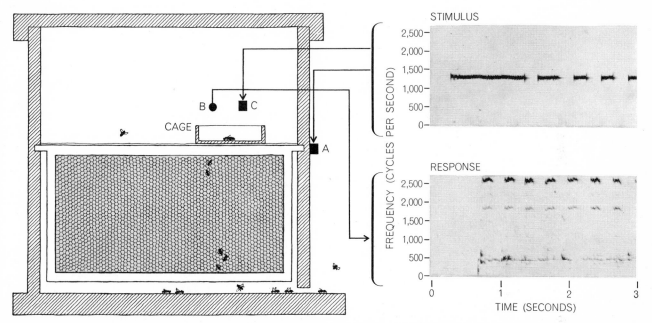

TOOTING was simulated (*upper tracing*) and played to a caged queen via a vibrator touching the hive (*A*). It elicited from the queen a response that was picked up by a microphone (*B*) and analyzed as quacking (*lower tracing*). When the tooting vibrator was suspended above the queen (*C*), there was no response, indicating that the queen perceived sound via the hive structure.

sound communication from another bee directly by touching the other bee's body with its antennae—as evidently occurs during the foraging bee's dance in the hive. The double receiving system would have a great advantage for bees in a noisy hive: in spite of the din of piping, which they apparently receive through their legs from the hive's vibrations, they would still be able to perceive the faint dance sounds by touching the dancer with their antennae.

Listening to the sounds of bees, recording them, analyzing them and designing experiments to explore their meaning, one cannot help feeling that much of this is akin to the problem of communicating with beings on another planet. With bees we have the advantage of being able to study them here and now.

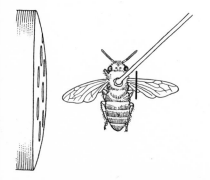

RELATION OF WING to sound production was demonstrated by severing most of two wings of a bee (*left*). Comparison with the sound produced by the intact animal (*center*) showed that loss of wing area reduced the intensity and changed the harmonics (*right*).

# THE EVOLUTION OF BEHAVIOR

KONRAD Z. LORENZ                    December 1958

A whale's flipper, a bat's wing and a man's arm are as different from one another in outward appearance as they are in the functions they serve. But the bones of these structures reveal an essential similarity of design. The zoologist concludes that whale, bat and man evolved from a common ancestor. Even if there were no other evidence, the comparison of the skeletons of these creatures would suffice to establish that conclusion. The similarity of skeletons shows that a basic structure may persist over geologic periods in spite of a wide divergence of function.

Following the example of zoologists, who have long exploited the comparative method, students of animal behavior have now begun to ask a penetrating question. We all know how greatly the behavior of animals can vary, especially under the influence of the learning process. Psychologists have mostly observed and experimented with the behavior of individual animals; few have considered the behavior of species. But is it not possible that beneath all the variations of individual behavior there lies an inner structure of inherited behavior which characterizes all the members of a given

species, genus or larger taxonomic group —just as the skeleton of a primordial ancestor characterizes the form and structure of all mammals today?

Yes, it is possible! Let me give an example which, while seemingly trivial, has a bearing on this question. Anyone who has watched a dog scratch its jaw or a bird preen its head feathers can attest to the fact that they do so in the same way. The dog props itself on the tripod formed by its haunches and two forelegs and reaches a hindleg forward in front of its shoulder. Now the odd fact is that most birds (as well as virtu-

SCRATCHING BEHAVIOR of a dog and a European bullfinch is part of their genetic heritage and is not changed by training. The widespread habit of scratching with a hindlimb crossed over a forelimb is common to most Amniota (birds, reptiles and mammals).

**DISPLAY BEHAVIOR** of seagulls shows how behavior traits inherent in all gulls have adapted to the needs of an aberrant species. At top is a typical gull, the herring gull, which breeds on the shore. It is shown in the "choking" posture which advertises its nest site. In middle the herring gull is shown in the "oblique" and "long call" postures, used to defend its territory. At bottom is the aberrant kittiwake, which unlike other gulls breeds on narrow ledges and has no territory other than its nest site. The kittiwake does not use the "oblique" or "long call" postures, but employs the "choking" stance for both advertisement and defense.

ally all mammals and reptiles) scratch with precisely the same motion! A bird also scratches with a hindlimb (that is, its claw), and in doing so it lowers its wing and reaches its claw forward in front of its shoulder. One might think that it would be simpler for the bird to move its claw directly to its head without moving its wing, which lies folded out of the way on its back. I do not see how to explain this clumsy action unless we admit that it is inborn. Before the bird can scratch, it must reconstruct the old spatial relationship of the limbs of the four-legged common ancestor which it shares with mammals.

In retrospect it seems peculiar that psychologists have been so slow to pursue such clues to hereditary behavior. It is nearly 100 years since T. H. Huxley, upon making his first acquaintance with Charles Darwin's concept of natural selection, exclaimed: "How stupid of me, not to have thought of that!" Darwinian evolution quickly fired the imagination of biologists. Indeed, it swept through the scientific world with the speed characteristic of all long-overdue ideas. But somehow the new approach stopped short at the borders of psychology. The psychologists did not draw on Darwin's comparative method, or on his sense of the species as the protagonist of the evolutionary process.

Perhaps, with their heritage from philosophy, they were too engrossed in purely doctrinal dissension. For exactly opposite reasons the "behaviorists" and the "purposivists" were convinced that behavior was much too variable to permit its reduction to a set of traits characteristic of a species. The purposivist school of psychology argued for the existence of instincts; the behaviorists argued against them. The purposivists believed that instincts set the goals of animal behavior, but left to the individual animal a boundless variety of means to reach these goals. The behaviorists held that the capacity to learn endowed the individual with unlimited plasticity of behavior. The debate over instinct versus learning kept both schools from perceiving consistent, inherited patterns in behavior, and led each to preoccupation with external influences on behavior.

If any psychologist stood apart from the sterile contention of the two schools, it was Jakob von Uexküll. He sought tirelessly for the causes of animal behavior, and was not blind to structure. But he too was caught in a philosophical trap. Uexküll was a vitalist, and he denounced Darwinism as gross materialism. He believed that the regularities he observed

in the behavior of species were manifestations of nature's unchanging and un-
changeable "ground plan," a notion akin
to the mystical "idea" of Plato.

## The Phylogeny of Behavior

But even as the psychologists debated,
evolutionary thought was entering the
realm of behavior studies by two back
doors. At Woods Hole, Mass., Charles
Otis Whitman, a founder of the Marine
Biological Laboratory, was working out
the family tree of pigeons, which he had
bred as a hobby since early childhood.
Simultaneously, but unknown to Whitman, Oskar Heinroth of the Berlin
Aquarium was studying the phylogeny
of waterfowl. Heinroth, too, was an
amateur aviculturist who had spent a
lifetime observing his own pet ducks.
What a queer misnomer is the word
"amateur"! How unjust that a term
which means the "lover" of a subject
should come to connote a superficial
dabbler! As a result of their "dabbling,"
Whitman and Heinroth acquired an in-
comparably detailed knowledge of pigeon and duck behavior.

As phylogenists, Whitman and Heinroth both sought to develop in detail
the relationship between families and
species of birds. To define a given group
they had to find its "homologous" traits:
the resemblances between species which
bespeak a common origin. The success
or failure of their detective work hinged
on the number of homologous traits they
could find. As practical bird-fanciers,
Whitman and Heinroth came to know
bird behavior as well as bird morphology, and each independently reached an
important discovery: Behavior, as well
as body form and structure, displays
homologous traits. As Whitman phrased
it just 60 years ago: "Instincts and organs are to be studied from the common
viewpoint of phyletic descent."

Sometimes these traits of behavior are
common to groups larger than ducks or
pigeons. The scratching habit, which I
have already mentioned, is an example
of a behavior pattern that is shared by
a very large taxonomic group, in this
case the Amniota: the reptiles, birds and
mammals (all of whose embryos grow
within the thin membrane of the am-
niotic sac). This widespread motor pattern was discovered by Heinroth, who
described it in a brief essay in 1930. It is
noteworthy that Heinroth observed the
extreme resistance of such inborn habits
to changes wrought by learning. He noticed that while most bird species maintain their incongruous over-the-shoulder

"HEAD-FLAGGING" is another form of display in which the kittiwake has adapted its behavioral birthright to meet unusual needs. Most gulls—like this pair of black-faced gulls—
use this stance in courtship (by averting its menacing facial and bill coloration, the bird
"appeases" the aggressive instinct of its mate). Kittiwakes alone evince this posture not
only in mating adults but in ledge-bound nestlings, which use it to "appease" invaders.

scratching technique, some have lost
this behavior trait. Among these are the
larger parrots, which feed with their
claws and use the same motion—under
the wing—for scratching. Parakeets,
however, scratch in the unreconstructed
style, reaching around the lowered wing,
and do not pick up food in their claws.
There are a few exceptions to this rule.
The Australian broadtailed parakeet has
learned to eat with its claw. When eating, it raises its claw directly to its bill.
But when scratching, it still reaches its
claw around its lowered wing! This oddity is evidence in itself of the obstinacy of
the old scratching habit. So far no one
has been able to teach a parakeet to
scratch without lowering its wing or to
train a parrot to scratch around a lowered wing.

Today a growing school of investigators is working in the field opened up by
Whitman and Heinroth. They have set
themselves the task of discovering inherited patterns of behavior and tracing
them from species to species. Many of
these patterns have proved to be reliable
clues to the origin and relationship of
large groups of animals. There is no
longer any doubt that animals in general
do inherit certain deep-seated behavioral
traits. In the higher animals such traits
tend to be masked by learned behavior,
but in such creatures as fishes and birds
they reveal themselves with great clarity. These patterns of behavior must
somehow be rooted in the common phys-

iological inheritance of the species that
display them. Whatever their physiological cause, they undoubtedly form a
natural unit of heredity. The majority of
them change but slowly with evolution
in the species and stubbornly resist
learning in the individual; they have a
peculiar spontaneity and a considerable
independence of immediate sensory
stimuli. Because of their stability, they
rank with the more slowly evolving skel-
etal structure of animals as ideal subjects
for the comparative studies which aim to
unravel the history of species.

I am quite aware that biologists today
(especially young ones) tend to think of
the comparative method as stuffy and
old-fashioned—at best a branch of research that has already yielded its treas-
ures, and like a spent gold mine no longer pays the working. I believe that this
is untrue, and so I shall pause to say a
few words in behalf of comparative morphology as such. Every time a biologist
seeks to know *why* an organism looks
and acts as it does, he must resort to the
comparative method. Why does the ear
have its peculiar conformation? Why is
it mounted behind the jaw? To know the
answer the investigator must compare
the mammalian frame with that of other
vertebrates. Then he will discover that
the ear was once a gill slit. When the
first air-breathing, four-legged vertebrates came out of the sea, they lost all
but one pair of gill slits, each of which
happened to lie conveniently near the

"INCITING" is a threatening movement used by the female duck to signal her mate to attack invaders of their territory. At left a female of the European sheldrake (*with head lowered*) incites her mate against an enemy that she sees directly before her. The female at right (*with head turned*) has seen an enemy to one side. Each female watches her enemy regardless of her own body orientation.

labyrinth of the inner ear. The water canal which opened into it became filled with air and adapted itself to conducting sound waves. Thus was born the ear.

This kind of thinking is 100 years old in zoology, but in the study of behavior it is only now coming into its own. The first studies leading to a true morphology of behavior have concentrated largely on those innate motor patterns that have the function of expression or communication within a species. It is easy to see why this should be so. Whether the mode of communication is aural, as in the case of bird songs, or visual, as in the "dis-

play" movements of courtship, many of these motor patterns have evolved under the pressure of natural selection to serve as sharply defined stimuli influencing the social behavior of fellow-members of a species. The patterns are usually striking and unambiguous. These qualities, so essential to the natural function of the behavior patterns, also catch the eye of the human observer.

## Gulls, Terns and Kittiwakes

For some years N. Tinbergen of the University of Oxford has intensively

studied the innate behavior of gulls and terns: the genus *Laridae*. He has organized an international group of his students and co-workers to conduct a worldwide study of the behavior traits of gulls and terns. They are careful to observe the behavior of their subjects in the larger context of their diverse life histories and in relationship to their different environments. It is gratifying that this ambitious project has begun to meet with the success which the enthusiasm of its participants so richly deserves.

Esther Cullen, one of Tinbergen's students, has been studying an eccentric

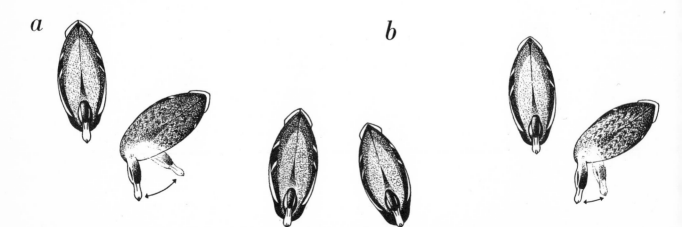

*a*    *b*

"RITUALIZED" INCITING is exhibited by mallards. In this species turning the head—as a female sheldrake does when inciting against an enemy to one side—has become an innate motor pat-tern. In situation *a* the female mallard turns her head toward the enemy. In *b*, with the enemy in front of her, she still turns her head even though this results in her turning it away from the enemy.

among the seagulls—the kittiwake. Most gulls are beachcombers and nest on the ground, and it is safe to assume that this was the original mode of life of the gull family. The kittiwake, however, is different. Except when it is breeding, it lives over the open sea. Its breeding ground is not a flat shore but the steepest of cliffs, where it nests on tiny ledges.

Mrs. Cullen has listed 33 points, both behavioral and anatomical, in which the kittiwake has come to differ from its sister species as a result of its atypical style of life. Just as the whale's flipper is a recognizable mammalian forelimb, so many of the kittiwake's habits are recognizably gull-like. But the kittiwake, like the whale, is a specialist; it has given its own twist to many of the behavior patterns that are the heritage of the *Laridae*.

For example, the male of most gull species stakes its claim to nesting territory by uttering the "long call" and striking the "oblique posture," its tail up and head down. To advertise its actual nesting site, it performs the "choking" movement. In the kittiwake the inherited patterns of behavior have been modified in accord with the habitat. On the kittiwake's tiny ledge, territory and nest sites are identical. So the kittiwake has lost the oblique posture and long call, and uses choking alone for display purposes.

Another example is the kittiwake gesture which Tinbergen calls "head-flagging." In other gull species a young gull which is not fully able to fly will run for cover when it is frightened by an adult bird. But its cliffside perch provides no cover for the young kittiwake. When it is frightened, the little kittiwake averts its head as a sign of appeasement. Such head-flagging does not occur in the young of other gulls, although it appears in the behavior of many adult gulls as the appeasement posture in a fight and in the rite of courtship. The kittiwake species has thus met an environmental demand by accelerating, in its young, the development of a standard motor habit of adult gulls.

Recently Wolfgang Wickler, one of my associates at the Max Planck Institute for Comparative Ethology, has found a similar case of adaptation by acceleration among the river-dwelling cichlid fishes. Most cichlids dig into the river bottom only at spawning time, when they excavate their nest pits. But there is an eccentric species (*Steatocranus*), a resident of the rapids of the Congo River, which lives from infancy in river-bottom burrows. In this cichlid the maturation of the digging urge of the mating fish is accelerated, appearing in

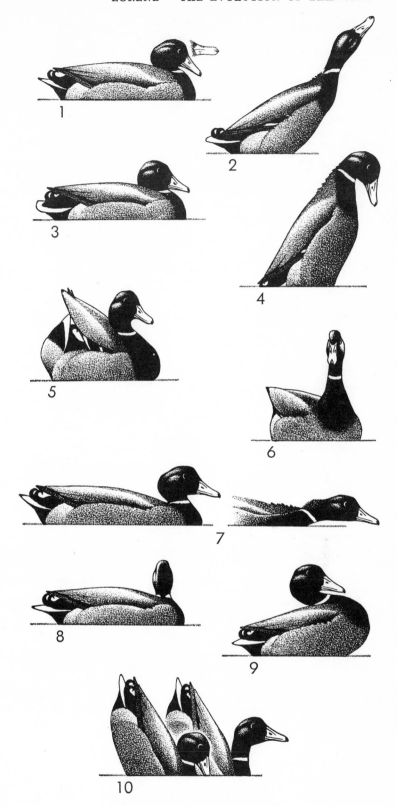

**TEN COURTSHIP POSES** which belong to the common genetic heritage of surface-feeding ducks are here shown as exemplified in the mallard: (1) **initial bill-shake**, (2) **head-flick**, (3) **tail-shake**, (4) **grunt-whistle**, (5) **head-up—tail-up**, (6) **turn toward the female**, (7) **nod-swimming**, (8) **turning the back of the head**, (9) **bridling**, (10) **down-up**. How the mallard and two other species form sequences of these poses is illustrated on pages 38 through 41.

the infant of the species. It is not hard to conceive how selection pressure could have led to this result.

The work of the Tinbergen school has had the important result of placing innate motor habits in their proper setting. He and his co-workers have shown that these traits are highly resistant to evolutionary change, and that they often retain their original form even when their function has diverged considerably. These findings amply justify the metaphor that describes innate patterns as the skeleton of behavior. More work of the Tinbergen kind is badly needed. There

is great value in his synthetic approach, uniting the study of the physical nature and environment of animals with study of their behavior. Any such project is of course a tall order. It requires concerted field work by investigators at widely separated points on the globe.

### Behavior in the Laboratory

Fortunately it is quite feasible to approach the innate motor patterns as an isolated topic for examination in the laboratory. Thanks to their stability they are not masked in the behavior of the

captive animal. If only we do not forget the existence of the many other physiological mechanisms that affect behavior, including that of learning, it is legitimate for us to begin with these innate behavior traits. The least variable part of a system is always the best one to examine first; in the complex interaction of all parts, it must appear most frequently as a cause and least frequently as an effect.

Comparative study of innate motor patterns represents an important part of the research program at the Max Planck Institute for Comparative Ethology. Our

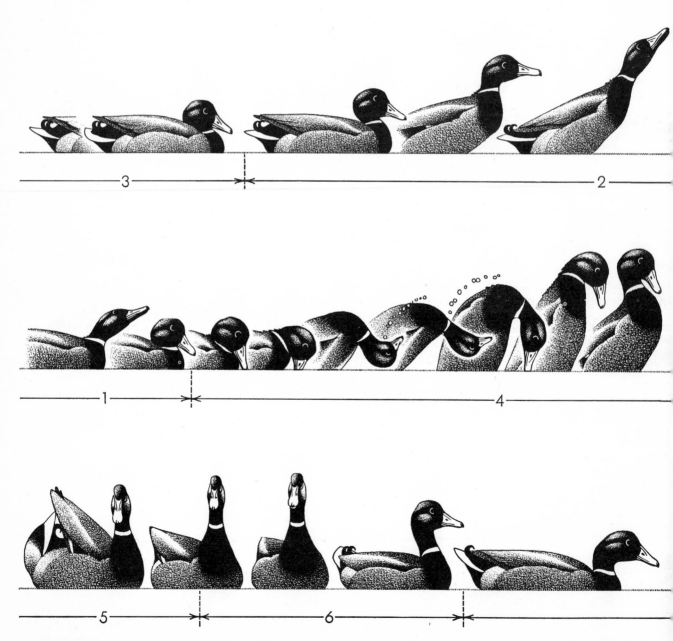

**COURTSHIP SEQUENCES OF MALLARD** are shown in this series of drawings, based on motion pictures made by the author at

his laboratory in Seewiesen, Germany. Each sequence combines in fixed order several of the 10 innate courtship poses illustrated on

subjects are the various species of dabbling, or surface-feeding, ducks. By observing minute variations of behavior traits between species on the one hand and their hybrids on the other we hope to arrive at a phylogenetics of behavior.

Our comparative studies have developed sufficient information about the behavior traits of existing species to permit us to observe the transmission, suppression and combination of these traits in hybrid offspring. Ordinarily it is difficult to find species which differ markedly with respect to a particular characteristic and which yet will produce fertile hybrids. This is true especially with respect to behavioral traits, because these tend to be highly conservative. Species which differ sufficiently in behavior seldom produce offspring of unlimited fertility. However, closely related species which differ markedly in their patterns of sexual display are often capable of producing fertile hybrids. These motor patterns serve not only to bring about mating within a species but to prevent mating between closely allied species. Selection pressure sets in to make these patterns as different as possible as quickly as possible. As a result species will diverge markedly in sexual display behavior and yet retain the capacity to interbreed. This has turned out to be the case with dabbling ducks.

The first thing we wanted to know was how the courtship patterns of ducks become fixed. Credit is due to Sir Julian Huxley, who as long ago as 1914 had observed this process, which he called "ritualization." We see it clearly in the so-called "inciting" movement of female dabbling ducks, diving ducks, perching ducks and sheldrakes.

To see "inciting" in its original unritualized form, let us watch the female

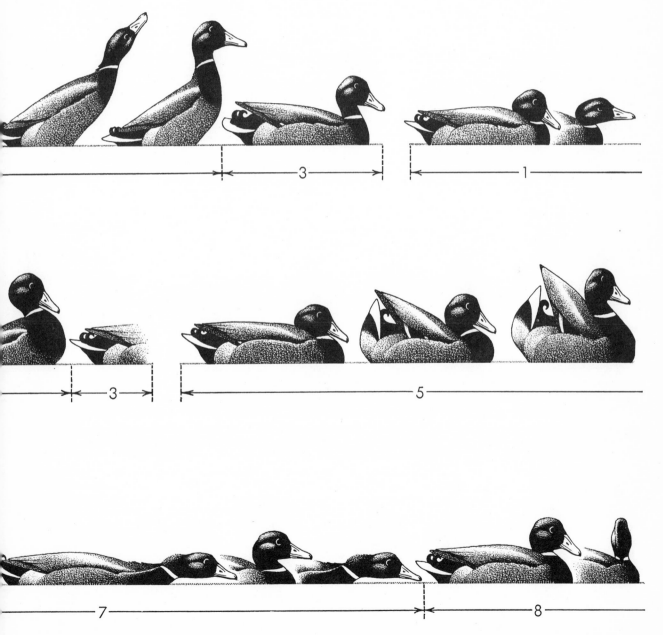

page 37. The numbers under the ducks refer to these poses. Shown here are the following obligatory sequences: tail-shake, head flick, tail-shake; bill-shake, grunt-whistle, tail-shake; head-up tail-up, turn toward female, nod-swimming, turning back of the head.

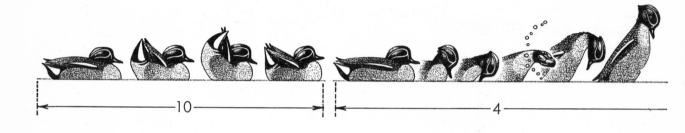

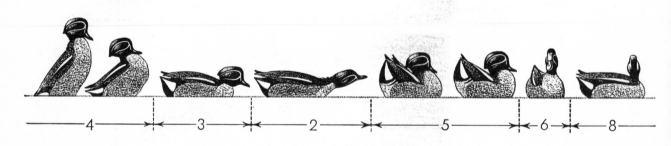

**COURTSHIP OF EUROPEAN TEAL**—another species of surface-feeding duck—includes tail-shake, head-flick, tail-shake (as in the mallard); down-up; grunt-whistle, tail-shake, head-flick, head-up-tail-up, turned toward the female, turning back of the head.

of the common sheldrake as she and her mate encounter another pair of sheldrakes at close quarters. Being far more excitable than her placid companion, the female attacks the "enemy" couple, that is, she adopts a threatening attitude and runs toward them at full tilt. It happens, however, that her escape reaction is quite as strong as her aggressive one. She has only to come within a certain distance of the enemy for the escape stimulus to overpower her, whereupon she turns tail and flees to the protection of her mate. When she has run a safe distance, she experiences a renewal of the aggressive impulse. Perhaps by this time she has retreated behind her mate. In that case she struts up beside him, and, as they both face the enemy, she makes threatening gestures toward them. But more likely she has not yet reached her mate when the aggressive impulse re-

turns. In that case she may stop in her tracks. With her body still oriented toward her mate, she will turn her head and threaten the enemy over her shoulder. In this stance she is said to "incite" an aggressive attitude in her partner.

Now the incitement posture of the female sheldrake does not constitute an innate behavior trait. It is the entirely plastic resultant of the pressure of two independent variables: her impulse to attack and her impulse to flee. The orientation of her head and body reflects the geometry of her position with respect to her mate and the enemy.

The same incitement posture in mallards, on the other hand, is distinctly ritualized. In striking her pose the female mallard is governed by an inherited motor pattern. She cannot help thrusting her head backward over her shoulder. She does this even if it means she must

point her bill away from the enemy! In the sheldrake this posture is the resultant of the creature's display of two conflicting impulses. In the mallard it has become a fixed motor pattern.

No doubt this motor pattern evolved fairly recently. It is interesting to note that while the female mallard is impelled to look over her shoulder when inciting, the older urge to look at the enemy is still there. Her head travels much farther backward when the enemy is behind her. If you observe closely, it is plain that her eyes are fixed on the enemy, no matter which way her head is turned.

Occasionally a female, impelled by the awkwardness of watching the enemy from the ritualized posture, will swing about and face them directly. In that case one may say that her old and new motor patterns are simultaneously active. Like the sheldrake, the mallard must once have faced the enemy during incitement. Overlying this instinct is a new one—to move her head backward over her shoulder regardless of the location of the enemy. The old orienting response survives in part. It usually displays itself at low levels of excitement. Especially at the beginning of a response, the female

mallard may stretch her neck straight forward. As her excitement mounts, however, the new motor pattern irresistibly draws her head around. This is one of many instances in which the mounting intensity of a stimulus increases the fixity of the motor coordination.

What has happened is that two independent movements have been welded together to form a new and fixed motor pattern. It is possible that all new patterns are formed by such a welding process. Sometimes two patterns remain rigidly welded. Sometimes they weld only under great excitement.

Recently we have been studying be-

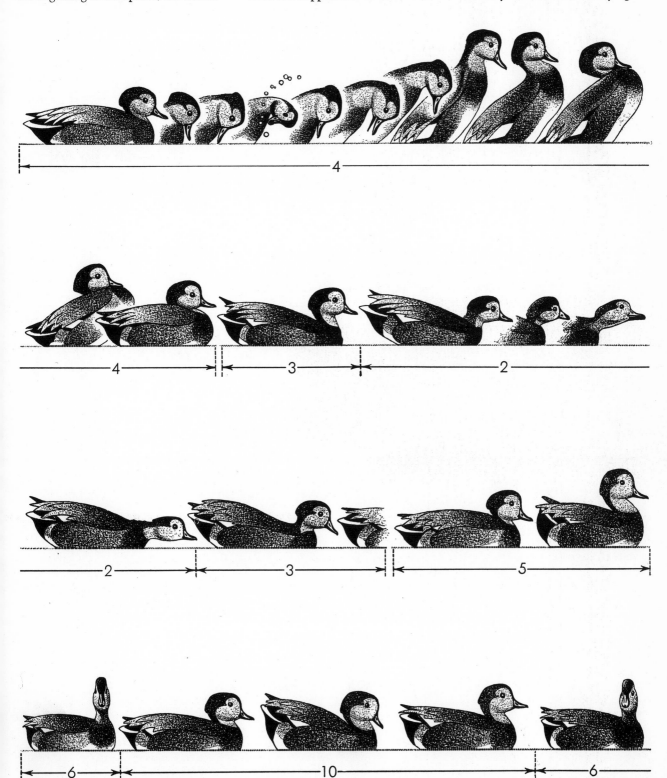

GADWALL COURTSHIP includes the grunt-whistle, always followed by the tail-shake, head-flick, tail-shake sequence also found in the other species illustrated. The head-up–tail-up (5) and the down-up (10) are always followed by a turn toward the female (6). During the most intense excitement of the courtship display, these pairs themselves become welded into the invariable sequence 5-6-10-6.

havior complexes in which more than two patterns are welded. In their courtship behavior our surface-feeding ducks display some 20 elementary innate motor patterns. We have made a special study of three species which have 10 motor patterns in common but display them welded into different combinations. As shown in the illustration on page 37, these patterns are (1) initial bill-shake, (2) head-flick, (3) tail-shake, (4) grunt-whistle, (5) head-up—tail-up, (6) turn toward the female, (7) nod-swimming, (8) turning the back of the head, (9) bridling, (10) down-up movement. Some of the combinations in which these motor patterns are displayed are shown on pages 38 through 42. In some species certain of the patterns occur independently (*e.g.*, 1 and 10 in the mallard). Some simple combinations have wide distribution in other species as well (*e.g.*,

4, 3 and 5, 6 in all the species). Many combinations are more complicated, as the illustrations show.

What happens when these ducks are crossbred? By deliberate breeding we have produced new combinations of motor patterns, often combining traits of both parents, sometimes suppressing the traits of one or the other parent and sometimes exhibiting traits not apparent in either. We have even reproduced some of the behavior-pattern combinations which occur in natural species other than the parents of the hybrid. Study of our first-generation hybrids indicates that many differences in courtship patterns among our duck species may also be due to secondary loss, that is, to suppression of an inherited trait. Crosses between the Chiloe teal and the Bahama pintail regularly perform the head-up—tail-up, although neither parent is ca-

pable of this. The only possible conclusion is that one parent species is latently in possession of this behavioral trait, and that its expression in a given species is prevented by some inhibiting factor. So far our only second-generation hybrids are crosses between the Chiloe pintail and the Bahama pintail. The results look promising. The drakes of this generation differ greatly from each other and display hitherto unheard-of combinations of courtship patterns. One has even fused the down-up movement with the grunt-whistle!

Thus we have shown that the differences in innate motor patterns which distinguish species from one another can be duplicated by hybridization. This suggests that motor patterns are dependent on comparatively simple constellations of genetic factors.

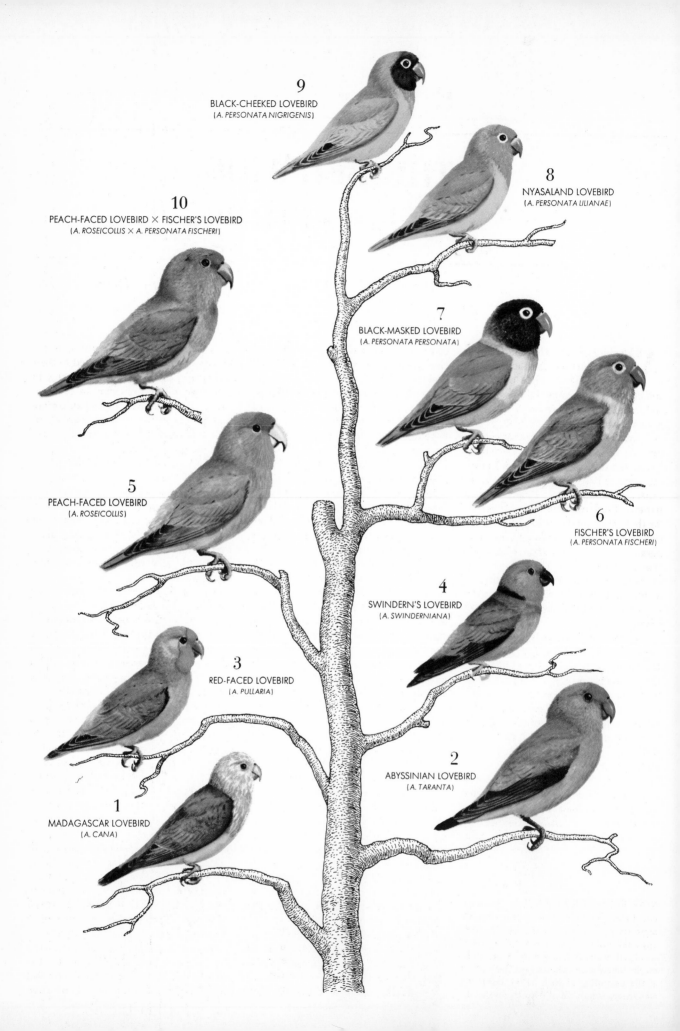

9
BLACK-CHEEKED LOVEBIRD
(*A. PERSONATA NIGRIGENIS*)

8
NYASALAND LOVEBIRD
(*A. PERSONATA LILIANAE*)

10
PEACH-FACED LOVEBIRD × FISCHER'S LOVEBIRD
(*A. ROSEICOLLIS × A. PERSONATA FISCHERI*)

7
BLACK-MASKED LOVEBIRD
(*A. PERSONATA PERSONATA*)

5
PEACH-FACED LOVEBIRD
(*A. ROSEICOLLIS*)

6
FISCHER'S LOVEBIRD
(*A. PERSONATA FISCHERI*)

4
SWINDERN'S LOVEBIRD
(*A. SWINDERNIANA*)

3
RED-FACED LOVEBIRD
(*A. PULLARIA*)

2
ABYSSINIAN LOVEBIRD
(*A. TARANTA*)

1
MADAGASCAR LOVEBIRD
(*A. CANA*)

# THE BEHAVIOR OF LOVEBIRDS

WILLIAM C. DILGER                    January 1962

All lovebirds display the behavior that gives them their anthropomorphic common name. They pair early, and once pairs are formed they normally endure for life. The partners exhibit their mutual interest with great constancy and in a variety of beguiling activities. For the student of the evolution of animal behavior the lovebirds have special interest. The genus comprises nine forms (species or subspecies). They show a pattern of differentiation in their behavior that corresponds to their differentiation in color and morphology. By comparative study of their behavior, therefore, one can hope to reconstruct its evolution and to observe how natural selection has brought about progressive variations on the same fundamental scheme.

Together with my colleagues in the Laboratory of Ornithology at Cornell University, I have been studying both the constants and the variables in lovebird behavior for the past five years. It is not too difficult to duplicate in the laboratory the basic features of the lovebirds' natural African environment, so the birds thrive in captivity. Our work has covered all the lovebirds except Swindern's lovebird; we have not been able to obtain any specimens of this species. Our findings in two areas—sexual behavior and the defense and construction of the nest—have been particularly fruitful, be-

cause in these areas the evolutionary changes in lovebird behavior stand out in sharp relief.

Lovebirds constitute the genus *Agapornis,* and are members of the parrot family. Their closest living relatives are the hanging parakeets of Asia (the genus *Loriculus*). Three species of lovebird—the Madagascar lovebird, the Abyssinian lovebird and the red-faced lovebird—resemble the hanging parakeets and differ from all other lovebirds in two major respects. The males and females of these three species differ in color and are easily distinguishable from each other. The male and female of the other lovebirds are the same color. In these three species the primary social unit is the pair and its immature offspring. The other lovebirds are highly social and tend to nest in colonies. In these respects, then, the Madagascar lovebird, the Abyssinian lovebird and the red-faced lovebird most closely resemble the ancestral form, and the other lovebirds are more divergent.

Our study of interspecies differentiation of behavior has begun to reveal the order in which the other species arrived on the scene. Next after the three "primitive" species is Swindern's lovebird. Then comes the peach-faced lovebird and finally the four subspecies of *Agapornis personata,* commonly referred to as the white-eye-ringed forms: Fischer's lovebird, the black-masked lovebird, the Nyasaland lovebird and the black-cheeked lovebird. There are significant differences in behavior between the peach-faced lovebird and the four white-eye-ringed forms.

Perhaps the sharpest contrasts in behavior are those that distinguish the three primitive species from the species that evolved later. Even the common generic characteristic of pairing at an

early age shows changes between the two groups that must be related to their contrasting patterns of life—nesting in pairs as opposed to nesting in colonies. Among the primitive species pair formation takes place when the birds are about four months old. At that time they are entirely independent of their parents and have already developed adult plumage. In the more recently evolved species, the colonial nesting pattern of which offers them access to their contemporaries virtually from the moment of their birth, pair formation takes place even earlier: the birds are about two months old and still have their juvenile plumage.

Among all the lovebird species pair formation is a rather undramatic event. Unpaired birds seek out the company of other unpaired birds and test them, as it were, by attempting to preen them and otherwise engage their interest. Couples quickly discover if they are compatible, and generally it takes no more than a few hours to establish lifelong pairs.

When the paired birds reach sexual maturity, their behavior with respect to each other becomes much more elaborate. This behavior as a whole is common to all lovebirds, and some activities are performed in the same way by all. Other activities, however, are not, and they show a gradation from the most primitive forms to the most recently evolved ones. One constant among all species is the female's frequent indifference to, and even active aggression against, the male each time he begins to woo her. Another is the essential pattern of the male's response—a combination of fear, sexual appetite, aggression and consequent frustration. Primarily motivated by both fear and sexual appetite, the male makes his first approach to his mate by sidling toward and then away from

NINE FORMS OF LOVEBIRD, as well as one hybrid (*top left*), are shown on the opposite page. They are arranged in their apparent order of evolution. The hybrid was bred in the laboratory for experiments on the inheritance of behavior. The letter *A.* at the beginning of each of the Latin species names stands for the genus *Agapornis.*

her while turning about on his perch. This switch-sidling, as it is called, is common to all species.

Two forms of male behavior initially associated with frustration, on the other hand, show a distinct evolutionary progression. The first of these activities is called squeak-twittering. Among the three primitive species—the Madagascar lovebird, the Abyssinian lovebird and the red-faced lovebird—the male utters a series of high-pitched vocalizations when the female thwarts him by disappearing into the nest cavity. The sounds are quite variable in pitch and purity of tone and have no recognizable rhythm. In the more recently evolved species—the peach-faced and the four white-eye-ringed forms—squeak-twittering is rather different. The sound is rhythmic, purer in tone and less variable in pitch. Nor does it occur only when the female has turned her back on the male and entered the nest cavity. The male usually vocalizes even when the female is present and gives no indication whatever of thwarting him. Squeak-twittering has undergone a progressive change not only in its physical characteristics but also in the context in which it appears.

A similar evolution toward more highly ritualized behavior has occurred in another sexual activity, displacement

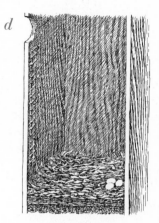

**BEHAVIOR OF MADAGASCAR LOVEBIRD** is outlined. Both sexes engage in courtship feeding (*a*). Accompanying head bobs are rapid and trace small arc (*b*). Nest materials, generally bark and leaves, are carried several pieces at a time and tucked among

**BEHAVIOR OF PEACH-FACED LOVEBIRD** suggests higher evolutionary stage. Only males perform courtship feeding; females fluff their feathers during this ritual (*a*). Slower head bobs trace wider arc (*b*). Nest materials, also bark and leaves, are

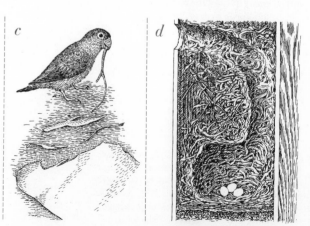

**BEHAVIOR OF FISCHER'S LOVEBIRD** indicates a further evolution. Courtship feeding (*a*), mobbing (*e*) and bill-fencing (*f*) are performed much as they are by the peach-faced lovebird. But other kinds of behavior are significantly different. Head bobs

scratching. This response derives from the habit, common to all species, of scratching the head with the foot when frustrated. Among the three primitive species displacement scratching is still close to its origins. Only two things distinguish it from ordinary head-scratching: its context and the fact that it is always performed with the foot nearest the female. Purely practical considerations govern this behavior: the male already has that foot raised preparatory to mounting his mate. In the more recently evolved species, displacement scratching has become primarily a form of display. Its progressive emancipation from the original motivation with which it is associated becomes more and more apparent as one observes it in the species from the peach-faced lovebird through the white-eye-ringed forms. Among all these the scratching is far more rapid and perfunctory than it is among the primitive species. Nor is it uniformly directed at the feathered portions of the head. In the peach-faced lovebird it is sometimes directed at the bill instead, and among the Nyasaland and black-cheeked lovebirds it is nearly always so directed. Moreover, these species use the far foot as well as the near one in displacement scratching; among the Nyasaland and black-cheeked lovebirds one is

 *e*     *f*

all feathers of the body (*c*). Short strips are used to make an unshaped nest pad (*d*). **The young join the mother in cavity-**

defense display (*e*). In *f* birds show threat and appeasement display. It usually averts combat; if it fails, the birds fight furiously.

*e*     *f*

carried several at a time in back plumage (*c*); long strips are used to make a well-shaped nest (*d*). **Birds join in "mobbing" to**

protect nest (*e*). Bill-fencing (*f*) has a display function. It never leads to real harm; the birds bite only their opponents' toes.

*e*     *f*

(*b*) are still slower and trace an even wider arc. Nest materials are carried in the bill, one piece at a time (*c*); twigs as well

as strips of bark and leaf are used. This permits construction of an elaborate covered nest, entered through a tunnel (*d*).

used as often as the other. Finally, as in the case of squeak-twittering, which is often performed at the same time as displacement scratching among these species, the display occurs even when the female does not seem to be thwarting her mate.

All species engage in courtship feeding: the transfer of regurgitated food from one member of the pair to the other. In the three primitive species the female often offers food to her mate. This behavior has never been observed among the peach-faced and white-eye-ringed forms; here courtship feeding seems exclusively a male prerogative.

One can also discern an evolutionary progression in the manner in which the birds carry out the rather convulsive bobbing of the head associated with the act of regurgitation that immediately precedes courtship feeding. Among the primitive species these head-bobbings describe a small arc, are rapid and numerous and are usually followed by rather prolonged bill contacts while the food is being transferred. In the other forms the head-bobbings are slower, fewer in

number and trace a wider arc; the bill contacts usually last for only a short time. Moreover, among the more recently evolved forms head-bobbing has become pure display; it is no longer accompanied by the feeding of the female. Unlike the females of the primitive lovebird species, which have no special display activity during courtship feeding, the females of the more recently evolved species play a distinctly ritualized role. They ruffle their plumage throughout the entire proceeding.

Females of all species indicate their fluctuating readiness to copulate by subtle adjustments of their plumage, particularly the feathers of the head. The more the female fluffs, the readier she is, and the more the male is encouraged. Finally she will solicit copulation by leaning forward and raising her head and tail. Females of the primitive species do not fluff their plumage during copulation; females of the more recently evolved species do. This is undoubtedly related to the morphological differences among the lovebirds. Since males and females of the more recently evolved species have the same coloring and patterning, the

females must reinforce their mates' recognition of them, both in courtship and in copulation, by some behavioral means.

Although the forms of precopulatory behavior seem to be innate among all species, learning appears to play a major role in producing the changes that occur as the members of a pair become more familiar with each other. Newly formed pairs are rather awkward. The males make many mistakes and are frequently threatened and thwarted by their mates. After they have had a few broods, however, and have acquired experience, they become more expert and tend more and more to perform the right activity at the right time. As a result the female responds with aggression far less often, and the male engages more rarely in the displays that are associated with frustration and thwarting. Squeak-twittering and displacement scratching in particular become less frequent. Switch-sidling is still performed, but with a perceptibly diminished intensity. Altogether precopulatory bouts become less protracted. In spite of the male's reduced activity, the female seems to become receptive fairly quickly.

Disagreements among members of the same species are handled in quite different ways by those lovebirds that nest in pairs and those that nest colonially. Among the less social primitive species an elaborate pattern of threat and appeasement display has developed. For example, a formalized series of long, rapid strides toward an opponent signalizes aggression; a ruffling of the feathers, fear and the wish to escape. The loser in a bout of posturing may indicate submission by fleeing or by remaining quiet, turning its head away from its opponent and fluffing its plumage. By means of this code the birds can communicate rather exact items of information as to their readiness to attack or to flee. As a result actual fights seldom occur. When they do, however, the birds literally tear each other apart.

The peach-faced lovebird and the white-eye-ringed forms, which nest colonially, are thrown in contact with members of their own species much more often. This is undoubtedly related to the fact that they have developed a ritualized form of display fighting that goes far beyond a mere code of threat and appeasement and that replaces serious physical conflict. Display fighting among these more recently evolved species consists primarily of bill-fencing. The two birds parry and thrust with their bills and aim sharp nips at each other's toes.

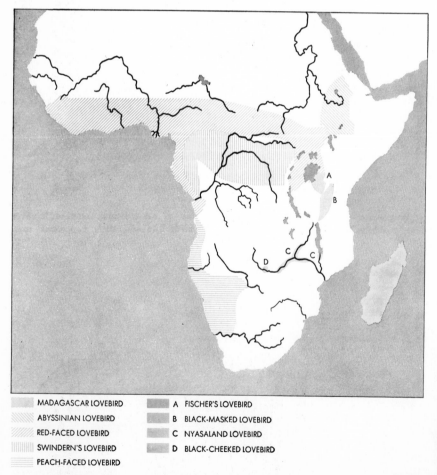

MADAGASCAR LOVEBIRD
ABYSSINIAN LOVEBIRD
RED-FACED LOVEBIRD
SWINDERN'S LOVEBIRD
PEACH-FACED LOVEBIRD

A  FISCHER'S LOVEBIRD
B  BLACK-MASKED LOVEBIRD
C  NYASALAND LOVEBIRD
D  BLACK-CHEEKED LOVEBIRD

**DISTRIBUTION OF LOVEBIRDS** is shown on this map of Africa and the island of Madagascar. All nine of the lovebird species and subspecies inhabit different areas.

SQUEAK-TWITTERING in male Madagascar lovebird is seen on sound spectrogram. The horizontal axis represents time; the vertical axis, frequency. Uneven distribution of spots along both axes shows an arhythmic quality and a wide variation in pitch.

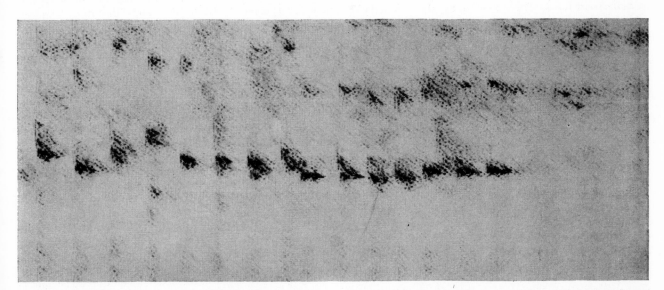

SOUND SPECTROGRAM of squeak-twittering in peach-faced lovebird shows greater rhythmicity and less variation in pitch. In Madagascar lovebird behavior is displayed only when female thwarts male. In peach-faced lovebird this is not always the case.

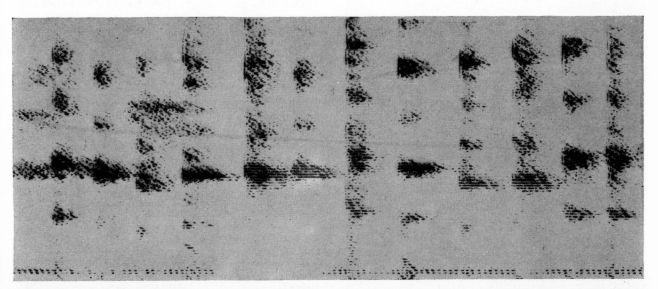

FURTHER EVOLUTION in squeak-twittering is seen in behavior of Nyasaland lovebird. Sounds are very rhythmic and show almost no variation in pitch; wide vertical distribution of spots reflects the large number of harmonics contained in the monotonous note.

The toe is the only part the birds ever bite, and the inhibition against biting a member of the same species in any other place seems to be, like bill-fencing itself, an innate pattern. Though bill-fencing appears to be innate, it must be perfected by learning. The colonial nesting pattern offers young birds considerable practice with their contemporaries, and they quickly become skilled.

If lovebirds have had experience in rearing their own young, they will not rear the young of those other forms that have a natal down of a different color. On the other hand, a female that is given the egg of such a form at the time of her first egg-laying will rear the bird that emerges. Indeed, if a peach-faced lovebird has her first experience of motherhood with a newly hatched Madagascar

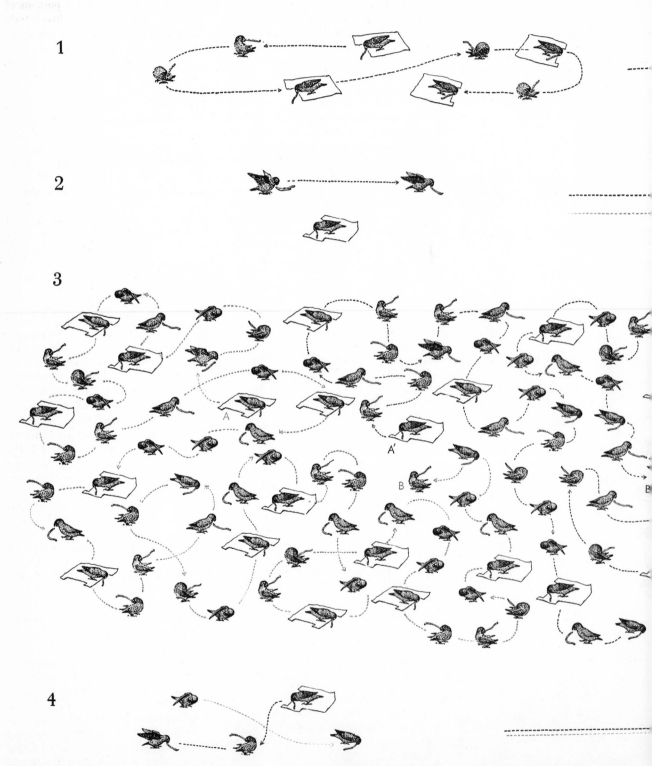

**HYBRID LOVEBIRD** inherits patterns for two different ways of carrying nest-building materials. From the peach-faced lovebird (1) it inherits patterns for carrying strips several at a time, in feathers. From Fischer's lovebird (2) it inherits patterns for carrying strips one at a time, in the bill. When the hybrid first begins to build a nest (3), it acts completely confused. Colored lines from *A* to *B* and black lines from *A'* to *B'* indicate the number of activities necessary for it to get two strips to the nest site, a feat achieved only when the strips are carried singly, in the bill. It takes three years before the bird perfects its bill-carrying behavior (4).

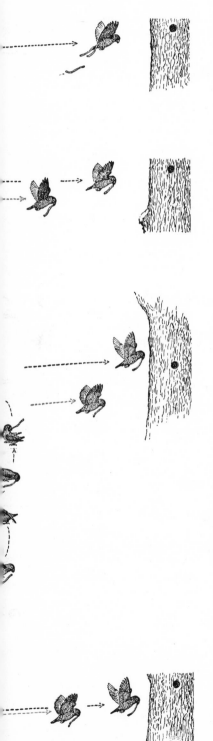

lovebird, she will thereafter refuse to raise her own offspring. The down of the peach-faced lovebird's newly hatched young (like the down of the white-eye-ringed forms) is red, and the down of newly hatched Madagascar, Abyssinian and red-faced lovebirds is white.

and even then it makes efforts to tuck its nest materials in its feathers. As the bird gains experience it becomes more and more proficient in this activity, which, however, never results in successful carrying.

Unlike most of the other members of the parrot family, which simply lay their eggs in empty cavities, all lovebird species make nests. The red-faced lovebird constructs its nest in a hole it digs in the hard, earthy nests certain ants make in trees. All other species, however, make their nests in pre-existing cavities, which are usually reached through small entrances. The nests of the Madagascar lovebird, the Abyssinian lovebird and the red-faced lovebird are quite simple, consisting essentially of deposits of soft material on the cavity floor. These three species have developed an elaborate cavity-defense display. The moment an intruder appears, the female ruffles her feathers, partly spreads her wings and tail and utters a rapid series of harsh, buzzing sounds. If the intruder persists, she will suddenly compress her plumage, utter a piercing yip and lunge toward it. She does not bite, but she gives every indication of being about to do so. Her older offspring may join her at this time, ruffling their feathers and making grating sounds.

The effect of this performance is quite startling; it can even give pause to an experienced investigator! The Madagascar lovebird, the most primitive of all the species, is the quickest to engage in the cavity-defense display and is the only species we have seen carry the display through both stages. A stronger stimulation is necessary before the Abyssinian lovebird engages in this behavior, and we have not seen the bird go any further than ruffling its body plumage and making the harsh, rasping sounds.

The white-eye-ringed lovebirds build rather elaborate nests, consisting of a roofed chamber at the end of a tunnel within the cavity. This fact and their strongly social nature combine to make their response to a threat to their nests different from the response of the primitive species. They have no cavity-defense displays at all. If a predator actually reaches the cavity, the birds within it will either cower or, if possible, flee through the entrance. But if the predator, encouraged by this show of fear, enters the cavity, it is likely to find that its troubles have just begun. It faces a journey down a narrow tunnel, defended at the end by a bird with a powerful and sharp bill. Moreover, a predator is seldom allowed to come close to the cavity. As soon as it is seen approaching, the entire colony engages in a form of behavior called mobbing: holding their bodies vertically, the birds beat their wings rapidly and utter loud, high-pitched squeaks. The sight and sound of a whole flock mobbing is quite impressive and probably serves to deter many would-be predators.

All female lovebirds prepare their nest materials in much the same way: by punching a series of closely spaced holes in some pliable material such as paper, bark or leaf. The material is held between the upper and lower portions of the bill, which then works like a train conductor's ticket punch. The pieces cut out in this way vary in size and shape among the various lovebirds. So do the forms of behavior that now ensue.

The three primitive species and the peach-faced lovebird tuck the pieces they have cut into the feathers of their bodies and fly off with them. The Madagascar lovebird, the Abyssinian lovebird and the red-faced lovebird use very small bits of material. (This is one of the reasons their nests are so unstructured.) The entire plumage of the bird is erected as it inserts the six to eight bits of material in place and remains erect during the whole operation. The peach-faced lovebird cuts strips that are considerably longer. (This permits the more elaborate structuring of its cuplike nest.) Indeed, the strips are so long that they can be carried only in the feathers of the lower back. These are the feathers erected when the strips are tucked in, and the feathers are compressed after each strip is inserted. The peach-faced lovebird loses about half of its cargo before it gets to its nest site; either pieces fall out while others are being cut or tucked in, or they fall out while the bird is flying. The lovebirds that use smaller bits of nest material are more successful in carrying them.

Carrying nest material in the feathers is unique to these birds and the related hanging parakeets. What is more, speculation about its origin must begin with the fact that no other parrots (with one unrelated exception) build nests at all. It is almost certain that this behavior arose from fortuitous occurrences associated with two characteristic parrot activities: chewing on bits of wood, bark and leaf to keep the bill sharp and properly worn down; and preening, which serves to keep the plumage clean and properly arranged. Some parrots that do not build nests will accidentally leave bits of the material in their feathers when they proceed directly from chewing to preening. Such oversights almost certainly initiated the evolution of the habit of carrying nest materials in the feathers.

The four white-eye-ringed forms are completely emancipated from this ancestral pattern. Fischer's lovebird, the black-masked lovebird, the Nyasaland lovebird and the black-cheeked lovebird all carry their nest materials as do most birds—in their bills. They lose little material in the process of carrying, and they pick up twigs in addition to cutting strips of pliable material. With these materials, they can build their characteristically elaborate nests.

Although the peach-faced lovebird normally carries its nest-building material in its feathers, on about 3 per cent of its trips it carries material in its bill. This peculiarity suggested an experiment. We mated the peach-faced lovebird with Fischer's lovebird (the birds hybridize readily in captivity) to see what behavior would show up in the hybrids. In confirmation of the thesis that patterns of carrying nest materials are primarily innate, the hybrid displays a conflict in behavior between the tendency to carry material in its feathers (inherited from the peach-faced lovebird) and the tendency to carry material in its bill (inherited from Fischer's lovebird).

When our hybrids first began to build their nests, they acted as though they were completely confused. They had no difficulty in cutting strips, but they could not seem to determine whether to carry them in the feathers or in the bill. They got material to the nest sites only when they carried it in the bill, and in their first effort at nest building they did carry in their bills 6 per cent of the time. After they had cut each strip, however, they engaged in behavior associated with tucking. Even when they finally carried the material in the bill, they erected the feathers of the lower back and rump and attempted to tuck. But if they were able to press the strips into their plumage—and they were not always successful in the attempt—they could not carry it to the nest site in that fashion. Every strip dropped out.

Two months later, after they had become more experienced, the hybrids carried many more of their nest strips in their bills—41 per cent, to be exact. But they continued to make the movements associated with the intention to tuck: they erected their rump plumage and turned their heads to the rear, flying away with material in their bills only after attempting to tuck.

After two more months had passed they began to learn that strips could be picked up in the bill and carried off with a minimum of prior abortive tucking. But it took two years for them to learn to diminish actual tucking activity to any great extent, and even then they continued to perform many of the movements associated with tucking.

Today the hybrids are behaving, by and large, like Fischer's lovebird, the more recently evolved of their two parents. Only infrequently do they attempt to tuck strips into their plumage. But it has taken them three years to reach this stage—evidence of the difficulty they experience in learning to use one innate pattern at the expense of another, even though the latter is never successful. Moreover, when they do carry out the activities associated with tucking, they perform them far more efficiently than they did at first. Evidently this behavior need not achieve its normal objective in order to be improved.

So far our hybrids have proved to be sterile and therefore unable to pass on their behavior to a second generation. Even in the first generation, however, one can see the ways in which nature interweaves innate and learned elements to produce the behavior characteristic of a species. Further comparative studies can add much to our understanding, not only of the behavior of lovebirds but also of the behavior of all vertebrates, including man.

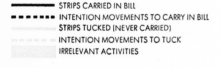

STRIPS CARRIED IN BILL
INTENTION MOVEMENTS TO CARRY IN BILL
STRIPS TUCKED (NEVER CARRIED)
INTENTION MOVEMENTS TO TUCK
IRRELEVANT ACTIVITIES

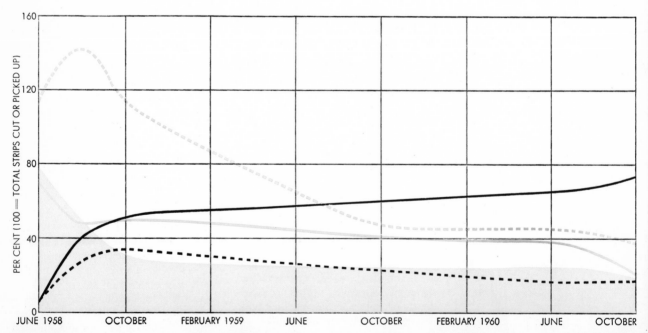

**CONFLICTING PATTERNS** of carrying nest-building materials are inherited by a hybrid lovebird, produced by mating the peach-faced and Fischer's lovebirds. The hybrid's behavior is charted here for a period of almost three years. As the bird progressively learns to carry nest materials as Fischer's lovebird does, the number of irrelevant movements and inappropriate activities decreases.

# Part II

# PHYSIOLOGICAL DETERMINANTS OF INSTINCTIVE BEHAVIOR

# II

## PHYSIOLOGICAL DETERMINANTS OF INSTINCTIVE BEHAVIOR

*Introduction*    As stated earlier, instinct theories for many years have implied that there exist in the brain genetically coded motivational centers which control particular behavior patterns. This notion was based upon extensive observations and analyses of behavior, but not upon direct studies of the brain. In recent years, however, physiological analyses of behavior have been carried out, which reveal much of interest about the nature of the biological bases of behavior.

Working in Europe in the 1930's, W. R. Hess was one of the first to show definitively that centers that control behavior do exist in the brain. Hess developed techniques for stimulating electrically certain structures deep in the brains of cats and was able to show that such stimulation would induce the cats to exhibit organized defensive reactions and also behavior associated with going to sleep. In "Electrically Controlled Behavior" (page 56), E. von Holst and U. von Saint Paul present a modern version of the Hess-type experiment. They show that electrical stimulation in the chicken brain can induce all the types of behavior and vocalization that naturally occur in chickens. Von Holst and von Saint Paul also make the important observation that the elicitation of one motivational state by electrical stimulation simultaneously inhibits other drive states, a finding which may help to clarify many behavioral observations about the interactions between drive states. The article deals with the problem of drive interaction in some detail—and with good reason, for this is an area in which we have too little information.

Of course, stimulation of the brain need not be by electrical means. In "Chemical Stimulation of the Brain" (page 66) A. E. Fisher shows us that chemicals and hormones, if applied directly to brain tissue, will cause changes in behavior. Fisher's work leads to the very important idea that the neurons in the brain are not only spatially organized, but are "chemically coded" in the sense that they respond to specific chemicals as part of their control of behavior.

The fact that different brain cells are particularly sensitive to different chemicals raises the question of why this is so. Although it would be easy to explain these differential sensitivities in terms of gene action, we must be cautious in so doing. S. Levine demonstrates in "Sex Differences in the Brain" (page 76) that the sensitivity of brain cells is in part determined by the hormonal environment of the cells during maturation. Levine points out that the type of control the brain exerts over the pituitary gland—and thus over behavior—is different in male and female animals, and that this difference depends upon whether or not the animal is stimulated by hormone during a critical period in its development. Proper control over the hormone environment in infancy can lead to masculinized female animals and feminized male animals.

In the rat, the hormonal control of mating behavior is relatively simple. This is not the case in birds, as D. S. Lehrman explains in "The Reproductive Behavior of Ring Doves" (page 82). The reproductive sequence in the dove contains several components—courtship, nest building, egg laying, and incubation—each under control of a different hormone state and stimulus condition. Apparently, the behavior occurring at one point produces stimuli that cause internal changes, which then bring about the appearance of another component of the pattern. Lehrman shows that the changes produced by behavior are changes in the secretion of pituitary and gonadal hormones. By selectively administering these hormones to the doves, Lehrman is able to show which component of the behavior is controlled by which hormone. His research indicates that the total behavior pattern is controlled by a sequence of events: stimuli→brain→hormone secretion→brain→behavior.

All of these studies make clear the fact that the brain, the glands, and the sense organs do not act alone in the modulation of behavior. All components interact to produce the complex behavior patterns that we observe in the laboratory and in the field.

# 7

# ELECTRICALLY CONTROLLED BEHAVIOR

ERICH VON HOLST AND
URSULA VON SAINT PAUL

March 1962

We all recognize that many human actions are controlled by drives, which we can steer but which we cannot easily ignore. We become hungry, thirsty, sleepy; we crave affection; sometimes we are angry or frightened. If we classify an action as controlled by drives when it is not planned or directed by conscious intelligence, then we can maintain that nearly all kinds of animal behavior, and rather large portions of human behavior, are drive-controlled. Often we are not aware of why we act as we do. This lack of awareness takes a number of forms.

A boy who stops in front of several grocery stores on his way home from school may not realize that it is hunger that makes the window displays so attractive to him. He may remember only later that he has missed his lunch that day. In this example the drive accentuates whatever is most important among the things that can be perceived.

A man who is kept waiting by a young lady may approach a complete stranger, thinking her to be the person he is expecting. He does not realize that it is his longing that transforms the stranger into the person he is expecting; he is only annoyed by his poor eyesight. Here the drive has led to a change in perception, an illusion.

A child who wakes up crying with fear in a strange room, quite sure that he sees a tiger, does not know it is his own fear that creates the animal, which disappears as soon as the light is turned on. Here the drive produced a hallucination.

Thus our moods, feelings, drives and wishes constantly color and change the so-called objective world around us. Our actions are guided by a variety of unconscious drives on which are superimposed those needs and wishes of which we are aware.

Presumably animals other than man have no awareness of drives. Moreover, if a drive in an animal is fully satisfied, it cannot be elicited by any stimulus. On the other hand, the longer a drive is held in check, the more urgent it becomes and the wider is the range of stimuli that will elicit the corresponding behavior, be it eating, sexual activity, flight or care of another animal of the same species. In many kinds of behavior if the drive is held in check too long, the behavior pattern will begin in the total absence of the appropriate stimulus.

An example is described by the eminent student of animal behavior Konrad Z. Lorenz. When a captive starling accustomed to receiving its food from a dish was allowed to fly freely, it performed, as if in pantomime, the entire pent-up cycle of catching an insect in the air. It would appear to fixate on an insect, swoop down on it, catch it and

URGE TO FLEE is elicited by a weak electric current delivered by an electrode implanted in the brain stem of a rooster. Before stimulation (*left*) the rooster feeds calmly. On stimulation (*center*) the rooster fixates intently on a nonexistent object approaching from

swallow it—all in the absence of an insect. It is hard to believe that in such cases an animal does not have a hallucinatory perception of the absent prey.

We know from observations of people with brain damage, from electrical stimulation of regions of the brain in patients undergoing brain surgery while conscious, and particularly from the celebrated experiments on cats by Walter R. Hess of Zurich, that in mammals the chief center for the regulation of drives lies in a part of the brain stem called the diencephalon. When various areas of the brain of a surgical patient are stimulated, a number of spontaneous desires and feelings and their corresponding perceptions are elicited. Hess implanted electrodes in the brain stem of cats and found that in the presence of the appropriate object he could stimulate the cats to eat, attack or flee. If the stimulation was very intense, the animal would chew inedible objects or attack a human observer instead of a natural enemy. The cats behaved as they would have if the corresponding drives had been abnormally pent up. Perceptual accentuation, illusion and hallucination all seem to have been involved in these experiments.

Hess began his pioneering studies in the early 1930's and in 1949 shared the Nobel prize for medicine and physiology. His methods allowed him to identify many reactive regions in the brain stem. He sacrificed his animals following stimulation, cut their brains into serial sections and mapped the points of effective stimulation, which had been stained. Certain moods or drives, such as fatigue, turned out to be associated with specific zones, whereas others were related to larger regions or interspersed with the locations associated with other drives. Unfortunately simple spatial separation into discrete centers, each representing one specific function, is not to be found.

Such localization of function in the nervous system has considerable importance for the physician. The physiologist, however, must remember that localization studies answer the question of "where" but not the questions of "how" and "why." In order to answer these physiological questions one must try to penetrate into the dynamics of the drive mechanism. It is on this topic that I wish to report.

There are two methods of studying the way in which animal behavior is controlled by drives. The first is careful observation of one species over many years and under various conditions. In this way one acquires expert knowledge that enables one to predict with some certainty how an animal of this species will behave in a particular situation. Predictive ability of this sort is largely intuitive; it cannot be reduced to its components or used to make measurements. Analysis and measurement become possible, however, with the second method, namely the technical mastery of electrical stimulation of regions in the brain stem. Even with this method a detailed understanding of the species and its behavior remains indispensable. To recognize the delicate interplay of drives one must be able to judge the significance of individual behavior sequences, as seen under normal conditions, and to appreciate their place within the animal's behavioral repertory.

The richest inventory of behavior can be found among animals that form social groups. In addition to the egoistic drives that every organism needs for survival, these animals display a variety of altruistic drives for regulating their social interactions, which are not unlike

a distance; the object gets closer as the stimulus increases in strength and duration. (The stimulus voltage can be read on the meter at right.) Finally (*right*) the rooster jumps away fearfully. On repeated stimulation the frightening object always seems to come from the same direction. These photographs were made by the authors at the Max Planck Institute for the Physiology of Behavior.

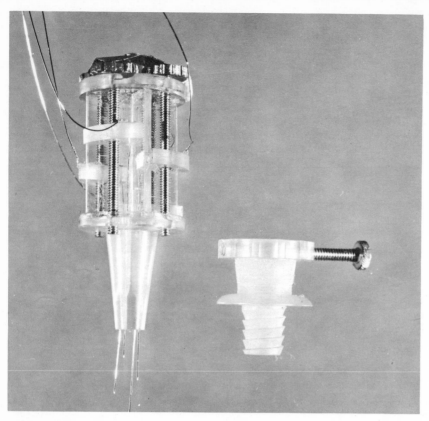

**STIMULATING APPARATUS** consists of a plastic fitting (*right*), which heals in place after being threaded into the skull of an animal, and an electrode carrier (*left*), which goes into the fitting. The carrier holds four electrodes, the lengths of which are adjustable.

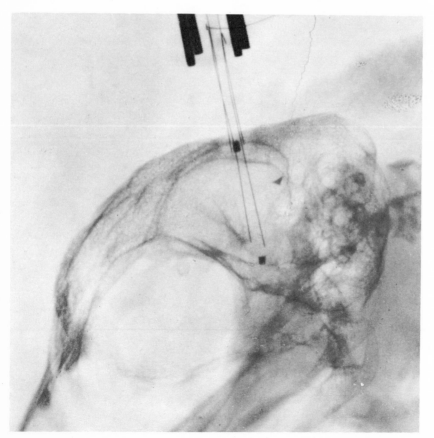

**X-RAY VIEW** shows electrodes penetrating the brain of a chicken. The drawing at the bottom left on the opposite page delineates the brain and the brain stem region. The electrodes and the stimuli they carry cause no pain, and the experiments do the animal no harm.

human social behavior. Such a species, the domestic chicken, has served as our experimental subject at the Max Planck Institute for the Physiology of Behavior in Seewiesen, Germany.

Chickens have a large repertory of gestures and a language consisting of several dozen "words." To be sure, their language is not learned, as is the language of man; their sounds and the understanding of these sounds are inborn. In the chicken yard there is a definite "pecking order" among the hens, which has been established as the result of fights in early youth. The hen of highest rank is entitled to the best sleeping place and the best food; the others take what is left in sequence. Transgression by a hen of lower rank is punished by pecking and the pulling of feathers.

The rooster is both ruler and cavalier. He warns the others with several distinct sounds against approaching enemies on the ground or in the air. He defends the hens against attackers, announces the presence of food, seeks out a nesting place for the young hen who is ready to mate and summons her with gentle, whispering sounds. Half-asleep, he watches over the sleeping flock. The call "cock-a-doodle-doo," which each rooster emits in his own distinctive fashion, may be freely translated to mean: "Here I am, ready to stand by you as mate and defender." Rival males are threatened and fought with vigor; the defeated rooster leaves the scene and may hide for days. All these forms of behavior, which I have merely sketched, are accompanied or preceded by specific gestures or sounds that tell the expert much about what is happening. It takes years to recognize and appreciate the complex social activity of the chicken yard. But until one understands chicken society there is no point in using electrical stimulation methods to study the role of drives in behavior.

At our institute these methods begin with anesthetizing a chicken and inserting in its skull a small threaded plastic fitting that remains in place permanently. To conduct an experiment we introduce into an opening in the fitting a small device bearing four electrode wires, each of which can be positioned in the brain by a screw [*see top illustration at left*]. The electrodes can be inserted while the animal is conscious, since the brain itself is totally insensitive to touching or probing. The damage done by this procedure is so slight that the experimental animal remains normal and healthy after 100 or more experiments extending over a period of years.

The initial experiment is to advance an electrode slowly into the brain stem, applying at intervals a low-voltage alternating current (usually of 50 cycles). We observe the animal's reaction closely and record, often with motion pictures, the behavior that is elicited as the tip of the electrode reaches different levels. When the electrode tip is still some distance away from a reactive structure, a relatively strong current will be needed to evoke a particular response. As the electrode tip penetrates deeper, the response can be evoked with less and less current: the threshold decreases. As the electrode tip moves away from this response zone the threshold increases again. One thereby obtains, on traversing the brain stem, a varying number of threshold curves for different types of behavior [see illustration at right below]. If an interesting reaction is encountered, the electrode is left at this depth and is allowed to remain for hours or days in the animal's skull.

The chickens are kept on a table to which they have become accustomed before testing, and they are connected with fine wires to the stimulating apparatus. Alternatively the animals are equipped with a tiny radio receiver, weighing about 25 grams, and are permitted to wander about freely. The remote-control procedure is valuable for studying behavior within a social group.

By stimulating the brain stem in this way we have evoked almost all the forms of activity and vocalization familiar to those acquainted with chickens. We have also obtained various composite forms of behavior, some of which do not occur in nature. The natural modes of behavior can be classified provisionally into simple movements and complex behavior sequences. Simple movements are, for example, sitting, standing, preening, grooming, looking about alertly, and stretching the neck as if peering at something in the distance. The last response is sometimes accompanied by a special call used to warn against airborne predators. Other simple responses are scratching with one foot, which is part of a courtship sequence, and the various orienting attitudes such as turning the head to the right or left or moving it up or down.

More complex behavior sequences include seeking and eating food, seeking and drinking water, escaping from predators on the ground, escaping from flying predators, the sequence of settling down and falling asleep and the sequence of guiding a hen to a nest, which is of course performed only by the rooster. These complex activities consist of a chain of different individual movements that are all related to a single goal. For example, a series of steps is interposed between an initiating stimulus, delivered to the "sleep" region in a waking and active rooster, and the final stage of deep sleep. The animal stops eating, looks around and walks; it flutters its eyelids, yawns and sits down; it fluffs its plumage, retracts its head and closes its eyes. All these effects—each of which, incidentally, can be evoked individually from other foci—are subordinated to a single drive, that associated with fatigue or the desire to sleep. Another meaningful series, having to do with disgust, is depicted at the top of page 62. Here also individual components can be evoked by stimulating other specific regions of the brain stem.

The ability to evoke at will either individual movements or complex drive sequences has theoretical significance. In the case of individual movements

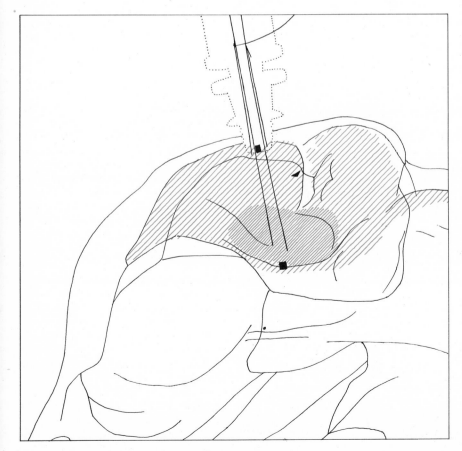

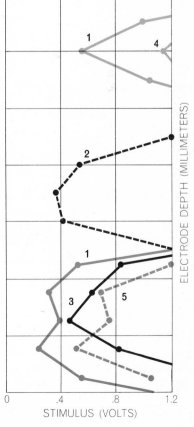

**REGION STIMULATED AND RESPONSES** are shown in these two illustrations. The brain is indicated (*left*) by colored hatching, and the brain stem, the region actually stimulated, is doubly hatched. As an electrode is lowered gradually to different depths and activated, the animal may respond in various ways. The charted responses (*right*) are: *1*, alertness; *2*, watchful staring; *3*, shaking the head; *4*, turning to left; *5*, turning to right. Overlapping represents responses at the same depth but at different sites.

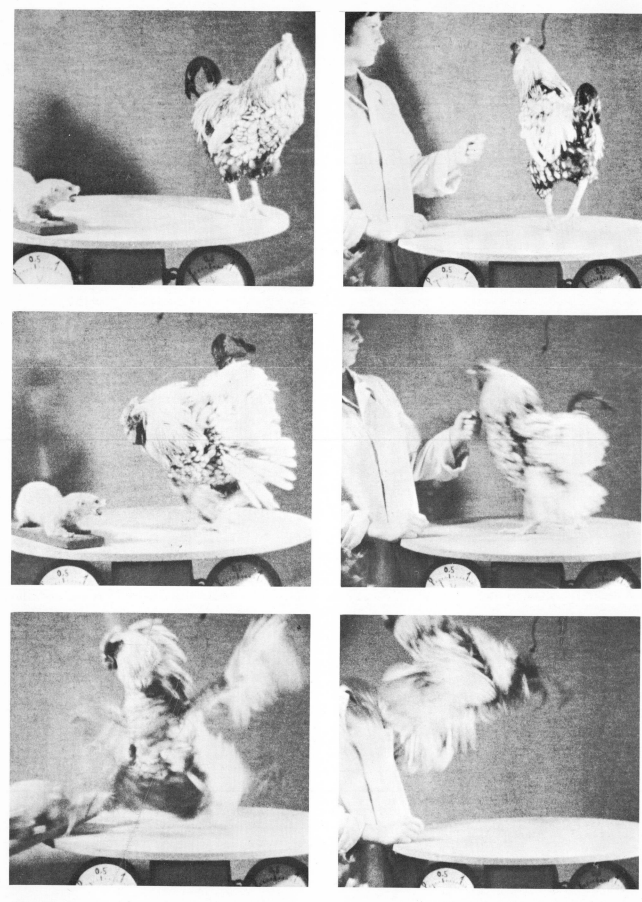

ATTACK ON AN "ENEMY" can be elicited by a particular stimulus. In the absence of the stimulus (*top*) the rooster ignores the stuffed predator. When the stimulus is applied, the bird turns on the stuffed animal and attacks it furiously, spurs flying.

ATTACK ON A FRIEND, the rooster's keeper, is provoked if the natural "enemy" is absent and if the stimulus used in the film sequence shown at left is prolonged. The rooster prefers to aim its attack at the keeper's face rather than at her hand.

the stimulus merely furnishes an impulse for a particular movement; in the case of the drives the stimulus sets up a goal that can be attained in different ways, depending on external circumstances. It is not always easy to decide, however, whether a stimulus activates an isolated movement or an entire drive sequence. Many complex behavior sequences occur in their entirety only under certain external circumstances. To be sure, escape reactions can be evoked in the absence of the appropriate external object (or its substitute) if the brain stimulation is sufficiently intense. In such cases it is probable that the absent object of fear is being hallucinated. Hallucination, or apparent hallucination, does not seem to occur, however, when aggressive behavior is evoked by stimulation. Let me explain further.

Chickens exhibit different kinds of attack behavior. For example, stimulation of a certain region of the brain activates the characteristic attack that one hen makes against another hen of lower rank. If the stimulated hen is confronted with another hen (alive or stuffed), it pecks at the other hen and pulls its feathers. When a human hand is proffered as a substitute object, it is pecked in the same way if the stimulation has been increased somewhat. When no object is provided, however, and if the brain stimulation is strong, the hen looks about in great excitement and pecks the ground several times, much as an angry man may hit a table with his fist if the object of his anger is out of reach. But the other part of this form of natural attack, the plucking of feathers, is missing.

A totally different form of aggression is directed against natural enemies of the species. The behavior that accompanies this drive never arises unless an enemy, real or artificial, is present. The three photographs at the left on the opposite page, taken from a motion picture, shows an electrically stimulated rooster attacking a small stuffed predator. Before stimulation the rooster had hardly noticed that an "enemy" was present. The stimulation brought out the full behavioral sequence: alertness, visual fixation, approach, attitude of rage, attack with spurs and triumphant call.

The second series of motion-picture frames on the opposite page shows the behavior of the same rooster toward a keeper who had always been treated as a friend. After sustained stimulation the rooster flew up and attacked the keeper's face with its spurs. (The human face is apparently a better substitute for an enemy than the human hand.) If all substitutes for an enemy are lacking—when

there is, so to speak, no hook on which to hang an illusion—the rooster exhibits only motor restlessness. Moreover, the same motor restlessness is observed if one stimulates brain areas associated with hunger, thirst, courtship or fighting under conditions in which the environment does not permit the unreeling of the entire behavior sequence. For this reason it is often necessary to vary the external conditions to be sure which particular behavior sequence—which complex drive —has in fact been activated.

Simple behavior patterns other than motor restlessness can be observed in a variety of complex drive systems. Sitting down occurs whether the hen simply wants to sit down, to incubate eggs or to

go to sleep. Standing up marks the onset of all those behavior sequences that entail a change in position. A particular excited cackling (poh-poh-poh) accompanies a number of behavior sequences that involve a mood of anxious tension. Another kind of cackling that sounds oddly like scolding (cock-cock-cock-colay) accompanies various forms of relaxation of function, such as landing after a brief flight or "relief" after laying an egg. The frozen stance, with head pulled in, can be an element in the behavior toward a predator threatening from the air (in which case the chicken seems to feign death), or it can be an attitude of humility brought on by a rival of superior strength. Even the pecking

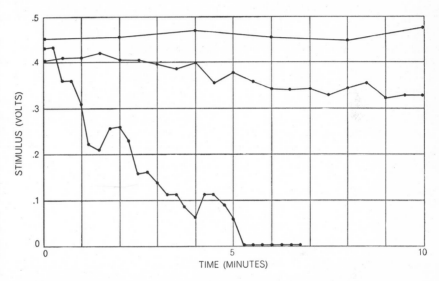

**EFFECT OF STIMULATION FREQUENCY** is found by plotting the threshold voltage needed to elicit "attentive reconnoitering" in a sleepy hen. The voltage is raised slowly; the dots indicate the voltage reached when the hen's head begins to move. If the stimuli are two minutes apart (*top curve*), the threshold voltage is virtually the same each time. If the stimuli are only 30 seconds apart (*middle curve*), the threshold voltage tends to drop. If the stimuli are closely spaced (*bottom*), the hen becomes fully awake in about five minutes.

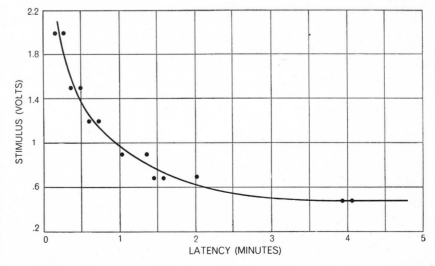

**EFFECT OF VOLTAGE STRENGTH** is found by plotting the interval between stimulus and response, called the latency. In this case the response is a warning call (clucking).

STIMULUS

⟶ TIME

**"DISGUST REACTION"** can be elicited by stimulating the hen's brain stem in the appropriate place. The hen, which has been eating, stops (*1*), spits out the food in its beak (*2*), shakes its head (*3*) and wipes its beak on the ground before eating again (*4*).

of food on the ground can be either an element in the behavior associated with hunger or an element of fights between rivals. Fighting cocks tend to peck hastily at food or, if a rival is present, they peck the bare ground. The latter form of pecking, known as displacement pecking, is a threatening gesture [for other patterns of aggression see "The Fighting Behavior of Animals," by Irenäus Eibl-Eibesfeldt, Offprint #470].

From such observations we can conclude that a fairly large number of movements or behavior elements are subordinated to a smaller number of more complex drives. The drives employ the repertory of simple movements as a means of reaching various goals. The existence of such a hierarchic system of drives is well supported by the observation that only the complex "high level" drives give the impression of completely spontaneous activity. In contrast, the individual acts induced by stimulation, such as particular sounds, head-turning, sitting down, pecking, swallowing and the like, all have a certain mechanical character, as if they did not concern the animal as a whole.

Before turning to our experimental attempts to combine drives, I should say something about thresholds and the variation in the strength of the current needed to evoke particular forms of activity. During and after stimulation there are conspicuous changes in behavior. When a particular behavior is evoked in a given brain region for the first time, the threshold is usually quite high; that is, one has to apply a strong stimulus in order to elicit the behavior. With rapidly repeated or protracted stimulation the threshold decreases markedly and may even fall to zero, in which case the activity may continue for a fairly long time without further stimulation [*see upper illustration on preceding page*]. Later on, if the stimulus is maintained over a

*a*

STIMULUS 1

*b*

STIMULUS 2

*c*

STIMULUS 1

STIMULUS 2

⟶ TIME

**COMBINATION OF TWO STIMULI** may result in the suppression of the weaker response, followed by its delayed expression. One stimulus causes the hen to flatten its feathers and stretch out its neck (*a*). A different stimulus induces it to fluff its feathers (*b*). Combination of the two elicits the two responses in succession, but the second does not appear until all stimulation has ended (*c*).

period of time, the threshold gradually rises again and often becomes so high that, for several minutes or as much as an hour afterward, the particular behavior cannot be elicited.

By combining brain stimuli in certain ways we have found that the initial decline in threshold and its subsequent rise are attributable to two different processes. The initial decline in threshold represents a change in what can be called central set, or predisposition, so that it favors a particular activity to which the animal was initially more or less indifferent. Simultaneously there is a rise in threshold for other activities that are antagonistic to the one evoked. For instance, if by stimulation one makes a sleepy animal hungry and it begins to eat, the threshold for inducing sleep has been concurrently increased. Similarly, if an animal that spontaneously exhibits a slight tendency toward flight is made sleepy by the appropriate brain stimulation, the threshold for flight is simultaneously increased. These shifts in central set represent a shift in dynamic balance. In contrast, the kind of increase in threshold that occurs after prolonged activation of a particular behavior represents a form of central blocking, or central adaptation, that makes the animal in-

creasingly less sensitive to the continuing stimulation. This blocking occurs in the brain stem close to the stimulated region, whereas the central change of set seems to take place higher in the brain, closer to the cortical regions associated with motor activity.

In addition to these quantitative changes in behavior, qualitative changes also appear. I shall cite only one striking example. In roosters a number of behavioral states manifest a certain underlying depressive quality, such states as the desire to escape, crying, "freezing," warning, reconnoitering, scolding. If, through appropriate stimulation, one of these activities is maintained over a period of time, there is usually a change five to 10 seconds after the end of the stimulation that transforms the depressive mood into a euphoric, self-assured one. The rooster stands up alertly, flaps its wings and crows. In much the same way, people often feel happy and cheerful after a prolonged depression.

The foregoing illustrates the necessity for controlling conditions carefully if one hopes to discover exact relationships between stimulus and response. Fortunately such control is attainable, and it is possible to maintain a desired mood

over long periods without change. Clear stimulus-response relationships then become evident. For many types of behavior we have been able to draw simple curves showing the interval between onset of the stimulus and onset of the response—that is, showing latency as a function of stimulus strength [*see lower illustration on page 61*]. For example, with a stimulus current of about .5 volt the latency in a given response may be four seconds; with four times the voltage the latency may be only about .2 second. In general we find a simple reciprocal relationship between stimulus intensity and stimulus duration.

In addition to latency we can measure such variables as the speed of a motor sequence, the frequency of a rhythmic repetitive movement or the length of time a given kind of behavior continues beyond the end of the stimulation. Reproducible quantitative relationships can be observed in all these cases. The freely moving animal, steered by the experimenter in its spontaneous activities, proves to be a complicated yet precisely functioning physical apparatus.

All this had to be considered before we could turn to the problem of combining different drives. Such a combination is achieved by means of two differ-

*a*

STIMULUS 1

*b*

STIMULUS 2

STIMULUS 1

⟶ TIME

ANOTHER COMBINATION OF STIMULI leads to suppression of certain components of one of the responses. Gradual activation of an urge to flee in a sitting hen (*a*) causes the hen to stand and look about alertly before it finally jumps. When a continuous stimulus for sitting is applied at the same time (*b*), the hen becomes restless but keeps sitting until it finally jumps away.

ent electrodes that activate different drives concurrently in different regions of the brain. For safety's sake this is done by stimulating one region intermittently and the other region during the intervals. In this way only one region is physically stimulated at a time, although two drives are activated simultaneously. If the alternation of the two stimuli is between four and 10 per second, the physiological effects in both regions become perfectly continuous.

When two drives are intermingled in this way, several types of interplay can be observed. The simplest type results when two different elementary movements are stimulated: one movement is simply added to the other without mutual influence. If, for example, one stimulus makes the chicken sit down and the other makes it look to the left, then the chicken does both simultaneously. Similarly, one can combine pecking and head-turning, rising and cackling, sitting down and preening, and so on.

More interesting is a combination in which the animal strikes a balance, so to speak, between the two forms of behavior. For instance, one can combine reconnoitering (peering into the distance, with neck stretched and head immobile) with a totally different searching gesture (in which the head sweeps quickly back and forth). This combination results in a compromise movement in which the neck protrudes only a little and the head moves only slightly.

In a fairly rare type of combined reaction both forms of behavior appear in full strength but alternate rhythmically. An example would be eating and reconnoitering: the animal makes a few pecking movements, then raises its head abruptly to look about, pecks and looks about again. When two responses are mutually antagonistic, an attempt to evoke them together will lead to mutual cancellation, provided that the two brain stimuli have been properly adjusted. Thus a stimulus to turn to the left can be exactly canceled by a stimulus to turn to the right.

In an even rarer type of combined reaction two stimuli lead to a new type of behavior containing elements not normally evoked by either stimulus alone. So far we have found only one particularly clear example of this reaction. One of two stimuli induces the hen to peck aggressively; the other induces it to take flight, with its feathers smoothed down. Both stimuli together, if properly balanced, induce neither attack nor flight. Instead the hen emits piercing cries and rushes frantically back and forth with its feathers raised and its wings spread. In nature this behavior would occur if the hen were confronted by an antagonist of superior strength near its nest, where it would not be inclined to flee.

A frequent result of combining two stimuli is that the stronger drive suppresses the weaker one, even though more voltage is applied to evoke the weaker drive. One can often show that the weaker drive has been activated but that its expression has somehow been blocked. One stimulus makes the hen appear anxious, stretch out its neck and flatten its plumage; the other stimulus induces it to fluff up its plumage (a component of grooming). If the relative strength of the two stimuli is appropriate, the animal acts, on simultaneous delivery of both stimuli, as if only the first stimulus were present. If both stimuli are stopped at the same time, the fluffed-up plumage appears afterward. Evidently this response too must have been activated during the period of stimulation, although it remained latent.

The phenomenon of suppression exhibits still other peculiarities. Complex drive systems, which consist of several behavior elements, are rarely suppressed as a whole; instead their components are eliminated successively, as if they had different thresholds for suppression. If one slowly activates a tendency to flee in a chicken that has been sitting quietly on the ground, there appear successively, like links in a chain, the following movements: attentive alertness, getting up, walking about, freezing and finally jumping away. The sequence mimics flight from an air-borne predator. Let us now deliver to another region of the brain in the same chicken a stimulus inducing a strong tendency to sit while simultaneously activating the tendency to flee. At first nothing happens, until the urge to flee becomes quite intense. Then

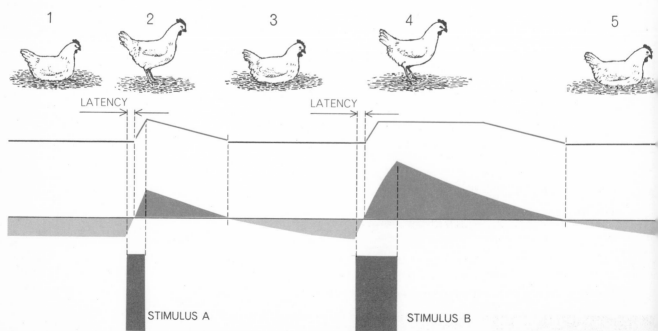

URGE TO STAND, induced by electrical stimulation, can be made to override a spontaneous urge to sit. If the stimulus (A) is strong but brief, the chicken stands up quickly and promptly sits down again (1, 2, 3). If the stimulus is repeated at the same strength but is maintained twice as long (B), the chicken remains standing for an appreciable time (4). With a weaker but longer stimulus (C), the bird gets up more slowly and remains standing for a still longer time (6). Note, however, that the time the bird

the chicken suddenly jumps away as the last phase of the suppressed escape sequence erupts explosively. This behavior resembles the natural behavior of a bird that continues to incubate its eggs in the nest as an enemy comes gradually closer. The bird jumps from the nest only at the last moment.

So far I have discussed only those drive combinations that result from two kinds of brain stimulation. It is possible, however, to activate and combine two different drives by inducing one form of behavior through an environmental stimulus (visual or auditory) and letting it interact with an artificially induced drive. One can say that there is no essential difference between these two methods, and the situation is no different when brain stimulation is combined with a spontaneous drive. It is easier, however, to make measurements if both drives are associated with voltages. These facts strongly suggest that stimulation of the brain stem indeed sets off, in the responding centers, what are essentially complete and normal processes. The effects of stimulation are therefore not mere imitations of natural processes. They are not "pseudoaffective" states but genuine drives.

I shall now attempt to give a somewhat more detailed theoretical interpretation of what goes on within the nervous system when two drives interact. Let us consider a simple case of antagonism between drives, for example the one found

in a hen that has a spontaneous urge to sit (because it is in the "incubating mood") but that can be induced to get up by stimulation of a particular brain region. The illustration on the bottom of these two pages depicts the situation. We stimulate such a hen, which sits spontaneously, three separate times to make it stand. The three stimuli differ in intensity and duration.

We record all those aspects of resulting behavior that can be measured: the latency, the speed with which the animal gets up and the length of time that the animal continues to stand after cessation of the stimulus. All these values are represented schematically in the upper curve of the illustration. One can see how the latency depends on the strength of the stimulus, as already discussed. One can also see how the speed with which the animal gets up (steepness of the curve) depends on strength and duration of the stimulus. In theory one could reduce all these data by ascribing them to a single process, which is depicted by the intermediate curve. The horizontal zero line should represent that central condition in which standing and sitting are in equilibrium. Below this line the central drive to sit is dominant; above the line the drive to stand is dominant. The stimulus for getting up alters this central state; when the drive for sitting becomes zero, the threshold has been reached and the animal begins to stand up.

If the stimulus for getting up is in-

tense, the threshold is reached rapidly and the latency is short. If the stimulus for standing is weak, the curve rises less steeply, intersects the zero line later, and the latency is prolonged. The steepness of this rising curve similarly determines the speed with which the animal gets up. The length of time it remains standing after the stimulus to stand up has been turned off depends only on the height reached by the central drive level for standing.

The intermediate curve shown in the illustration may seem to be nothing but a hypothetical construct. But if we now fit the chicken with a second electrode to activate sitting, we can see that the intermediate curve does in fact represent something real. We deliver a stimulus for sitting, at various times, while the animal is spontaneously standing and measure the strength of the stimulus needed to induce the animal to sit down at any given moment. The values obtained are in complete agreement with the intermediate curve, which had at first been based on mere conjecture. In other words, there must be, within the central nervous system, some kind of process that takes the course described by the form of our intermediate curve. It is too early to say anything about the nature of this process, whether it is chemical or electrical or whether it is a combination of both (which is the most likely).

As one can see, it is possible to measure the inner dynamics of drives in a rather complicated animal and thereby measure processes that ordinarily elude us when we simply observe behavior; so far as we are concerned an animal that sits is merely sitting; a rooster that crows is merely crowing; a hen that eats is merely eating. But observation alone cannot as a rule tell us how strongly the animal "feels inclined" to sit, crow or eat. We do not know how strong the inner drives are at any given instant or what other drives may be operating. A more detailed analysis of these central phenomena is likely to reveal a complicated interplay of forces. It is only infrequently the case that two drives, such as those that involve sitting and standing, are mutually antagonistic. On the whole the momentary situation within the brain is much more like a knot of numerous threads that pull in the most diverse directions. The organism comprises a bundle of drives, which support one another or oppose one another to greater or lesser extent. "Spontaneous" activity is the result of a continual and shifting interplay of forces in the central nervous system.

STIMULUS C

remains standing when the stimulus has been turned off is about the same after each of the last two stimuli. Evidently some process in the central nervous system of the chicken takes the form of the intermediate curve. The colored area above the "zero line" symbolizes the urge to stand; the gray area below the line symbolizes the urge to sit.

# 8

# CHEMICAL STIMULATION OF THE BRAIN

ALAN E. FISHER                                                    June 1964

It was once customary to think of the brain as an intricate switchboard and decoding system, operating by essentially electrical means. As neurophysiologists learned more about the central nervous system, however, they came to recognize that chemical mediators play an important role in brain activity. To examine this role more closely it is now possible with new techniques to apply chemical substances directly to local areas deep within the brain.

As usually happens in pioneering a new technique, there have been disappointments, puzzles, surprises and, most fruitful of all, findings that seem to contradict previous understanding. But the operation of the brain is so complex that it is only by piecing together knowledge gained in many different ways, and by reconciling conflicting data, that we can hope to penetrate its secrets.

The tracing of specific behavior to stimulation of particular areas in the brain was pioneered by Walter Rudolph Hess of the University of Zurich. In a series of illuminating experiments for which he received the Nobel prize in physiology and medicine in 1949, Hess found that by gentle electrical stimulation of certain areas in the hypothalamus of cats he could evoke fear, anger and reactions connected with digestion and other body functions. These discoveries started a train of highly fruitful experiments in electrical stimulation by many investigators, culminating in the discovery of nerve circuits that appear to control pleasure and punishment [see "Pleasure Centers in the Brain," by James Olds, page 183, for a discussion of these areas].

Nevertheless, electrical stimulation of the brain has definite limitations. The effects are often blurred or mixed, and the method has generally failed to elicit some of the basic forms of behavior, such as those prompted by the maternal and sexual drives. Two factors may account for these limitations. Electrical stimulation is not selective as far as nerve cells are concerned; it will fire any nerve cell indiscriminately. And the indications are that the neurons responsible for a particular form of behavior are not usually clumped in one place but are dispersed widely in the brain, overlapping with other functional fields or systems of neurons.

These facts prompted some neurophysiologists to search for a more specific type of stimulator: something that would selectively stimulate only the system of cells controlling a particular behavior. With the growing appreciation of the role of chemistry in brain function it seemed that carefully chosen chemical substances might exhibit the discrimination desired.

It was known, for example, that chemical messengers, or hormones, are deeply involved in the brain's activities and that other chemical substances control the basic process of transmission of nerve impulses. Acetylcholine, noradrenalin and probably other substances are released at the ends of the nerve cells and carry impulses across the synaptic gap from one neuron to the next. Other chemicals mimic or interfere with the action of these transmitters. Chemical "modulators" have also been found that alter the threshold for the cell's firing of an impulse.

## The Case of the Mixed-up Rat

Was it possible that neurons or chains of neurons might be sensitive to specific substances to which they would respond selectively? Experimenters began to test this intriguing idea. The first results were not encouraging, but in 1953 Bengt Andersson in Sweden reported a significant success. Experimenting with goats, he injected a 5 per cent solution of salt into a precisely defined area in the middle of the hypothalamus, the governing center of the autonomic nervous system. The goats immediately began to drink large quantities of water. Evidently they had been induced to drink by some effect on the brain cells caused by the rise in osmotic pressure produced by the salt.

Late in 1954, while working in D. O. Hebb's laboratory at McGill University, I began to experiment with substances I hoped would produce direct chemical stimulation of specific brain cells. I started with the male sex hormone, testosterone, and injected it into specific sites in the hypothalamus of male rats. These particular regions seemed the most likely ones for action by the hormone because it was already known that they are involved in the primary drives of rats, such as courtship, care of the young, eating and drinking. I had expected, of course, that injection of the male sex hormone into the rat's brain would trigger male sex behavior.

By one of those ironic twists that are so typical of scientific research, the behavioral change produced in my first "successful" subject was a completely unexpected one. Within seconds after the male hormone was injected into his brain he began to show signs of extreme restlessness. I then put in his cage a female rat that was not in the sexually receptive state. According to the script I had in mind, the brain injection of male hormone should have driven the male to make sexual advances, although normally he would not do so with a nonreceptive female. The rat, however, followed a script of his own. He grasped the female by the tail with his teeth

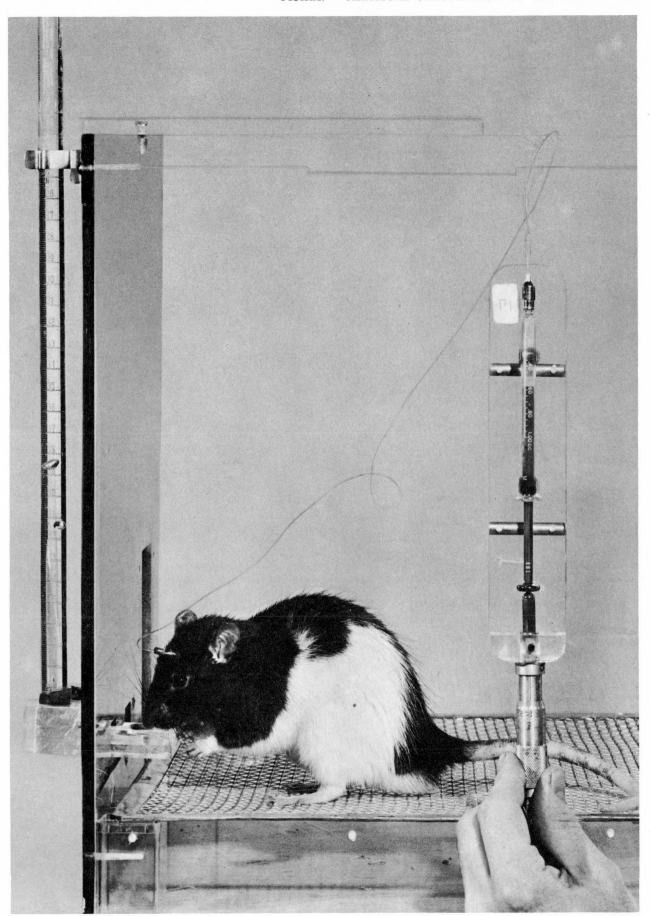

WATER-SATED RAT returns to trough to drink more within a few minutes after the brain circuit that controls the animal's thirst drive has been triggered by injection of acetylcholine. A single stimulus can make the rat drink a day's normal ration in an hour.

**SELECTIVE STIMULATION** is a primary advantage in the use of chemicals. When an electrical stimulus is applied (*left*) to a group of neurons belonging to three separate circuits, all circuits operate (*color*) and no integrated response occurs. When a chemical stimulus is applied (*right*), only one circuit, for which the chemical is specific, operates. The other two remain inactive.

and dragged her across the cage to a corner. She scurried away as soon as he let go, whereupon he dragged her back again. After several such experiences the male picked her up by the loose skin on her back, carried her to the corner and dropped her there.

I was utterly perplexed and so, no doubt, was the female rat. I finally guessed that the male was carrying on a bizarre form of maternal behavior. To test this surmise I deposited some newborn rat pups and strips of paper in the middle of the cage. The male promptly used the paper to build a nest in a corner and then carried the pups to the nest. I picked up the paper and pups and scattered them around the cage; the male responded by rebuilding the nest and retrieving the young.

After about 30 minutes the rat stopped behaving like a new mother; apparently the effect of the injected hormone had worn off. Given a new injection, he immediately returned to his adopted family. With successive lapses and reinjections, his behavior became disorganized; he engaged in all the same maternal activities, but in a haphazard, meaningless order. After an overnight rest, however, a new injection the next day elicited the well-patterned motherly behavior.

The case of the mixed-up male rat was a most auspicious one. Although the rat had not followed the experimenter's script, the result of this first experiment was highly exciting. It was an encouraging indication that the control of behavior by specific neural systems in the brain could indeed be investigated by chemical means. We proceed-

ed next to a long series of experiments to verify that the behavior in each case was actually attributable to a specific chemical implanted at a specific site in the brain rather than to some more general factor such as mechanical stimulation, general excitation of the brain cells, or changes in acidity or osmotic pressure.

We have now administered many different chemicals to the brains of hundreds of animals, mostly rats. For this work we have had to develop simple surgical techniques for implanting tiny hollow guide shafts in the animals' brains so that chemicals can be delivered to selected points. The location of each shaft is carefully established with

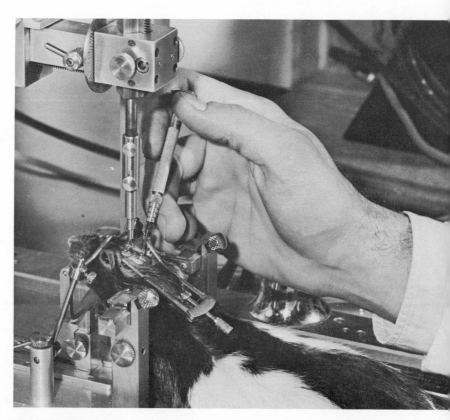

**TRACING THE ROUTE OF A BRAIN CIRCUIT,** one undertaking made possible by the selectivity of chemical stimuli, requires delicate techniques. At left a vernier-adjusted stereotactic machine is used in conjunction with a sectional atlas of the brain to implant

the help of a three-dimensional brain map and a stereotactic instrument, which holds the head of the anesthetized animal and guides the surgical instruments. After a tiny hole has been made in the brain the shaft is inserted and antiseptically fastened to the skull with jewelers' screws and an adhesive. Each animal can be equipped with several guide shafts at different locations. In a rat four or five shafts may be inserted; in a monkey, as many as 100. The animal recovers quickly and resumes its normal laboratory existence. Through these permanent shafts we can deliver as little as one microgram of a chemical in crystalline form or as little as a ten-thousandth of a milliliter of a solution [see illustration below].

## Arousing Male Behavior

Our extended program of tests confirmed, first of all, the elicitation of maternal behavior by an injection of a testosterone solution at a specific location in the brain. When we placed the hormone in a site in the center of the brain just in front of the hypothalamus at the level of the optic tracts below it, many of the rats tested, male and female, responded with some form of maternal behavior.

An injection of the same hormone in the same general region- but slightly to one side instead of in the center, brought forth a dramatically different response. Many of the animals now reacted as I had expected the original male to do—with male sexual activity. This was true even of female rats. Presented with a partner, whether male or female, the injected rat (male or female) soon tried to mount the partner. One heroic female persisted in this malelike behavior over a period of eight weeks in tests conducted every other day. The behavior was elicited only by testosterone; it did not appear when the same site was injected with other chemicals or stimulated by electricity.

When the male hormone injection was placed between the central and lateral sites in the hypothalamus, so that it impinged on both, some rats exhibited a curious combination of maternal and male behavior. They took care of the young and at the same time tried to copulate with any partner available. In several instances a male rat that had received such an injection tried to mount a nonreceptive female or male at the same time that it was carrying a rat pup in its mouth!

This was particularly puzzling because it seemed to deny the hypothesis that functionally related brain cells are selectively sensitive to specific substances. How could the neurons that mediate two different kinds of behavior respond to one and the same hormone? The question has not yet been fully answered, but we can offer a reasonable conjecture. Testosterone is known to act not only as a male hormone but also, under appropriate circumstances, as a weak substitute for the female hormone progesterone, which is linked to pregnancy and maternal behavior. (This versatility is generally true of the family of steroid hormones; most of them can mimic one another's actions.) Therefore a concentrated injection of testosterone into the brain cells may carry enough progestational potency to stimulate the cells that are sensitive to progesterone.

This hypothesis would explain how testosterone injected into the brain of a male rat can evoke maternal behavior. The male body contains little or no progesterone, and presumably its circulating testosterone, at normal levels, has no significant progestational potency. But when a concentration of testosterone is injected directly into cells that are susceptible to progestational stimulation, the hormone's secondary activity is strong enough to stimulate them.

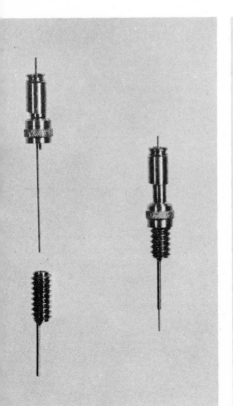

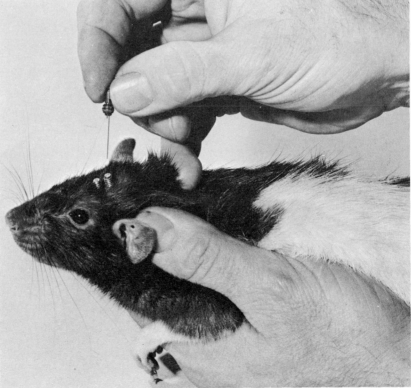

guide shafts leading to precisely calculated regions in the brain of an anesthetized rat. In the middle, unassembled and assembled, are the permanent guide shaft and the removable cannula that carries the chemical to the brain tissue. At right a rat with two guide shafts is about to receive a brain stimulus. The cannula in this instance contains the chemical agent in the form of a solid.

Whether or not this particular hypothesis is correct, the experiments in chemical stimulation seem to show that the male brain and the female brain are essentially identical in the character and organization of the neurons. In the rat, at least, both brains contain cells that can direct male behavior and other cells that can direct female behavior. Differences in sexual behavior can be attributed largely to differences in the kinds of sex hormone that enter the animal's circulatory system.

Yet even this concept is an oversimplification. Evidence obtained recently suggests that during early development sex hormones also play an organizational role, determining degrees of maleness or femaleness by permanently altering the response thresholds or growth within neural systems that will direct male and female behavior. Thus the presence or absence of a hormone during early life may determine the extent to which a nerve circuit develops the capacity for effective function. This may explain why many of our rats are unaffected by brain hormone stimulation, and why, under ordinary conditions, some males and females of every species display the behavior of the opposite sex.

## The Puzzle of Steroid Action

Investigators at several other laboratories have now confirmed our finding that steroid hormones act selectively on nerve cells at specific sites in the brain. They have found, for example, that implants of estrogen in selected sites in the hypothalamus can produce sexual receptivity in a cat whose ovaries (the main natural source of estrogen) have been removed. Tracer experiments with radioactively labeled estrogen have shown further that the estrogen tends to concentrate around certain cells of the hypothalamus. A puzzling aspect of the experiment is that the radioactivity (and presumably the hormone itself) has disappeared from the brain by the time the cats become sexually receptive, which is not until five days or more after implantation.

Other puzzling findings have emerged from related studies, and there are many questions to be answered before any comprehensive or confident conclusions can be presented. One of the chief questions has to do with the speed of action of the hormones I have injected into the brain. When a steroid hormone is injected into the muscle tissue or the bloodstream of a male rat, it does not take effect until 24 to 48 hours later. Our injections into the brain, on the other hand, usually produce changes in the rat's behavior within seconds or minutes. Part of the explanation may lie in the form of the injection. Normally steroids are soluble only in oils, and it is in such a solution that they are injected into the blood or peripheral tissues. For the injections into the brain we have generally used a rare steroid that is soluble in water. Possibly an oil-soluble hormone can act rapidly only after it has been converted to a water-soluble form.

R. D. Lisk of Princeton University has recently demonstrated, however, that even an oil-soluble steroid will take effect quickly under certain conditions. He experimented with injections of progesterone to stimulate sexual receptivity in the female rat. He found that when he injected progesterone into the veins of a female that had been primed with injections of estrogen for several days, she became sexually receptive in less than 10 minutes. It takes six hours for such a female to respond fully when the progesterone is injected into muscle tissue rather than the bloodstream.

## Control of Hunger and Thirst

With the chemical technique we have gone on to explore the rat brain for the location of the neural systems responsible for the control of other drives besides the sexual. Foremost among these drives, of course, are hunger and thirst. Several regions in the brain that help to control eating and the hunger drive are located in the hypothalamus and are well known. One center acts as an "appestat" (by analogy with the thermostat), and its setting can be raised or lowered. Electrical stimulation of this center will cause even a sated animal to increase its food intake sharply, whereas injury to the same center will drastically reduce an animal's appetite. The other center, in the lower middle region of the hypothalamus, acts as a satiation center, or "brake," for eating.

Some investigators have proposed that the main factor regulating the ac-

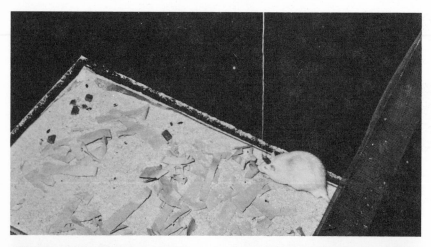

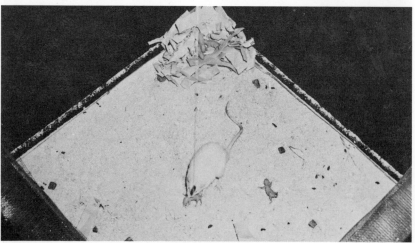

INJECTION of testosterone (*upper photograph*) induces maternal behavior in this male rat. The male gathers scattered paper strips to make a nest (*lower photograph*), ignores food pellets and carries rat pups (which males normally would eat) to shelter in the nest.

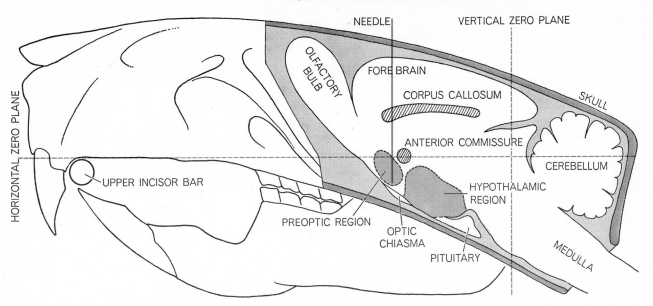

**RAT'S HEAD** is positioned by hooking the upper incisors over a bar on the stereotactic machine. The brain, in sagittal section (*right*), is labeled to show major anatomical features. The broken lines (*color*) show the zero coordinates for implant measurements.

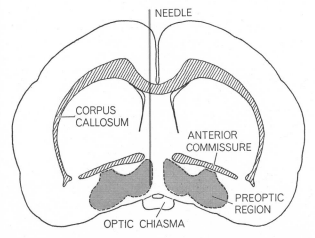
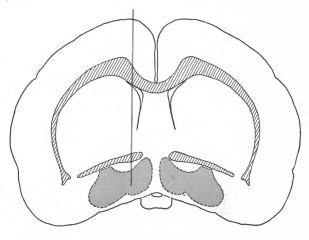

**TRANSVERSE SECTIONS** of rat brain were taken about eight millimeters forward of the vertical zero coordinate. The needles, or cannulas, touch points in preoptic region where testosterone induced maternal behavior (*left*) and male sexual behavior (*right*).

tivity of the appestat is the sugar level in the blood [see "Appetite and Obesity," by Jean Mayer; SCIENTIFIC AMERICAN, November, 1956]. Our first conjecture, therefore, was that the two oppositely working hormones of the pancreas that regulate the blood-sugar level—insulin and glucagon—might be the primary chemical modulators for the hunger drive, determining the settings or thresholds of the brain centers by acting directly on them. In an extensive series of attempts to stimulate these centers with the two hormones, however, we found no evidence that insulin or glucagon had any effect on them. (Indeed, it has not been conclusively proved that the blood-sugar level itself is a major factor in the regulation of appetite.)

Subsequently a Yale University graduate student, Sebastian P. Grossman, discovered that eating and drinking could be elicited in rats by brain injections of two other chemicals. They were none other than noradrenalin and acetylcholine, the substances that have long been known as transmitters of nerve impulses. Noradrenalin, injected into a site in the brain just above the hypothalamus, would cause even a well-fed rat to start eating again. Acetylcholine, injected into the same site, would drive the rat to drink. Grossman also found that these stimulating effects could be blocked by injection of chemicals that were known to block the transmitting action of noradrenalin and acetylcholine at nerve synapses.

### A Circuit Theory of Drives

I was naturally interested to learn that these two nerve-impulse transmit-ting chemicals can do their work within the tissue of the brain itself. But even more intriguing, Grossman had shown that different chemicals released different inherent drives even though injected at exactly the same site in the brain. This immediately suggested that the neurons composing each of these major drive circuits were chemically selective and would respond only to the appropriate chemical stimulus. If such a theory were correct, a specific chemical could be released almost at random in the midst of several quite separate circuits but would selectively excite only one of them. In this way it would be possible to probe various parts of the brain with a specific chemical and actually chart the circuit responsive to that particular stimulus.

In our laboratory at the University of Pittsburgh John N. Coury and I set

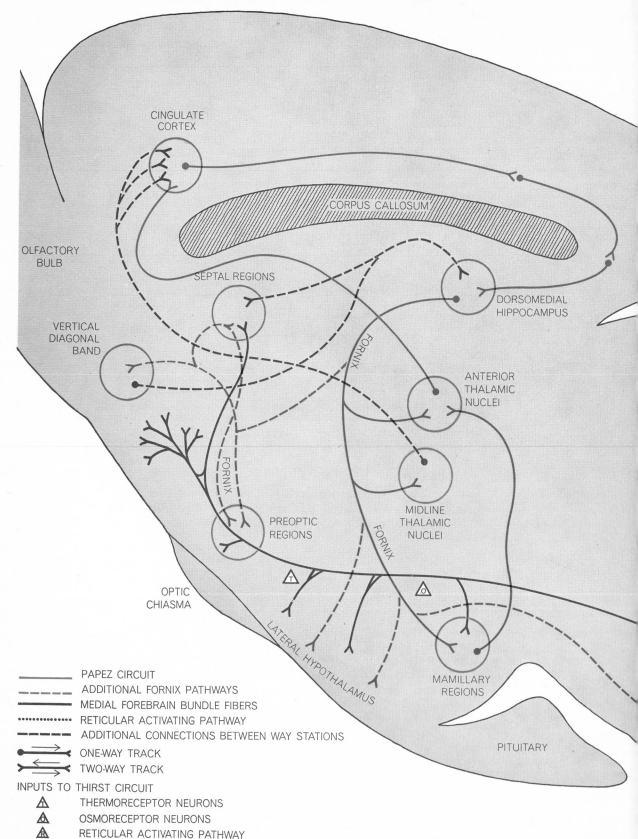

CINGULATE
CORTEX

CORPUS CALLOSUM

OLFACTORY
BULB

SEPTAL REGIONS

DORSOMEDIAL
HIPPOCAMPUS

VERTICAL
DIAGONAL
BAND

FORNIX

ANTERIOR
THALAMIC
NUCLEI

FORNIX

PREOPTIC
REGIONS

MIDLINE
THALAMIC
NUCLEI

FORNIX

OPTIC
CHIASMA

LATERAL HYPOTHALAMUS

MAMILLARY
REGIONS

PITUITARY

——————— PAPEZ CIRCUIT
– – – – – ADDITIONAL FORNIX PATHWAYS
━━━━━━ MEDIAL FOREBRAIN BUNDLE FIBERS
·············· RETICULAR ACTIVATING PATHWAY
– – – ADDITIONAL CONNECTIONS BETWEEN WAY STATIONS
●——→ ONE-WAY TRACK
◄——► TWO-WAY TRACK

INPUTS TO THIRST CIRCUIT
△ THERMORECEPTOR NEURONS
△ OSMORECEPTOR NEURONS
△ RETICULAR ACTIVATING PATHWAY

SCHEMATIC CIRCUITRY of the thirst drive is superimposed on a simplified outline of a rat's brain. Although all structures appear to lie on a single plane, they are actually distributed at varying depths in each brain hemisphere. The central figure eight (*solid color*) is a limbic circuit that links the hippocampal, the hypothalamic and the thalamic regions with the cingulate cortex of the forebrain. First postulated by James W. Papez in the 1930's, this circuit proves to be part of the thirst-drive system. Chemical ex-

ploration has identified other pathways (*broken colored lines*) extending the Papez circuit; in general, all involve the brain structure called the fornix. The second major component of the thirst-drive system (*solid black*) connects many forward limbic regions with the medial midbrain; the structures involved are the descending and ascending fibers of the medial forebrain bundle. Additional circuit elements (*broken black lines*) have been found to provide alternate connections between various system

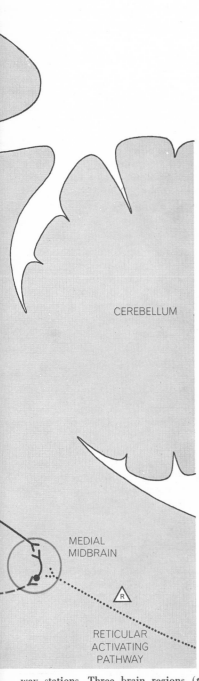

CEREBELLUM

MEDIAL
MIDBRAIN

R

RETICULAR
ACTIVATING
PATHWAY

way stations. Three brain regions (*triangles*), although not sensitive to cholinergic stimuli, can trigger the thirst-drive system. These are (*left to right*) neurons that respond to an increase in blood temperature, neurons that respond to an increase in the blood's salt concentration, and the reticular activating pathway leading to the midbrain.

out to try to chart the circuit that mediates drinking. Our design was to stimulate various sites in the rat brain by injections of the thirst-inducing substance acetylcholine or a chemical that mimics its transmitter action, such as muscarine. Tests were conducted at hourly intervals. As controls for the experiment some rats received no injections and some got injections of chemicals that have no impulse-transmitting action, but which can excite or depress nerve-cell activity. All the rats were given free access to as much water and food as they wanted, and an exact record was kept of their water consumption.

Normally rats drink 25 to 35 milliliters of water a day. Some rats we stimulated with brain injections of acetylcholine or muscarine quickly developed a colossal thirst. Within 10 minutes after the injection they began to consume large quantities of water, and within an hour some rats drank as much as twice a whole day's normal intake.

We found that this behavior could be evoked by injection of the drug at any one of many sites distributed widely in the brain [*see illustration on next page*]. Almost all the sites lie within what is known as the brain's limbic system, or the primitive "smell brain." It turned out that our initial map of the thirst circuit virtually coincided with one that James W. Papez, a Cornell University Medical College neuroanatomist, had described in 1937 as a closed-loop system that seemed to be responsible for emotion-directed behavior.

Our tests have shown that all the structures Papez outlined are implicated in thirst, but there are also a few thirst-inducing regions outside his circuit [*see illustration at left*]. We are exploring the entire brain to trace the full extent of the thirst system. We are now convinced that it involves a fiber trunk in the forebrain that connects limbic structures in the front of the brain with the hypothalamus and midbrain. Presumably suitable chemical stimulation of any of these regions alerts the entire thirst-drive system. We believe that the whole circuit normally utilizes acetylcholine, or a similar cholinergic chemical, as a neurotransmitter, and that when a cholinergic chemical is injected locally into the brain it initiates the chain release of cholinergic substances at nerve-fiber terminals throughout the system. It seems significant that Olds has found the same system to be involved in the mediation of "pleasure," or reward.

Our present model of the thirst-drive circuit in the brain, based on experiments, is a highly complex affair, and its very complexity strongly supports the model's plausibility. One obvious requirement for a basic drive system is stability; that is, it should not be easily knocked out or blocked by a simple disorder or injury to the animal. The complexity of the thirst system, as traced by our experiments, provides such protection, because the circuit contains many alternate pathways that can serve to maintain its integrity if some of the pathways are blocked.

This model of the thirst-drive system has some interesting parallels to Hebb's model of the memory system in the brain. Hebb believes that even the simplest perceptual learning involves hundreds of neurons widely dispersed in the brain and is established only gradually by the development of neuronal interconnections. The perception of a given event activates a certain pattern of sensory, associational and motor neurons. At first the pattern is a comparatively simple one and its durability is precarious. But as the perception is repeated and the neurons involved become more practiced in firing as a team, their functional interconnections become more firmly established. In time additional neurons are recruited, alternate pathways develop and the system becomes less and less vulnerable to disruption.

Hebb's model helps to explain the well-known fact that long-established memories are much less subject to obliteration by brain damage or stress than are the memories of recent events. Extending the analogy to the thirst-drive system, we can say that this system resists disruption because it is solidly established with a wealth of alternate pathways. It differs from a memory pattern, however, in that most of the neuronal interconnections are present at birth, having been established by genetic inheritance rather than by perception and learning.

The complexity of the thirst-drive circuit also helps to explain how a drive is maintained over a period of time. Obviously a nerve circuit that mediates a primary drive must be able to dominate brain activity long enough to permit the organism to search for environmental stimuli that will satisfy the drive. The thirst-drive circuit shown in the illustration at the left exhibits both closed-loop and reciprocal pathways. Such a system is ideally designed to continue functioning over a period of time, even after the cessation of the input that triggered the activity. Messages can continue to circulate, or "reverberate," through such a system until an inhibitory brake is applied.

Another set of experimental facts emphasizes the complexity of the thirst-drive system. It is clear that thirst can be triggered by several different means. For example, Andersson in Sweden has found two types of specialized neurons in the hypothalamus that increase thirst. One type responds to increased osmotic pressure, the other is sensitive to a rise in temperature. There is also other evidence suggesting that thirst-triggering inputs come from other parts of the brain, including the amygdala and the reticular activating system. Our map of the thirst-drive system, picturing it as a complex circuit with many way stations, helps to explain how these various inputs may be fed into the system.

So far we have little information about the chemical substances and brain circuits that control the primary drives other than thirst. Evidence from electrical-stimulation experiments, however, suggests that the same structures and pathways are involved in these other drives. It looks more and more as if the primary-drive circuits all follow a roughly parallel course in the brain. Thus in our laboratory we are seeking to determine whether each is stimulated and modulated by specific chemicals. We recently tested a male rat by injecting three different chemicals, on separate occasions, into the same site in the brain. An injection of acetylcholine into this site stimulated the animal to drink, noradrenalin prompted him to eat and testosterone caused him to build nests! Coury and I are now trying to trace a hunger circuit through the brain. Curiously enough we had very little success until a mixture of chemicals was tried that both suppresses acetylcholine action and enhances the action of noradrenalin.

## The Cat Is Not a Rat

I must point out that so far the only animal in which we have succeeded in tracing a brain circuit for a primary drive is the rat. The brain of the cat, for example, does not respond the same way when we inject acetylcholine into regions anatomically similar to those that stimulate thirst in the rat. Instead of stimulating cats to drink, these injections elicit anger, fear or a sleeplike trance. Independently, Raúl Hernández-Peón in Mexico City has reported tracing in the cat's brain a sleep circuit that follows much the same course as the thirst circuit in the rat. The chemical that induces sleep is acetylcholine. We interpret this to mean that there are species differences in the relations between specific chemicals and nerve circuits, but that the general principle of chemical specificity of separate functional systems still applies.

Whether or not our present theories are correct, chemical explorations of the brain have established at least two significant facts: first, that certain brain cells are stimulated selectively by specific chemicals and, second, that drive-oriented behavior can be triggered and sustained by chemical means. It seems safe to predict that chemical stimulation of the brain will become an increasingly important tool in the investigation of the neurophysiological bases of behavior.

EXCESSIVE WATER INTAKE during the hour after stimulus is related to the area of the brain that was stimulated. The light bars show the mean amount of water consumed in the course of multiple tests with a series of rats. The dark bars show the maximum water intake by a single animal. Normally a rat will drink about 1.5 milliliters per hour. A greater intake is evidence that the stimulated structure is part of the brain's thirst-drive system.

# 9

# SEX DIFFERENCES IN THE BRAIN

SEYMOUR LEVINE                                            April 1966

What makes a male mammal male and a female mammal female? We might sum up the answer in the word heredity, but this would evade the question. How is the genetic information translated into the differentiation of the sexes, as expressed in their physiology and behavior? Again we might summarize the answer in a single word: hormones. Recent investigations have revealed, however, that sexual differentiation in mammals cannot be explained solely in terms of hormones. There is now considerable evidence that the brain is also involved. According to this evidence there are distinct differences between the male brain and the female brain in a mammal, differences that determine not only sexual activity but also certain other forms of behavior.

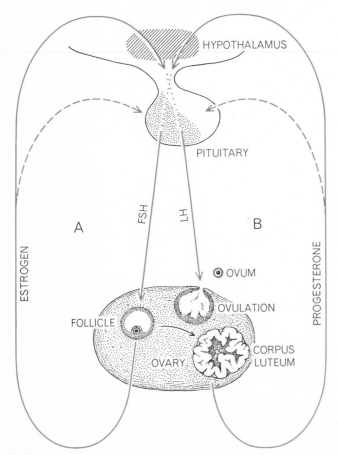
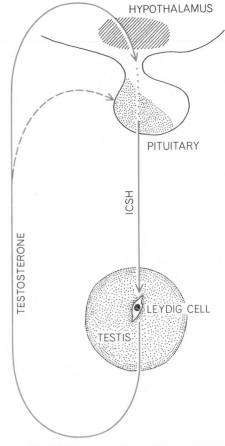

INTERPLAY OF SEX HORMONES differs in the female mammal (*left*) and the male (*right*). In the cyclic female system the pituitary initially releases a follicle-stimulating hormone (FSH) that makes the ovary produce estrogen (*colored arrows at A*): the estrogen then acts on the hypothalamus of the brain to inhibit the further release of FSH by the pituitary and to stimulate the release of a luteinizing hormone (LH) instead. This hormone both triggers ovulation and makes the ovary produce a second hormone, pro-gesterone (*colored arrows at B*). On reaching the hypothalamus the latter hormone inhibits further pituitary release of LH, thereby completing the cycle. In the noncyclic male system the pituitary continually releases an interstitial-cell-stimulating hormone (ICSH) that makes the testes produce testosterone; the latter hormone acts on the hypothalamus to stimulate further release of ICSH by the pituitary. Broken arrows represent the earlier theory that the sex hormones from ovaries and testes stimulated the pituitary directly.

Let us begin by examining one of the principal distinctions between males and females. In most species of mammals the female has a cyclic pattern of ovulation. The human female ovulates about every 28 days; the guinea pig, about every 15 days; the rat, every four to five days. The process is dominated by hormones of the pituitary gland. In cyclic fashion the anterior (front) part of the pituitary delivers to the ovary a follicle-stimulating hormone (FSH), which promotes the growth of Graafian follicles, and a luteinizing hormone (LH), which induces the formation of corpora lutea and triggers ovulation. The formation of corpora lutea is clear evidence that ovulation has occurred. The ovary in turn responds to FSH by releasing the female sex hormone estrogen and to LH by releasing the female sex hormone progesterone [*see illustration on opposite page*].

The male mammal shows no such cycle. Its testes continually receive from the pituitary the same hormone (LH) that stimulates formation of corpora lutea in the female's ovary; in the male, however, this hormone is known as the interstitial-cell-stimulating hormone (ICSH) because it causes the interstitial cells of the testes to secrete testosterone. Thus the patterns of pituitary effects on the sex organs are distinctly different in the two sexes: cyclic in the female, noncyclic in the male.

What might account for this difference? When the interaction of the pituitary and sex organs was discovered, it was natural to suppose that the sex hormones regulated the pituitary's secretions. In the female the pituitary hormones controlled the process that led to ovulation; the consequent output of estrogen and progesterone by the ovary caused the pituitary to cut down production of its stimulating hormones, and the cycle might therefore be described as a negative-feedback system.

Thirty years ago the endocrinologist Carroll A. Pfeiffer, then working at the Yale University School of Medicine, reported a series of studies unequivocally demonstrating that the process of sexual differentiation occurred very early in the course of a mammal's development. In these studies he undertook to exchange the sex organs in the formative period of early life. In newborn male rats he removed the testes and replaced them with transplanted ovaries; in newborn females he replaced the ovaries with testes; other animals in his experiments were provided with both organs—testes and ovaries. The

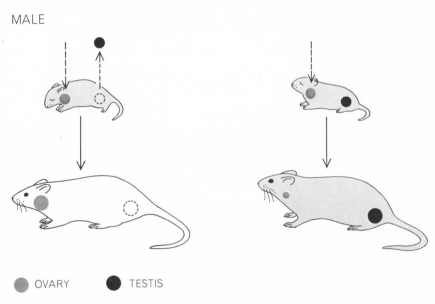

FEMALE

● OVARY    ● TESTIS

**REVERSAL OF SEX** in young female rats was achieved experimentally by Carroll A. Pfeiffer of the Yale University School of Medicine 30 years ago in proof of the action of the male sex hormone testosterone. When the ovaries of a young female (*at top left in color*) were removed and testes were implanted, the animal in effect became male (*gray*) and showed no estrus at maturity. Even when a female's ovaries were left intact (*top right*), the output of testosterone from the implant prevented normal functioning of the ovaries.

MALE

● OVARY    ● TESTIS

**LACK OF TESTOSTERONE** permitted a similar reversal of sex among young male rats in the Pfeiffer experiment. When the rat's testes were removed and an ovary was then implanted (*top left*), the ovary continued to function and the animal in effect became female (*color*). When an ovary was implanted in a normal male, however (*top right*), the male's output of testosterone kept the ovary from functioning and the rat remained male (*gray*).

main findings that emerged were these: Males with ovaries in place of testes showed the female capacity for producing corpora lutea in the ovarian tissues. Those that possessed testes as well as ovaries failed to form any corpora lutea in the implanted ovaries. Of the females that had testes implanted, many failed to show estrous cycles or any formation of corpora lutea in their ovaries if the ovaries were left intact.

From these results Pfeiffer deduced that, since the controlling factor seemed to be the presence or absence of testosterone, in the newborn rat testosterone acted to induce a permanent sexual differentiation of the pituitary. If testosterone was present during this critical early period, it would cause the pituitary to produce stimulating secretions thereafter in the noncyclic, male mode; if testosterone was absent, the pituitary would behave throughout life as if it belonged to a female.

Pfeiffer's hypothesis that the pituitary itself was sexually differentiated did not stand up, however. Direct evidence on this question was produced in the 1950's by Geoffrey W. Harris of the University of Oxford and investigators working with him at the Institute of Psychiatry in London. Harris and Dora Jacobsohn found that when the pituitary gland of a male rat was transplanted under the hypothalamus of a female, her reproductive functions and behavior remained entirely female and normal. The same absence of change was noted when pituitaries from female rats were implanted in males. Meanwhile the late F. H. A. Marshall of the University of Cambridge was able to demonstrate that a close relation exists between the external environment and reproduction. In many species of mammals the female cycle of ovulation is affected by light, diet, temperature and emotional stress. Moreover, electrical stimulation of the hypothalamus could induce ovulation, and lesions of the hypothalamus could block ovulation.

Reviewing Pfeiffer's findings and the other experimental evidence, Harris and another investigator, the late William C. Young of the University of Kansas, suggested that it was the brain (not the pituitary, as Pfeiffer had proposed) that was subject to differentiation by the action of hormones. According to this view, the brain of a mammal was essentially female until a certain stage of development (which in the rat came within a short time after birth). If testosterone was absent at this stage, the brain would remain female; if testosterone was present, the brain would develop male characteristics.

Under Harris' leadership the author and other investigators working in the department of neuroendocrinology at the Institute of Psychiatry started a systematic and extensive program of experiments to test this hypothesis. The

FEMALE

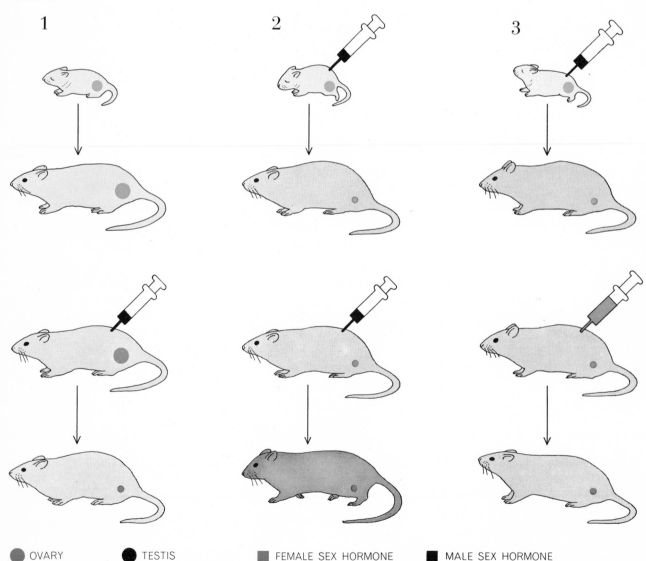

● OVARY    ● TESTIS    ■ FEMALE SEX HORMONE    ■ MALE SEX HORMONE

MASCULINIZED FEMALE RATS were produced by injections of testosterone (*black syringe*) at birth. In Column 1 a normal female (*color*) is injected with male hormone when mature; the animal exhibits some male sexual behavior (*gray*). In Column 2 the female is injected with male hormone in infancy; when reinjected at maturity, it exhibits full male sexual behavior. In Column 3, in spite of an injection of female hormone (*colored syringe*) at maturity, the masculinized female fails to exhibit female sexual behavior.

program has been continued at the Stanford University School of Medicine. We worked mainly with rats, and the basic procedure entailed alteration of the newborn animal's normal exposure to sex hormones within the first four days after birth. Instead of transplanting organs we simply injected the hormone whose effects we wished to test; it was already known that a single injection of testosterone (in the form of the long-acting compound testosterone propionate) in a newborn female rat could produce the same effects as the implantation of male testes.

We found that females injected with testosterone in this critical early period did not develop the normal female pattern of physiology when they became adults. Their ovaries were dwarfed and they failed to produce corpora lutea or show the usual cycle of ovulation. On the other hand, males that were castrated (and thus deprived of testosterone) within the first days after birth did show signs of female physiology; when ovaries were implanted in them as adults, they developed corpora lutea. It was clear that a permanent control over the activity of the pituitary in the rat was established by the absence or presence of testosterone in the critical first few days after birth. In the absence of testosterone a pattern of cyclic release of FSH and LH by the pituitary was formed; if testosterone was present, it abolished the cycle.

Essentially the same effect has been demonstrated in guinea pigs and monkeys, but the critical period for these longer-gestating mammals occurs before birth. A series of injections of testosterone in the fetal stage of a female guinea pig or monkey produces permanent masculinizing effects such as we have observed in the female rat.

What are the effects of the early administration of testosterone on the rat's sexual behavior? In this area, as in physiology, there are measurable

MALE

1 2 3

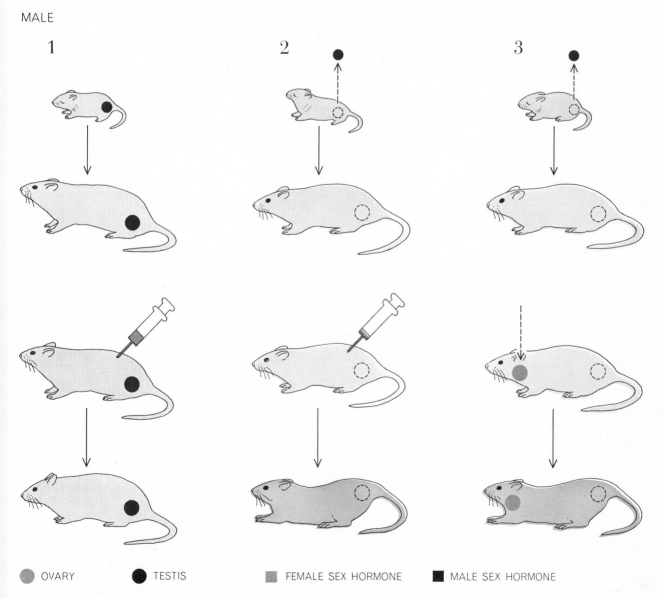

● OVARY  ● TESTIS  ■ FEMALE SEX HORMONE  ■ MALE SEX HORMONE

**FEMINIZED MALE RATS** were produced by injections of estrogen and progesterone or by ovary implants only when the males had been castrated at birth and thereby deprived of testosterone during the critical first days of life. In Column 1 a normal male (gray) is unaffected by the injection of female hormones (*colored syringe*) at maturity. In Column 2 a castrated male is similarly injected; it then assumes the female's permissive sexual posture. In Column 3 the same behavior is produced by implanting an ovary.

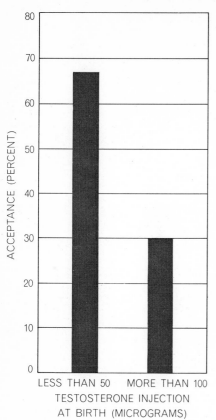

**SEXUAL BEHAVIOR** of female rats was substantially modified by the injection of male hormone at birth. Although dosed with female hormones at maturity, females that had received 100 micrograms or more of testosterone at birth were less than half as responsive to male sexual advances as rats that had received little or no male hormone.

criteria for male and female behavior. The male goes through a complex pattern of behavior that begins with mounting of the female and proceeds through several stages to the final ejaculation. The female's display of sexual receptivity is marked by a "lordosis response" (which consists of arching the back and elevating the pelvis) when she is mounted by the male. Now, in most subprimate mammals, including the rat, the female's sexual behavior depends entirely on the hormones circulating in her bloodstream. Removal of the ovaries (and hence the elimination of estrogen and progesterone) will completely suppress her normal female sexual behavior, and conversely injections of estrogen and progesterone will restore it. Hence it was no surprise to find that the testosterone treatment of newborn female rats, which disrupted their normal secretion of sex hormones, affected their sexual behavior. The effects were marked, however, by several unusual features.

These masculinized females not only lost the usual female sexual receptivity, including the normal lordosis response to a male, but also failed to show the normal response even when they were given large replacement injections of estrogen and progesterone. Moreover, they showed male behavior that went beyond any previously observed. Male sex behavior is not uncommon even in normal female animals; they can often be observed going through the motions of mounting. A normal adult female rat, if injected with testosterone, will sometimes go so far as to mimic some components of the male's act of copulation. Some of our female rats that had been testosteronized at birth went further, however. Although such females lack any semblance of male genitalia, when they were given a new dose of testosterone as adults, they performed the entire male sexual ritual, including the motions that accompany ejaculation.

The male rats in our experiments showed a similarly striking change of sexual behavior as a result of hormonal alteration at birth. Normally it is extremely difficult to elicit female sexual behavior in an adult male merely by injecting him with female hormones. When, however, newborn male rats were castrated, so that they lacked testosterone at the critical stage of development occurring in the few days after birth, it was found that injection of very small doses of estrogen and progesterone in these males as adults caused them to display sexual behavior precisely like that of normal females. Clearly the change in these animals involved the central nervous system; the system's response to female hormones, as reflected in the animal's behavior, had been altered.

Thus all the experiments, both on males and on females, left little doubt that testosterone could determine the sexual differentiation of the brain in the first few days after birth. In some manner testosterone produced a profound and permanent change in the sensitivity of the brain to sex hormones. In the female it made the brain tissue much more sensitive to testosterone and insensitive to estrogen and progesterone, so that the animal did not display normal female behavior in response to these female hormones. In the male the absence of testosterone at the critical period caused the animal to be sensitive to estrogen and progesterone. To put it another way, the absence of testosterone at the differentiation stage would leave both males and females

sensitive to the female hormones and capable of displaying female behavior; the presence of testosterone, on the other hand, would desensitize females as well as males, so that both sexes failed to display feminine behavior when they were challenged with female hormones.

That the sex hormones can act directly on the brain was clearly demonstrated in experiments by Harris and Richard Michael. They implanted a synthetic estrogen (stilbestrol) into the hypothalamus of female cats and found that the implant evoked full female sexual behavior although the cats did not show the usual physiological signs of estrus. In similar experiments with males Julian M. Davidson of Stanford University showed that implants of testosterone in the brain of a castrated male rat would elicit male sexual behavior, although again there was no sign of effects on the anatomy of the male reproductive system.

If the brain differentiates into male and female types, may not the difference be reflected in fields of behavior other than the sexual? A few experiments looking into this question have been conducted; they suggest that other forms of behavior can indeed be influenced by hormonal treatment during the critical period of sexual differentiation.

One of these studies involved a difference between male and female behavior that Curt P. Richter of the Johns Hopkins School of Medicine observed many years ago. He used an activity wheel that measured the amount of voluntary running activity an animal would perform each day. The activity of females, he found, went in cycles, rising to a peak at the time of ovulation; males, on the other hand, performed more uniformly from day to day. Harris recently applied this activity test to male rats that had been castrated shortly after birth and then implanted with an ovary as adults. They showed a cyclic pattern of running activity corresponding to the cycle of ovulation (covering four to five days) of the female rat.

Another test employed the open-field apparatus with which we have gauged animals' behavior in response to various emotion-evoking stimuli [see "Stimulation in Infancy," by Seymour Levine, page 93, for an account of this]. In this apparatus females tend to be more exploratory and to defecate less often than males. We found that female rats to which testosterone had been administered at birth displayed the male pattern of defecation behavior instead of the female pattern [*see illustration on this page*].

Analyzing the play of young monkeys before they reach sexual maturity, Young and his co-workers found that the juvenile male's behavior is distinctly different from the female's: the male is more inclined to rough-and-tumble play, more aggressive and more given to threatening facial expressions. Again experiments showed that injections of testosterone during the critical differentiation period (before birth in the monkey's case) caused females to display the male type of behavior in play.

Obviously the findings so far are only first steps in what promises to be an important new field of investigation. They invite a full exploration of the extent to which behavior, nonsexual as well as sexual, can be masculinized by testosterone treatment or feminized by castration at the critical stage of sexual differentiation. It presents a new biological mystery: If testosterone at the critical period does indeed produce sexual differentiation in the brain, by what mechanism does it do so? The studies on animals may well have clinical implications for human beings with respect to the problem of homosexuality. Human homosexual behavior undoubtedly involves many psychological factors that do not apply to the lower animals, but it may also depend in a fundamental sense on what the hormonal makeup of the individual happens to be during the development of the nervous system.

There are other questions of broader interest. Do the hormones of the thyroid

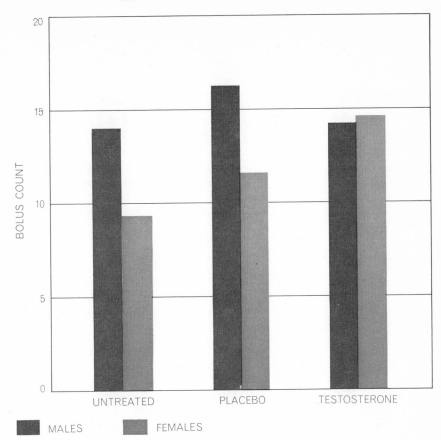

EXPLORATORY BEHAVIOR, more extensive among female rats than among males, was modified when the females were injected with male hormones at birth. The bar chart shows the frequency of defecation, which is inversely proportional to exploration, in three minutes' exposure in an open-field apparatus. When the females had not been injected at birth (*left and center*), their count was significantly lower than the males'. Females that had been masculinized (*right*), however, defecated at a rate insignificantly different from the males'.

gland, the adrenal cortex and other organs of the endocrine system exert differentiating effects on the developing brain? To what extent may the various hormones acting on the brain during infancy shape the future behavior of an individual? The artificially masculinized female rat and the feminized male have opened a wide field for speculation and research.

# 10

# THE REPRODUCTIVE BEHAVIOR OF RING DOVES

DANIEL S. LEHRMAN

November 1964

In recent years the study of animal behavior has proceeded along two different lines, with two groups of investigators formulating problems in different ways and indeed approaching the problems from different points of view. The comparative psychologist traditionally tends first to ask a question and then to attack it by way of animal experimentation. The ethologist, on the other hand, usually begins by observing the normal activity of an animal and then seeks to identify and analyze specific behavior patterns characteristic of the species.

The two attitudes can be combined. The psychologist can begin, like the ethologist, by watching an animal do what it does naturally, and only then ask questions that flow from his observations. He can go on to manipulate experimental conditions in an effort to discover the psychological and biological events that give rise to the behavior under study and perhaps to that of other animals as well. At the Institute of Animal Behavior at Rutgers University we have taken this approach to study in detail the reproductive-behavior cycle of the ring dove (*Streptopelia risoria*). The highly specific changes in behavior that occur in the course of the cycle, we find, are governed by complex psycho-

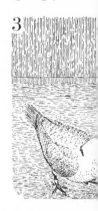

REPRODUCTIVE-BEHAVIOR CYCLE begins soon after a male and a female ring dove are introduced into a cage containing nest-ing material (hay in this case) and an empty glass nest bowl (1). Courtship activity, on the first day, is characterized by the "bowing

CYCLE CONTINUES as the adult birds take turns incubating the eggs (6), which hatch after about 14 days (7). The newly hatched squabs are fed "crop-milk," a liquid secreted in the gullets of the adults (8). The parents continue to feed them, albeit reluctantly,

biological interactions of the birds' inner and outer environments.

The ring dove, a small relative of the domestic pigeon, has a light gray back, creamy underparts and a black semicircle (the "ring") around the back of its neck. The male and female look alike and can only be distinguished by surgical exploration. If we place a male and a female ring dove with previous breeding experience in a cage containing an empty glass bowl and a supply of nesting material, the birds invariably enter on their normal behavioral cycle, which follows a predictable course and a fairly regular time schedule. During the first day the principal activity is courtship: the male struts around, bowing and cooing at the female. After several hours the birds announce their selection of a nest site (which in nature would be a concave place and in our cages is the glass bowl) by crouching in it and uttering a distinctive coo. Both birds participate in building the nest, the male usually gathering material and carrying it to the female, who stands in the bowl and constructs the nest. After a week or more of nest-building, in the course of which the birds copulate, the female be-

comes noticeably more attached to the nest and difficult to dislodge; if one attempts to lift her off the nest, she may grasp it with her claws and take it along. This behavior usually indicates that the female is about to lay her eggs. Between seven and 11 days after the beginning of the courtship she produces her first egg, usually at about five o'clock in the afternoon. The female dove sits on the egg and then lays a second one, usually at about nine o'clock in the morning two days later. Sometime that day the male takes a turn sitting; thereafter the two birds alternate, the male sitting for about six hours in the middle of each day, the female for the remaining 18 hours a day.

In about 14 days the eggs hatch and the parents begin to feed their young "crop-milk," a liquid secreted at this stage of the cycle by the lining of the adult dove's crop, a pouch in the bird's gullet. When they are 10 or 12 days old, the squabs leave the cage, but they continue to beg for and to receive food from the parents. This continues until the squabs are about two weeks old, when the parents become less and less willing to feed them as the young birds

gradually develop the ability to peck for grain on the floor of the cage. When the young are about 15 to 25 days old, the adult male begins once again to bow and coo; nest-building is resumed, a new clutch of eggs is laid and the cycle is repeated. The entire cycle lasts about six or seven weeks and—at least in our laboratory, where it is always spring because of controlled light and temperature conditions—it can continue throughout the year.

The variations in behavior that constitute the cycle are not merely casual or superficial changes in the birds' preoccupations; they represent striking changes in the overall pattern of activity and in the atmosphere of the breeding cage. At its appropriate stage each of the kinds of behavior I have described represents the predominant activity of the animals at the time. Furthermore, these changes in behavior are not just responses to changes in the external situation. The birds do not build the nest merely because the nesting material is available; even if nesting material is in the cage throughout the cycle, nest-building behavior is concentrated,

coo" of the male (2). The male and then the female utter a distinctive "nest call" to indicate their selection of a nesting site (3).

There follows a week or more of cooperation in nest-building (4), culminating in the laying of two eggs at precise times of day (5).

as the young birds learn to peck for grain themselves (9). When the squabs are between two and three weeks old, the adults ignore

them and start to court once again, and a new cycle begins (10). Physical changes during the cycle are shown on the next page.

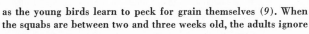

as described, at one stage. Similarly, the birds react to the eggs and to the young only at appropriate stages in the cycle.

These cyclic changes in behavior therefore represent, at least in part, changes in the internal condition of the animals rather than merely changes in their external situation. Furthermore, the changes in behavior are associated with equally striking and equally pervasive changes in the anatomy and the physiological state of the birds. For example, when the female dove is first introduced into the cage, her oviduct weighs some 800 milligrams. Eight or nine days later, when she lays her first egg, the oviduct may weigh 4,000 milligrams. The crops of both the male and the female weigh some 900 milligrams when the birds are placed in the cage, and when they start to sit on the eggs some 10 days later they still weigh about the same. But two weeks afterward, when the eggs hatch, the parents' crops may weigh as much as 3,000 milligrams. Equally striking changes in the condition of the ovary, the weight of the testes, the length of the gut, the weight of the liver, the microscopic structure of the pituitary gland and other physiological indices are correlated with the behavioral cycle.

Now, if a male or a female dove is placed alone in a cage with nesting material, no such cycle of behavioral or anatomical changes takes place. Far from producing two eggs every six or seven weeks, a female alone in a cage lays no eggs at all. A male alone shows no interest when we offer it nesting material, eggs or young. The cycle of psychobiological changes I have described is, then, one that occurs more or less synchronously in each member of a pair of doves living together but that will not occur independently in either of the pair living alone.

In a normal breeding cycle both the male and the female sit on the eggs almost immediately after they are laid. The first question we asked ourselves was whether this is because the birds are always ready to sit on eggs or because they come into some special condition of readiness to incubate at about the time the eggs are produced.

We kept male and female doves in isolation for several weeks and then placed male-female pairs in test cages, each supplied with a nest bowl containing a normal dove nest with two eggs. The birds did not sit; they acted almost as if the eggs were not there. They courted, then built their own nest (usually on top of the planted nest and its eggs, which we had to keep fishing out to keep the stimulus situation constant!), then finally sat on the eggs—five to seven days after they had first encountered each other.

This clearly indicated that the doves are not always ready to sit on eggs; under the experimental conditions they changed from birds that did not want to incubate to birds that did want to incubate in five to seven days. What had induced this change? It could not have been merely the passage of time since their last breeding experience, because this had varied from four to six or more weeks in different pairs, whereas the variation in time spent in the test cage before sitting was only a couple of days.

Could the delay of five to seven days represent the time required for the birds to get over the stress of being handled and become accustomed to the strange cage? To test this possibility we placed pairs of doves in cages without any nest bowls or nesting material and separated each male and female by an opaque partition. After seven days we removed the partition and introduced nesting material and a formed nest with eggs. If the birds had merely needed time to recover from being handled and become acclimated to the cage, they should now have sat on the eggs immediately. They did not do so; they sat only after five to seven days, just as if they had been introduced into the cage only when the opaque partition was removed.

The next possibility we considered was that in this artificial situation stimulation from the eggs might induce the change from a nonsitting to a sitting "mood" but that this effect required five to seven days to reach a threshold value at which the behavior would change.

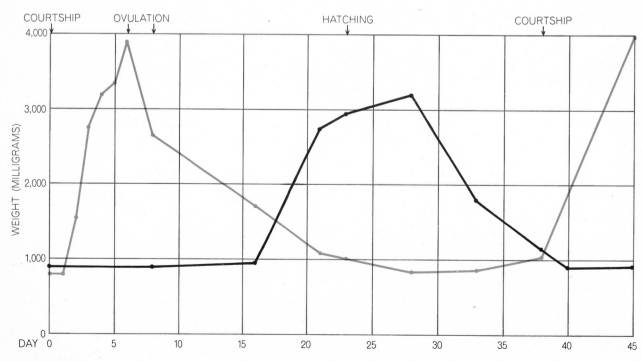

**ANATOMICAL AND PHYSIOLOGICAL** changes are associated with the behavioral changes of the cycle. The chart gives average weights of the crop (*black curve*) and the female oviduct (*color*) at various stages measured in days after the beginning of courtship.

We therefore placed pairs of birds in test cages with empty nest bowls and a supply of nesting material but no eggs. The birds courted and built nests. After seven days we removed the nest bowl and its nest and replaced it with a fresh bowl containing a nest and eggs. All these birds sat within two hours.

It was now apparent that some combination of influences arising from the presence of the mate and the availability of the nest bowl and nesting material induced the change from nonreadiness to incubate to readiness. In order to distinguish between these influences we put a new group of pairs of doves in test cages without any nest bowl or nesting material. When, seven days later, we offered these birds nesting material and nests with eggs, most of them did not sit immediately. Nor did they wait the full five to seven days to do so; they sat after one day, during which they engaged in intensive nest-building. A final group, placed singly in cages with nests and eggs, failed to incubate at all, even after weeks in the cages.

In summary, the doves do not build nests as soon as they are introduced into a cage containing nesting material, but they will do so immediately if the nesting material is introduced for the first time after they have spent a while together; they will not sit immediately on eggs offered after the birds have been in a bare cage together for some days, but they will do so if they were able to do some nest-building during the end of their period together. From these experiments it is apparent that there are two kinds of change induced in these birds: first, they are changed from birds primarily interested in courtship to birds primarily interested in nest-building, and this change is brought about by stimulation arising from association with a mate; second, under these conditions they are further changed from birds primarily interested in nest-building to birds interested in sitting on eggs, and this change is encouraged by participation in nest-building.

The course of development of readiness to incubate is shown graphically by the results of another experiment, which Philip N. Brody, Rochelle Wortis and I undertook shortly after the ones just described. We placed pairs of birds in test cages for varying numbers of days, in some cases with and in others without a nest bowl and nesting material. Then we introduced a nest and eggs into the cage. If neither bird sat within three hours, the test was scored as nega-

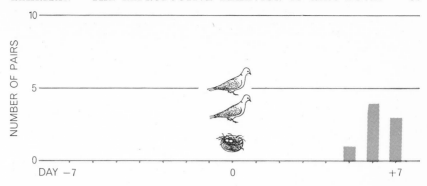

**READINESS TO INCUBATE** was tested with four groups of eight pairs of doves. Birds of the first group were placed in a cage containing a nest and eggs. They went through courtship and nest-building behavior before finally sitting after between five and seven days.

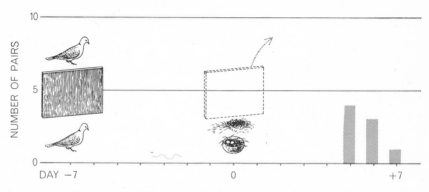

**EFFECT OF HABITUATION** was tested by keeping two birds separated for seven days in the cage before introducing nest and eggs. They still sat only after five to seven days.

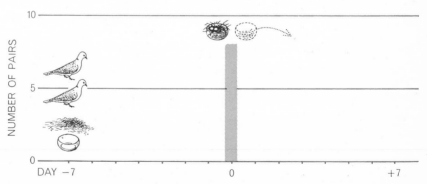

**MATE AND NESTING MATERIAL** had a dramatic effect on incubation-readiness. Pairs that had spent seven days in courtship and nest-building sat as soon as eggs were offered.

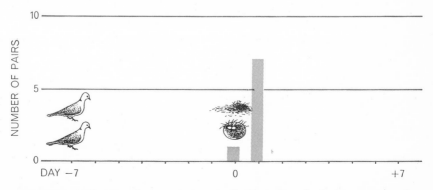

**PRESENCE OF MATE** without nesting activity had less effect. Birds that spent a week in cages with no nest bowls or hay took a day to sit after nests with eggs were introduced.

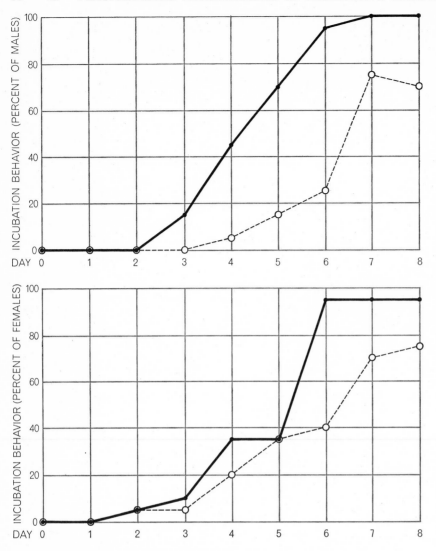

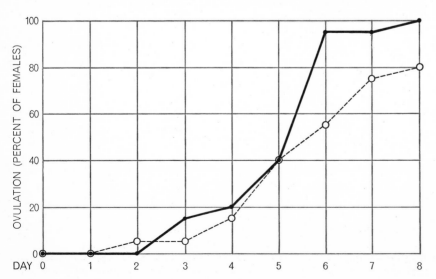

**DURATION OF ASSOCIATION** with mate and nesting material affects incubation behavior. The abscissas give the length of the association for different groups of birds. The plotted points show what percentage of each group sat within three hours of being offered eggs. The percentage increases for males (*top*) and females (*bottom*) as a function of time previously spent with mate (*open circles*) or with mate and nesting material (*solid dots*).

**OVULATION** is similarly affected. These curves, coinciding closely with those of the bottom chart above, show the occurrence of ovulation in the same birds represented there.

tive and both birds were removed for autopsy. If either bird sat within three hours, that bird was removed and the other bird was given an additional three hours to sit. The experiment therefore tested—independently for the male and the female—the development of readiness to incubate as a function of the number of days spent with the mate, with or without the opportunity to build a nest.

It is apparent [*see top illustration at left*] that association with the mate gradually brings the birds into a condition of readiness to incubate and that this effect is greatly enhanced by the presence of nesting material. Exposure to the nesting situation does not stimulate the onset of readiness to incubate in an all-or-nothing way; rather, its effect is additive with the effect of stimulation provided by the mate. Other experiments show, moreover, that the stimulation from the mate and nesting material is sustained. If either is removed, the incidence of incubation behavior decreases.

The experiments described so far made it clear that external stimuli normally associated with the breeding situation play an important role in inducing a state of readiness to incubate. We next asked what this state consists of physiologically. As a first approach to this problem we attempted to induce incubation behavior by injecting hormones into the birds instead of by manipulating the external stimulation. We treated birds just as we had in the first experiment but injected some of the birds with hormones while they were in isolation, starting one week before they were due to be placed in pairs in the test cages. When both members of the pair had been injected with the ovarian hormone progesterone, more than 90 percent of the eggs were covered by one of the birds within three hours after their introduction into the cage instead of five to seven days later. When the injected substance was another ovarian hormone—estrogen—the effect on most birds was to make them incubate after a latent period of one to three days, during which they engaged in nest-building behavior. The male hormone testosterone had no effect on incubation behavior.

During the 14 days when the doves are sitting on the eggs, their crops increase enormously in weight. Crop growth is a reliable indicator of the secretion of the hormone prolactin by the birds' pituitary glands. Since this growth coincides with the development of incubation behavior and culminates in the secretion of the crop-milk the birds feed to their young after the eggs hatch, Brody and I have recently examined the effect of injected prolactin on incubation behavior. We find that prolactin is not so effective as progesterone in inducing incubation behavior, even at dosage levels that induce full development of the crop. For example, a total prolactin dose of 400 international units induced only 40 percent of the birds to sit on eggs early, even though their average crop weight was about 3,000 milligrams, or more than three times the normal weight. Injection of 10 units of the hormone induced significant increases in crop weight (to 1,200 milligrams) but no increase in the frequency of incubation behavior. These results, together with the fact that in a normal breeding cycle the crop begins to increase in weight only after incubation begins, make it unlikely that prolactin plays an important role in the initiation of normal incubation behavior in this species. It does, however, seem to help to maintain such behavior until the eggs hatch.

Prolactin is much more effective in inducing ring doves to show regurgitation-feeding responses to squabs. When 12 adult doves with previous breeding experience were each injected with 450 units of prolactin over a seven-day period and placed, one bird at a time, in cages with squabs, 10 of the 12 fed the squabs from their engorged crops, whereas none of 12 uninjected controls did so or even made any parental approaches to the squabs.

This experiment showed that prolactin, which is normally present in considerable quantities in the parents when the eggs hatch, does contribute to the doves' ability to show parental feeding behavior. I originally interpreted it to mean that the prolactin-induced engorgement of the crop was necessary in order for any regurgitation feeding to take place, but E. Klinghammer and E. H. Hess of the University of Chicago have correctly pointed out that this was an error, that ring doves are capable of feeding young if presented with them rather early in the incubation period. They do so even though they have no crop-milk, feeding a mixture of regurgitated seeds and a liquid. We are now studying the question of how early the birds can do this and how this ability is related to the onset of prolactin secretion.

The work with gonad-stimulating hormones and prolactin demonstrates that the various hormones successively produced by the birds' glands during their reproductive cycle are capable of inducing the successive behavioral changes that characterize the cycle.

Up to this point I have described two main groups of experiments. One group demonstrates that external stimuli induce changes in behavioral status of a kind normally associated with the progress of the reproductive cycle; the second shows that these behavioral changes can also be induced by hormone administration, provided that the choice of hormones is guided by knowledge of the succession of hormone secretions during a normal reproductive cycle. An obvious—and challenging—implication of these results is that external stimuli may induce changes in hormone secretion, and that environment-induced hormone secretion may constitute an integral part of the mechanism of the reproductive behavior cycle. We have attacked the problem of the environmental stimulation of hormone secretion in a series of experiments in which, in addition to examining the effects of external stimuli on the birds' behavioral status, we have examined their effects on well-established anatomical indicators of the presence of various hormones.

Background for this work was provided by two classic experiments with the domestic pigeon, published during the 1930's, which we have verified in the ring dove. At the London Zoo, L. H. Matthews found that a female pigeon would lay eggs as a result of being placed in a cage with a male from whom she was separated by a glass plate. This was an unequivocal demonstration that visual and/or auditory stimulation provided by the male induces ovarian development in the female. (Birds are quite insensitive to olfactory stimulation.) And M. D. Patel of the University of Wisconsin found that the crops of breeding pigeons, which develop strikingly during the incubation period, would regress to their resting state if the incubating birds were removed from their nests and would fail to develop at all if the birds were removed before crop growth had begun. If, however, a male pigeon, after being removed from his nest, was placed in an adjacent cage from which he could see his mate still sitting on the eggs, his crop would develop just as if he were himself incubating! Clearly stimuli arising from participation in incubation, including visual stimuli, cause the doves' pituitary glands to secrete prolactin.

Our autopsies showed that the incidence of ovulation in females that had associated with males for various periods coincided closely with the incidence of incubation behavior [see bottom illustration on opposite page]; statistical analysis reveals a very high degree of association. The process by which the dove's ovary develops to the point of ovulation includes a period of estrogen secretion followed by one of progesterone secretion, both induced by appropriate ovary-stimulating hormones from the pituitary gland. We therefore conclude that stimuli provided by the male, augmented by the presence of the nest bowl and nesting material, induce the secretion of gonad-stimulating hormones by the female's pituitary, and that the onset of readiness to incubate is a result of this process.

As I have indicated, ovarian development, culminating in ovulation and egg-laying, can be induced in a female dove merely as a result of her seeing a male through a glass plate. Is this the result of the mere presence of another bird or of something the male does because he is a male? Carl Erickson and I have begun to deal with this question. We placed 40 female doves in separate cages, each separated from a male by a glass plate. Twenty of the stimulus animals were normal, intact males, whereas the remaining 20 had been castrated several weeks before. The intact males all exhibited vigorous bow-cooing immediately on being placed in the cage, whereas none of the castrates did so. Thirteen of the 20 females with intact males ovulated during the next seven days, whereas only two of those with the castrates did so. Clearly ovarian development in the female is not induced merely by seeing another bird but by seeing or hearing it act like a male as the result of the effects of its own male hormone on its nervous system.

Although crop growth, which begins early in the incubation period, is apparently stimulated by participation in incubation, the crop continues to be large and actively secreting for quite some time after the hatching of the eggs. This suggests that stimuli provided by the squabs may also stimulate prolactin secretion. In our laboratory Ernst Hansen substituted three-day-old squabs for eggs in various stages of incubation and after four days compared the adults' crop weights with those of birds that had continued to sit on their eggs dur-

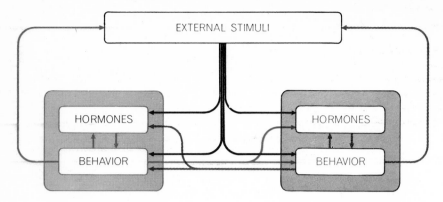

**INTERACTIONS** that appear to govern the reproductive-behavior cycle are suggested here. Hormones regulate behavior and are themselves affected by behavioral and other stimuli. And the behavior of each bird affects the hormones and the behavior of its mate.

ing the four days. He found that the crops grow even faster when squabs are in the nest than when the adults are under the influence of the eggs; the presence of squabs can stimulate a dove's pituitary glands to secrete more prolactin even before the stage in the cycle when the squabs normally appear.

This does not mean, however, that any of the stimuli we have used can induce hormone secretion at *any* time, regardless of the bird's physiological condition. If we place a pair of ring doves in a cage and allow them to go through the normal cycle until they have been sitting on eggs for, say, six days and we then place a glass partition in the cage to separate the male from the female and the nest, the female will continue to sit on the eggs and the male's crop will continue to develop just as if he were himself incubating. This is a simple replication of one of Patel's experiments. Miriam Friedman and I have found, however, that if the male and female are separated from the beginning, so that the female must build the nest by herself and sit alone from the beginning, the crop of the male does

not grow. By inserting the glass plate at various times during the cycle in different groups of birds, we have found that the crop of the male develops fully only if he is not separated from the female until 72 hours or more after the second egg is laid. This means that the sight of the female incubating induces prolactin secretion in the male only if he is in the physiological condition to which participation in nest-building brings him. External stimuli associated with the breeding situation do indeed induce changes in hormone secretion.

The experiments summarized here point to the conclusion that changes in the activity of the endocrine system are induced or facilitated by stimuli coming from various aspects of the environment at different stages of the breeding cycle, and that these changes in hormone secretion induce changes in behavior that may themselves be a source of further stimulation.

The regulation of the reproductive cycle of the ring dove appears to depend, at least in part, on a double set of reciprocal interrelations. First, there

is an interaction of the effects of hormones on behavior and the effects of external stimuli—including those that arise from the behavior of the animal and its mate—on the secretion of hormones. Second, there is a complicated reciprocal relation between the effects of the presence and behavior of one mate on the endocrine system of the other and the effects of the presence and behavior of the second bird (including those aspects of its behavior induced by these endocrine effects) back on the endocrine system of the first. The occurrence in each member of the pair of a cycle found in neither bird in isolation, and the synchronization of the cycles in the two mates, can now readily be understood as consequences of this interaction of the inner and outer environments.

The physiological explanation of these phenomena lies partly in the fact that the activity of the pituitary gland, which secretes prolactin and the gonad-stimulating hormones, is largely controlled by the nervous system through the hypothalamus. The precise neural mechanisms for any complex response are still deeply mysterious, but physiological knowledge of the brain-pituitary link is sufficiently detailed and definite so that the occurrence of a specific hormonal response to a specific external stimulus is at least no more mysterious than any other stimulus-response relation. We are currently exploring these responses in more detail, seeking to learn, among other things, the precise sites at which the various hormones act. And we have begun to investigate another aspect of the problem: the effect of previous experience on a bird's reproductive behavior and the interactions between these experiential influences and the hormonal effects.

# Part III

# EXPERIENTIAL DETERMINANTS OF ANIMAL BEHAVIOR

# EXPERIENTIAL DETERMINANTS OF ANIMAL BEHAVIOR

*Introduction*  Genes determine the direction and limits of development of animals, but these directions and limits are not reached solely through the action of genes. Organisms develop in environments that provide stimuli, and these stimuli interact with genetic influences to control the ontogenesis of form, function, and behavior. External physical stimuli such as light, sound, and pressure and temperature changes help to determine the ultimate expression of the genetic potential. During maturation external stimuli facilitate the functioning of sensory receptors and the growth and functioning of the brain. The full development of the receptors and brain, of course, are crucial for the development of the animal's ability to behave normally.

In the past decade we have come to appreciate the importance of stimulation during the early period of postnatal development upon the behavioral potential of the adult. Seymour Levine in "Stimulation in Infancy" (page 93 ) describes how so simple a process as daily handling during the first few weeks of life can greatly influence the maturation of the rat's adaptation to stressful stimuli. Stimulation, as Levine shows, accelerates the functioning of the adrenal gland system, a system which plays a major role in the animal's adult behavior.

With the higher mammals the effects of stimulation—or rather, the effects of the absence of normal stimulation during development—are much more profound than in the rat. To a large extent, adult experience can substitute for the absence of stimulation in infancy in the rat, but this is not so in the monkey, as H. F. Harlow points out in "Love in Infant Monkeys" (page 100). Monkeys that are reared without mothers or adequate surrogate mothers may completely fail to develop normal social relationships when they mature. Of particular interest in this work is Harlow's finding that it is tactile stimulation, rather than suckling, that is important in the development of affectional behavior.

In the studies by Levine and Harlow, stimulation is found to have effects upon many different facets of the animal's behavior. E. H. Hess, in " 'Imprinting' in Animals" (page 107), discusses a form of "early learning" that is quite different from that studied by Levine and by Harlow. Imprinting is the term applied to the formation of the social attachment of young precocial birds, such as chickens and ducks, to their parents. In 1937 Lorenz stated that imprinting is different from the usual kinds of learning because (1) it does not require trial-and-error training, (2) it can occur only during a "critical period" of maturation, and (3) it is irreversible. Hess adds to this list the statement that the amount of imprinting that occurs depends upon how much effort the chick exerts while following its mother during the critical period. Although the exact validity of these characterizations of imprinting remains open to question, Lorenz and Hess have raised important questions about how early learning can influence an animal's adaptation to his environment.

We should not, of course, be led to think that the social behavior of organisms is determined entirely by experiences that occur during the first weeks and months of life. Most animals do modify their behavior in adulthood in ways that maximize their own survival and the survival of the species. A. M. Guhl discusses one such case of learning during adulthood in "The Social Order of Chickens" (page 113). Chicken flocks exhibit a social order that may be characterized as a linear dominance hierarchy. This "peck order" is based on learning to avoid aggression and contributes greatly to the social harmony of the flock.

Each of the four articles in this section describes how experience modifies the behavior of animals. Behavior is not "set" entirely by genes, but is clearly the result of gene-environment interactions. The next section explores in more detail the nature of the learning process.

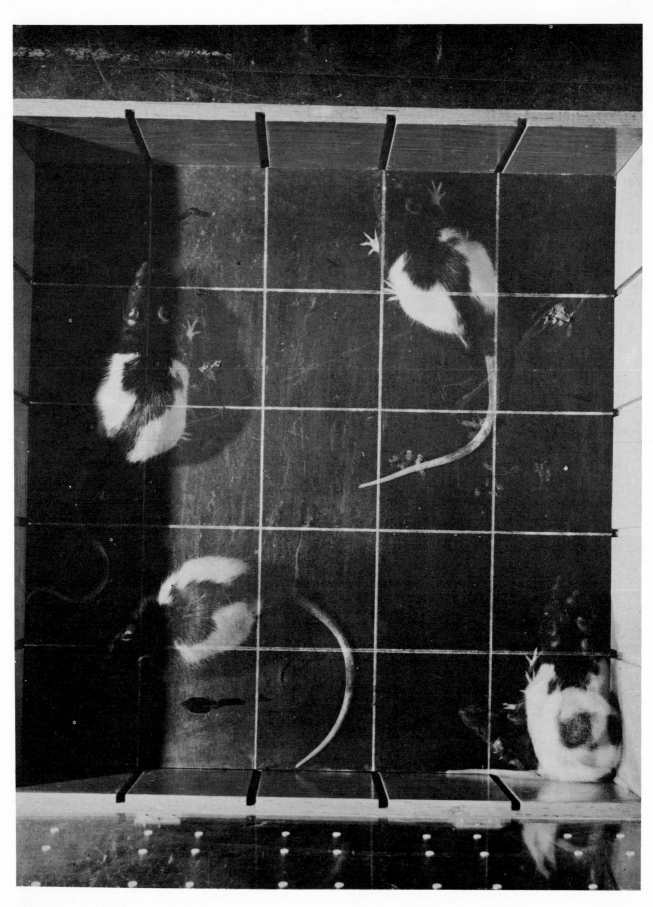

**OPEN-FIELD EXPERIMENT** illustrates how the behavior of a full-grown rat stimulated during infancy differs from that of a previously nonstimulated one. This multiple-exposure photograph shows how a nonstimulated rat (*lower right*) cowers in a corner when placed in an unfamiliar environment; the stimulated animal is much more willing to run about and explore his surroundings.

# II

# STIMULATION IN INFANCY

SEYMOUR LEVINE                                    May 1960

When the Emperor of Lilliput accepted Lemuel Gulliver into favor, His Most Sublime Majesty first secured Gulliver's solemn oath upon an agreement to observe certain rules of etiquette. The fourth article of the agreement stipulated that Gulliver should not take any Lilliputian subjects into his hands without their consent. Gulliver learned later to appreciate the sentiments behind this article in an intensely subjective way. In the country of Brobdingnag he was himself picked up in the huge hand of a Brobdingnagian. He recalled his reactions: "All I ventured was to raise my eyes towards the sun, and place my hands together in a supplicating posture, and to speak some words in an humble melancholy tone, suitable to the condition I then was in."

What Jonathan Swift describes here is the essence of an experience that befalls children and small animals every day. It happens whenever a parent picks up a baby, or a child tussles with his puppy. Almost all experiences of infancy involve some handling by a parent or some other larger and supremely powerful figure. Even the tenderest handling must at times be the occasion of emotional stress. Perhaps the only children insulated from such experience are those reared in orphanages and other institutions, and the only animals those that live in laboratories. Certainly the laboratory animal must find a minimum of stress and little stimulation of any other kind in an environment controlled for temperature, humidity, light and so on. In the ordinary world the infant must grow under the changing pressures and sudden challenges of an inconstant environment. One may well wonder how the stressful experiences of infancy affect the behavior and physiology of the adult organism later on.

When in 1954 we began our investigations into the broad area defined by this question, we naturally turned first to the presumably more obvious effects of early painful or traumatic experience. We subjected a group of infant rats to mild electric shocks, scheduled at the same hour each day. For control purposes we routinely placed the members of another group in the shock cage for the same length of time each day but did not give them shocks. A third group of infant rats was left in the nest and not handled at all. We expected that the shocked rats would be affected by their experience, and we looked for signs of emotional disorder when they reached adulthood. To our surprise it was the second control group—the rats we had not handled at all—that behaved in a peculiar manner. The behavior of the shocked rats could not be distinguished from that of the control group which had experienced the same handling but no electric shock. Thus the results of our first experiment caused us to reframe our question. Our investigation at the Columbus Psychiatric Institute and Hospital of Ohio State University has since been concerned not so much with the effects of stressful experience—which after all is the more usual experience of infants—as with the effects of the absence of such experience in infancy.

We have repeated our original experiment many times, subjecting the infant animals to a variety of stresses and degrees of handling. Invariably it is the nonmanipulated "controls" that exhibit deviations of behavior and physiology when they are tested as adults. Significantly these deviations involve the organism's response to stress, and they show up in most of the diverse aspects of that response. In a standard behav-

ioral test, for example, the animal is placed in the unfamiliar, but otherwise neutral, surroundings of a transparent plastic box. The nonmanipulated animals crouch in a corner of the box; animals that have been handled and subjected to stress in infancy freely explore the space. The same contrast in behavior may be observed and recorded quantitatively in the "open field": an area three feet square marked off into smaller squares. In terms of the number of squares crossed during a fixed time period, shocked and manipulated animals show a much greater willingness to run about and explore their surroundings. In both situations the nonmanipulated animals, cowering in a corner or creeping timidly about, tend to defecate and urinate frequently. Since these functions are largely controlled by the sympathetic nervous system, and since certain responses to stress are principally organized around the sympathetic nervous system, this behavior is a sure sign of reactivity to stress.

Another objective and quantitative index of stress response is provided by the hormones and glands of the endocrine system. Under stress, in response to prompting by the central nervous system, the pituitary releases larger quantities of various hormones, one of the principal ones being the adrenal-corticotrophic hormone (ACTH). Stimulation by ACTH causes the outer layer, or cortex, of the adrenal gland to step up the release of its several steroids; distributed by the bloodstream, these hormones accelerate the metabolism of the tissues in such a way as to maintain their integrity under stress. The activity of the endocrine system may be measured conveniently in a number of ways: by the enlargement of the adrenal glands, by the volume of adrenal steroids in circulation or by the depletion of ascorbic acid (vitamin C) in the adrenals. By some of these measurements the nonstimulated animals showed a markedly higher reactivity when subjected to a variety of stresses, including toxic injection of glucose, conditioning to avoid a painful stimulus and swimming in a water maze.

The conclusion that these animals are hyperreactive to stress is, however, an oversimplification that conceals an even more important difference in their stress response. Recently we measured the steroids in circulation in both stimulated and nonstimulated animals during the period immediately following stress by electric shock. Whereas the two groups showed the same volume of steroids in circulation before shock, the animals that had been exposed to stress in infancy showed a much higher output of steroids in the first 15 minutes after shock. The nonstimulated animals achieve the same output but more slowly, and appear to maintain a high level of steroid secretion for a longer period of time. There is thus a distinct difference in the pattern of the stress response in the two kinds of animal.

This observation acquires its full significance when it is considered in the light of the biological function of the stress response. The speed and short duration of the response in the stimulated animal obviously serve the useful purpose of mobilizing the resources of the organism at the moment when it is under stress. The delay in the endocrine response of the nonstimulated animal

**MILD STIMULATION** consisted of picking up the infant rats, removing them from their breeding cage and enclosing them in a small compartment for three minutes a day. The rats were then returned to their nests. The rats shown here are about 11 days old.

is thus, by contrast, maladaptive. Moreover, the prolongation of the stress response, as observed in these animals, can have severely damaging consequences: stomach ulcers, increased susceptibility to infection and eventually death due to adrenal exhaustion.

The maladaptive nature of the stress response in the nonmanipulated animal is further manifested in the fact that it may be elicited in such a neutral situation as the open-field test. The animal that has been manipulated in infancy shows no physiological stress response in this situation although it exhibits a vigorous and immediate endocrine response when challenged by the pain and threat of an electric shock.

In this connection we have made the interesting discovery that stimulation by handling and stress hastens the maturation of the stress response in the infant animal. Although the adrenal glands begin to function shortly after birth and the pituitary appears to contain ACTH early in the course of development, the nerve mechanism that controls the release of ACTH does not seem to come into operation until the rat is about 16 days of age. When we exposed infant rats that had been handled from birth to severe cold stress, however, they showed a significant ACTH response as early as 12 days of age. This four days' difference represents a considerable acceleration of development in the rat, equivalent to several months in the growth of a human infant. The manipulated animals, more-

**PAINFUL STIMULATION** consisted of subjecting the infant rats to an electric shock lasting from several seconds to several minutes. The effects on the rat's behavior as an adult were indistinguishable from those produced by the routine shown on the opposite page.

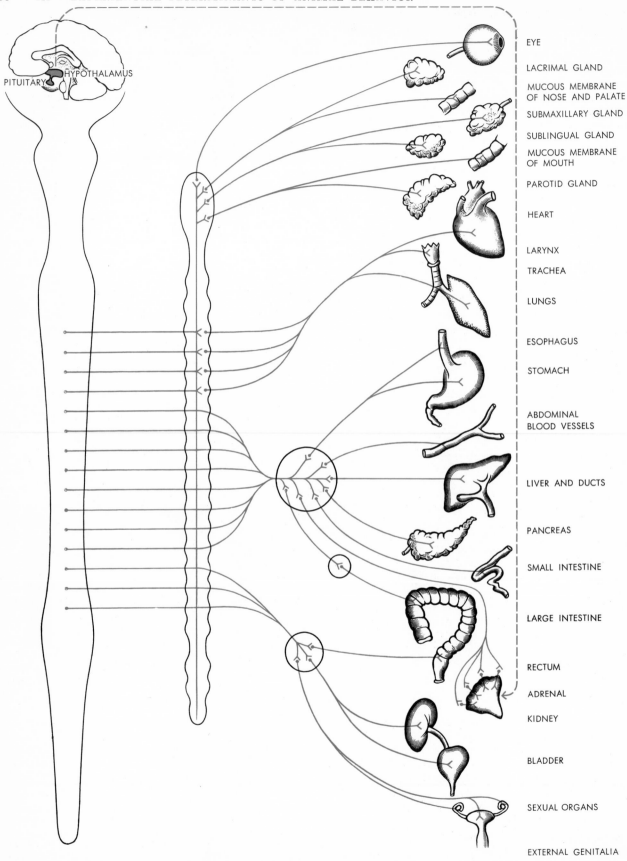

PITUITARY    HYPOTHALAMUS

EYE

LACRIMAL GLAND

MUCOUS MEMBRANE
OF NOSE AND PALATE

SUBMAXILLARY GLAND

SUBLINGUAL GLAND

MUCOUS MEMBRANE
OF MOUTH

PAROTID GLAND

HEART

LARYNX

TRACHEA

LUNGS

ESOPHAGUS

STOMACH

ABDOMINAL
BLOOD VESSELS

LIVER AND DUCTS

PANCREAS

SMALL INTESTINE

LARGE INTESTINE

RECTUM

ADRENAL

KIDNEY

BLADDER

SEXUAL ORGANS

EXTERNAL GENITALIA

**RESPONSES TO STRESS** are partly controlled by the pathways shown in this diagram of the human sympathetic nervous system. Sympathetic fibers (*solid colored lines*) originating in the spinal cord (*far left*) innervate the internal organs via the chain ganglia (*left center*) and the ganglia of the celiac plexus (*right center*).

Extreme stress upsets the normal rhythm of this system, causing disturbances such as loss of bladder control and increased pulse rate. Stress also stimulates the hypothalamus and the pituitary to produce ACTH, which reaches the adrenals via the bloodstream (*broken line*) and stimulates them to produce steroid hormones.

over, reached an adult level of response considerably earlier than their untreated litter mates.

From the evidence it may be inferred that stimulation must have accelerated the maturation of the central nervous system in these animals. We have direct evidence that this is so from analysis of the brain tissue of our subjects. The brains of infant rats that have been handled from birth show a distinctly higher cholesterol content. Since the cholesterol content of the brain is related principally to the brain's white matter, this is evidence that in these animals the maturation of structure parallels the maturation of function.

In all respects, in fact, the manipulated infants exhibit a more rapid rate of development. They open their eyes earlier and achieve motor coordination sooner. Their body hair grows faster, and they tend to be significantly heavier at weaning. They continue to gain weight more rapidly than the nonstimulated animals even after the course of stimulation has been completed at three weeks of age. Their more vigorous growth does not seem to be related to food intake but to better utilization of the food consumed and probably to a higher output of the somatotrophic (growth) hormone from the pituitary. These animals may also possess a higher resistance to pathogenic agents; they survive an injection of leukemia cells for a considerably longer time.

Another contrast between the stimulated and unstimulated animals developed when we electrically destroyed the septal region of their brains, the region between and under the hemispheres of the midbrain. Such damage makes an animal hyperexcitable, vicious and flighty. It will attack a pencil extended to it, react with extreme startle to a tap on the back, is exceedingly difficult to capture and upon capture will bite wildly and squeal loudly. In systematic observation of these responses we found that manipulated animals are far tamer postoperatively than nonmanipulated ones. The latter rank as the most excitable and vicious rats we have ever observed in the laboratory; it was not unusual for one of these animals to pursue us around the room, squealing and attacking our shoes and pants legs.

At the very least our experiments yield an additional explanation for the variability among laboratory animals that so often confuses results in experimental biology. This has been attributed to genetic differences, unknown factors and sometimes to experimental error. It

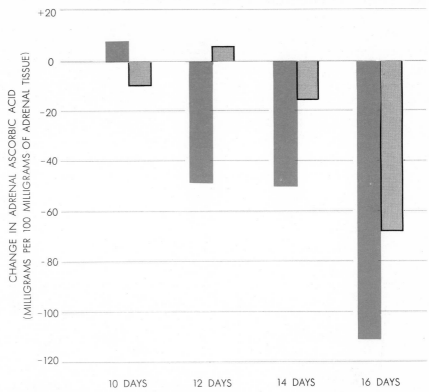

**EXPOSURE TO COLD** produced a marked drop in the ascorbic acid (vitamin C) concentration in the adrenal glands of stimulated rats more than 10 days old (*colored bars*), but produced no significant effect on the nonstimulated rats until they were 16 days old.

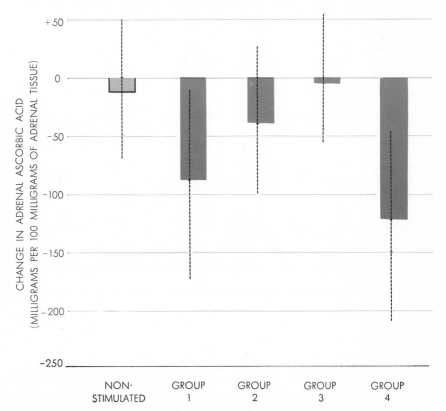

**CRITICAL PERIOD** in the development of the stress response was determined by stimulating infant rats at different stages of life. They were then exposed to cold and the drop in their adrenal ascorbic acid level was analyzed. Rats in Group 1 (stimulated from the second to the fifth days of life) and in Group 4 (stimulated from the second to the 13th days) responded better than both the nonstimulated rats and those in Groups 2 and 3 (stimulated from the sixth to the ninth and from the 10th to the 13th days, respectively). The bars show the average drop in the concentration and the broken lines the range.

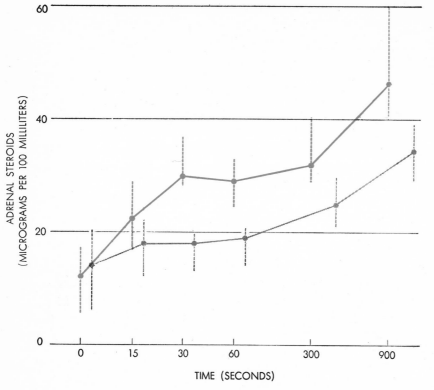

**SLUGGISH RESPONSE** to an electric shock is indicated by the slow rise in the concentration of circulating steroid hormones in previously nonstimulated rats (*gray curve*). In the stimulated animals (*colored curve*) the level increases rapidly for about 15 minutes. The points on the curve indicate the average level and the broken lines the range of values.

many problems in psychosomatic medicine and may explain in part why one individual develops ulcers, another migraine headaches and yet another shows little or no psychosomatic involvement under the same pressures of living.

One of the most encouraging aspects of our research is that it has raised more questions than it has answered. We have not yet, for example, identified the critical element in our stimulation procedures that leads to such predictable and profound effects. Painful and extreme forms of stimulation seem to have effects indistinguishable from those produced by merely picking up an animal and placing it in another location for a brief period of time. Is picking up an infant organism as casual and insignificant a procedure as it appears? Or is the experience of the infant closer to that of Gulliver in Brobdingnag? Mere handling may, in fact, constitute a stimulation as compelling and severe as the more obviously traumatic forms of stimulation. It may be that some degree of stressful experience in infancy is necessary for successful adaptation of the organism to the environment it encounters in later life.

Another important question is whether there is a critical infantile period (or periods) during which stimulation is most effective. The evidence so far points to a period following immediately after birth. In one study we handled the animals in three separate groups for four days each, from the second through the fifth day, from the sixth through the ninth day and from the 10th through the 13th day. When we tested them for stress response on the 14th day, only the first group showed any evidence that they were capable of an endocrine response. Other investigators have had similar results. This should not be taken to mean, however, that stimulation has no effect after the critical period is past or that one critical period sets all responses.

Still other questions have not yet been satisfied by even partial answers. There is, for example, the question of therapy: Can the effects of lack of stimulation in the critical period be counteracted by stimulation of any sort after the critical period has passed? The most pressing question—the most "stimulating" question—is how stimulation causes change in the infant organism. The answer to this question should lead to a fuller understanding of the differences between individual constitutions and of the physiological mechanisms that are involved in behavior.

is apparent that the character of early infant experience is another important determinant of individual differences in animals.

The same consideration leads to the broader question of "nature *v.* nurture," that is, the contribution of genetic factors as opposed to the influence of the environment. Both sets of factors are essential and they interact to give rise to the individual organism. The basic patterns of development are most likely determined by heredity. But the genetic determinants do not find expression except in interaction with various aspects of the environment. In the normal course of events the environment provides the substance, energy and milieu for the unfolding of the organism's potentialities; in the extreme, environmental influences can determine whether the process of development will continue and produce an organism. In other words, organisms do not grow in a vacuum. This is true even of our nontreated animals. Litter mates and the routine laboratory procedures furnish stimulation of all kinds. Such stimulation does not compare, however, with that provided by our experimental treatments. We have dealt with only a limited range of effects, and

have focused primarily on the physiological and behavioral responses to stress. But our results clearly indicate that stimulation of the infant organism has quite universal consequences upon the behavior and physiology of the adult.

One must be careful in attempting to bridge the gap between animal experimentation and human biology. The effects of early experience have proved to be significant, however, in many species of mammal, including the monkey, dog, cat, guinea pig and mouse, and in such nonmammals as fish and fowl. It cannot be said that the phenomenon is species-limited. A great deal of clinical evidence, moreover, clearly indicates that infant experience in humans has a profound effect in shaping the character and constitution of the adult. Investigators concerned with maternal deprivation report that children raised in foundling homes develop at a retarded rate and are more susceptible to disease. These observations are similar to those we have made in our animal experiments. It may be that the detrimental effects of the foundling home have less to do with maternal deprivation than with the simple lack of stimulation that is inevitable in most such environments. The character of early experience may thus also underlie

# 12

# LOVE IN INFANT MONKEYS

HARRY F. HARLOW                                    June 1959

The first love of the human infant is for his mother. The tender intimacy of this attachment is such that it is sometimes regarded as a sacred or mystical force, an instinct incapable of analysis. No doubt such compunctions, along with the obvious obstacles in the way of objective study, have hampered experimental observation of the bonds between child and mother.

Though the data are thin, the theoretical literature on the subject is rich. Psychologists, sociologists and anthropologists commonly hold that the infant's love is learned through the association of the mother's face, body and other physical characteristics with the alleviation of internal biological tensions, particularly hunger and thirst. Traditional psychoanalysts have tended to emphasize the role of attaining and sucking at the breast as the basis for affectional development. Recently a number of child psychiatrists have questioned such simple explanations. Some argue that affectionate handling in the act of nursing is a variable of importance, whereas a few workers suggest that the composite activities of nursing, contact, clinging and even seeing and hearing work together to elicit the infant's love for his mother.

Now it is difficult, if not impossible, to use human infants as subjects for the studies necessary to break through the present speculative impasse. At birth the infant is so immature that he has little or no control over any motor system other than that involved in sucking. Furthermore, his physical maturation is so slow that by the time he can achieve precise, coordinated, measurable responses of his head, hands, feet and body, the nature and sequence of development have been hopelessly confounded and obscured. Clearly research into

the infant-mother relationship has need of a more suitable laboratory animal. We believe we have found it in the infant monkey. For the past several years our group at the Primate Laboratory of the University of Wisconsin has been employing baby rhesus monkeys in a study that we believe has begun to yield significant insights into the origin of the infant's love for his mother.

Baby monkeys are far better coordinated at birth than human infants. Their responses can be observed and evaluated with confidence at an age of 10 days or even earlier. Though they mature much more rapidly than their human contemporaries, infants of both species follow much the same general pattern of development.

Our interest in infant-monkey love grew out of a research program that involved the separation of monkeys from their mothers a few hours after birth. Employing techniques developed by Gertrude van Wagenen of Yale University, we had been rearing infant monkeys on the bottle with a mortality far less than that among monkeys nursed by their mothers. We were particularly careful to provide the infant monkeys with a folded gauze diaper on the floor of their cages, in accord with Dr. van Wagenen's observation that they would tend to maintain intimate contact with such soft, pliant surfaces, especially during nursing. We were impressed by the deep personal attachments that the monkeys formed for these diaper pads, and by the distress that they exhibited when the pads were briefly removed once a day for purposes of sanitation. The behavior of the infant monkeys was reminiscent of the human infant's attachment to its blankets, pillows, rag dolls or cuddly teddy bears.

These observations suggested the series of experiments in which we have sought to compare the importance of nursing and all associated activities with that of simple bodily contact in engendering the infant monkey's attachment to its mother. For this purpose we contrived two surrogate mother monkeys. One is a bare welded-wire cylindrical form surmounted by a wooden head with a crude face. In the other the welded wire is cushioned by a sheathing of terry cloth. We placed eight newborn monkeys in individual cages, each with equal access to a cloth and a wire mother [see illustration on opposite page]. Four of the infants received their milk from one mother and four from the other, the milk being furnished in each case by a nursing bottle, with its nipple protruding from the mother's "breast."

The two mothers quickly proved to be physiologically equivalent. The monkeys in the two groups drank the same amount of milk and gained weight at the same rate. But the two mothers proved to be by no means psychologically equivalent. Records made automatically showed that both groups of infants spent far more time climbing and clinging on their cloth-covered mothers than they did on their wire mothers. During the infants' first 14 days of life the floors of the cages were warmed by an electric heating pad, but most of the infants left the pad as soon as they could climb on the unheated cloth mother. Moreover, as the monkeys grew older, they tended to spend an increasing amount of time clinging and cuddling on her pliant terry-cloth surface. Those that secured their nourishment from the wire mother showed no tendency to spend more time on her than feeding required, contradicting the idea that affection is a response that is learned or derived in asso-

**CLOTH AND WIRE MOTHER-SURROGATES** were used to test the preferences of infant monkeys. The infants spent most of their time clinging to the soft cloth "mother," (*foreground*) even when nursing bottles were attached to the wire mother (*background*).

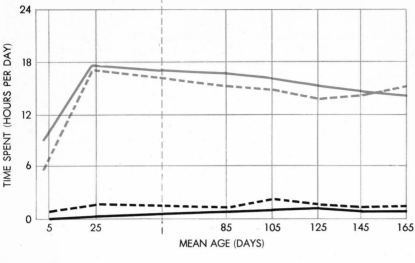

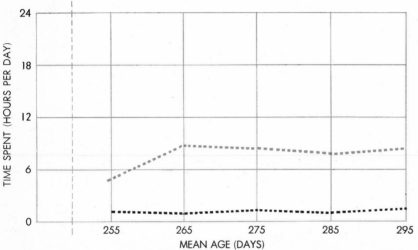

**STRONG PREFERENCE FOR CLOTH MOTHER** was shown by all infant monkeys. Infants reared with access to both mothers from birth (*top chart*) spent far more time on the cloth mother (*colored curves*) than on the wire mother (*black curves*). This was true regardless of whether they had been fed on the cloth (*solid lines*) or on the wire mother (*broken lines*). Infants that had known no mother during their first eight months (*bottom chart*) soon came to prefer cloth mother, but spent less time on her than the other infants.

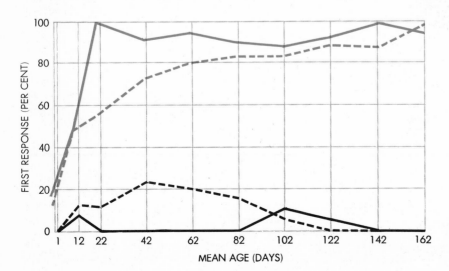

**RESULTS OF "FEAR TEST"** (*see photographs on opposite page*) showed that infants confronted by a strange object quickly learned to seek reassurance from the cloth mother (*colored curves*) rather than from the wire mother (*black curves*). Again infants fed on the wire mother (*broken lines*) behaved much like those fed on cloth mother (*solid lines*)

ciation with the reduction of hunger or thirst.

These results attest the importance—possibly the overwhelming importance—of bodily contact and the immediate comfort it supplies in forming the infant's attachment for its mother. All our experience, in fact, indicates that our cloth-covered mother surrogate is an eminently satisfactory mother. She is available 24 hours a day to satisfy her infant's overwhelming compulsion to seek bodily contact; she possesses infinite patience, never scolding her baby or biting it in anger. In these respects we regard her as superior to a living monkey mother, though monkey fathers would probably not endorse this opinion.

Of course this does not mean that nursing has no psychological importance. No act so effectively guarantees intimate bodily contact between mother and child. Furthermore, the mother who finds nursing a pleasant experience will probably be temperamentally inclined to give her infant plenty of handling and fondling. The real-life attachment of the infant to its mother is doubtless influenced by subtle multiple variables, contributed in part by the mother and in part by the child. We make no claim to having unraveled these in only two years of investigation. But no matter what evidence the future may disclose, our first experiments have shown that contact comfort is a decisive variable in this relationship.

Such generalization is powerfully supported by the results of the next phase of our investigation. The time that the infant monkeys spent cuddling on their surrogate mothers was a strong but perhaps not conclusive index of emotional attachment. Would they also seek the inanimate mother for comfort and security when they were subjected to emotional stress? With this question in mind we exposed our monkey infants to the stress of fear by presenting them with strange objects, for example a mechanical teddy bear which moved forward, beating a drum. Whether the infants had nursed from the wire or the cloth mother, they overwhelmingly sought succor from the cloth one; this differential in behavior was enhanced with the passage of time and the accrual of experience. Early in this series of experiments the terrified infant might rush blindly to the wire mother, but even if it did so it would soon abandon her for the cloth mother. The infant would cling to its cloth mother, rubbing its body against hers. Then, with its fears assuaged through intimate contact with the moth-

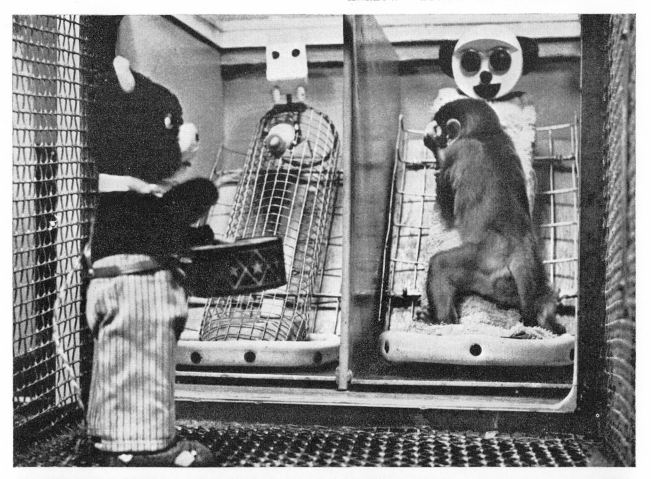

**FRIGHTENING OBJECTS** such as a mechanical teddy bear caused almost all infant monkeys to flee blindly to the cloth mother, as in the top photograph. Once reassured by pressing and rubbing against her, they would then look at the strange object (*bottom*).

"OPEN FIELD TEST" involved placing a monkey in a room far larger than its accustomed cage; unfamiliar objects added an addi-tional disturbing element. If no mother was present, the infant would typically huddle in a corner (*left*). The wire mother did

er, it would turn to look at the previously terrifying bear without the slightest sign of alarm. Indeed, the infant would some-times even leave the protection of the mother and approach the object that a few minutes before had reduced it to abject terror.

The analogy with the behavior of hu-man infants requires no elaboration. We found that the analogy extends even to less obviously stressful situations. When a child is taken to a strange place, he usually remains composed and happy so long as his mother is nearby. If the moth-er gets out of sight, however, the child is often seized with fear and distress. We developed the same response in our infant monkeys when we exposed them to a room that was far larger than the cages to which they were accustomed. In the room we had placed a number of unfamiliar objects such as a small arti-ficial tree, a crumpled piece of paper, a folded gauze diaper, a wooden block and a doorknob [*a similar experiment is depicted in the illustrations on these two pages*]. If the cloth mother was in the room, the infant would rush wildly to her, climb upon her, rub against her and cling to her tightly. As in the previous experiment, its fear then sharply di-minished or vanished. The infant would begin to climb over the mother's body and to explore and manipulate her face. Soon it would leave the mother to inves-tigate the new world, and the unfamiliar objects would become playthings. In a typical behavior sequence, the infant might manipulate the tree, return to the mother, crumple the wad of paper, bring it to the mother, explore the block, ex-

plore the doorknob, play with the paper and return to the mother. So long as the mother provided a psychological "base of operations" the infants were unafraid and their behavior remained positive, exploratory and playful.

If the cloth mother was absent, how-ever, the infants would rush across the test room and throw themselves face-down on the floor, clutching their heads and bodies and screaming their distress. Records kept by two independent ob-servers—scoring for such "fear indices" as crying, crouching, rocking and thumb-and toe-sucking—showed that the emo-tionality scores of the infants nearly tripled. But no quantitative measure-ment can convey the contrast between the positive, outgoing activities in the presence of the cloth mother and the stereotyped withdrawn and disturbed behavior in the motherless situation.

The bare wire mother provided no more reassurance in this "open field" test than no mother at all. Control tests on monkeys that from birth had known only the wire mother revealed that even these infants showed no affection for her and obtained no comfort from her presence. Indeed, this group of animals exhibited the highest emotionality scores of all. Typically they would run to some wall or corner of the room, clasp their heads and bodies and rock convulsively back and forth. Such activities closely re-semble the autistic behavior seen fre-quently among neglected children in and out of institutions.

In a final comparison of the cloth and wire mothers, we adapted an experiment originally devised by Robert A. Butler

at the Primate Laboratory. Butler had found that monkeys enclosed in a dimly lighted box would press a lever to open and reopen a window for hours on end for no reward other than the chance to look out. The rate of lever-pressing de-pended on what the monkeys saw through the opened window; the sight of another monkey elicited far more activi-ty than that of a bowl of fruit or an emp-ty room [described in "Curiosity in Mon-keys," by Robert A. Butler, in this vol-ume, page 173]. We now know that this "curiosity response" is innate. Three-day-old monkeys, barely able to walk, will crawl across the floor of the box to reach a lever which briefly opens the window; some press the lever hundreds of times within a few hours.

When we tested our monkey infants in the "Butler box," we found that those reared with both cloth and wire mothers showed as high a response to the cloth mother as to another monkey, but dis-played no more interest in the wire mother than in an empty room. In this test, as in all the others, the monkeys fed on the wire mother behaved the same as those fed on the cloth mother. A con-trol group raised with no mothers at all found the cloth mother no more inter-esting than the wire mother and neither as interesting as another monkey.

Thus all the objective tests we have been able to devise agree in showing that the infant monkey's relationship to its surrogate mother is a full one. Com-parison with the behavior of infant mon-keys raised by their real mothers con-firms this view. Like our experimental monkeys, these infants spend many

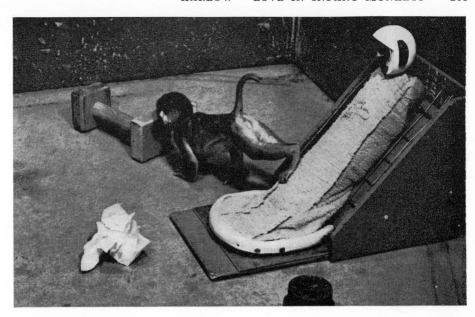

not alter this pattern of fearful behavior, but the cloth mother provided quick reassurance. The infant would first cling to her *(center)* and then set out to explore the room and play with the objects *(right)*, returning from time to time for more reassurance.

hours a day clinging to their mothers, and run to them for comfort or reassurance when they are frightened. The deep and abiding bond between mother and child appears to be essentially the same, whether the mother is real or a cloth surrogate.

While bodily contact clearly plays the prime role in developing infantile affection, other types of stimulation presumably supplement its effects. We have therefore embarked on a search for these other factors. The activity of a live monkey mother, for example, provides her infant with frequent motion stimulation. In many human cultures mothers bind their babies to them when they go about their daily chores; in our own culture parents know very well that rocking a baby or walking with him somehow promotes his psychological and physiological well-being. Accordingly we compared the responsiveness of infant monkeys to two cloth mothers, one stationary and one rocking. All of them preferred the rocking mother, though the degree of preference varied considerably from day to day and from monkey to monkey. An experiment with a rocking crib and a stationary one gave similar results. Motion does appear to enhance affection, albeit far less significantly than simple contact.

The act of clinging, in itself, also seems to have a role in promoting psychological and physiological well-being. Even before we began our studies of affection, we noticed that a newborn monkey raised in a bare wire cage survived with difficulty unless we provided it with a cone to which it could cling. Re-

cently we have raised two groups of monkeys, one with a padded crib instead of a mother and the other with a cloth mother as well as a crib. Infants in the latter group actually spend more time on the crib than on the mother, probably because the steep incline of the mother's cloth surface makes her a less satisfactory sleeping platform. In the open-field test, the infants raised with a crib but no mother clearly derived some emotional support from the presence of the crib. But those raised with both showed an unequivocal preference for the mother they could cling to, and they evidenced the benefit of the superior emotional succor they gained from her.

Still other elements in the relationship remain to be investigated systematically. Common sense would suggest that the warmth of the mother's body plays its part in strengthening the infant's ties to her. Our own observations have not yet confirmed this hypothesis. Heating a cloth mother does not seem to increase her attractiveness to the infant monkey, and infants readily abandon a heating pad for an unheated mother surrogate. However, our laboratory is kept comfortably warm at all times; experiments in a chilly environment might well yield quite different results.

Visual stimulation may forge an additional link. When they are about three months old, the monkeys begin to observe and manipulate the head, face and eyes of their mother surrogates; human infants show the same sort of delayed responsiveness to visual stimuli. Such stimuli are known to have marked ef-

fects on the behavior of many young animals. The Austrian zoologist Konrad Lorenz has demonstrated a process called "imprinting"; he has shown that the young of some species of birds become attached to the first moving object they perceive, normally their mothers [see "'Imprinting' in Animals," by Eckhard H. Hess, page 107, reporting on such experiments]. It is also possible that particular sounds and even odors may play some role in the normal development of responses or attention.

The depth and persistence of attachment to the mother depend not only on the kind of stimuli that the young animal receives but also on when it receives them. Experiments with ducks show that imprinting is most effective during a critical period soon after hatching; beyond a certain age it cannot take place at all. Clinical experience with human beings indicates that people who have been deprived of affection in infancy may have difficulty forming affectional ties in later life. From preliminary experiments with our monkeys we have found that their affectional responses develop, or fail to develop, according to a similar pattern.

Early in our investigation we had segregated four infant monkeys as a general control group, denying them physical contact either with a mother surrogate or with other monkeys. After about eight months we placed them in cages with access to both cloth and wire mothers. At first they were afraid of both surrogates, but within a few days they began to respond in much the same way as the other infants. Soon they were

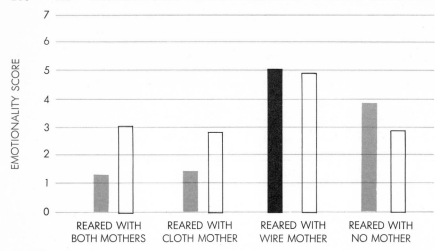

**SCORES IN OPEN FIELD TEST** show that all infant monkeys familiar with the cloth mother were much less disturbed when she was present (*color*) than when no mother was present (*white*); scores under 2 indicate unfrightened behavior. Infants that had known only the wire mother were greatly disturbed whether she was present (*black*) or not (*white*).

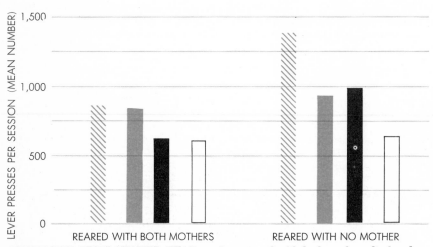

**"CURIOSITY TEST" SHOWED THAT** monkeys reared with both mothers displayed as much interest in the cloth mother (*solid color*) as in another monkey (*hatched color*); the wire mother (*black*) was no more interesting than an empty chamber (*white*). Monkeys reared with no mother found cloth and wire mother less interesting than another monkey.

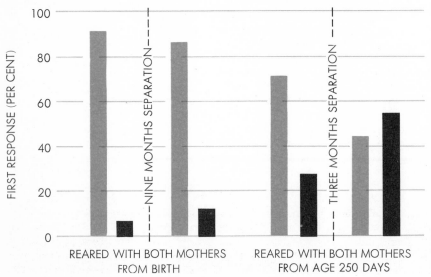

**EARLY "MOTHERING"** produced a strong and unchanging preference for the cloth mother (*color*) over the wire mother (*black*). Monkeys deprived of early mothering showed less marked preferences before separation and no significant preference subsequently.

spending less than an hour a day with the wire mother and eight to 10 hours with the cloth mother. Significantly, however, they spent little more than half as much time with the cloth mother as did infants raised with her from birth.

In the open-field test these "orphan" monkeys derived far less reassurance from the cloth mothers than did the other infants. The deprivation of physical contact during their first eight months had plainly affected the capacity of these infants to develop the full and normal pattern of affection. We found a further indication of the psychological damage wrought by early lack of mothering when we tested the degree to which infant monkeys retained their attachments to their mothers. Infants raised with a cloth mother from birth and separated from her at about five and a half months showed little or no loss of responsiveness even after 18 months of separation. In some cases it seemed that absence had made the heart grow fonder. The monkeys that had known a mother surrogate only after the age of eight months, however, rapidly lost whatever responsiveness they had acquired. The long period of maternal deprivation had evidently left them incapable of forming a lasting affectional tie.

The effects of maternal separation and deprivation in the human infant have scarcely been investigated, in spite of their implications concerning child-rearing practices. The long period of infant-maternal dependency in the monkey provides a real opportunity for investigating persisting disturbances produced by inconsistent or punishing mother surrogates.

Above and beyond demonstration of the surprising importance of contact comfort as a prime requisite in the formation of an infant's love for its mother —and the discovery of the unimportant or nonexistent role of the breast and act of nursing—our investigations have established a secure experimental approach to this realm of dramatic and subtle emotional relationships. The further exploitation of the broad field of research that now opens up depends merely upon the availability of infant monkeys. We expect to extend our researches by undertaking the study of the mother's (and even the father's!) love for the infant, using real monkey infants or infant surrogates. Finally, with such techniques established, there appears to be no reason why we cannot at some future time investigate the fundamental neurophysiological and biochemical variables underlying affection and love.

# 13

# "IMPRINTING" IN ANIMALS

ECKHARD H. HESS                    March 1958

What is meant by "imprinting" in animals? The best answer is to describe an experiment performed on geese by the Austrian zoologist Konrad Lorenz. On an estate near Vienna Lorenz divided a clutch of eggs laid by a graylag goose into two groups. One group was hatched by the goose; the other group was hatched in an incubator. The goslings hatched by the goose immediately followed their mother around the estate. The goslings hatched in the incubator, however, did not see their mother; the first living thing they saw was Lorenz. They then followed Lorenz about the estate!

Lorenz now marked the two groups of goslings to distinguish them. He placed all the goslings under a large box, while the mother watched anxiously. When the box was lifted, the two groups of

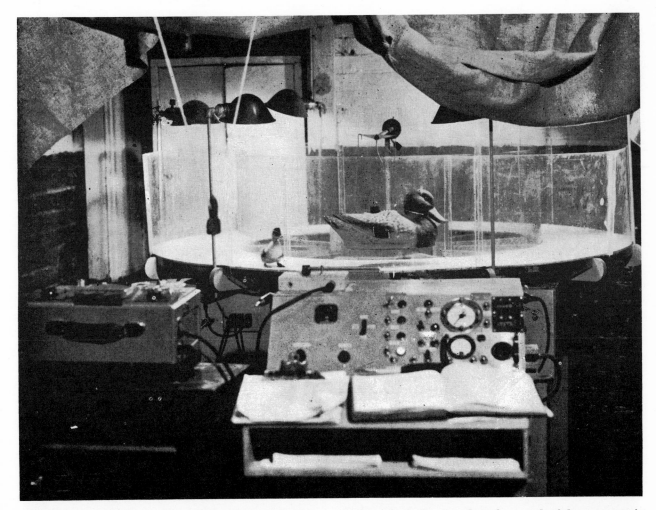

APPARATUS used by Hess and A. O. Ramsay in the study of imprinting consists primarily of a circular runway around which a decoy duck can be moved. In this photograph a duckling follows the decoy. In the foreground are the controls of the apparatus. At the top of the photograph is a cloth which is normally dropped so that movements of the experimenter will not distract the duckling.

**DUCKLING IS IMPRINTED** by placing it in the runway behind a model of a male duck which is wired for sound. Below the duckling is a trap door through which it is removed.

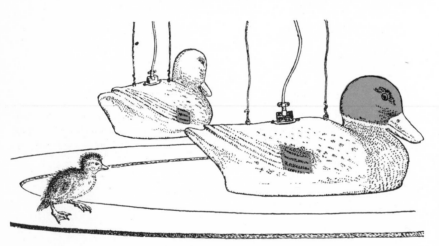

**DUCKLING IS TESTED** for imprinting by placing it between the male model and a female model which emits a different sound. If it follows the male, response is scored as positive.

**DUCKLING SCALES AN OBSTACLE** in the runway in an experiment to determine whether the effort it expends during imprinting is related to its score when it is tested.

goslings streamed to their respective "parents." Lorenz called this phenomenon, in which an early experience of the goslings determined their social behavior, "imprinting." Although earlier investigators had observed the effect, he was the first to name it and to point out that it appeared to occur at a critical period early in the life of an animal. He also postulated that the first object to elicit a social response later released not only that response but also related responses such as sexual behavior.

Students of behavior generally agree that the early experiences of animals (including man) have a profound effect on their adult behavior. D. O. Hebb of the University of Montreal goes so far as to state that the effect of early experience upon adult behavior is inversely correlated with age. This may be an oversimplification, but in general it appears to hold true. Thus the problem of the investigator is not so much to find out *whether* early experience determines adult behavior, but rather to discover *how* it determines adult behavior.

Three statements are usually made about the effects of early experience. The first is that early habits are very persistent and may prevent the formation of new ones. This, of course, refers not only to the study of experimental animals but also to the rearing of children. The second statement is that early perceptions deeply affect all future learning. This concept leads to the difficult question whether basic perceptions—the way we have of seeing the world around us—are inherited or acquired. The third statement is simply that early social contacts determine adult social behavior. This, of course, is imprinting.

Although imprinting has been studied mainly in birds, it also occurs in other animals. It has been observed in insects, in fishes and in some mammals. So far as mammals are concerned the phenomenon appears to be limited to those animals whose young are able to move about almost immediately after birth. For example, imprinting has been described in sheep, goats, deer and buffalo. For better or worse these observations have not been made under controlled laboratory conditions. One exception is a study begun in our laboratories at the University of Chicago. One of our students has observed that imprinting appears to occur in guinea pigs. Our work has dealt mainly, however, with imprinting in birds.

Lorenz and other European workers

have shown that a variety of birds are most easily imprinted during the first day after they are hatched, and that the birds will follow not only other animals but also inanimate objects. In this country A. O. Ramsay of the McDonogh School in McDonogh, Md., succeeded in making young Canada geese and mallard ducklings follow a small green box containing an alarm clock. Some ducklings and goslings responded to a football. In the early 1950s I met Ramsay and we decided to begin a cooperative study of imprinting under laboratory conditions. Among our goals were the following. What is the critical age at which imprinting occurs? How long must young birds be exposed to the imprinting object in order for them to discriminate between it and similar objects?

The subjects used in the experiments described here were mallard ducklings. We were fortunate in that our laboratory in Maryland had access to a small duck pond in which we could keep relatively wild mallards. The birds laid their eggs in nesting boxes, so the eggs could be regularly collected and hatched in laboratory incubators. Our experimental apparatus consisted of a circular runway about five feet in diameter and 12 inches wide, the walls of which were made of transparent plastic. Our imprinting object was a model of a male mallard duck, of the sort used by duck hunters as a decoy. The model was suspended from a motor-driven arm pivoted at the center of the apparatus; thus it could be moved around the runway at various speeds. Inside the model was a loudspeaker through which tape-recorded sounds could be played.

After the mallard eggs were collected, they were placed in a dark incubator. When the young birds were hatched, they were kept in individual cardboard boxes so that they would have no visual experience until they were put into the imprinting apparatus. The boxes were then kept in a brooder until we were ready to work with the birds. After each duckling was exposed to the imprinting object (the decoy duck) in the apparatus, it was automatically returned to its box by means of a trap door in the floor of the runway. The bird was then lodged in another brooder until it was to be tested for the imprinting effect.

The imprinting itself was accomplished first by placing the young mallard in the runway of the apparatus about a foot away from the decoy. As the bird was released, the loudspeaker inside the decoy was made to emit a human rendition of the sound "GOCK gock gock gock gock," and after a short interval the decoy was moved around the runway. The imprinting period, during which the duckling followed the decoy, usually lasted 10 minutes. We can also imprint ducklings with a silent object, or even with sound alone. In one experiment we tried to imprint ducklings with the "gock" sound while they were still in the egg. This effort was unsuccessful.

The bird was tested for imprinting by releasing it between two decoys four feet apart. One decoy was the male model with which the duckling had been imprinted; the other was a female model which differed from the male only in its coloration. One minute was allowed for the duckling to make a decisive response to the silent models. At the end of this time, regardless of the duckling's response, sound was turned on in both models. The male model made the "gock" call; the female emitted the sound of a mallard duck calling her young. This latter sound was a recording of a real female. Four test situations were run off in sequence: (1) both models stationary and silent; (2) both models stationary and calling; (3) male stationary and female moving, both calling; (4) male stationary and silent, female moving and calling. Each bird was scored according to the percentage of its positive responses, i.e., the number of times it moved toward the male model as opposed to doing something else.

To determine the age at which an imprinting experience was most effective we imprinted our ducklings at various ages after hatching. In this series of experiments the imprinting experience was standard: it consisted of having the duckling follow the model 150 to 200 feet around the runway during a period of 10 minutes. It appears that some imprinting occurs immediately after hatching; however, only those ducklings imprinted between 13 and 16 hours after hatching consistently made a maximum score [see chart below].

To answer the question how long the imprinting experience must last in order to be most effective we varied not only the time during which the duckling was exposed to the model but also the distance traveled by the duckling as it followed the model around the runway of our apparatus. We exposed groups of ducklings to the model for the same length of time (10 minutes), but during that time moved the model at different speeds so that the ducklings in each group moved a different distance (1,

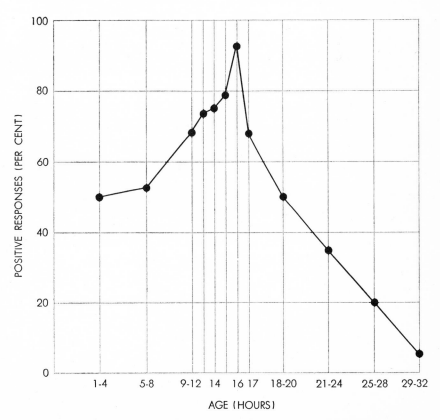

**CRITICAL AGE** at which ducklings are most strongly imprinted is reflected by this curve. Each black dot on the curve is the average test score of ducklings imprinted at that age.

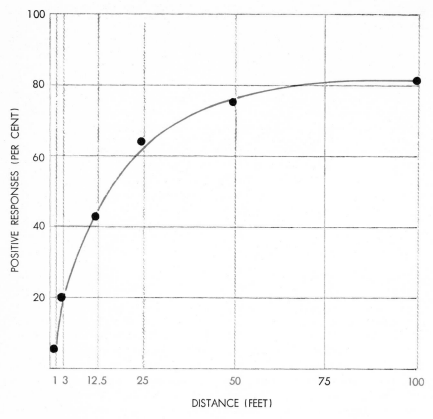

**DISTANCE TRAVELED** during imprinting affected the scores of ducklings as indicated by this curve. The farther the ducklings had traveled, the more strongly they were imprinted.

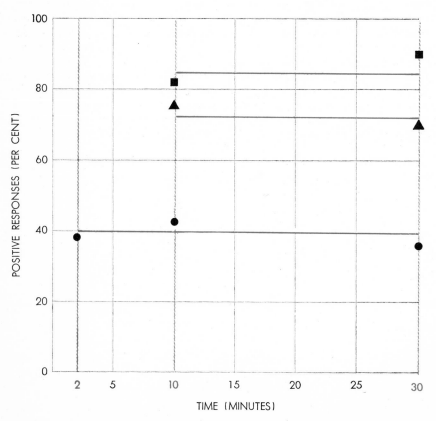

**TIME ELAPSED** during imprinting had little effect on the scores. The squares represent ducklings which had traveled 100 feet during imprinting; triangles, 50 feet; dots, 12.5 feet.

12½, 25, 50 and 100 feet). All the ducklings were imprinted between 12 and 17 hours after hatching. The results showed that at distances up to 50 feet the strength of imprinting increased with the distance traveled [*see chart at top of this page*].

We now allowed other groups of ducklings to travel the same distance, but over different periods of time. One turn around our runway is 12½ feet; a duckling can walk this distance in something less than two minutes. We moved the decoy so that groups of ducklings made one turn around the runway in 2, 10 and 30 minutes. The scores of these animals were essentially identical [*see chart at bottom of this page*]. Moreover, there was no significant difference between the scores of ducklings which followed the decoy 100 feet in 10 minutes and those which traveled the same distance in 30 minutes.

In other words, the strength of imprinting appeared to be dependent not on the duration of the imprinting period but on the effort exerted by the duckling in following the imprinting object. To confirm this notion we tried two supplementary experiments. In the first we placed four-inch hurdles in the runway so that the ducklings not only had to follow the model but also had to clear the obstacles. As we suspected, the birds which had to climb the hurdles, and thus expend more effort, made higher imprinting scores than those which traveled the same distance without obstacles. In the second experiment we allowed the duckling to follow the decoy up an inclined plane, with similar results. After further experiments we came to the conclusion that we could write a formula for imprinting: the strength of imprinting equals the logarithm of the effort expended by the animal during the imprinting period.

Now that we had this basic information, we began to explore other aspects of imprinting. We had been puzzled by the fact that the imprintability of ducklings rapidly declines soon after they are 16 hours old. We had noticed, as had other workers, that ducklings develop their first emotional response when they are 16 to 20 hours old. This response is an avoidance or fear of moving objects. Twenty-four hours after hatching almost 80 per cent of the ducklings exhibit this fear; the proportion increases to 100 per cent at about 32 hours. Does this fear response knock out imprinting?

At the time we were reflecting on this

question the tranquilizing drugs had just been introduced, and it occurred to us that these drugs which reduce fear and anxiety might solve our problem. We administered meprobamate (Miltown) to 24-hour-old ducklings; their fear response was indeed reduced. We then imprinted the drugged birds 26 hours after hatching. Ducklings 26 hours old are of course imprinted very weakly, but we were surprised that the imprinting scores of these animals were even lower than normal. In other words, eliminating fear did not improve imprintability. Later we found that the tranquilizer also interfered with the imprinting of young mallards at an age when they were normally most imprintable. So far our best conclusion is that meprobamate, being a muscle relaxant, nullifies the effectiveness of the imprinting experience by relaxing muscular tension. It is also possible that in the imprinting process some degree of anxiety is necessary. This anxiety, from an admittedly human viewpoint, may merely be the fear of being left alone; the duckling might thus tend to follow the imprinting object as it moved away. We are continuing our study of these drugs because we feel that it may not only shed some light on the mechanism of imprinting but also may give us valuable information about the action of the drugs themselves.

We have also considered the genetic side of imprinting. We have kept ducklings which were highly imprintable and bred them separately from ducklings which showed very little imprinting response. Significant differences appeared even in the first generation: the offspring of imprintable parents were easily imprinted; those of less imprintable par-

REMOTE-CONTROLLED DECOY was used by Hess and his colleagues in other imprinting experiments. Here both decoy and duckling move about freely rather than on a runway.

ents were difficult to imprint. We are also following up those animals which have had experimental imprinting experiences to determine what influence, if any, these experiences have on their adult behavior. So far the results are inconclusive, but they do suggest that experimental imprinting of mallards affects their adult behavior, particularly with respect to courtship patterns.

We have performed imprinting experiments not only with mallards and, as indicated earlier, guinea pigs, but also with other kinds of ducks, several varieties of geese, with sheep, turkeys, pheasants, quail and chickens. We have had some success in imprinting certain breeds of chicks (mainly Cochin bantams and Seabright bantams), but in general domestic fowl cannot be as clearly imprinted as wild birds.

What does all this have to do with human behavior? Of course it is not really necessary to relate our work to such behavior; it is interesting and important in its own right because it tells us something about the way an organism adapts itself to the world. We do feel, however, that the work has some implications which are relevant to humans. It has long been known, for example, that in order for a child to develop normally it must have a certain amount of attention and handling during a critical period of its infancy. This period is doubtless not as sharply defined as the imprinting period in birds, but it may lie within the first six months of life. Jere Wilson of our group is studying the smiling response of infants in an effort to get at some aspects of human behavior which may involve imprinting.

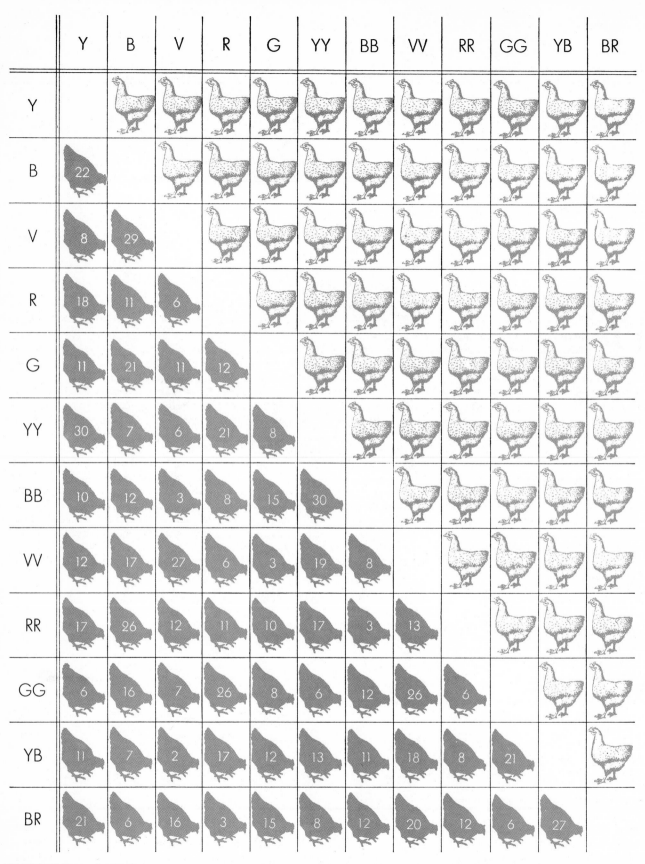

**PECK-ORDER IS DEPICTED** in this chart of an experimental flock of 12 Rhode Island Red hens. Each hen in the flock was marked with either one or two colors: yellow (Y), blue (B), violet (V), red (R) and green (G). The hen with a yellow marking (*column at far left*) pecked all 11 of the other hens and was pecked by none of them. The number of times it pecked each of them is indicated by the numbers in the column. The hen with a blue marking (*second column*) pecked nine of the other hens but was pecked by the hen with a yellow marking. The hen with a blue and red marking (*column at far right*) pecked none of the other hens and was pecked by all. The hens with bowed heads (*solid color*) indicate the number of hens submissive to the hen in that column. The hens with upright heads (*open color*) indicate the number of hens that are dominant over the hen in that column.

# 14

# THE SOCIAL ORDER OF CHICKENS

A. M. GUHL                    February 1956

During the past 30 years the social organization and behavior of chickens has interested many investigators, and its study has produced a great deal of fascinating information. The main theme of the investigation has been the trait of dominance, or bossism, but it has also shed important light on other questions of psychology, sociology and biology, and has been helpful in practical poultry husbandry. This article will report recent findings at our zoology laboratory at Kansas State College.

It was T. Schjelderup-Ebbe, a Norwegian psychologist, who discovered the peck-order among chickens. He found that in any flock one hen usually dominated all the others: she could peck any without being pecked in return. Second came a hen which pecked all but the top hen, and the rest were arranged in a descending hierarchy ending in a hapless hen which was pecked by all and could peck no one. Cocks do not normally peck hens, but they have their own peck-order, so a breeding flock usually has two hierarchies, one for each sex.

The late W. C. Allee and his students at the University of Chicago found that the male sex hormone increases aggressiveness, so that hens given injections of this hormone fight their way up the social ladder. The female hormone tends to have the opposite effect, making injected individuals more submissive. It is common knowledge that a castrate is more docile than the normal of the species. However, capons will and do form peck-orders and may engage in some harmless fighting.

When grown birds that are strangers to one another are put together in a pen, they engage in a series of single combats, each pairing off against one opponent at a time, until a peck-order has been established for the whole flock. Some in-

dividuals submit without a fight, because of lack of aggressiveness, poor health or lack of fighting skill. Once the peck-order has been determined, pecking begins to decline in frequency as members of the hierarchy recognize their superiors; eventually a mere raising or lowering of the head may be enough to signify dominance or submission, respectively. Thus the flock becomes comparatively peaceful and conserves energy.

In flocks of birds reared together from hatching, the dominance order develops gradually. Downy chicks rarely peck: they go no farther than a threatening posture or jump. As they grow older, fighting begins, and it may be repeated

frequently before certain individuals learn to give way habitually to others. Peck-orders may be established at 10 weeks of age among pullets and somewhat earlier among cockerels.

A chicken's memory is short. Hens that have been separated for two weeks or more will fight the battle for dominance all over again when they are brought together. If a strange bird enters an organized flock, it has to fight each of the residents to establish its status. Obviously only an exceptionally aggressive outsider can win a respectable rank in the social scale under these circumstances. W. C. Sanctuary at the University of Massachusetts found that when flocks of hens were mixed, there

**PECK-ORDER IS FORMED** by a series of individual combats among the members of a newly established flock. This drawing depicts two Rhode Island Red pullets fighting.

was severe disruption, sometimes causing some birds to stop laying.

Such is the basic social structure of chickens. Now let us examine it more closely. To begin with, what are the advantages of high social status?

Naturally hens that rank high in the peck-order have privileges—first chance at the food trough, the dusting areas, the roost and the nest boxes. The low members of the hierarchy may find themselves driven about ruthlessly in the pen, especially during the earlier phase of peck-order formation. Much of the time they keep out of the way of their superiors in secluded places. They have a cowed, submissive appearance—the head usually lowered, the body feathers ruffled and unpreened. By contrast the high-ranking hens strut proudly like pampered show horses.

We have found that in a flock of young hens the high-ranking birds feed regularly during the day and crowd together on the roosts for warmth at night, whereas the low-ranking birds have to feed at twilight or early in the morning while their superiors are roosting, and at night they hover timidly on the fringes of the roosting group, often singly, even

when temperatures drop below freezing. The low-ranking pullets take longer to reach sexual maturity than those of privileged status.

To see how social disorganization affected productivity, we compared two flocks, of which one was allowed to attain a stable peck-order and the other was kept disrupted by frequent shifting of its membership. Birds in the unstable flock fought more, ate less food, gained less weight and suffered many more wounds. The latest comers had the poorest position; the top ranks were occupied by those that had been in the shifting flock longest. In other words, chickens have seniority rights. There are, however, variations of individual aggressiveness: a hen that spends a short time daily with each of several flocks may have different ranks in the different flocks.

How does the peck-order influence sexual behavior? The question of course has considerable practical importance for poultrymen. We investigated it by several rather complex observational experiments.

The observable sexual activity of a male chicken follows a characteristic

pattern: courting, treading and the act of coition itself. Most conspicuous of his courting maneuvers is a wing-flutter and dance, but sometimes he uses a more subtle approach to the female, merely extending his head toward or over her, with or without raising his hackle. If the hen responds by assuming what is called a sexual crouch, the male grips her comb or hackle with his beak and, standing on her outstretched wings, moves his feet up and down with a treading action prior to coition. A female chicken, in response to a male's courting, may react in one of three simple ways: indifference, avoidance or the cooperative crouch.

We were interested first to find out how hens would respond to courtship by males which lacked the normal male dominance over them. We therefore castrated some cockerels, depriving them of the advantage of masculine aggressiveness, and raised them in a flock of pullets where they were subjected to the peck-order contest. Some of the capons fell in the intermediate ranks, being dominated by some females. We then treated these capons with the hormone estrogen, which restored their sex drive without increasing their ag-

SEXUAL BEHAVIOR of chickens involves four kinds of maneuver: courting, avoiding, crouching and treading. In the first drawing a White Leghorn rooster (*foreground*) courts a hen by performing a waltz. The hen may respond either by avoiding the

gressiveness. Hens that ranked below these males in the peck-order mated readily with them. But hens that outranked them repelled their advances and drove them wildly about the pen. Evidently among chickens dominance by the male is a prerequisite for sexual acceptance by the female. However, we also noted that females fled from males which were too aggressive sexually.

In all-male flocks of young chickens the males often perform sexual treading upon one another, presumably because they have no normal outlet for their sexual drive. Usually the low-ranking males are the objects of these aberrant treadings, and some are driven and trodden so incessantly that they are killed. In flocks of hens, similarly, dominant females may act the male role and tread on hens lower in the peck-order. This behavior is difficult to explain, for the treading hens are not necessarily masculine in any way; they usually respond normally to the advances of a male in the same flock.

Another experiment showed, as was to be expected, that males at the top of the peck-order win out over their inferiors in any competition for mating with hens. When a small group of cocks which had previously shown no significant individual differences in sex drive was placed in a pen with hens, the dominant male was most successful in mating with the hens, while the male ranking lowest in the group's peck-order was least successful. The dominant one suppressed his inferiors' treading to varying degrees. One male was completely suppressed sexually; he failed to react to the hens he knew even when the other males were removed. This condition was called psychological castration.

One would naturally assume that the males most successful in mating would also sire the most offspring, but to make sure we carried out some special experiments with the cooperation of the poultry geneticist D. C. Warren. We used males of different breeds (Rhode Island Red, Barred Rock, White Leghorn), and the distinctively marked offspring demonstrated that the most dominant males did indeed father the most chicks. The lowest-ranking cock in one flock failed to fertilize even one egg.

What of the hens; how does their rank in the peck-order affect their sexual activity? There were already hints that the more dominant females are less likely to submit to coition, and we undertook to investigate this systematically. We raised some large flocks of 30 to 40 pullets each, and after they had established peck-orders, we divided each flock into three groups—the top third, the middle third and the bottom third of the peck-order. The ranking within each group remained the same as before, but each pullet now had fewer birds to dominate or be dominated by. This significantly changed their receptivity to male courtship. The hens in the top third, which had been comparatively unreceptive to males, became more submissive to them (as evidenced by the frequency of crouching), and the middle and bottom thirds became less submissive. In other words, the higher hens stand on the social scale, the less likely they are to mate, whereas the male improves his chances by high social status.

In these tests we noted that the females' sexual interest was stimulated each time a new male was released in their pen, but their interest was soon sated (within six to nine minutes), and thereafter they tended to avoid the male. On the other hand, the more reluctant the females were, the more ardently the males pressed their courtship: they com-

rooster (*second drawing*) or crouching with her wings spread out (*third drawing*). Crouching is a strong stimulus for the rooster to mount the hen. Before coition he stands on her wings, seizes her hackle with his beak and moves his feet with a treading action.

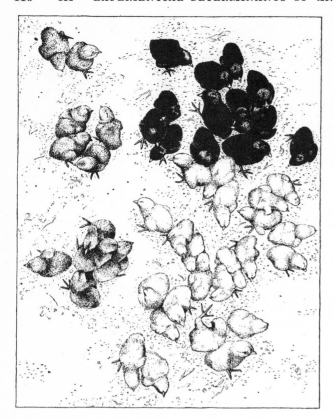

CHICKS at left hatched from eggs laid by hens artificially insem- Rock (*lighter chicks*) and a White Leghorn (*white chicks*). The
inated with a mixture of sperm from three roosters: a Rhode chicks at right were sired by the same roosters in a flock of hens.
Island Red (*siring darkest chicks in drawing*), a Barred Plymouth Difference in distribution was due to social status of the roosters.

pensated for the hens' reduced recep- may reduce the fertility of a flock of hens gation of general principles of social be-
tivity by increasing their displays. by preventing other males from mating. havior. They add a great deal to the

Male chickens vary considerably in This suggests that for breeding flocks understanding of various matters, such
sex drive. Their sexuality is not neces- poultrymen should select males of high as aggressiveness and courtship, which
sarily related to their aggressiveness, or sexuality and effectiveness in courting. is being gained from studies of many
standing in the peck-order. Consequent- We have found that chickens are ex- animals, from the stickleback fish to the
ly a dominant male with a low sex drive cellent animals for experimental investi- chimpanzee.

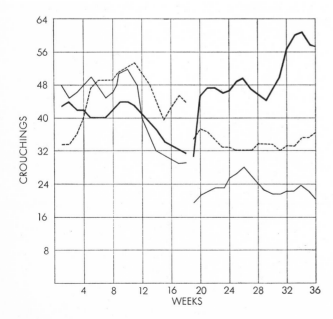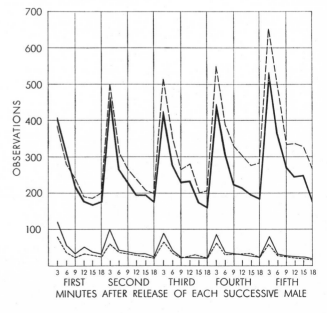

CROUCHINGS of hens per week were altered by dividing flock OBSERVATIONS of courting (*solid line at top*), avoiding (*broken
into top third of the peck order (*heavy line*), middle third (*bro- line at top*), crouching (*solid line at bottom*) and treading (*broken
ken line*) and bottom third (*light line*) after 18 weeks of courting. line at bottom*) changed with introduction of each new rooster.

# Part IV

## LEARNING AND MEMORY

# IV

## LEARNING AND MEMORY

*Introduction*     As the articles in the preceding sections have clearly emphasized, behavior plays a central role in animals' adaptation to their environments. The adaptiveness of genetically based "instinctive" behavior is insured only if the patterns of behavior are appropriate for the environment in which the animals live. Stable or at least highly predictable environments are required if animals are to survive and reproduce on the basis of relatively stereotyped, genetically based responses. Fortunately, most responses in animals are not highly fixed or stereotyped, and behavior can be modified by a wide variety of environmental influences. As the article by Hess pointed out, certain animals have the capacity to become imprinted. But the nature and degree of the imprinting is determined by the specific environmental stimulation occurring at a critical period in the animal's life.

A new dimension was added to behavioral adaptation when animals evolved the capacity to learn—that is, to record specific experiences and to modify their behavior in terms of the experiences. Animals that can learn have the possibility of adjusting their behavior to meet the requirements of specific environments and the ability to change their behavior as the environment changes. In a changing environment, the behavioral flexibility that is provided by learning ability is clearly an advantage over that provided by the more slowly acting genetic changes produced by mutations. Learning is thus clearly one of the most important phenomena of biology. For this reason attempts to understand the nature and bases of learning have to considerable extent dominated research in psychobiology for the past half century.

The papers in this section present but a small sample of current theories and research concerned with the problem of learning. In the first paper, "Place-Learning" (page 118), H. Gleitman examines some of the evidence bearing on fundamental questions concerning the nature of learning in animals. What does an animal learn when it is acquiring a response? Does the animal learn merely to make a patterned sequence of responses, or does learning consist of the acquisition of information? Can animals learn without responding? The evidence reviewed by Gleitman indicates that (1) animals can learn about their environment even under conditions which prevent their making relevant responses, and (2) a learned response is not merely a movement pattern. Such evidence indicates that it is essential to distinguish between learning and performance. Performance must be observed in order to make inferences about the animals' learning, but learning as indexed by performance is based on the animals' ability to acquire and retain information about features of the environmental stimulation.

Animals are able to record experiences and either to change or to repeat their behavior in terms of the recorded experience. The ability to learn obviously requires memory, but what is memory? How are traces of experiences stored in animals' nervous systems and how do the traces influence subsequent behavior? As R. W. Gerard points out in the second article in this section, "What Is Memory?" (page 126), the nature of the physiological processes underlying memory are as yet unknown. The problem is enormously complex. Memory of well-learned responses is unaffected by a variety of experimental procedures—cooling of the brain, electric shock sufficient in intensity to produce convulsions, and multiple incisions in the cerebral cortex. Recently acquired memory, however, is destroyed by convulsive electric shock. Research published since the appearance of Gerard's article continues to provide support for the view that the fixation of permanent memory traces involves processes occurring for at least an hour following training and that the processes involve a pattern of changes throughout much of the brain.

The more recent findings of studies of "Learning in the Octopus" (page 132), reported by B. B. Boycott, are generally consistent with Gerard's earlier conclusions. Under some experimental circumstances the formation of permanent memory is prevented by removal of the vertical lobe of the brain. Short-term memory is unimpaired by the operation. Boycott points out that these results closely parallel results of studies of memory in human patients with surgically removed temporal lobes. These findings suggest that memory may involve two mechanisms: a short-term mechanism and a longer-term mechanism that requires time for fixation.

Studies of "Short-Term Memory" (page 141) on human subjects, reviewed by L. R. Peterson, provide still further support for the view that short-term memory and long-term memory involve separate mechanisms. The rapid forgetting that characterizes short-term memory seems to arise from spontaneous decay as well as from interference from other messages. Support for the view that long-term memory is attributable to a separate mechanism is based in part upon evidence that, with repeated presentations, spacing of the presentation results in better retention. As Peterson points out, ". . . it is a paradox that in order to remember something better you should allow some forgetting to occur." Apparently we have just begun to explore in depth the problem of the nature and bases of learning and memory. Most of the important questions remain unanswered. Whether memory is in fact based on one, two, or many separate mechanisms or processes, is at present one of the important unanswered questions.

# 15

# PLACE-LEARNING

HENRY GLEITMAN

October 1963

When we see a circus animal performing a trick, we know that this is learned behavior. But exactly what is it that the animal has learned? Has it merely learned a pattern of response to a given situation or has it acquired concepts of broader application? Obviously this is a question of considerable importance for the theory of learning.

Consider a young child adding sums on the blackboard. He has been taught that three plus six equals nine. Confronted with the symbols $3 + 6 =$, he promptly fills in the answer. Suppose now we present the class with a new form of the question: $6 + 3 =?$ One child is hopelessly puzzled, another readily answers nine. It is clear that the two pupils have learned different things: the first child has learned a specific answer to a specific question; the second has learned an arithmetical concept.

This example illustrates the truism that successful performance in any particular task does not necessarily indicate what has been learned. The point is a crucial one in theoretical studies of the nature of the learning process, and for half a century psychologists have investigated it with a great variety of experimental tests. They have swung between two rival theories about the learning process, which we might call the "response," or "motor," theory and the "cognitive," or perhaps "concept," theory.

In order to study the essentials of the learning process psychologists naturally have worked mainly with animals, which allow closely controlled experiments in relatively simple situations. The rat is a particularly convenient animal, and one of the favorite instruments for investigating its learning performances is the maze (a natural testing apparatus for an animal that normally lives in tunnels and burrows). Very early in this work it was established that a rat could learn to find its way through a highly complex maze involving 20 or more choices. How did it learn, and of what exactly did its learning consist?

One of the first to suggest an answer (around 1910) was John B. Watson, then a graduate student at the University of Chicago. He argued that what the rat (indeed, any animal) learned was a certain sequence of physical acts that got it through the maze. This sequence was based on sensory stimulations and motor responses: as the rat tried various paths, those muscle responses that took it along the correct path (for example, turning right, then left, then left again and so on) were gradually chained more and more strongly to specific sensory messages. In short, the animal eventually was propelled along the correct pathway automatically by connections forged between certain kinesthetic sensory patterns and specific motor innervations.

Watson and his mentor Harvey Carr performed an experiment that seemed to support this idea. They trained rats to run a certain maze perfectly, then they substituted a maze with exactly the same sequence of turns but with the alleys either shortened or lengthened substantially. In the shortened maze the rats ran headlong into the ends of the alleys; in the lengthened alleys they turned too soon and bumped into the walls. It did indeed look as if the animals had learned very specific muscular patterns, with the result that in the new mazes they tried to run the same distance up each alley as before.

But some further experiments by Watson threw doubt on his motor theory. In one experiment he rotated the original maze 90 degrees; in another he reversed its direction in the room. In both cases the rats performed poorly, making many errors. This indicated that in their original learning the animals had been guided to some degree by cues from outside the maze itself—perhaps by the light from a window or by the sounds from cages of rats at one side of the room.

Opposed to Watson's theory was one that had been proposed by the British sociologist and philosopher Leonard T. Hobhouse. Noting that a dog, even in a strange house, would quickly learn to run to its master wherever the master called from, Hobhouse argued that an animal learned not a sequence of movements but the location of the goal, that is, some idea of spatial relations. Through the years many experiments have strongly upheld this view and contradicted Watson's "muscle twitch" theory, as its opponents dubbed it.

In one classic experiment D. A. Mac-Farlane of the University of California at Berkeley trained rats in a maze and then flooded the alleys with eight inches of water. The animals no longer could employ their running pattern and now had to swim, using an entirely different set of muscle movements. Nevertheless, they went through the maze almost without error. Other experimenters used more drastic methods to make sure that their experimental subjects could not employ the original motor pattern. They operated on the rat's cerebellum, upsetting its postural equilibrium, or they cut the spinal cord, severing the connection between the kinesthetic receptors and the brain, or they amputated a leg. None of these handicaps made any difference in the performance of a rat that had learned the maze thoroughly: swimming, staggering, limping or hobbling, the rat made its way through by the correct path.

Although these experiments strongly

contested the Watson motor theory, it could still be argued that they were not decisive; the animals might be guided solely by the learned sequence of turns—by a "body twitch" pattern instead of the "muscle twitch" complex. But this point was decisively answered by another type of experiment. It turned out that rats could easily learn to reach a given goal without error even when they had to make different turns from one trial to the next.

The instrument used for these experiments was the "elevated maze," a maze without walls consisting of a raised runway from which the subject can see and hear cues from outside the maze itself. (In the language of experimental psychology, "maze" does not necessarily mean a tortuous enclosure; it can be a simple T-shaped affair in which the subject merely chooses whether to turn right or left.) Edward C. Tolman, Benbow F. Ritchie and D. Kalish of the University of California at Berkeley tested rats on an elevated T-maze that could be ar-

ranged so that the starting point was on one side or the other of the crossbar [see illustrations below]. For one group of rats the experimenters always placed the food reward at the same point, namely at the same end of the crossbar. In order to find the food the animals had to turn right if they started from one side of the maze and left if they started from the opposite side. In other words, these rats had to learn the place where the food was located, not a particular turn. In order to learn

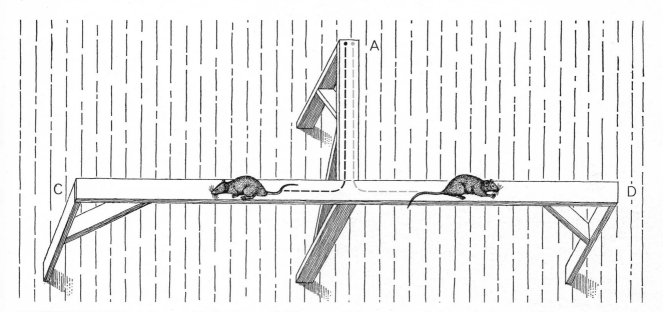

ELEVATED T-MAZE is used to test the effectiveness of different learning processes in rats. In this hypothetical test situation both rats set out from the same starting position (A). The "response-learner" (rat following black broken path) has been trained to turn right to receive a food reward, whereas the "place-learner" (rat following colored broken path) has been trained to use various visual and auditory cues outside the maze itself to find a food reward at point D. In actuality only one rat is tested on the maze at a time.

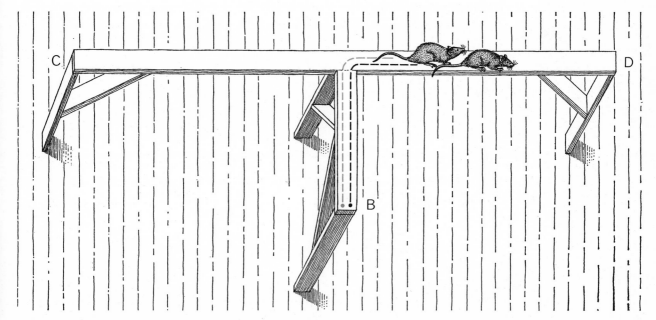

T-MAZE IS REVERSED in order to compare the performances of the response-learner and the place-learner in a new test situation. Both rats now start from point B. The response-learner again turns right, which now happens to be toward D rather than C. The place-learner also heads for D but this time must make a right turn rather than a left turn. Given a sufficient number of distinct spatial cues in the room, the place-learners were able to master the problem of the T-maze much more quickly than the response-learners were.

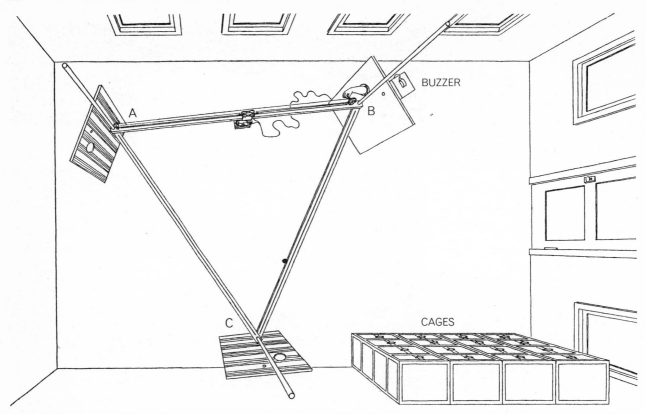

**RATS WERE TRANSPORTED** over three different 10-foot courses in a transparent Plexiglas trolley car in this experiment conducted by the author. Between the starting and terminal point of each trip the rat was subjected to a continuous electric shock. Windows, striped screens, cages and a loud buzzer provided a variety of spatial cues for the rats to learn the course without actually running it.

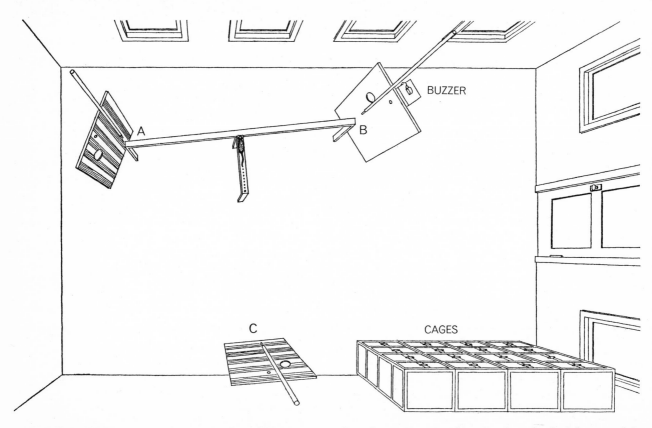

**RATS WERE TESTED** 24 hours later on an elevated T-maze set up at the same height at which the car had traveled. The object was to determine whether or not the rat could locate, by spatial cues alone, the starting point of its trip, where the shock began, and the terminal point of the trip, where the shock ceased. The T-maze was also set up between points *A* and *C* and between points *B* and *C*.

this they had to use cues in the room. For purposes of comparison another group of rats was trained to make the same *turn* each time, the food being placed at the end of the arm that corresponded to the correct turn at each trial. The animals in the first group were called "place-learners"; in the second, "response-learners."

Given distinct cues in the room, the place-learners, as it turned out, mastered their problem much more quickly than the response-learners did theirs. This suggests that animals learn how to reach a goal from spatial cues more easily than from practice in a pattern of turning movements. Tolman concluded that an animal acquires a "cognitive map" that enables it to locate objects of interest to it.

By broadening the definition of "response" one might still contend that these animals were learning only an automatic response to cues, such as the response of "turning toward the light" or of "avoiding the noise." Such a theory was far removed from its muscle-bound predecessor, but it betrayed its parentage by insisting that what is learned *is* the response (a more broadly defined response, to be sure, but a response nonetheless). In contrast, those psychologists who believed that the animal achieves a cognitive map pointed out that the experimental response was only an *index* of learning—a convenient measuring stick, to be sure, but not the thing that was being measured.

The theoretical debate quickly led to an experimental question: Could learning occur without actual performance of the response? The motor-response theory argued, of course, that it could not—that practice in the response was an essential part of the learning process. The general experimental approach has been to render an animal incapable of making its normal response to a stimulus and then test it later to determine whether or not it has learned anything simply from its exposure to the stimulus.

Edward C. Beck and Robert Doty of the University of Utah conducted experiments with cats immobilized by the drug bulbocapnine hydrochloride. While the cat was in this paralytic stupor the experimenters repeatedly applied an electric shock to its foreleg and at the same time sounded a short tone. Normally the cat would have pulled back its leg in response to the shock and then to the tone alone as a conditioned reaction, but the drugged cat of course was unable to

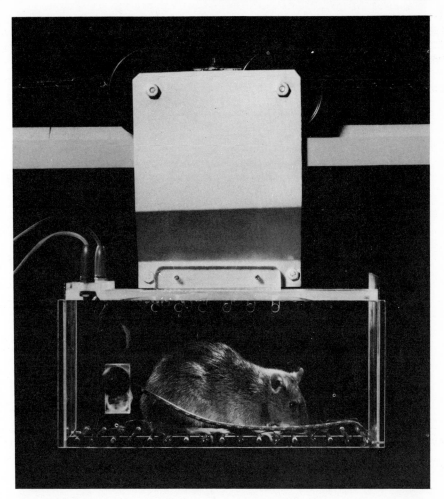

TROLLEY CAR used in the experiment at top of page 122 is made of transparent Plexiglas and is suspended from the track by an aluminum carriage. The floor is wired to shock the rat.

do so. After the drug had worn off, the experimenters tested the animal by sounding the tone without the shock. In most cases the cat promptly bent its foreleg. To make sure that no motor response was possible during administration of the shock, Beck and Doty repeated the experiment with a doubly paralyzing treatment: the drug and an operation on the roots of the motor nerves in the leg. Some 10 weeks later, after the cat had recovered the ability to move its foreleg, they again gave it the tone test, and the cat again responded by bending its leg. The responses of the cats treated in this way were essentially the same as those of control animals that were fully capable and reacted immediately at the time the shock was applied.

At Swarthmore College we carried out experiments of a similar nature, employing somewhat less drastic means of preventing the animals' responses. In these experiments rats were imprisoned and transported over a certain course while they were receiving the electric shock; they were then allowed to run the course

themselves to show what they had learned. It was a test of both place-learning and postponed performance.

The chief instrument of the experiment was a small trolley car just large enough to hold a rat. Made of transparent Plexiglas, with a wire-grid floor, the car was suspended from a track 10 feet long. Three tracks were laid out in different directions in the room so that the cues to location would vary; the cues were windows, cages along one wall and a loud buzzer [*see top illustration on page 122*]. The starting and terminal points of the tracks were also differentiated sharply from each other by a different screen at each point, one striped vertically, one horizontally and the third unpainted.

Each rat was placed in the car and drawn over the 10-foot track between two points, the trip lasting about 20 seconds. It was a dolorous journey: the rat was subjected to a severe electric shock throughout the trip. Each rat made 18 trips (over the same route and in the same direction each time), with

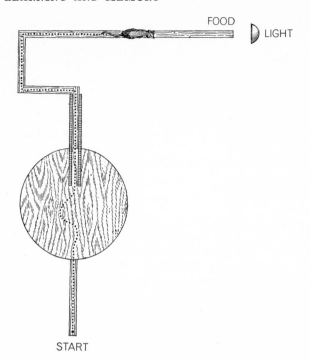

**TRAINING MAZE** used by Edward C. Tolman and his colleagues at the University of California is shown here. The rats set out from the starting point, crossed a circular table and traversed a path with several turns in it before reaching the food reward. The light was presumably used as a visual cue by the rats in forming a "cognitive map" of the test situation.

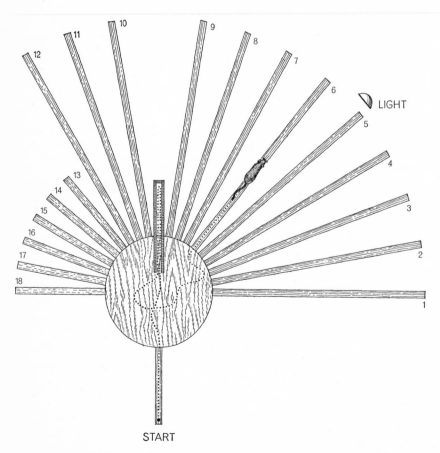

**"SUNBURST" MAZE** is a modification of the training maze shown at the top of this page. As before, the rats ran into the alley only to find it blocked at the end. They then returned to the table and, after some exploration, chose the path whose end was closest to where the food had been, near the light. Paths *13* through *18* were abbreviated by the size of the room.

a 90-second rest period between rides. Twenty-four hours later it was tested on an elevated maze related to the track it had traveled.

What, if anything, had the rat learned about the spatial aspects of the situation during its journeys in the car? The test was designed to determine whether or not the animal could locate the starting point of its trip, where the shock began (presumably a "bad" place), and the end point of the trip, where the shock ceased (presumably a "good" place). In the maze the rats were given a choice between the good and the bad place, or between the good place and a neutral place, or between the bad place and a neutral place. The track and cars were removed from the room and an elevated T-maze was set up at the same height above the floor at which the cars had traveled. The maze consisted of a three-foot stem leading to two five-foot arms. When the choice was between the good and the bad place, the arms were in the same path as the track had been, with one arm leading to the track's starting point and the other to the terminal point; for the choice between the good (or bad) and the neutral place, one arm ended at an end point of the former track and the other at some point in the room not in the path of the track. The animals' selection of good and bad places in the room would depend, of course, on whether or not they had located, and could remember, those places with reference to the room cues: the different screens, the windows, the buzzer, the cages and so on.

Deprived of food for a full day, the hungry rats went looking for food on the maze (having previously been trained to find such a reward on elevated pathways in another room). Would they show a preference for the good arm of the T (leading to the end of their shocking trip) rather than the bad arm (leading to the beginning of shock)? The results were clear: of the animals offered this choice, 26 chose the good arm and only nine the bad. This seems strong evidence that, without any previous exploration of the room by their own locomotion, most of the rats had formed a cognitive map during their trips in the trolley car.

On the other hand, it surprisingly turned out that the animals showed no particular preference between the bad (or good) place and a neutral place. Those that were given such a choice selected the bad arm almost as often as the neutral one and the good arm slightly less often than the neutral one. Their place-learning, it seems, was not broad enough to discriminate between a known location and an area of the room where they had not been before.

Other experiments, however, have shown that rats can acquire cognitive maps of considerable breadth and complexity. This was demonstrated in a famous experiment by Tolman, Ritchie and Kalish. They trained rats to run an elevated maze on which, to reach the food reward, the animals had to cross a circular table, go through a short alley, turn left, right, then right, then right again and finally go to the end of a straight path. Near the goal was a light that could serve as a cue to its location in the room [see top illustration on opposite page].

After the rats had run this maze for 12 trials the experimenters changed the design drastically. They cut off the original route at the end of the alley and set up instead a "sunburst" of 18 paths radiating in different directions from the circular table [see bottom illustration on opposite page]. Tested on this new maze, the rats ran as before into the alley only to find it blocked at the end. They then returned to the table and began to explore the other paths radiating from it. But in fairly short order they chose one particular path: the one whose end was closest to where the goal had been before, near the light. Typically the rat would nose a few inches into some of the other paths, then select the correct path and go all the way to the end.

Hobhouse, had he still been alive, would have been highly pleased by this convincing confirmation that animals are capable of place-learning. The pendulum

had indeed swung far away from Watson's view that animals learned only a pattern of movements. But it is not often (at least in psychology) that when a theory is found to be false, its exact opposite is found to be true. Soon the pendulum began to swing back: it developed that rats were not quite as shrewd as the Tolman experiment had suggested.

Other investigators failed to get the same results in spite of earnest efforts to duplicate the conditions of Tolman's experiment. A possible explanation may lie in the fact that their animals were less sophisticated than Tolman's rats. As it happens, his rats had previously been trained to solve a rather complex multiple maze that took about 50 trials to master. The rats used by the other experimenters had had no such training in a complicated problem. It may be, therefore, that in order to form spatial "concepts" a rat must have some prior experience in exploring space by perceptual and motor means. That is to say, an untutored rat may solve a problem by a process of learning that lies somewhere between the theory of Watson and that of Hobhouse.

That complex learning does require a considerable background of sensory experience and other forms of stimulation is indicated by the performances of animals that have been raised under conditions of deprivation. For example, a puppy reared alone in a small cage with little exposure to normal sensory and social stimuli performs very poorly when tested in mazes or in other problems demanding ability in spatial organization. The same is true of primates similarly deprived of experience. For that matter, most of the laboratory rats bred

for maze studies are also carefully restricted in experience, so that their performance in experiments will not be contaminated by prior learning. The result is that all these "experimentally naïve" animals perform much less successfully in maze tests than animals that have been raised normally and allowed some modicum of sophistication. The maps of the first are narrow and confined.

We are still far from any complete or detailed description of the learning process. The evidence so far indicates that neither of the two theories we have considered tells a full story. The rat in a maze is neither a mechanical automaton nor a sagacious geometer surveying spatial relations. For naïve animals, at least, it appears that the truth lies somewhere between the two theoretical extremes.

|  | GROUP I | GROUP II | GROUP III |
|---|---|---|---|
| STARTING POINT | 9 |  |  |
| TERMINAL POINT | 26 | 16 | 15 |
| NEUTRAL POINT |  | 19 | 18 |

RESULTS of the experiment depicted at bottom of page 122 revealed a preference for a terminal, or "good," place over a starting, or "bad," place. The rats' capacity for place-learning, however, did not enable them to distinguish between a good and a neutral place or between a bad and a neutral place.

# 16

# WHAT IS MEMORY?

RALPH W. GERARD                                                September 1953

A textbook of biochemistry widely used early in this century had a famous passage on the memory of linseed oil. Exposure to light makes the oil turn gummy. A brief exposure may not cause any observable change. But on later illumination the oil will change more rapidly than if it had not already been exposed. The oil "remembers" its past experience and behaves differently because of it. Its memory consists in the fact that light produces, among other things, substances which aid the light-induced oxidations that make it gummy.

However far removed this may be from remembering the Gettysburg address, it clearly points up one way in which memory can work—by means of material traces of the past—and the difficulty of defining what memory is. Actually the behavior of the oil and of a human being memorizing the Gettysburg address are but extremes of a spectrum of such behavior in nature. Between these extremes there is a pretty smooth continuity, and any concept which defines memory much more narrowly than "the modification of behavior by experience" will run into trouble. Consciousness, for example, is not necessary to memory, for men remember, and recall under hypnosis, innumerable details never consciously perceived.

Where, then, shall we draw the line? A pebble, rubbed smooth in a stream, rolls differently from the original angular stone. Experience has here modified behavior; the past has been stored in a changed structure. Yet this does not greatly interest us as an instance of memory. Perhaps we should restrict the notion of memory to changes in systems which participate actively in causing the change. Then linseed oil "remembers," and so does the bulging calf muscle of a ballet dancer. Does a developing em-

bryo "remember" the major steps, and missteps, in the long evolution of the species? Do trees "remember" good and bad seasons in the thickness of their rings? Is a film a memory of light in chemicals and a tape recording a memory of sound in magnetism? Is a library a memory of thoughts in books and a brain a memory of thoughts in protoplasm? Even to identify memory, let alone explain it, is no simple matter.

Without memory the past would vanish; intelligence, often called the ability to learn by experience, would be absent, and life would indeed be "a tale told by an idiot, full of sound and fury, signifying nothing." Today the search for the fundamental mechanisms of memory in the nervous system is being pressed with hopeful enthusiasm. The smell of success is in the air and great developments seem to wait just over the next ridge.

Let us consider as memory only that exhibited in man and in such sophisticated behavior as is usually close to conscious awareness. One great problem is: Why do certain impressions become conscious upon reception while others do not; why does awareness accompany some acts, not others; what, in general, invests certain neural events with a phosphorescence of subjective recognition? This question remains unanswered, but the answer is likely to come in terms of the evolution of awareness of certain types of neural events as useful to the organism.

Memory involves the making of an impression by an experience, the retention of some record of this impression and the re-entry of this record into consciousness (or behavior) as recall and recognition. The initial impression need not have entered awareness in order to be retained and recalled. Anyone asked to recall what he has just seen in a room or in

a picture does a less complete job than a subject under hypnosis even years later. I have been told of a bricklayer who, under hypnosis, described correctly every bump and grain on the top surface of a brick he had laid in a wall 20 years before!

Guesses have been made as to how many items might be accumulated in memory over a lifetime. Some tests of perception suggest that each tenth of a second is a single "frame" of experience for the human brain. In that tenth of a second it can receive perhaps a thousand units of information, called bits. In 70 years, not allowing for any reception during sleep, some 15 trillion bits might pour into the brain and perhaps be stored there. Since this number is more than 1,000 times larger than the total of nerve cells, the problem of storage is not exactly simple.

Whether or not all incoming sensations are preserved as potential memories, there is an important time factor in their fixation. Youthful, repeated or vivid experiences seem most firmly fixed. They are the last to survive disrupting conditions—old age, brain damage, concussion or mental shock—and the first to return after a period of amnesia. A goose seems to fix upon the first moving object it sees as its mother and thereafter follows it about. An infant, suddenly frightened by a barking dog, may fear dogs for the rest of its life.

More often experiences force themselves into attention and memory only gradually. Even learning to perceive is a long, troublesome matter. Adults gaining vision for the first time must labor for months to learn to recognize a circle and to distinguish it from a triangle, let alone to see letters and words.

After any experience, apparently considerable time must elapse between the arrival of the incoming nerve impulses and the fixing of the trace. If a photographic plate acted similarly, it could not be developed at once after exposure but only some time later. Recent experiments in our laboratory have emphasized this phenomenon. Hamsters daily were run in a maze and were given an electric shock afterward. When the shock was given four hours or more after the run, it did not influence the learning curve. (The question of cumulative damage is irrelevant here.) A shock one hour after the run impaired learning a little, and as the shock was brought closer it interfered more and more, until at one minute after the run, it destroyed learning completely. Clearly some process of fixing continues for at least an hour.

The nature of the fixing process must be left for the moment, while some related phenomena of memory are noted. One is a type of erasing. A memory wizard who can glance through a newspaper and then name the word at any position in any column on any page makes an effort to forget this mass of information at the close of a performance so as not to "clutter up" his memory. Perhaps similar is the removal by a pre-suggested signal of an instruction to a hypnotized subject to perform some act after arousal. In such instances stored experience traces seem to be expunged, but whether they are really irrecoverable is perhaps not fully established. Recall alone may be at fault, as in simple forgetting.

A second phenomenon has to do with the alteration of memory traces. The memory left by an experience can change progressively. Memory, as has been well said, is reconstructive rather than reduplicative. It is also highly associative. Pictures redrawn from memory at intervals become more regular (details are smoothed out) or more exaggerated (some salient feature is caricatured) or an object different from the original (a chair looks more like a horse at each redrawing).

Besides fixation and storage, there remain recall and recognition. Failure to recall does not imply loss of the trace: witness the frequent experience of temporary inability to say a familiar name "just on the tip of my tongue." The most intriguing problem about memory, however, is not the existence but the tremendous specificity of recall. Both in its positive and negative aspects—as seen in dreams, in amnesia, in suppression and repression, in hypnosis, in hysteria and dual personality—recall offers bi-

zarre phenomena, formidable to explain.

One day not long ago, as I left a lecture room I caught a fleeting glimpse of the head and shoulders of a person half-silhouetted against a window over a hundred feet away. I knew at once with certainty the name of the person standing there, although he had not crossed my path nor his name my mind for more than 15 years. A chord, a note, a word, a line can recall a long past experience. Or it may reawaken an intense emotion without the connected experience; I know of a young man who invariably faints at the sight of a stethoscope, yet has no general fear of doctors or illness and no idea of why he reacts so uncontrollably.

Recall may sometimes be disguised, seemingly to protect the subject from the anguish of fear or shame or pain. Parts of a story that touch upon a personal problem are often "forgotten" only to appear, modified, in a dream. A man who was unable to recall the telephone number of a girl friend while visiting her city dreamed of red objects that night and recognized in the morning that the numerical position of the letters $r$, $e$, $d$ in the alphabet gave the missing number. This opens the door to the whole edifice

of symbols. An unsophisticated youngster, directed under hypnosis to dream about bed-wetting, may report his dream in Freudian symbols which only an experienced psychoanalyst—or another naive youngster under hypnosis!—can recognize as referring to bed-wetting.

Finally, what of the compulsive neurotic whose affliction is banished when some infant experience is dredged up during psychotherapy? What of the psychoneurotic soldier, unable to recall a battle beyond a certain point, who relives under pentothal all the horror of seeing a companion's head blown off and is then able to remember and talk about it? What of aphasics, who can recognize words by sight or by sound but not both? And what of dream experiences, not actually sensed but presumably due to intrinsic brain activity, which may be recalled in wakefulness or only in other dreams, if at all? The problem of recall and its specificity is the real challenge to neurophysiology.

The human brain is composed of some 10 billion nerve cells, more or less alike, which interact in various ways. Each cell contributes to behavior, and

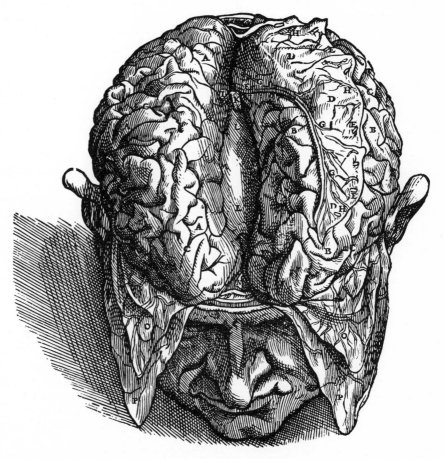

THE BRAIN was dissected by early anatomists seeking clues to its function. This woodcut is from the famous *De Humani Corporis Fabrica* of the pioneer Andreas Vesalius.

**HAMSTER RUNS THROUGH MAZE** as part of a memory experiment conducted by Robert E. Ransmeier at the University of Chicago. Each barrier in the maze has two doors, one open and one locked. After training hamster reaches food (*right*) in a few seconds.

**HAMSTER IS CHILLED** in a refrigerator. When its temperature is 40 degrees Fahrenheit, the electrical pulse of its brain ceases.

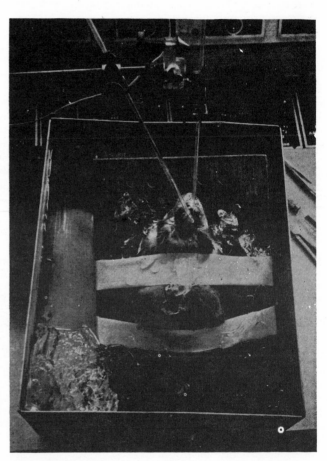

**ANOTHER HAMSTER IS TESTED** by electroencephalograph to determine the temperature at which the electrical activity stops.

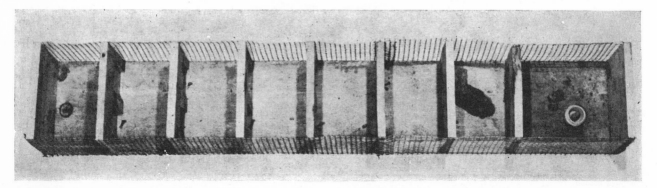

**HAMSTER RUNS THROUGH THE MAZE AGAIN** after it has been chilled to wipe out the electrical activity of its brain. The investigators discovered that hamsters trained to run through the maze suffered no impairment of this ability because of the chilling.

presumably to mental activity, by firing impulses or failing to fire. All the phenomena of memory must be explained in terms of the temporal and spatial patterns of these discharges.

If experience is to modify behavior, the activity of neurons connected with an experience must alter their subsequent activity patterns. Two general questions regarding the neural trace must be asked, and both can be given a reasonable, if not a certain, answer today. The first is: Does memory depend on a continuing activity or on some static residue, some structural alteration, left behind by past activity? Is a river the water flowing in it or the channel the water cuts? The answer today is tending strongly toward the latter. The second question is: Is the structural trace (or dynamic process) for each memory located in a particular region, or are memory traces suffused through the brain in some way? Are memories marks placed on violin strings or are they wave trains playing over these strings? The latter would imply dynamic memory, but the trace could still be structural, like the wiggled groove on a phonograph record. Whether the trace is localized or diffuse, its exact nature is a third, if somewhat subsidiary question. Current investigations suggest that there are multiple patterns of local traces rather than a single well-localized one, but the nature of the trace is almost pure guess.

A dynamic memory would depend on the continuous passage of nerve impulses or on the maintenance of some active metabolic or potential change in neurons, presumably reinforced by the repeated arrival of impulses. A nerve impulse traveling around a closed loop of connecting neurons would be a mechanism for such a dynamic memory, each remembered item depending on the activity of a particular loop or net of neurons. (Actually, since there are more memories than neurons, different memories would have to share portions of path, but this is physiologically possible without snarling traffic.) Such a memory device would, however, be metabolically expensive, and if the impulses really left no long-enduring trace, memories would be completely and irrevocably lost once the activity stopped.

There is a simple way to test the question as to whether a memory is purely dynamic. One need only stop all nerve impulses in the brain momentarily and observe whether a memory is lost. The problem, of course, is to stop the impulses reversibly. In sleep or under anesthesia the brain slows down but remains electrically active, and memories are largely undisturbed. But the brain's electrical activity can be stopped in several ways. When a hibernating animal, such as the hamster, is cooled to a body temperature of 40 degrees Fahrenheit, needles thrust into its brain fail to pick up electrical activity; it seems reasonably certain that the reverberating impulses are frozen in their tracks.

Another way of stopping the circulating nerve messages is to stimulate the neurons simultaneously by a vigorous electric shock, so that all the neurons presumably are unable to respond to a normal impulse. Such a shock does produce a period of complete electrical silence, measured in seconds or minutes. If the lower brain, controlling respiration, is included, the normal messages for breathing are suspended. Brain neurons may also be made electrically inactive by withholding oxygen for some two minutes or by withholding sugar. In all these cases the animals recover rapidly after the temporary treatment, and their memory can be investigated.

The experiment is now straightforward. Hamsters are first taught a simple maze. They are then hibernated or given electric shock or made to breathe nitrogen for a few minutes. After recovering, they are tested for their retention of learning. If they remember the way through the maze, the memory did not depend upon reverberating circuits or upon any other purely dynamic process. They remember!

This by no means excludes the initial dependence of memory on neuron activity. The passage of impulses is necessarily involved in the initial experience that leaves a memory trace. The fact that repetition makes for better memory reminds us of the analogy of the river cutting a channel in its bed. Indeed, the reason it takes time to fix a memory trace in the brain may be that impulses must circulate over their selected pathways many times in order to leave behind an enduring material change.

What, then, is this enduring static trace? Muscle fibers react to continued exercise by increasing their content of hemoglobin-like pigment; the meat becomes darker. No one has described an enduring chemical change in nerve or brain as a result of activity, but it must be conceded that this is a difficult quest and has not been undertaken very seriously. Muscle fibers swell and become hypertrophied on exercise. It has been shown recently that nerve fibers also swell slightly as they conduct impulses, and the swelling persists at least for minutes and hours if not for days and

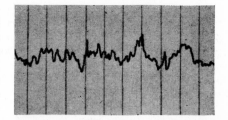

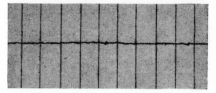

BRAIN WAVES of a hamster (*page 128*) are damped by chilling. Normal waves at top.

years. Nerve fibers also show alterations in potential which outlast the active period by many minutes. Any of these changes might occur at the critical junction between one neuron and the next—the synapse or gap across which conduction is considerably more precarious than it is along the uniform nerve fiber. The change might then make the passage of subsequent impulses easier or more difficult.

Certain it is that activity can facilitate and inactivity hinder the subsequent passage of an impulse across a synapse. This has been learned from experiments on simple spinal cord reflexes involving only one sensory neuron, one synapse and one motor neuron in each arc. If some of the sensory nerve fibers serving the knee-jerk reflex are stimulated, say a hundred times a second for 10 minutes, and are then tested with a single stimulus, the number of motor fibers responding (in effect, the size of the knee-jerk) is increased tenfold above the normal response to a single shock. The increased responsiveness dies out in two or three phases, one lasting for seconds and one certainly for hours. This suggests that the local trace left behind may have involved several changes. Conversely, when impulses are prevented from reaching the synapses of this reflex for days or weeks, by cutting the sensory nerve connections, the reflex elicited by a single shock is strikingly below normal. After a few shocks, however, the response begins to improve, and again the return toward normal seems to involve more than one phase.

Many suggestions have been made as to what kinds of changes may alter the response at a synapse. They must be structural—either in the fibers and contacts or at the molecular level, where displacement of ions might alter the electric potential or displacement of atoms change the chemistry. One observed change, already noted, is the swelling of fiber end-bulbs induced by activity. The swelling should favor the transmission of impulses. Actually this explanation is a modern version of one of the earliest theories of memory: that activity somehow causes a nerve fiber to sprout new twigs near its termination and so to increase its effective contact. Neurons from brains of older persons have in fact been reported to branch more extensively than those from the young, and the notoriously poor memory of old people for recent events might be attributed to the neurons' inability to grow more twigs or to accommodate more connections. A closely related suggestion, that electric-shock treatment of some psychoses is successful because it destroys certain existing connections and permits neurons to make "healthier" ones, is based upon the observation, made on transparent tadpole tails, that electric shocks cause nerve filaments to be torn off.

Another mechanism enjoying some current popularity is chemical. Since every type of cell of every individual of every species has its own chemical personality, and since this differentiation of cells depends on proteins, the specificity of memory might be due to changes in nerve proteins. Each trace could be limited to one or a few molecules in an end-bulb of a neuron. The body cells that manufacture and release antibodies against invading organisms "learn," as we know, from experience. When typhoid proteins, for instance, enter the body the first time, antibodies are produced slowly and in small amounts. But years later, when almost no antibody remains in the blood, a new invasion by this specific protein is met by a prompt and vigorous release of antibody that nips the disease before it gets started.

It is far from explained just how the passage of nerve impulses would alter protein molecules at a synapse, or how, in turn, an altered protein composition would aid or hinder the passage of a nerve impulse. Yet some such chemical mechanism cannot be discarded, for nerves and synapses can be highly specific and can change their specificity. For example, if an extra muscle is transplanted into the back of a salamander, the nerve to which it becomes attached will make the transplanted muscle contract simultaneously with the normal flexor if the transplant is a flexor muscle or with the normal extensor if it is an extensor. Somehow the central synapses have "discovered" what kind of muscle is attached at the far end of the motor neuron and they let through nerve impulses at the proper time for a muscle of this sort.

The essence of all these suggested mechanisms is that a given end-bulb of a neuron, initially ineffective, can become and remain effective as a result of activity. Indeed, mathematical theories of the behavior of complex nerve nets demand only such an assumption to account for the basic properties of memory. Moreover, the total number of end-bulbs on the neurons of the brain, some 10 trillion, about matches the number of bits of information the brain may store during a lifetime. But then each memory would have to have its exact microscopic spot in the brain, would have to stay put through life, and would somehow have to be deposited, once and once only, at a given end-bulb, despite the wide sweep of impulses through the brain during each experience. This raises sharply the problem of localization.

The degree of localization is probably the key problem of memory. If we could expect to find a given memory at a given place in the brain our experimental problem would be comparatively simple. We would locate the region and compare structural, chemical or physical changes there in animals with and without the appropriate experience. Some years ago there was an exciting report that electrical stimulation of a small spot in the cerebral cortex caused trained dogs to make a conditioned leg movement, while in unconditioned or deconditioned animals the same region was inactive. Alas, this claim has not been substantiated. There is, however, valid evidence of a kind of memory localization. When the exposed brain of a person under local anesthesia for a brain operation is stimulated electrically, various conscious effects are produced. Stimulating the occipital lobe, which receives the sensory fibers from the eyes, gives visual sensations. Similarly, stimulation of other specific regions produces sounds and skin sensations. These responses are not related to specific past experiences. However, other regions of the brain, particularly the temporal lobe, do respond to stimulation with the conscious recall of quite specific events from an individual's past.

The particularity, however, is at best only roughly localized, and localization largely vanishes when we look at the effects of brain damage. Large sections of nearly any part of the brain can be destroyed without loss of particular memories or, indeed, without disturbance of the memory function. Human brains have been extensively damaged by trauma, by tumors or abscesses, by loss of circulation, by operative removal, or by the shriveling away of extreme age. In these cases the ability to learn new things, to make sound judgments, to see new relations and to imagine new ideas may be profoundly disturbed, but the recollection of past experience is likely to remain reasonably intact. The frontal lobes of mental patients would not be amputated so freely as they are today if any serious defect in memory resulted.

So we are left with good reasons for believing that memories depend on static changes left behind by the passage of nerve impulses; that these changes occur somewhere along the paths the impulses traveled and are most likely at particular synapses; that the traces are to some extent gathered in certain regions, but that extensive brain damage is not accompanied by comparable losses of memories. One line of escape from the dilemma is to assume, as we can quite reasonably, that a given memory is not

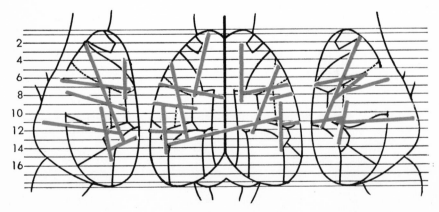

RAT'S BRAINS were incised by Karl S. Lashley of Harvard University and the Yerkes Laboratory of Primate Biology to determine the role of cortical connections in memory. This diagram shows the brain of the rat from the top (center) and both sides. Each red line represents an incision made in a single rat. None of the cuts impaired performance in maze.

represented by one specific local change but by a pattern of many changed loci—a pattern with sufficient redundancy so that if part of it is destroyed the rest will still suffice to represent the memory.

Such a view raises serious difficulties, but they do not appear to be insurmountable. For example, if thousands of neuron endings are involved in one memory, how can the brain store the huge number of memories we have assumed? Actually such indirect coding could greatly increase its storage capacity. Ten letters, each used to represent one item, give 10 items; but 10 letters used in groups as words give a vast number of items. Such patterned memory traces might also actually change with time, as particular neurons or synapses dropped out of the ensemble, and so permit the alteration of memories observed on successive recalls.

We come finally to the problem of recall. Recall is a matter of attention, a selecting or rejecting of particular memory traces. Here enter all the intriguing phenomena of specificity, suppression, symbolization and the like. The physiological explanation of these is certainly not yet at hand. Perhaps the best clue now available is the control of cortical activity and of conscious awareness by nerve centers in the older and deeper parts of the nervous system. Much recent experimentation has shown that these primitive jumbled masses of nerve cells in the upper part of the brain stem exercise a profound influence on the more recently evolved neurons of the cerebral cortex. Impulses from these deep cell groups continuously spray out to the cortex to regulate its activity. An excess of stimulation leads to cortical overactivity and convulsive seizures, followed by the unconsciousness of exhausted neurons. When the impulses are few and the cortex is comparatively inactive, the brain waves slow down and normal sleep results. One is tempted by the picture of an electron beam scanning the tube face of a television camera, picking up impressions left by the outside world from one tiny region after another. But whether such beams of nerve impulses, playing upon the cortex, do actually control attention, whether they are responsible for the evocation of specific memory traces, only the future can decide.

We are beginning to have some reasonable guesses as to the "gadgets" that would serve as a memory mechanism—guesses sufficiently concrete to permit testing by rigorous experimentation. I think it is realistic to hope for an understanding of memory precise enough to permit experimental modification of it in men.

# 17

# LEARNING
# IN THE OCTOPUS

BRIAN B. BOYCOTT                    March 1965

In recent years a number of British students of animal behavior, of whom I am one, have done much of their experimental work at the Stazione Zoologica in Naples. The reason why these investigations have been pursued in Naples rather than in Britain is that our chosen experimental animal—*Octopus vulgaris,* or the common European octopus—is found in considerable numbers along the shores of the Mediterranean. *Octopus vulgaris* is a cooperative experimental subject. If it is provided with a shelter of bricks at one end of a tank of running seawater, it takes up residence in the shelter. When a crab or some other food object is placed at the other end of the tank, the octopus swims or walks the length of the tank, catches the prey with its arms and carries it home to be poisoned and eaten. Since it responds so consistently to the presence of prey, the animal is readily trained. It is also tolerant of surgery and survives the removal of the greater part of its brain. This makes the

octopus an ideal animal with which to test directly the relation between the various parts of the brain and the various kinds of perception and learning.

There are many unanswered questions about such relations. We now know a great deal about conduction in nerve fibers, transmission from nerve fiber to nerve fiber at the synapses and the integrative action of nerve fibers in such aggregations of nerve cells as the spinal cord; we are almost wholly ignorant, however, of the levels of neural integration involved in such long-term activities as memory. We can still quote with sympathy the remark of the late Karl S. Lashley of Harvard University: "I sometimes feel, in reviewing the evidence on the localization of the memory trace, that the necessary conclusion is that learning is just not possible!"

It was J. Z. Young, then at the University of Oxford, who first began to exploit the possibility of using for memory studies various marine mollusks

of the class Cephalopoda. Shortly before World War II he undertook to work with the cuttlefish *Sepia officinalis.* In a simple experiment he and F. K. Sanders removed from a cuttlefish that part of the brain known as the vertical lobe. They found that a cuttlefish so deprived would respond normally—that is, attack—when it was shown a prawn. If the prawn was pulled out of sight around a corner after the attack began, however, the cuttlefish could not pursue it. The animal might advance to where the prawn had first been presented, but it was apparently unable to make whatever associations were necessary to follow the prawn around the corner. One might say it could not remember to hunt when the prey was no longer in sight. Young and Sanders found that surgical lesions in certain other parts of the cuttlefish's brain did not affect this hunting behavior.

In 1947 I had the privilege of joining Young in his studies. Financed by the Nuffield Foundation, we began

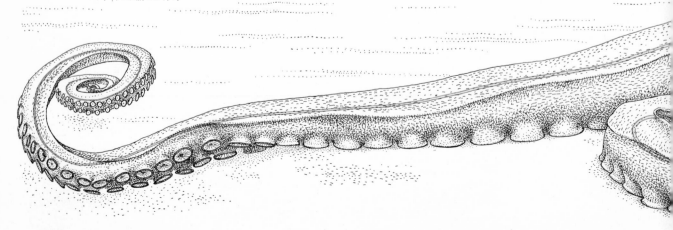

**COMMON EUROPEAN OCTOPUS** (*Octopus vulgaris*) is the experimental animal the author and his fellow-workers in Naples use for their investigations of perception and learning. The animal's brain (*in color between the eyes*) is about two cubic

work at the Stazione Zoologica, where both seawater aquariums and *Octopus vulgaris* were in abundant supply. The octopus was chosen in preference to the other common laboratory cephalopods—cuttlefishes and squids—because they do not survive so well in tanks and are less tolerant of surgery. At Naples today, in addition to Young's associates from University College London, there are investigators from the University of Oxford led by Stuart Sutherland and from the University of Cambridge led by Martin J. Wells, all going their various ways toward using the brains of octopuses for the analysis of perception and memory. At present most of the work is financed by the Office of Aerospace Research of the U.S. Air Force.

In our early experiments we attempted to train octopuses to do a variety of things, such as taking crabs out of one kind of pot but not out of another, to run a maze and so on. Our most successful experiment was to put a crab in the tank together with some kind of geometric figure—say a Plexiglas square five centimeters on a side—and give the octopus an electric shock when it made the normal attacking response. With this simple method we found that octopuses could learn not to attack a crab shown with a square but to go on attacking a crab shown without one [*see bottom illustrations on page 136 and 137*]. Or we could train the animals to stop taking crabs but to go on eating sardines or vice versa. The purpose of these experiments was to elucidate the anatomy and connections of the animal's brain and relate them to its learning behavior.

Like the brains of most other invertebrates, the brain of the octopus surrounds its esophagus [*see illustrations on next page*]. The lobes of the brain under the esophagus contain nerve fibers that stimulate peripheral nerve centers, for example the ganglia in the arms and the mantle. These peripheral ganglia contain the nerve cells whose fibers in turn stimulate the muscles and other effectors of the body; through

them local reflexes can occur. When all of the brain except the lobes under the esophagus is removed, the octopus remains alive but lies at the bottom of the tank; it breathes regularly but maintains no definite posture. If it is sufficiently stimulated, it responds with stereotyped behavior.

A greater variety of behavior can be obtained if some of the brain lobes above the esophagus are left intact. For instance, the upper brain's median basal lobe and anterior basal lobe send their fibers down to the lower lobes and through them evoke the patterns of nerve activity involved in walking and swimming. Above these two lobes are the vertical lobe, the superior frontal lobe and the inferior frontal lobe; their surgical removal does not result in any defects of behavior that are immediately obvious.

It is with these three lobes and the two optic lobes—which lie on each side of the central mass of the brain—that this article is mostly concerned. Using the electric-shock method of training

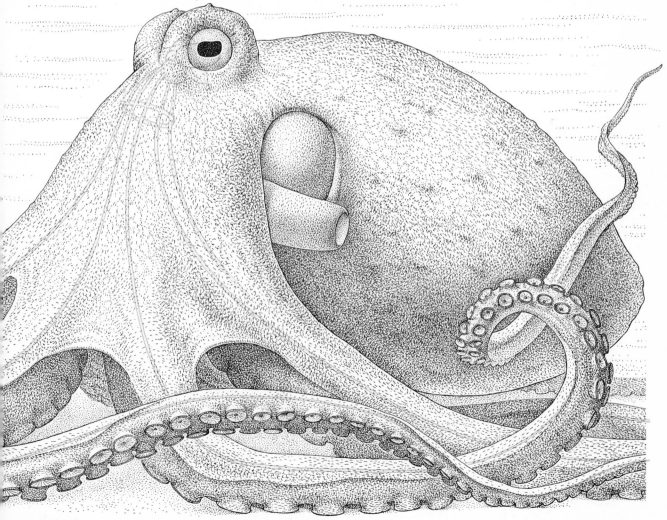

centimeters in size; the basket-like structure below it is composed of the eight major nerves of the arms, some of which are also outlined in color. The octopus adapts readily to life in a tank of seawater and can be trained easily through reward and punishment.

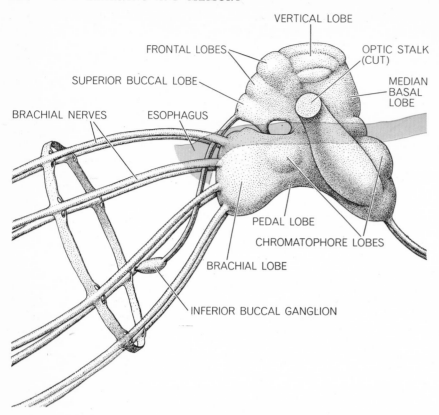

VERTICAL LOBE

FRONTAL LOBES

OPTIC STALK (CUT)

SUPERIOR BUCCAL LOBE

MEDIAN BASAL LOBE

BRACHIAL NERVES

ESOPHAGUS

PEDAL LOBE

CHROMATOPHORE LOBES

BRACHIAL LOBE

INFERIOR BUCCAL GANGLION

**OCTOPUS BRAIN** is shown in a side view with the left optic lobe removed (*see top view of brain below*). The labels identify external anatomical features of the brain and its nerve connections. As is the case with many other invertebrates, the brain of the octopus completely surrounds the animal's esophagus. Excision of the entire upper part of the brain is not fatal, but the octopus's behavior then exhibits neither learning nor memory.

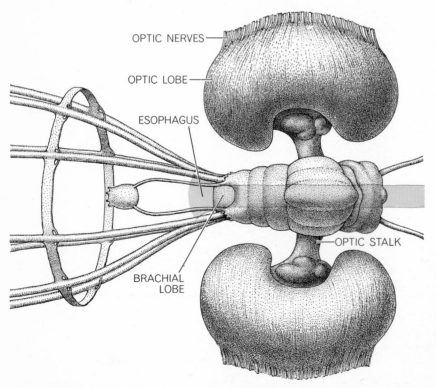

OPTIC NERVES

OPTIC LOBE

ESOPHAGUS

OPTIC STALK

BRACHIAL LOBE

**TOP VIEW OF BRAIN** relates the two large optic lobes and their stalks to the central brain structure situated above and below the octopus's esophagus (*color*). Combined, the mass of the two optic lobes roughly equals that of the brain's central structure; the fringe of nerves at each lobe's outer edge connects to the retinal structures of the octopus's eyes.

we soon found that, as far as visual learning goes, removing either the vertical lobe, the superior frontal lobe or both, or cutting the nerve tracts between these two lobes, left the octopus unable to learn the required discriminations (or, if they had already been learned, unable to retain them). Since operations on other parts of the brain—performed on control animals—had no effect either on learning or on previously learned behavior, we seemed to have demonstrated that the vertical lobe and superior frontal lobe of the octopus brain are memory centers. In a sense they are, but this is an unduly simple view; in a recent summary of findings Young has listed no fewer than six different effects caused by the removal of or damage to the vertical-lobe system alone.

Karl Lashley, who studied the cerebral cortex of mammals, concluded that, in the organization of a memory, the involvement of specific groups of nerve cells is not as important as the total number of nerve cells available for organization. A similar situation appears to hold true in the functioning of the vertical lobe of the octopus brain; there is a definite relation between the amount of vertical lobe left intact and the accuracy with which a learned response is performed [*see top illustration on page 138*]. This seems to suggest that, at least in the octopus's vertical lobe and the mammalian cerebral cortex, memory is both everywhere and nowhere in particular.

Some of the difficulties such a conclusion presents may be due to a failure to distinguish experimentally between the two constituents of a memory. Whatever its nature, a memory must consist not only of a representation, in neural terms, of the learned situation but also of a mechanism that enables that representation to persist. A distinction must be made between the topology of what persists (the coding and spatial relations involved in the memory of a particular animal) and the mechanisms of persistence (the neural change that is presumably the same in the memory of any animal). Indeed, it may be that some of the theoretical confusion in the study of memory arises from the fact that experiments showing a quantitative relation between memory and nerve tissue tell us something about how the neural representation of memory is organized but nothing about how the representation is kept going.

In our experiments demonstrating that an octopus deprived of its vertical lobe could not be trained to discriminate between a crab alone (that is, reward) and a crab accompanied by a geometric figure and a shock (that is, punishment) our groups of trials were separated by intervals of approximately two hours. When we spaced the trials so that they were only five minutes apart, however, we found that such animals were capable of learning [*see bottom illustration on page 138*]. Using the number of trials required as a criterion of learning, we found that these animals attained a level of performance as good as that of normal animals trained with longer time intervals between trials.

One significant difference remained: a normal octopus has a learning-retention period of two weeks or longer, but animals without a vertical lobe had retention periods of only 30 minutes to two hours. These observations suggest that the establishment of a memory involves two mechanisms. There is first a short-term, or transitory, memory that, by its continuing activity between intervals of training, leads to a long-term change in the brain. If there were no reinforcement, the short-term memory would wane; with reinforcement it keeps going and so induces the long-term—and by implication slower—changes that enable a brain to retain memories for long periods.

In 1957 Eliot Stellar of the University of Pennsylvania School of Medicine pointed out the parallels between our results with invertebrates and the unexpected discovery of a similar effect in man by Wilder Penfield, Brenda Milner and W. B. Scoville of the Montreal Neurological Institute. Epileptic patients who have been treated by surgical removal of the temporal lobes of the brain score as well in I.Q. tests after the operation as they do in tests before the onset of epilepsy. They remember their past, their profession and their relatives. They cannot, however, retain new information for more than short periods. Articles can be read and understood, but they are not remembered once they are finished and another topic is taken up. A relative may die but his death goes unremembered after an hour or so. This surgery involves the hippocampal system of the human brain; its effects seem to suggest that, although man's cerebral cortex incorporates a long-term memory system, the hippocampal system is essential to the establishment of new long-term memories.

Today a considerable body of behavioral and psychological evidence favors the separation of memory into short-term and long-term systems. At the neurological level this distinction has brought about a reaffirmation of the role in memory of what are called self-reexciting chains. A few years ago the concept of such chains had gone out of fashion because it had been found that neither convulsive shocks nor cooling the brain to a temperature so low that all activity ceased would abolish learned responses. It is now known that if such treatments are given during the early stages of learning—that is, before a memory is fully established—they have an effect; supposedly this is because they have interfered with the more active part of the process. As the surgical operations for epilepsy indicate, a long-term memory system is intact after removal of the temporal lobes. A short-

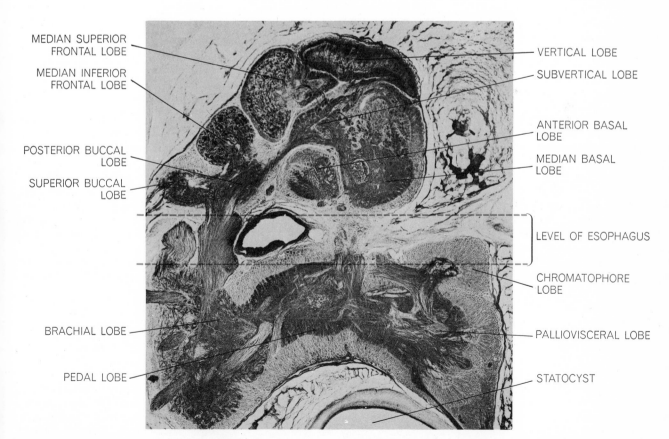

MEDIAN SUPERIOR FRONTAL LOBE — MEDIAN INFERIOR FRONTAL LOBE — POSTERIOR BUCCAL LOBE — SUPERIOR BUCCAL LOBE — BRACHIAL LOBE — PEDAL LOBE — VERTICAL LOBE — SUBVERTICAL LOBE — ANTERIOR BASAL LOBE — MEDIAN BASAL LOBE — LEVEL OF ESOPHAGUS — CHROMATOPHORE LOBE — PALLIOVISCERAL LOBE — STATOCYST

SAGITTAL SECTION stained with silver reveals some of the structures in the octopus brain. Broken lines (*color*) show the route of the esophagus, the boundary between the upper and lower parts of the brain. Labels identify eight lobes in the upper brain and four in the lower; experiments before and after surgical removal show that the vertical lobe (*top right*) plays a role in visual learning and that the inferior frontal lobe (*top left*) is one of two involved in tactile learning. The statocyst (*bottom right*) is not a part of the brain; it is one of the twin organs responsible for the octopus's sense of balance. Magnification is 15 diameters.

UNSCHOOLED OCTOPUS leaves the shelter at one end of its tank (*first photograph*) and walks toward the bait at the opposite end. The advancing animal uses only one of its eyes to guide it. When the bait, a crab, is in range, the octopus throws its leading

term memory system must also remain, however, because the patients can remember new information for short periods, particularly when they use mnemonic devices. On the basis of this interpretation it would appear that the hippocampal system may have the role of linking the two memory mechanisms—whatever that may mean.

For octopuses in our training situation it seems at first that when the vertical lobe of the brain is removed, the long-term memory system of the animal is completely abolished, leaving only the short-term system. We obtain a different result, however, if instead of showing such an animal a crab with or without a geometric figure we present it with figures only, rewarding it with a crab for an attack on one figure and punishing it with a shock for an attack on another. Under such conditions an octopus without its vertical lobe can learn the required discriminations and retain them. At least two conclusions can be drawn from this kind of result. The first is that the vertical lobe is essential to the memory system if the learned response involves a change in what might be termed innate behavior toward an object as familiar to an octopus as a crab. The second is that a long-term memory system for some responses

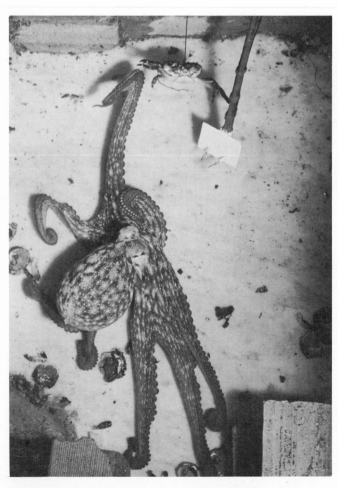

TRAINED OCTOPUS is cautious in its approach when a crab and a geometric figure are presented together (*first photograph*). If the animal seizes the crab, it receives an electric shock (*note darkened region at the base of the arm in second photograph*). As

arms forward to seize it (*second photograph*). Next it tucks the crab up toward its mouth (*third photograph*). The octopus then returns to its shelter (*fourth photograph*), where it kills the crab with a poisonous secretion from its salivary glands and eats it.

can be maintained in the absence of the vertical lobe.

Since we do not know (and probably never will know because it is so difficult to rear *Octopus vulgaris* from its larval stage) whether the octopus's response to a crab is learned or innate, our studies over the past eight years have involved experiments in which reward or punishment is given only after the animal has responded to an artificial situation, that is, the presentation of a figure of a given size, shape or color. It has been shown that animals without a vertical lobe can learn to attack unfamiliar figures for a reward, although they do so more slowly than normal animals. Once they have learned to attack such figures these octopuses retain their response for as long a time as normal animals do. If octopuses without a vertical lobe are required to reverse a learned visual response, however, they find it particularly difficult. When a shock is received for attacking a figure that formerly brought a reward, the animals can still learn to discriminate, but they make between four and five times as many mistakes as normal animals; moreover, their period of retention is shorter.

In addition to its large visual system

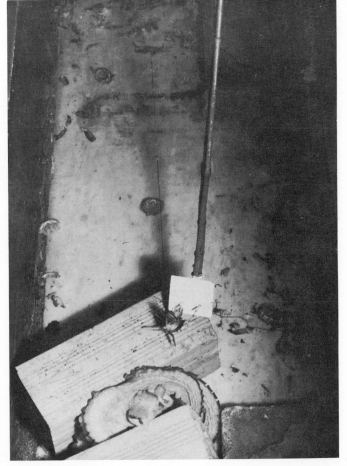

training continues, the octopus will often not even leave its shelter when crab and figure are presented (*third photograph*). If crab and figure are brought near a fully trained animal, it pales and pumps a jet of water at them (*fourth photograph*).

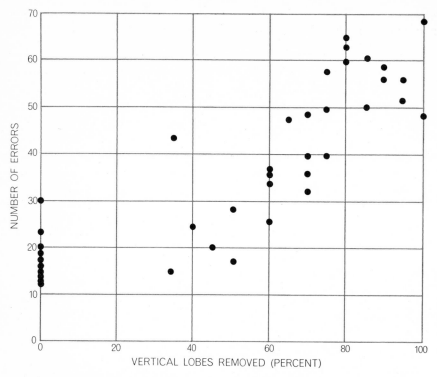

CONTRAST IN PERFORMANCE of normal (*far left*) and surgically altered octopuses shows that the number of errors increased more than threefold as larger and larger portions of the brain's vertical lobe were excised. This finding supports the conclusion that the organization of memory depends primarily on the number of brain cells available.

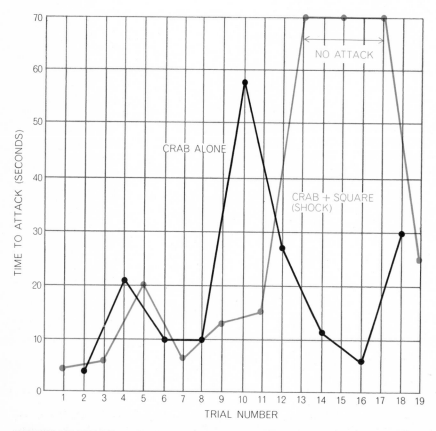

ABILITY TO LEARN can be demonstrated by an octopus deprived of the vertical lobes of its brain, provided that the trials are only a few minutes apart. In the example illustrated, little learning was apparent during 12 alternating exposures to negative and positive stimuli. Thereafter three successive negative stimuli were avoided by the octopus.

the octopus has a complex chemo-tactile sensory system. Most of the investigation of this system has been done by Martin Wells and his wife Joyce. By applying methods similar to those used for training the animals to make visual discriminations, they have been able to show that tactile learning in the octopus is about as rapid as visual learning. Octopuses have been trained to discriminate between a live bivalve and a counterfeit one consisting of shells of the same species that have been cleaned and filled with wax. They can discriminate between a bivalve with a ribbed shell and another species of comparable size but with a smooth shell. Just recently Wells has found that octopuses can detect hydrochloric acid, sucrose or quinine dissolved in seawater at concentrations 100 times less than those the human tongue can detect in distilled water. Presented with artificial objects, they can distinguish between grooved cylinders and smooth ones, although they cannot distinguish between two grooved objects that differ only in the direction in which the grooves run [*see illustration on opposite page*]. After intensive training they can discriminate a cube from a sphere about 75 percent of the time.

Through each arm of an octopus, which is studded with two rows of suckers, runs a cord of nerve fibers and ganglia. In these ganglia occur local reflexes along the arm and between the rows of suckers. It is supposed that, when the octopus makes a tactile discrimination, the state of excitation in the ganglia above each sucker is determined by the proportion of sense organs excited, and the degree to which these sense organs are stimulated determines the frequency with which nerve impulses are discharged in the fibers running from the ganglia to the brain. Learning in the isolated arm ganglia is probably not possible. Wells has found that for tactile learning to occur the upper brain's median inferior frontal lobe and subfrontal lobe are necessary. Damage to these regions of the brain does not affect visual learning, and for that reason the two lobes have often been used as the sites for control lesions in the investigation of visual learning.

The role of the median inferior frontal lobe seems to be to interrelate the information received from each of the octopus's eight arms; if the lobe is removed and one arm is trained to reject an object, then the other arms continue to accept the object. Without the subfrontal lobe the animals cannot even learn to reject objects by touch. As in the case of the vertical lobe in visual learning, the retention of small portions of the subfrontal lobe allows adequate learned performance. Wells believes that as few as 13,000 of the five million subfrontal-lobe cells may be sufficient for some learning to occur. The subfrontal lobe is structurally very similar to the vertical lobe; it must be considered the vertical lobe's counterpart in the chemotactile system. Removal of the vertical lobe nonetheless has an effect on chemotactile discrimination, mainly in the direction of slowing the rate at which learning occurs.

This account has discussed the main lines of work on memory systems that have been carried out with octopuses as experimental animals, together with some comparisons with human memory. Recently Young has summarized all the work on the cephalopod brain of the past 17 years and has devised a scheme of how such brains may work in the formation, storage and translation of memory into effective action.

Young proposes that in the course of evolution chemotactile and visual centers developed out of a primitive taste-and-bite reflex mechanism. As these "distance receptor" systems evolved, providing information as to where food might be obtained other than that received from direct contact, there came to be a more indirect relation between a change in the environment and the responses that such a change produced in the animal. As this happened, signal systems of greater duration than are provided by simple reflex mechanisms also had to evolve; learning had to become possible so that the animal could assess the significance of each distant environmental change.

Suppose, for example, a crab appears at a distance in the visual field of an octopus; as a result of what can be called "cue signals" there arises in the octopus brain a system for producing "graduated commands to attack." This command system will be weak at first but will grow stronger with reinforcement. The actual strengthening process will vary according to the reward or punishment met at each attack, because the outcome of each attack gives rise to a "result" signal. Such signals condition the distance-receptor systems that initially cued the attack—in the present example, the visual-receptor system. These result signals

become distributed throughout the nervous tissue that carries a record of a particular event.

There is, of course, a delay between the moment the cue signals are received in the brain and the moment the result signals arrive. If the result signals are to produce the appropriate conditioning of memory elements, the address of these elements, so to speak, has to be held to allow correct delivery of the information of, say, taste or pain. In the brain of the octopus each optic lobe contains "classifying" cells, among them vertically and horizontally oriented sets of nerve fibers that are presumably related to the vertical and horizontal arrangement of elements in the retina of the octopus's eye. These classifying cells form synapses with "memory" cells in the optic lobes that in their turn activate the cells that signal either attack or retreat. According to Young's hypothesis, each of the memory cells at first has a pair of alternative pathways; the actual neural change during learning consists in closing one of the two pathways. This closing may be accomplished by small cells that are

abundant in these learning centers and that can perhaps be switched on so as to produce a substance that inhibits transmission.

Suppose an attack has been evoked by means of this system; the memory cells activate not only an attack circuit but also a circuit reaching the vertical lobe of the upper brain. The signals indicating the results of the attack, such as taste or pain, arrive back and further reinforce the memory cells in the optic lobes, which have been under the influence of the appropriate pathways set up in the vertical lobe during the time interval between the cue signal and the result signal [see illustration on next page].

The hypothesis that the actual change represented by memory is produced by the small cells agrees with the fact that these cells are also present in the part of the brain that was shown by the Wellses to be the minimum necessary for tactile memory. Young suggests that the small cells were originally part of the primitive taste-and-bite reflex system, serving the function of

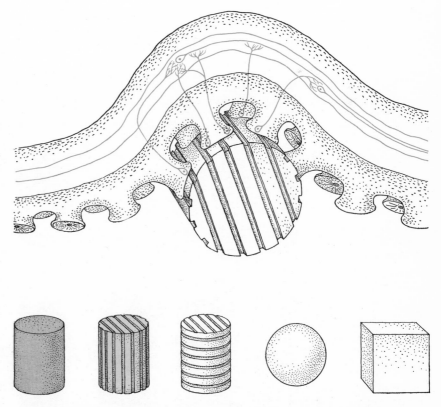

**LEARNING BY TOUCH** in the octopus was investigated by presenting objects with a variety of shapes and textures. In the case of a grooved cylinder (*top*) only the sense organs in contact with the surface are excited; those resting over the grooves remain inactive. Thus the octopus can learn to discriminate between a smooth cylinder (*gray*) and a grooved one (*color*), and even between a cube and a sphere; it cannot, however, discriminate between two cylinders that differ only in the orientation of the grooves.

temporary inhibition. The evolution of the memory consisted in making the inhibition last longer. The sets of auxiliary lobes associated with the memory system arose to allow for various combinations of inputs to be set up, to be combined with the signals that report the results of actions and finally to be "delivered to the correct address" in the memory.

There is much that is speculative about this description, but the fact remains that both the visual and the tactile memory systems of the octopus embrace sets of brain lobes arranged in similar circuits. This organization provides opportunities for study of the memory process that are made more challenging by Young's conviction that comparable circuits exist in the brains of mammals, including man.

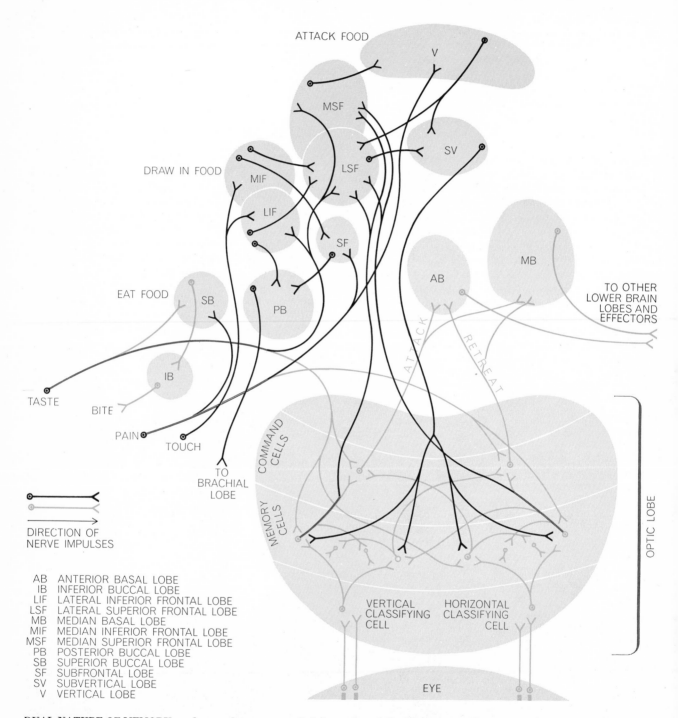

ATTACK FOOD

V

MSF

SV

DRAW IN FOOD

MIF

LSF

LIF

SF

MB

TO OTHER LOWER BRAIN LOBES AND EFFECTORS

EAT FOOD

SB

PB

AB

ATTACK

RETREAT

IB

TASTE

BITE

PAIN

TOUCH

TO BRACHIAL LOBE

COMMAND CELLS

MEMORY CELLS

OPTIC LOBE

DIRECTION OF NERVE IMPULSES

VERTICAL CLASSIFYING CELL

HORIZONTAL CLASSIFYING CELL

AB   ANTERIOR BASAL LOBE
IB   INFERIOR BUCCAL LOBE
LIF  LATERAL INFERIOR FRONTAL LOBE
LSF  LATERAL SUPERIOR FRONTAL LOBE
MB   MEDIAN BASAL LOBE
MIF  MEDIAN INFERIOR FRONTAL LOBE
MSF  MEDIAN SUPERIOR FRONTAL LOBE
PB   POSTERIOR BUCCAL LOBE
SB   SUPERIOR BUCCAL LOBE
SF   SUBFRONTAL LOBE
SV   SUBVERTICAL LOBE
V    VERTICAL LOBE

EYE

**DUAL NATURE OF MEMORY** can be traced out on an exploded view of the octopus brain. Circuits leading from the optic lobe (*color*) are the first to be activated on receipt of a visual cue by the lobe's classifying cells. The cue is then recorded in the memory cells and relayed to the command cells; the latter induce the octopus to attack or retreat. If an attack is rewarded, the returning "result" signal will reinforce a memory that registers the initiating cue favorably. If, instead, the attack brings pain, the reinforced memory will register the cue unfavorably and any similar cues encountered in the future will be channeled to the circuits governing retreat rather than attack. Additional circuits (*black*) connect the memory and command regions of the optic lobe to various lobes of the upper brain; thus each event and its outcome are also recorded and reinforced in these nervous tissues. In due course what appear to be the long-term components of the memory system become localized in individual upper brain lobes.

# 18

# SHORT-TERM MEMORY

LLOYD R. PETERSON                    July 1966

It is easy to forget information that has recently been acquired, as anyone knows who has failed to remember a name heard only a few minutes earlier at a social gathering. Such forgetfulness can be annoying, but it appears to have its uses. It might be distracting, for example, if one remembered every telephone number one had ever looked up. Considering all the information the memory does retain, it is probably just as well that something like an unfamiliar telephone number is remembered long enough for a single call and then forgotten. Besides, new information can usually be stored in the memory without undue effort if one has reason to think the material may be needed again.

The common experience of forgetfulness on the one hand and retentiveness on the other suggests that memory functions in two distinct ways—on a short-term basis and on a long-term one. For purposes of discussion it is often convenient to speak of a short-term memory and a long-term memory, although actually the two seem to be so closely related that they are described by some investigators as two aspects of the same phenomenon. Short-term storage serves well for many occasions in daily life. Long-term storage is, in fact, learning: the process by which information that may be needed again is stored for recall on demand.

A number of psychologists and physiologists who have investigated memory have suggested that two mechanisms are involved in it. One can be called an activity mechanism: a single experience gives rise to activity among neurons, or nerve cells. The activity soon dies out if the experience is not repeated. Here, then, is the basis for short-term storage. The second mechanism is structural change: with repetitions of an experience some kind of relatively permanent alteration occurs among neurons. This is the basis of long-term storage. The two mechanisms may be related in that the activity mechanism presumably assists in the production of the structural change.

Psychologists have traditionally studied short-term storage by presenting a sequence of digits to a subject and having him attempt immediately to recall them in the same order. The longest sequence of digits he can repeat correctly measures his span of immediate memory. Long-term storage has typically been studied by having a subject go over a list of words or other material repeatedly until he can recall the items without error. Hours or days after he has learned the list he is tested for recollection of it. The percentage of recall measures his long-term memory. Tests of these two kinds have resulted in considerable understanding of memory and have led to the design of further experiments intended to explore the re-

EXPERIMENTAL APPARATUS in the author's laboratory at Indiana University enabled the experimenter, at left in the photograph above, to show the subject various words paired with digits or with other words and to test his ability to recall the associations over varying periods of time.

lation between short-term and long-term storage. Although these experiments have provided some answers, they have also raised some intriguing questions that remain to be answered.

One type of experiment used to explore the relation between short-term and long-term retention involves a variation in the routine of the immediate recall of digits. The experimental subject is presented with a sequence of digits that is longer than he can be expected to recall after a single presentation. In a long series of these "superspan" tests one sequence of digits is repeated from time to time. Between repetitions several other sequences are presented and tested. For example, the first sequence might be 978263147; after hearing it the subject attempts to repeat it and then is given one or more different sequences, each of which he attempts to repeat immediately after presentation. Now and then the first sequence is repeated.

D. O. Hebb of McGill University designed this experiment, which was later elaborated by Arthur W. Melton of the University of Michigan. Their objective was to see if a single presentation leaves any lasting trace. They reasoned that if

a single presentation caused nothing but transient neural activity, succeeding sequences would obliterate the activity. If, however, the occasional repetition of a given sequence amid several others produced improvement in the recall of that sequence, then even a single presentation must have caused some structural change.

Hebb, Melton and others who have conducted this experiment have found that the sequence was indeed recalled with increasing accuracy the more it was repeated. Improvement occurred even when as many as five tests of new sequences were given between two successive repetitions. Beyond five there was little evidence of improvement, and up to five the rate of improvement tended to decline as the number of intervening sequences increased. Nevertheless, the finding of any improvement at all when other sequences intervened indicated that something more than transient neural activity results from a single presentation and test.

This experiment does not provide a way to measure changes in memory with time. Varying intervals of time separate the presentation of an individual digit from the recall of that digit. Undoubtedly the digit could have been recalled

immediately after it was presented. In a long sequence, however, the digit might be forgotten before testing. How long was it retained?

To examine this question we devised in our laboratory at Indiana University an experiment in which we presented a message of subspan length—a message that could be recalled immediately with complete accuracy—and introduced delays between presentation and recall. We chose the events of the delay interval carefully to fit two specifications. On the one hand we wanted to keep the subject talking so that he would have little or no opportunity to rehearse the message. On the other hand we wanted his activity during the delay to be as different as possible from the message in order to minimize confusion between the two. In this way we could plot a curve of forgetting for a single short message over a period of time.

A typical experiment proceeded as follows. The experimenter spoke a combination of three letters that did not constitute a word. Without any break he spoke a three-digit number, and the subject then counted backward rapidly from that number. On a signal from the experimenter the subject stopped counting and tried to recall the three-letter

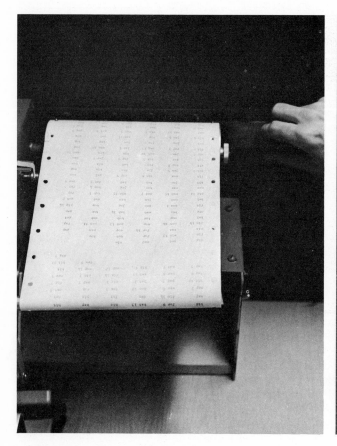

The apparatus used as seen from the experimenter's side.

A typical exposure seen by the subject.

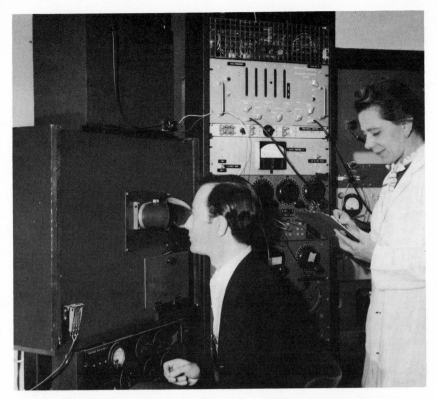

TACHISTOSCOPE was used by George Sperling of the Bell Telephone Laboratories to investigate short-term forgetting. For .05 second it showed arrays of letters such as those in the illustration below. A musical tone then told the subject which four-letter row to report.

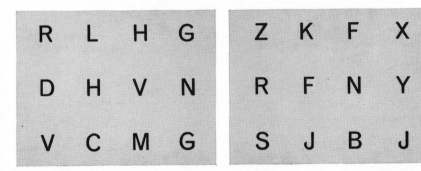

ARRAYS OF LETTERS shown in the tachistoscope included these. A tone of high pitch told the subject to report the top row, of medium pitch, the middle row, and of low pitch, the bottom row. The tone was helpful only if given within a second. The results suggested that a factor in short-term forgetting is decay in the retention of newly acquired information.

message. We found that recall dropped quite rapidly over an 18-second interval. When subjects were told to say the message aloud once or twice before counting, their retention curves were higher [see the illustration shown at left on the next page].

Bennet B. Murdock, Jr., of the University of Toronto and Melton have conducted similar experiments in which they found that the number of chunks in a message is a significant variable. A one-letter message is recalled very well over fairly long intervals of counting. The recall of a two-letter message is poorer and of a three-letter message poorer still. With each added letter the

retention curve (based on fully correct recall) is lower. As might be expected, this finding holds true only for unrelated letters. If the letters form a familiar word, retention of the word is as good as that of a single letter. The reason is that words have become units through use.

Our experiments established that rapid forgetting occurs after a single presentation of three unrelated letters. What causes the forgetting? One factor is undoubtedly competition from previous messages. A case can also be made for a second factor that can be termed spontaneous decay.

A contrast that appeared between the results of delayed-recall tests using visual presentation and the results of similar tests using auditory presentation will illustrate the point. In each case, as it was found in experiments conducted by Geoffrey Keppel of the University of California at Berkeley and Benton J. Underwood of Northwestern University, delayed recall on the first test of a session was much better than that on succeeding tests. With visual presentation, however, the entire curve was higher than that resulting from auditory presentation. In other words, a visual presentation produced almost no forgetting over an 18-second interval on the first test and more forgetting on subsequent tests, whereas an auditory presentation produced significant forgetting even on the first test. The contrast suggests that in the visual presentation interference from previous tests was the only source of forgetting but that in the auditory presentation another factor was at work to produce the relatively poor showing on the first test. Presumably the auditory presentation makes less of an impression on the memory, so that spontaneous forgetting occurs more readily.

Further evidence for the conclusion that earlier tests interfere with later tests comes from the errors made in delayed recall. A frequent error is the intrusion of a single letter from one message into the same position in the recall of a succeeding message. On one test, for example, the message might be KQF; on the next test the message is MHZ but the subject recalls MQZ. Evidently a letter from the first message has won out in competition with a letter from the second, and this is indicative of interference. A problem still unsolved is why the intruding letter tends to reappear in its original position. Apparently the memory somehow codes the letter for position, and this characteristic is retained in spite of failure to remember other aspects of the context in which the letter originally appeared.

The effect of competition from previous tests can be minimized in certain ways, with results that throw light on the process of retrieving a message from storage. Consider a delayed-recall experiment by Delos D. Wickens of Ohio State University in which the naming of colors was used as the intervening activity to curb rehearsal. The first few tests had digits for messages and resulted in the typical decrease in ability to recall as the tests progressed. Wickens then switched to a test in which the message consisted of three letters. On the first test the recall was virtually as good as it had been on the first test of the digit message. Evidently the subjects rejected intrusions from previous messages—those with the digits—as being of the wrong class, and so these messages did not interfere with recall of the message containing letters. The subject during retrieval remembers not just digits and letters; he remembers also that digits were not presented in the current trial. This kind of information is evidently useful in the organization of memory.

In this connection it seems reasonable to expect that the longer it has been since a subject heard or saw messages of one class, the less they will compete with another message of the same class. Previous messages should not interfere if they have been forgotten. This supposition is borne out in delayed-recall tests; the longer the rest interval between the end of one test and the beginning of the next, the better the retention has been. Moreover, a long rest interval results in fewer intrusions, such as that in the example of the letter Q from one message that appeared in the effort to recall a later message.

This finding raises the question of why the previous message weakens over

a rest interval. The answer appears to involve the spontaneous decay that I believe to be a factor in short-term memory. To the extent that short-term memory is based on activity of the neurons initiated by events in the outside world, it seems plausible that after the events have changed or disappeared the activity should diminish and eventually cease.

George Sperling of the Bell Telephone Laboratories has investigated a type of decay that is associated with visual presentation. He tested recall of messages presented by a tachistoscope, a device that enabled him to limit the duration of a visual message to .05 second. Subjects were required to give only a partial report of a superspan message. The experiment showed that there is more information available to a subject for a brief moment after presentation than he can report later.

Sperling's apparatus presented letters in an array four columns wide and three rows deep. A tone of high, medium or low pitch signaled to the subject which four-letter row he was to report. When this signal was given immediately after the presentation, the row it identified was reported with a high degree of accuracy. When the signal was delayed by a quarter of a second, the report was

less accurate. A delay of as much as a second made the signal valueless in aiding accuracy; the subject could not report the signaled row with any more accuracy than he showed in reporting the three rows.

This rapid decrease in the availability of the message strongly suggests a decay factor in short-term storage. The decrease occurred even though no interfering events could be identified; the subject just sat, waiting for a chance to report. Probably this type of decay is characteristic of storage near the sensory organ. Perhaps the decay should be considered a perceptual phenomenon rather than an element in what is traditionally called memory; it occurs before the subject has had time to process the message. Nonetheless, it is interesting to have clear evidence of spontaneous decay in neural systems. It may well be that decay is also characteristic of neural systems more closely related to memory.

Other experiments that indicate a decay factor in short-term memory have varied the rate of presentation and recall. In such experiments R. Conrad of the British Medical Research Council has found that in some circumstances fast rates will produce better recall than slow rates. It is difficult to interpret these

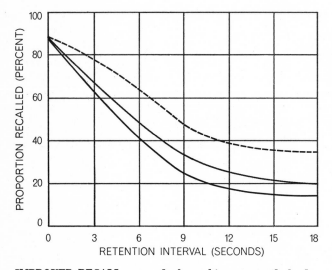

**IMPROVED RECALL** occurred when subjects repeated aloud a message of three unrelated letters before an interval of counting backward followed by a test for recall of the message. The curves, beginning at the bottom, represent zero, one and three repetitions.

**SPACING** between two presentations of the same pair of words affected short-term retention. Presentations were either successive (*dark curve*) or separated by eight seconds (*light curve*). Other pairs filled the interval between second presentation and test.

| EDGE | 8 | HOSE | | COOK | | APE | 6 | BOAT | 1 | MAD | 3 |
| COOK | 5 | EDGE | 8 | NOTE | 2 | LAW | 9 | APE | | BOAT | |
| HOSE | 4 | COOK | 5 | NOTE | | MAD | 3 | LAW | 9 | JOKE | 10 |
| SAW | 7 | JOKE | 10 | BOAT | 1 | SAW | 7 | LAW | | SAW | 7 |

**WORD-DIGIT PAIRS** were used in lists such as this to test short-term memory. The subject saw the pairs one at a time, beginning

with EDGE 8 and reading down. In a test a word was shown alone and the subject attempted to recall the number associated with it.

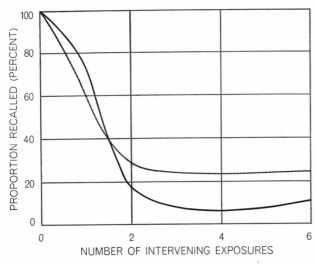

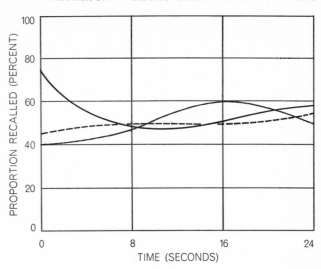

TIME FACTOR in short-term retention appeared when rate of presentation was varied. Paired words were shown every two seconds (*dark curve*) or four seconds (*light curve*), with other pairs filling the interval before test. Fast rate produced better recall with one intervening event; slow rate, with from two to six events.

RISING CURVES appeared when subjects tried to recall pairs of words after presentation of a list followed by varying intervals of digit-reading. The entire curve (*dark curve*) is shown for the fifth and last pair; for the first (*broken curve*) and third (*light*) pairs the drop is assumed to have occurred before the digit-reading began.

findings except in terms of decay. In the learning of lists a slow rate of presentation results in better learning than a fast rate, given an equal number of presentations. Furthermore, a longer time for recall should increase the chance of a correct response. Both considerations favor slow rates over fast ones. The fact that the faster rate produces better short-term recall indicates that at the slow rate the factor of decay with time has overridden the advantages of slow presentation and recall.

To sum up, short-term forgetting seems to be caused by two factors: interference from similar messages and decay. In most situations the effect of competing messages is so strong that it obscures any evidence of decay. An analogy can be drawn with the disappearance of an ice-cream cone in the hands of a small boy on a warm day. Undoubtedly the temperature contributes to the disappearance by causing some melting, but this effect is insignificant compared with that of the boy's appetite and enthusiasm. In short-term memory interference from other messages is the prime source of forgetting. It requires a special situation for the decay factor to be clearly observed.

The experiments described thus far provide good evidence that interference plays a strong role in short-term forgetting and that repetition improves short-term retention. Because the same factors produce similar effects in the learning of lists—that is, in long-term retention—Melton has suggested that short-term and long-term retention

are regions on a continuum. In this view there is a single underlying mechanism for both kinds of retention, and hence the effect of a single presentation can be described as the simplest kind of learning.

Several other investigators believe the situation is somewhat more complex than the single-mechanism argument suggests. They do not deny that learning occurs with a single presentation, but they suspect that a short-term storage mechanism operates in addition to a learning mechanism. The presence of a decay factor in short-term forgetting is considered to be one type of evidence for the existence of a short-term storage mechanism. This conclusion follows from the consideration that learned messages—those that are in long-term storage—do not appear to decay with time.

Another indication that memory is more complex than the single-factor interpretation suggests can be found in a variation of the usual type of cued-recall experiment. Normally in such an experiment the subject is repeatedly shown a list of pairs of words. Suppose one of the pairs is HANDLE–TREE. On a given test of learning HANDLE appears first—as a cue—and the subject is given a moment to see if he can recall TREE. He makes his response and then is shown HANDLE–TREE together again. The proportion of correct responses on successive trials provides an index of the subject's progress in learning.

Such an experiment is usually thought of as a measure of learning, but it can also be regarded as a measure of reten-

tion. The interval of retention is the time since the word being tested (TREE) was shown on the preceding trial; typically the interval will range from 15 seconds to several minutes. Experiments in short-term retention include tests at intervals within this range and also tests at much shorter intervals. Such experiments can be considered as testing both short-term memory and learning, or long-term memory. In this light the experiments in short-term retention of paired words might be expected to provide information not only on learning but also on the relation between learning and short-term memory. If variables such as rate of presentation and spacing of tests have an effect on the early portion of the retention curve that is different from that on the later portion, then one can infer differences between short-term memory and learning.

It was against this background that several investigators undertook to modify the standard type of cued-recall experiments by making them miniature paired-associate tests. Murdock tried varying the number of pairs of words. He presented a list once and tested for some member of the list by showing one member of a pair as a cue. In general, the more pairs in the list, the lower the asymptote, or leveling-off point, of the retention curve. Interestingly enough, however, the initial slopes of the curves were similar regardless of how many pairs Murdock showed. In other words, the variable—the number of pairs—affected the later part of the curve but not the earlier part. It seemed to affect learning rather than short-term memory.

In a similar experiment repetitions of pairs were found to raise the asymptote of the retention curve, but again the initial slope was not significantly affected. Then the duration of presentations was varied, and this variation too exerted its most pronounced effect on the final portion of the curve. The effect of all these experiments was to provide more evidence that the single-mechanism explanation of short-term and long-term memory does not go far enough.

We have found an even more striking discrepancy between the effect of a variable on the early part of a retention curve and its effect on the later part. In this case the variable was the spacing interval between two presentations of the same pair. Sometimes we gave the second presentation immediately after the first; sometimes we put several other pairs or tests between the two presentations. In both cases the retention interval from second presentation to test was filled with verbal material of the same class.

Forgetting occurs rapidly in this situation because of the large amount of interference from other pairs. For this reason it might be predicted that the effect of the first presentation would be strongest when it was immediately followed by the second presentation. In the case where other pairs separate the two presentations it would seem that forgetting between the first and the second presentation should reduce the cumulative effect of the two presentations. Such forgetting is invariably shown if a test is given instead of a second presentation after a spacing interval.

These commonsense predictions turn out to be true only for the early part of the curve that measures retention after the second presentation. Spaced presentations do produce poorer recall if only one or two events fill the retention interval, but with more events the curves cross [see upper illustration at right on page 144]. Thereafter the spaced presentations are recalled better than those that were not spaced.

The significance of these spacing studies is twofold. First, the fact that

the curves cross suggests that there is something different about recall when one or two events have intervened between second presentation and test and recall when more events filled that interval. One storage system would seem to dominate recall in the first case and another in the second. Although a learning mechanism is evidently assisting in both early and late retrieval, the early retrieval appears to have in addition the assistance of a short-term storage process.

The second point concerns the higher effectiveness of spaced presentations rather than of successive presentations at the longer retention intervals. The explanation of this phenomenon may be that the second presentation has a different effect in a successive situation than it does in a spaced situation. The subject may pay less attention to a pair he has just seen than to one that occurred earlier. Another possibility is that the long-term effect of the first presentation has time to consolidate during the spacing interval. This is one of the questions that goes unanswered. It remains a paradox that in order to remember something better you should allow some forgetting to occur.

A crossing of curves also appeared in some experiments we conducted involving changes in the rate of presentation and test. In these experiments pairs of words were presented at either a two-second rate or a four-second rate; various pairs in each block were tested after from zero to six intervening exposures of other pairs. A sample block of exposures appears in the illustration below. In that sample the third pair presented is FACE–ARMY. After one intervening pair (CAR–APPLE) the word FACE is shown to the subject again to see if he remembers its associate, ARMY.

In these experiments the fast rate was found to produce better recall with one intervening exposure, whereas the slow rate produced better recall when from two to six events intervened [see illustration at left on preceding page]. Evidently, then, time is a factor in the relation between short-term and long-term memory and must be regarded as a significant variable along with the

number of intervening events. Thus these experiments provide another bit of evidence that there is a decay factor in short-term memory.

An intriguing question that so far can be answered only speculatively involves retention curves that rise. In one of our experiments we presented a list of pairs once and tested for recall at periods ranging from zero to 24 seconds. If the test did not follow the presentation immediately, the subject filled the interval by reading digits aloud as rapidly as possible. On these cued-recall tests pairs from the first part of the list were recalled better after 24 seconds of digit-reading than they were immediately after presentation of the list. Pairs from the last part of the list showed first a decreasing retention curve and then a slight increase [see illustration at right on preceding page].

Undoubtedly each pair at the beginning of the list could have been recalled with complete accuracy if the subject had been tested on it right after it was presented. It is also clear that the availability of these pairs must have declined during presentation of the succeeding pairs. This picture of declining recall followed by increasing recall suggests several factors interacting in short-term and long-term retention.

The surprising fact is not that forgetting occurs soon after presentation but that the retention curve subsequently rises. The rapid forgetting could be ascribed to the short-term memory and the rise to the long-term memory. Even so, a question remains. Why should there be any rise?

Perhaps there is a characteristic of the retrieval process that enables it to work more efficiently after an interval of irrelevant activity. A related possibility is that recall itself is a disrupting process, tending to interfere with storage activities. If so, then the passage of time may allow some consolidation of information to take place so that the memory is less easily disrupted. We hope that further experimentation will clarify situations such as this one and lead to an improved understanding of human thought processes.

| | | | |
|---|---|---|---|
| HOUSE–ITEM | FACE | CLUB–BARN | SIGN–HAIR |
| BROOK–TOOTH | ARM–BOOK | ARM | CHECK–DOOR |
| FACE–ARMY | TABLE–EYE | EGG–BOTTLE | CLUB |
| CAR–APPLE | HORSE–MOON | EGG | WORM–TREE |

PAIRED WORDS in blocks such as this were used in the tests involving changes in the rate of presentation. Pairs were shown to the subject one at a time at either a two-second or a four-second rate. The first two pairs were dummies. Tests for recall, such as that involving the associate of FACE, were given either immediately or after the presentation of from one to six other associated pairs.

# Part V

## COMPARATIVE ASPECTS OF LEARNING

# V

## COMPARATIVE ASPECTS OF LEARNING

*Introduction*  Observations of "intelligent" behavior have long been of interest to both the layman and the scientist. It is clear that animals are not just "mechanical automata" (to use Gleitman's term) but it is equally clear that (1) animals are not unlimited in their capacity to learn and perform, and (2) different species have different capacities. What is the nature and what is the basis of species differences in "mental ability"? Answers to these questions are of great importance for evolutionary theory. Unfortunately there is no adequate taxonomy of mental processes; there is neither a simple nor adequate way of ordering species in terms of "intelligence." This is because it is difficult, if not impossible, to decide exactly what behavior is to be used as an index of "intelligence." Would it be possible to develop a single test appropriate for all species? Attempts to do so have failed. Simple learning problems typically do not reveal systematic species differences in intelligence.

Although the problem of studying species differences in "intelligence" is extremely difficult, it is, according to some investigators, not a hopeless task. M. E. Bitterman has attempted to study species differences in intelligence by training animals on problems that involve processes somewhat more complex than those required for simple learning. In "the Evolution of Intelligence" (page 150) Bitterman observes that two types of tasks—habit reversal and probability learning—reveal systematic species differences in learning capacity. He suggests that the evolution of intellectual behavior is not continuous: the more complex tasks appear to tap an intellectual capacity that is present in higher animals but is poorly developed in the turtle and absent in the fish. It may be that the species differences result from the evolution of brain structures—particularly the cerebral cortex.

The elephant is generally considered to be highly intelligent beast, but is it? In "The Intelligence of Elephants" (page 158) B. Rensch describes some experimental studies of learning in these animals. Although the performance of the elephant was not systematically compared with that of other species (or even of other elephants), it does appear that the elephant is capable of learning and retaining a large number of fairly complex responses. Rensch concludes that size is a decisive factor in the brain's learning capacity. Acceptance of this interesting conclusion will obviously require considerable additional research with other species.

One assumption frequently made in studies of intelligent behavior is that the ability investigated is innate. This assumption is challenged by

Harry and Margaret K. Harlow in "Learning to Think" (page 165). They report experiments which suggest that, in children and monkeys, the ability to solve complex problems is not inborn but is acquired by experience in solving problems. This conclusion would suggest that searches for species differences in intellectual ability are bound to be complicated. It may be that the capacity to acquire the ability to solve problems is a basic feature of species differences in intellectual functioning. The problem of discovering the nature and bases of species differences in intelligence remains as challenging as it is complex.

# 19

# THE EVOLUTION
# OF INTELLIGENCE

M. E. BITTERMAN                    January 1965

Suppose an animal is given a choice between two alternative courses of action, one of which is rewarded consistently and the other never. If the alternatives are readily discriminable, the animal will, after a number of trials, develop the habit of choosing the rewarded one. By plotting trials against errors, the experimental psychologist constructs a curve called a learning function that summarizes the course of the animal's mastery of the problem.

It has been known for some time that learning functions based on such simple problems do not differ significantly among diverse animals; the curves for a monkey and a fish, for example, have a similar shape. This fact, implying some intellectual continuity throughout the evolutionary hierarchy of animals, tended to corroborate a theory of animal intelligence that prevailed during the first half of the 20th century.

According to this theory, an animal is born with tendencies to react in certain ways to certain stimuli—tendencies based on inherited neural connections between sensory and motor systems. The animal's ability to learn is simply its ability to modify these connections (to break some and to form others) as needs and circumstances dictate. Differences in intelligence from species to species are differences only of degree. The higher animals can form more connections than the lower animals because of better sensory and motor development and because their nervous systems afford more elements for this purpose. Hence the evolution of intelligence merely entails refining old processes and replicating old neural equipment.

Since learning was thought to involve qualitatively similar processes throughout the evolutionary hierarchy it seemed that there was nothing to be gained

from studying many different species, and that there was much to be lost in terms of experimental efficiency. Attention became concentrated on a few mammals—primarily the rat—selected for reasons of laboratory custom or convenience and treated as being representative of animals in general. The number of animals under study narrowed, and so did the likelihood of discovering any differences that might in fact exist.

The investigations I have been conducting for several years with my associates at Bryn Mawr College were inspired by the conviction that the traditional theory called for more critical scrutiny than it had received. We began with the knowledge that the simplest problems would not serve to reveal distinct modes of intelligence and different neural mechanisms at work in various animals. Hoping that experiments based on more complex problems would point to such differences, we complicated matters for our test animals by introducing certain inconsistencies in reward. Thus we developed several kinds of experiment on which our diverse subjects (monkey, rat, pigeon, turtle and fish) gave diverse performances. The two I shall describe in this article are habit-reversal and probability-learning experiments.

In habit-reversal experiments animals are rewarded for choosing alternative A rather than B until a preference for A has been established, then B rather than A is rewarded. When a preference for B has been established, A is again rewarded, and so forth. Trained in this way, a rat or monkey shows a steady improvement in performance. It may make many errors in mastering early reversals, persisting in the choice of previously rewarded alternatives, but as

training continues it shifts its preference more and more readily. A fish, in contrast, shows no improvement at all; later reversals are accomplished no more readily than earlier ones.

Although the various sensory, motor and motivational characteristics of the five species we have been studying call for different experimental environments, we have been able to keep certain elements of the test apparatus analogous. In each case the animal is confronted with a pair of translucent Plexiglas panels on which various colors and patterns are projected from behind, and it makes a choice by pressing against one or the other of the panels in its own way: the fish strikes or bites, the pigeon pecks, the monkey pushes with its hand, the turtle or the rat presses with its head or forefoot or both. A correct choice is rewarded with food (a *Tubifex* worm for the fish, a bit of fish for the turtle, some grain for the pigeon, a pellet of sucrose for the rat, a peanut for the monkey), after which there is a brief interval of darkness and then the next choice is offered. If the animal makes an incorrect choice, there is a six-second interval of darkness (called a "time-out"), after which the correct panel alone is illuminated (a procedure called "guidance") and the animal is rewarded for responding to it. Guidance after error guarantees that the animal will not stop responding altogether in the course of a reversal before it has had a chance to learn that the previously unrewarded alternative now is rewarded. The time-out between error and guidance delays access to the reward and thus penalizes precipitous, undiscriminating choice. Without the time-out it would not matter much to the animal whether its choices were correct or not.

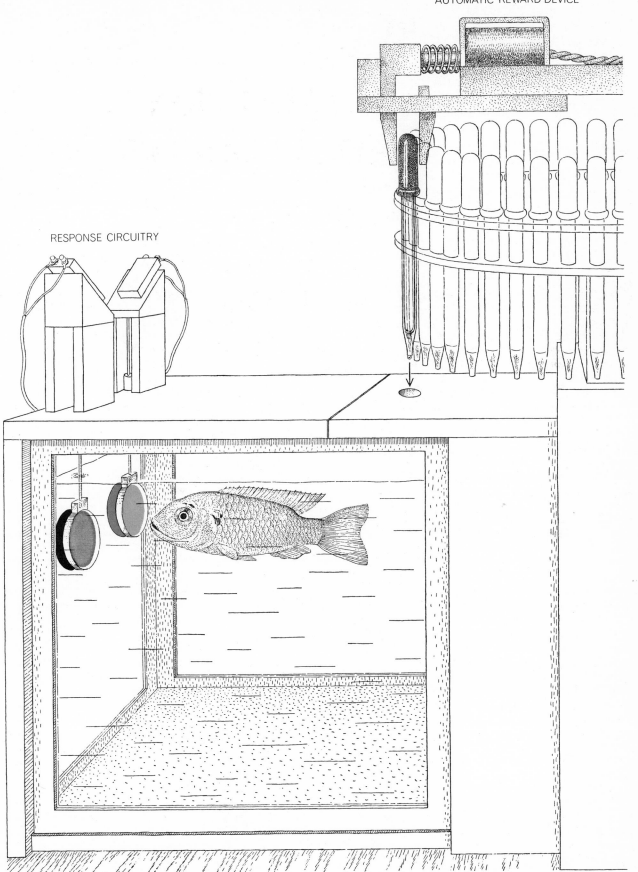

AUTOMATIC REWARD DEVICE

RESPONSE CIRCUITRY

**FISH IN A DISCRIMINATION TANK** is presented with a visual problem in which the lights projected on two stimulus disks are differently colored. By pressing its head against the proper disk the fish triggers an automatic reward device: the pincers above the eyedropper (*top right*) close, squirting a *Tubifex* worm into the tank. The experimental apparatus was designed by the author.

The entire experimental sequence is programmed by some simple relay circuitry and the responses are graphically recorded. With this introduction of automatic control and the removal of the experimenter there is a gain in objectivity: the animals can no longer be influenced by features of the experimenter's behavior. The task of data collection also becomes less arduous and can be entrusted to a co-worker of limited training, who can take data from several subjects concurrently.

In our experiments we employ both spatial and visual problems. A spatial problem is one in which the alternatives are identical to the eye (that is, the stimuli projected on the two Plexiglas panels are the same) and reward is correlated with the position of the panel. A visual problem is one in which the alternatives look different—blue light and green light, for example, or a triangle and a circle—and reward is correlated with appearance, regardless of position. The results of experiments based on spatial and visual problems can be plotted in comparable fashion, as the two graphs on page 154 indicate.

The experiment that provided the data plotted in the top graph was conducted with rats. Each animal was given 40 trials per day and was reversed whenever it made no more than six errors on any given day. The curve traces the average number of errors made in accomplishing each reversal by the group of rats tested. It reveals that the original problem (Reversal 0) was mastered with few errors, that the first reversal was mastered with difficulty and that adjustment to succeeding reversals was progressively less difficult. The bottom graph shows a similar progressive improvement in habit reversal made by pigeons as they were confronted with a visual problem. The plot of average errors per reversal points to a stage of increasing difficulty followed by a stage of steady improvement. Both for the pigeon and for the rat the first reversal is usually the point of maximum difficulty in spatial problems; the point of maximum difficulty tends to occur later in visual problems.

The fish follows a markedly different pattern. Neither of the two types of fish used in our experiments has shown progressive improvement in habit reversal. In two representative experiments fish were tested on spatial and visual problems, and each animal was reversed whenever it made six or fewer errors on a given 40-trial day. When

**PIGEON MAKING A CHOICE** is offered two visually distinct stimuli. (The center light is used in another type of test.) If the correct choice is made, some grain is presented in the rectangular opening. The experimental sequence is programmed by relay circuitry.

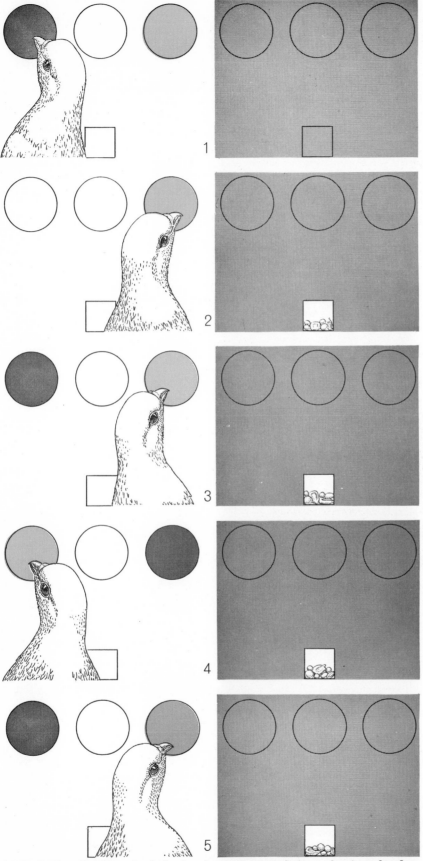

**GUIDANCE is offered an animal after it makes an incorrect choice, as the pigeon has done on its first trial (*top left*). No reward is given and the lights go out in the box for six seconds (*top right*). Then the correct panel alone is lighted and the pigeon is rewarded for pecking at it (2). Thereafter the pigeon is shown selecting the proper panel even when faced with the wrong alternative (3) or a change in the position of the correct panel (4 and 5).**

we plot the results in terms of average errors per reversal, both curves rise from the original problem to the first reversal but then fail to decline with continued training [*see upper illustrations on page 155*].

Before we can conclude that the fish is incapable of improvement in habit reversal, two other possibilities must be considered. The first is that the fish is in fact capable of progressive improvement, but only after more reversals than higher animals require. This possibility seems unlikely; in experiments with fish as many as 150 reversals have failed to yield evidence of improvement. Another possibility is that the conditions under which the fish has been tested are to blame for its poor showing, that the difference in performance is to be traced not to a difference in capability but to an inequality in some contextual variable such as sensory demand, motor demand, degree of hunger or attractiveness of reward.

Although the environments we construct for the various animals are roughly analogous, there is no way of equating them exactly with respect to such variables. Do a fish and a pigeon distinguish between a pair of red and green lamps with equal ease? Probably not. Does a *Tubifex* worm have the same reward value for a fish that a sucrose pellet has for a rat? Probably not. We do not know how to select stimuli that will be equally discriminable or rewards that will be equally attractive. Can we ever, then, rule out the possibility that a difference in performance of two different animals in such an experiment stems from a difference in some confounded contextual variable?

Fortunately, yes, thanks to a technique known as systematic variation. Consider, for example, the hypothesis that a fish fails to show progressive improvement in a given experiment because it is far less hungry (or far more hungry) than a rat that does show improvement. This hypothesis implies that at some level of hunger the fish will show progressive improvement. Thus we can test it—although we cannot produce in the fish the precise degree of hunger in a given rat—by repeating the experiment with subjects of widely different degrees of hunger. Hypotheses about other contextual variables have been tested by similar systematic variation. Progressive improvement in habit reversal has been sought without success in the fish under a wide variety of conditions, whereas the rat and the pigeon do progress under an equally wide range of conditions. Indeed, it is difficult to find a set of conditions under which the pigeon and the rat fail to show improvement.

The results of experiments on habit reversal in the painted turtle are in a sense intermediate between those for the fish on the one hand and those for the pigeon and the rat on the other. In spatial problems the turtle shows progressive improvement; in visual problems it does not. The data from two recent experiments with turtles, one group trained in a spatial problem and the other trained in a visual problem, are plotted at the bottom of page 155. Both curves give the average number of errors made per reversal. The curves rise from the initial presentation of the problem to the first reversal; then the spatial curve declines but the visual curve does not. We conclude simply that experiments on habit reversal tap an intellectual capability of higher animals that is not at all developed in the fish and is manifested by the turtle only in a restricted class of problems.

Other intellectual differences between our test animals appear when the rewarded alternative is changed within a given trial session (not from session to session). Experiments involving this technique are called probability-learning experiments. In a typical probability-learning experiment alternative A would be rewarded on, say, a random 70 percent of the trials and B would be rewarded the other 30 percent. As in experiments on habit reversal, we confront the animal with either a visual task or a spatial one. We can employ either the guidance method (in which an incorrect choice is followed by a time-out, presentation of only the correct alternative and finally a reward) or the noncorrection method (in which the trial ends whether the rewarded or the unrewarded alternative is chosen). Trained without guidance, subjects of all species tend to "maximize," choosing the 70 percent alternative on all the trials. (An occasional subject comes to the situation with a preference for the 30 percent alternative and persists in choosing it.) If guidance is used, however, striking differences appear among the various species.

Some representative results for the rat and the fish are presented in the two graphs on page 156. During the first stage of the experiments reflected in the graphs the animals were trained on a visual problem—horizontal

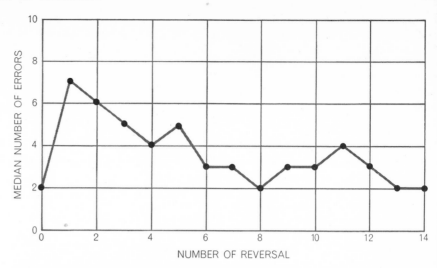

PROGRESSIVE IMPROVEMENT of a group of rats tested on spatial problems that required habit changes is plotted. In solving the original problem (*Reversal 0*) the group made a median number of two errors. When the rewarded alternative was switched (*Reversal 1*), many errors were made before the rats mastered the problem and the rewarded alternative could be switched again. The rats then made fewer errors in achieving reversals.

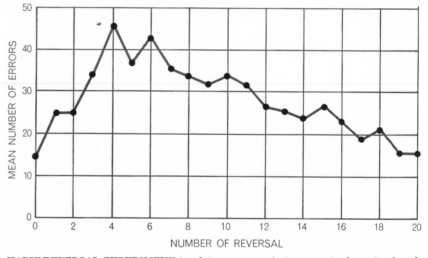

HABIT-REVERSAL EXPERIMENT involving a group of pigeons trained on visual problems yielded the results summarized in this graph. The birds were given 40 trials per day. They made a mean number of 15 errors in mastering the original problem. Difficulty in coping with reversals continued past the first one, reaching a maximum on the fourth reversal, when most animals had to be trained for six days before achieving reversal.

v. vertical stripes—by the guidance method. The choice of horizontal stripes was rewarded in 70 percent of the trials for the first 30 days and in 100 percent of the trials for the next 10 days. The rat tended to maximize under these conditions: after several days it began to choose the 70 percent alternative much more than 70 percent of the time; with the shift in the reward ratio to 100 percent the trend toward absolute preference continued as it might have even without the shift. In contrast, the fish showed a choice pattern we characterize as "matching." It began to choose the 70 percent alternative about 70 percent of the time after a few days of training,

and when the reward ratio was shifted to 100 percent, it rapidly began choosing the rewarded alternative in every instance. In other words, the fish produced a choice ratio that tended to match the reward ratio. We found that in spatial problems too the rat maximizes and the fish matches as long as guidance is used (although without guidance both species tend to maximize).

Whereas the rat and the monkey usually maximize in experiments on probability learning even when guidance is used, they sometimes show a correspondence between choice ratio and reward ratio of a rather different kind from that revealed by the fish. The mammals produce a pattern of systematic matching. Occasionally, for example, a group of rats will choose the rewarded alternative of the preceding trial. This tendency toward reward-following produces a 70 percent choice of the 70 percent alternative when the reward ratio is 70 to 30, and a 50 percent choice of each alternative in a problem in which the ratio is 50 to 50. An opposite strategy—to avoid the rewarded alternative of the preceding trial—sometimes has been used by the monkey. No such systematic tendencies are reflected in the matching of the fish, which can be characterized as random.

A pattern of random matching is also produced by the pigeon when it is tested on a visual problem. Since the rat either maximizes in such cases or begins

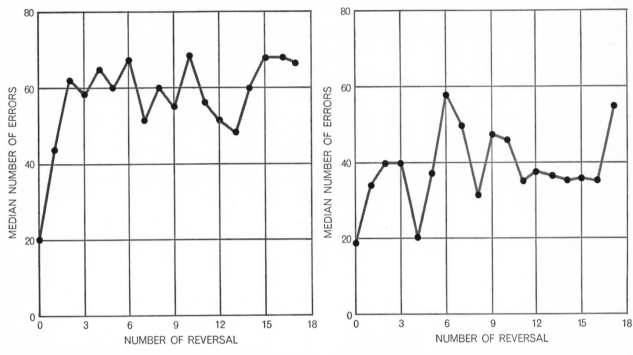

FISH TESTED ON SPATIAL PROBLEM yielded data for this graph, which reveals no progressive improvement in habit reversal. The curve remains approximately level after the first reversal.

FISH TESTED ON A VISUAL PROBLEM show no progressive improvement in habit-reversal experiments. Even graphs of experiments involving 150 reversals do not reveal any downward slope.

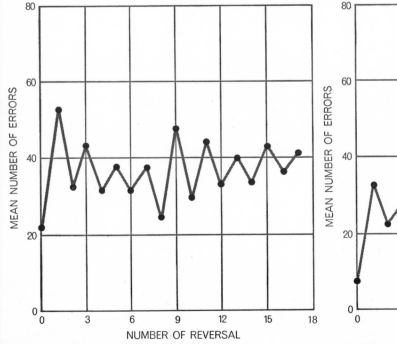

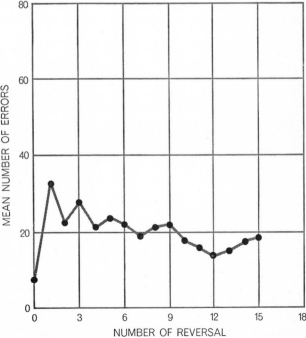

TURTLES TESTED VISUALLY failed to show any progressive improvement in habit reversal. Occasional drops between reversals have no significant statistical effect on the slope of the curve.

TURTLES SOLVING SPATIAL PROBLEMS do show progressive improvement when the results of a habit-reversal experiment are plotted. In this graph improvement follows the initial reversal.

reward-following, the experiments on probability learning have provided us with a clear functional difference between the rat and the pigeon.

Experiments on probability learning yield results for the turtle that are reminiscent of the result of experiments on habit reversal. The efforts of the turtle can be described as random matching in visual problems but maximizing or reward-following in spatial problems. In both kinds of experiment, then, its behavior is ratlike in spatial problems but fishlike in visual problems.

We can use such categories of intellectual behavior (ratlike or fishlike) to tabulate the results of our experiments on habit reversal and probability learning. Such a table [*see bottom illustration on page 157*] suggests the following generalizations: As we ascend the evolutionary scale we do not find a pattern of intellectual continuity but one of discontinuity. Moreover, the modes of adjustment evolved by the higher animals appear earlier in spatial than in visual contexts.

The monkey and the rat are not differentiated by the criteria used to construct our table. The two mammals do, however, show differences in their styles of probability learning, with the reward-following of the rat giving way in the monkey to the opposite strategy (avoiding the rewarded alternative of the preceding trial). It is notable that this strategy of the monkey has been observed so far only in spatial problems, providing support for the generalization that as we go up the evolutionary scale new modes of adjustment appear earlier in spatial than in visual settings.

The idea of advance has long been implicit in the idea of evolution. We are thus led to ask if the ratlike modes of adjustment are really effective in the sense that they help the animal to cope with its environment. Do they actually represent a higher intelligence? In general the answer is yes. Progressive improvement in habit reversal represents a flexibility that cannot help but be of value in an animal's adaptation to changing circumstances. As for probability learning, the ability to maximize produces a higher percentage of correct choices than does matching. In a problem where the reward ratio is 70 to 30, for example, the probability of correct choice is 70 percent if the subject is maximizing but only 58 percent—$(.70 \times .70) + (.30 \times .30)$—for an animal that is matching. Systematic matching is no more successful than random matching

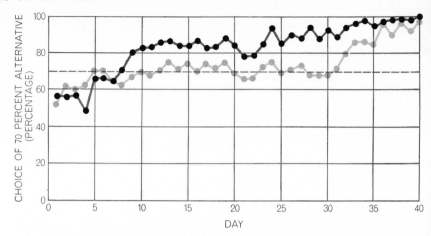

PROBABILITY LEARNING is the subject of experiments such as the one summarized in this graph. The graph compares results for a group of rats (*black curve*) and fish (*colored curve*) tested on visual problems. One alternative was rewarded on 70 percent of the trials for 30 days and on 100 percent of the trials thereafter. Almost from the outset the rat "maximized," tending to make the advantageous choice on 100 percent of the trials. The fish "matched," keeping its choice ratio equal to the reward ratio throughout the experiment.

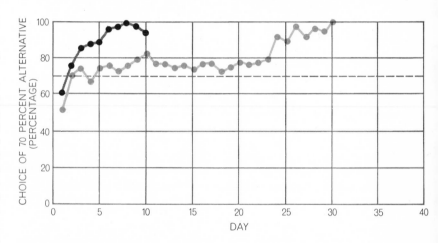

MAXIMIZING is illustrated for rats (*black curve*) and fish (*colored curve*). The animals were trained on spatial problems in which one alternative was rewarded on 70 percent of the trials. The rat, after 10 days, chose the advantageous alternative almost invariably. The fish matched its choice ratio with the reward ratio for 20 days, at which time guidance was discontinued and it tended to choose the advantageous alternative on almost every trial.

by this criterion, and yet we know that human subjects employ systematic matching in trying to find a principle that will enable them to make the correct choice 100 percent of the time. If the use of systematic matching by lower animals is based on some crude, strategic capability, it represents a considerable functional advance over random matching.

Having found behavioral differences among the various types of animal, we are now trying to trace them to physiological differences. My colleague R. C. Gonzales has lately been conducting experiments on habit reversal and probability learning with adult rats lacking extensive portions of the cerebral cortex, a prominent feature of the

mammalian brain that is absent from the brain of the fish and first appears in the reptilian brain. The decorticated rats showed progressive improvement in habit reversal on spatial but not on visual problems. In experiments on probability learning they maximized on spatial problems but took to random matching on visual problems. The intellectual behavior of these decorticated rats was exactly like that of the turtle, an animal with little cortex.

Summarizing the meaning of these experiments calls for sketching the origins of the study of animal intelligence. A century ago, as Charles Darwin developed his theory of evolution, he denied not only the physical uniqueness of man but also the intellectual uniqueness. In doing so he used the only evidence available to him: episodes described by naturalists, hunters, pet-owners and zoo-keepers. It was not until the start of the 20th century that the study of animal intelligence was brought from the realm of the anecdote into the laboratory by Edward L. Thorndike, who was then working at Harvard University. Thorndike's experiments led him to deny the existence of intellectual uniqueness anywhere in the evolutionary hierarchy of animals. It was he who set forth the theory that differences from species to species are only differences of degree, and that the evolution of intelligence involves only the improvement of old processes and the development of more neural elements.

Our studies of habit reversal and probability learning in the lower animals suggest that brain structures evolved by higher animals do not serve merely to replicate old functions and modes of intellectual adjustment but to mediate new ones (a contradiction of the Thorndike hypothesis). Work with decorticated rats points to the same conclusion. Yet it should be observed that these recent studies represent a new turn in the investigative path founded by Thorndike himself. Clearly bringing the study into the laboratory was the real first step toward replacing guesses with facts about the evolution of intelligence and its relation to the evolution of the brain.

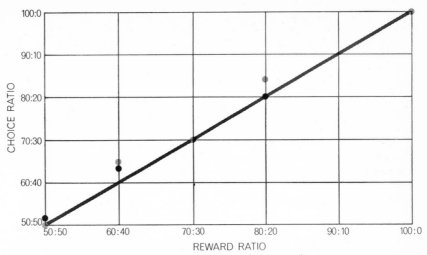

**MATCHING** of choice ratio (*vertical axis*) with reward ratio (*horizontal axis*) approaches a linear relation for both the pigeon (*colored dots*) and the fish (*black dots*). The graph is based on studies of fish given visual and spatial problems and pigeons given visual ones.

| TEST ANIMAL | SPATIAL PROBLEMS | | VISUAL PROBLEMS | |
|---|---|---|---|---|
| | REVERSAL | PROBABILITY | REVERSAL | PROBABILITY |
| MONKEY | RAT | RAT | RAT | RAT |
| RAT | RAT | RAT | RAT | RAT |
| PIGEON | RAT | RAT | RAT | FISH |
| TURTLE | RAT | RAT | FISH | FISH |
| FISH | FISH | FISH | FISH | FISH |

**DIFFERENCE IN INTELLIGENCE** of the five animals studied by the author (*column at left*) are tabulated according to the subject's response to spatial and visual problems in experiments on habit reversal and probability learning. The behavior of each animal in each test situation is characterized as ratlike (progressive improvement in habit reversal and maximizing or nonrandom matching on probability-learning tests) or fishlike (no such improvement in habit reversal and random matching on probability-learning tests).

# 20

# THE INTELLIGENCE OF ELEPHANTS

BERNHARD RENSCH                    February 1957

The bigger the brain, the greater the brain power—this seems to be a general rule among comparable members of the animal kingdom. In view of that interesting relation, it is rather surprising that so little scientific attention has been given to the brain of the elephant. It is not only the biggest of all land animals but also has the most massive brain (about 6,000 grams, or more than 13 pounds). Zoo keepers, circus trainers and jungle dwellers who use elephants as work animals have long known that the elephant is an intelligent creature. But just how intelligent is it? We have recently been examining its mental capacity in a systematic way at our Zoological Institute in Münster in Westphalia.

We had started to compare the brain anatomy or learning ability of closely related animals of different size: rats *v.* mice, a giant Indian squirrel *v.* a dwarf Indian squirrel, large *v.* small races of chickens and so on. Broadly speaking we found that the larger animals had developed the complicated parts of the cerebral cortex to a greater degree and also had greater learning ability. These findings suggested the idea of testing the learning ability of the elephant. It is true that the elephant is somewhat unusual and not particularly convenient as a "laboratory animal," but we had a five-year-old female Indian elephant available to work on in the Münster Zoo and we made some field trips to study working elephants in the jungles of southern India.

In India people tell fantastic stories about the feats and "cleverness" of elephants. Even so experienced an observer as J. H. Williams, who worked and lived with elephants in the forests of Burma for 25 years, says in his excellent book *Elephant Bill* that the elephant "never stops learning because he is always thinking." Williams reports quite seriously that domesticated elephants have been known to stuff mud into the bells round their necks to muffle them before going forth to steal bananas at night. Most of these tales credit elephants with far too much insight into the future to be believable. But authentic reports of their performances are not lacking. It is known that they sometimes use a branch to switch away flies and will take a stick to scratch parts of their bodies unreachable by the trunk.

When we went to India, we were offered a good opportunity to study the taming and training of working elephants in the southern part of the state of Mysore. A newly caught elephant is fettered and assigned to a mahout (elephant boy). The trainers calm the animal and accustom it to the presence of man by rubbing its back and flanks with grass and leaves and singing monotonous, soothing melodies. After two or three weeks of daily training the elephant learns to respond to the commands "Go!", "Stop!", "Kneel down!" and "Get up!" given in the Urdu language. In the training procedure the new elephant is tied between two tame ones, which drag the "apprentice" along at the command *"Mall-mall"* ("Go forward"). The young animal soon learns the meaning of this and a few other expressions, but it takes several years to master all the verbal commands necessary to qualify it for work in the forest or in road building.

One of our main objects was to find out how large a vocabulary a trained elephant could "understand" and whether it was capable of ideational behavior. We found that fully trained animals between 20 and 60 years old knew some 21 to 24 commands. The most important words of their vocabulary were: *mall-mall* (go forward), *tschoro* (stop), *datt-datt* (go backward), *tschei beri* (turn around), *tol-tol* (lift your foot) and the

INDIAN ELEPHANT obeys the command *"Derr-tol"* ("Squirt water on your back"). A trained elephant can distinguish this command from one to squirt water under its belly.

**TWO INDIAN ELEPHANTS** delicately coordinate their efforts in response to commands. At the top the elephants obey the command *"Toker·toker"* ("Push the object with your feet"); at the bottom, the command *"Djouk"* ("Push the object with your head").

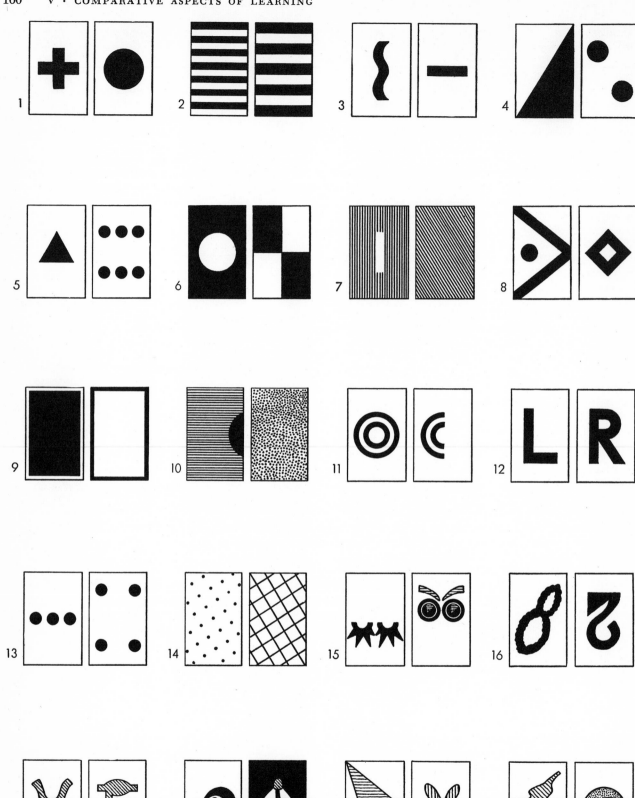

**VISUAL VOCABULARY** of an Indian elephant in the Münster Zoo is represented by these 20 pairs of cards. The card at the left in each pair is "positive"; *i.e.*, when the elephant chose the card, she was given a piece of bread. The card at right is "negative."

Urdu expressions for "Lie down on your belly," "Lie down on your side," "Lift up your trunk," "Give me the object," "Drink," "Squirt water under your belly," "Squirt water on your back," "Duck under [the water]," "Push the object with your foot," "Push it with your head," "Pass the obstacle," "Break the obstacle" (*e.g.*, a wooden bar).

Actually, experienced elephants did much of their work with only a minimum of commands, as if they "knew" what they were expected to accomplish. The main task of the elephants we observed was to push and drag heavy logs through the jungle to a road and there load the logs on trucks. They did all this with only occasional orders and shouts by the mahouts. It was remarkable how efficiently the elephants used their feet, trunks and heads to push the heavy logs up a pair of inclined bars onto a truck. Two elephants worked together in a team, assisting each other with wonderful balance and coordination [*see photographs on page 159*]. Their performances suggest that elephants must be credited with true ideation, *i.e.*, anticipating what will come of certain actions.

In Münster we carried out a series of experiments with our five-year-old zoo animal to measure the learning capacity of elephants more precisely. Her task was to discriminate among various visual patterns. The training apparatus was simple enough. Two small wooden boxes with cardboard lids were placed on the ground one meter apart, and the elephant had to remove the correct lid to get a food reward, a piece of bread. The lids were marked with different patterns: in the first pair presented, one had a black cross and the other a black circle [*see top of opposite page*]. Since the elephant showed a slight spontaneous tendency to prefer the circle, we made the circle the negative, nonrewarded stimulus and the cross the positive one. We took precautions to avoid giving the animal any clues except the visual pattern itself and uncovered both patterns simultaneously. It took the elephant about 330 trials, over a period of several days, to learn that the cross was the "correct" symbol. She learned by trial and error, though we tried to assist her at first by shouting *"Nein"* when she tried to open the "wrong" lid. Once the elephant had learned the correct pattern, she opened only that lid: if she started to reach toward the other, she would back away as soon as she saw it was the circle and go for the right one. This behavior clearly showed that she

really knew which pattern was "wrong."

After she had mastered this pair we presented a series of others: a pattern of narrow black stripes *v.* one of broad stripes, a curvy line *v.* a straight line, three dots in a row *v.* four dots arranged in a square, the letter L *v.* the letter R, and so on [*see opposite page*]. All these patterns were well within the discrimination ability of the elephant's eyesight, as my assistant R. Altevogt proved later by experiment. (He found that the visual acuity of the elephant is considerably inferior to man's and about equal to that of the goat and the deer.)

Our elephant learned to discriminate more and more rapidly in the successive tests, apparently gaining "know-how" as she proceeded (*e.g.*, acquiring the "idea" that there was one "wrong" and one "right" pattern in each pair). By the fourth pair she was able to choose the right one after only 10 trials.

As she added to her "vocabulary," we kept her refreshed on what she had learned by repeated tests, so that she was able to choose the correct one of each pair when they were presented in a series in irregular rotation. These tests required quite a tough effort from the elephant, but apparently the method of serial rotation aroused her interest, and she did not flag in the task.

We were surprised to find that the elephant could keep simultaneously in memory the "meaning" of 20 stimulus pairs. In a final multiple choice test in serial rotation, each of the 20 pairs was presented 30 times according to a previously established sequence. The elephant mastered all 20 discrimination pairs superbly. In most of them she made only one or two wrong choices or no error at all. The test covered 600 trials lasting several hours, yet the elephant not only showed no symptoms of fatigue but actually improved in performance toward the end.

Her excellent scores in this test on 40 patterns suggest that the elephant could have mastered a bigger vocabulary, but we did not pursue this because the teaching would have taken long months and would not have added any fundamentally significant information about learning ability.

I have mentioned that our elephant gave evidence of recognizing a "wrong" pattern as negative by backing away from it. To find out whether she also knew the meaning of positive patterns we gave her a special test. We presented her with four patterns at a time, one of which was positive and the other three negative. In a long series of tests she

recognized the positive pattern at first sight on about half of the occasions and after one wrong choice in the remaining trials. When she was given a choice between a positive pattern and a "neutral" card without any visual pattern, she almost always chose the positive pattern, showing that she very well knew its "meaning."

On the other hand, the choice between a negative card and a neutral one disturbed her. When she made a choice, she would often take the neutral one. But sometimes she would become excited and tear or bite the cardboard lid or

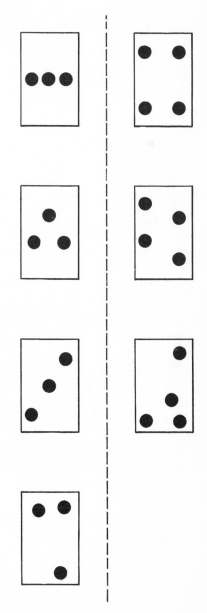

POSITION OF DOTS in the pair of cards numbered 13 on the opposite page was changed in several experiments. No matter what the position of the dots, the elephant was able to distinguish the positive card from the negative without further training.

trample on it. Her behavior suggested the kind of experimental neurosis that has been produced by conflict situations in many other subjects, from fish to man.

After the elephant had learned a good deal of her visual vocabulary, we tried some experiments to see whether she would recognize patterns when they were altered. This was a test of her ability to transpose learning or to form an abstract concept. For example, we turned the black cross (a positive stimulus) to the X position, we changed the relative length of the arms, and so on. Regardless of such changes, the elephant still recognized the figure as a positive sign, and she would choose the altered version as often as the original one. We may say that the elephant had got the "idea" that the essential feature of the pattern was the crossing of two black bars. (She did not respond to a white cross on a black background.)

An even clearer case of her ability to grasp an idea emerged in experiments with the striped patterns. In the original pair the stripes were respectively two centimeters and four centimeters wide (roughly three quarters of an inch *v.* an inch and a half), and the positive card was the one with the narrower stripes. We changed the widths to 1.5 and two centimeters, respectively. The elephant then chose the 1.5-centimeter pattern rather than the two-centimeter one. In short, she had mastered the idea that the pattern with the narrower stripes was the right choice. Presented with a choice between stripes of three centimeters and four centimeters, she again took the narrower stripes.

We tested our elephant's comprehension of numbers. Using the pair of cards with three dots and four dots, we first tried shifting the three dots on the positive card in various arrangements [*see preceding page*]. The elephant still chose this card in the majority of trials. We then switched about the positions of the four dots on the negative card as well. The elephant seemed at a loss for a while and made some wrong choices, but soon she solved the problem. She was able to distinguish three from four circular dots of equal size regardless of their arrangement, not by new learning but by extension of what she had learned. When we changed the objects to irregularly shaped spots instead of circular dots, she had to start anew, and it took her 440 trials to learn which was the "right" card.

We proceeded to a test of the elephant's memory, with very interesting results. She was presented with 13 pairs of cards which she had learned earlier but had not seen for about a year. In a total of 520 trials she scored between 73 and 100 per cent on all the pairs except one which was a difficult discrimination problem (*i.e.*, the double circle *v.* the double half-circle, on which she scored 67 per cent). In other words, the elephant had retained the meaning of 24 different visual patterns for the period of about one year. This was a truly impressive scientific demonstration of the adage that "elephants never forget."

Our observations of the Indian working elephants' ability to learn a vocabulary of verbal commands prompted us to make a precise laboratory examination of our elephant's acoustic discrimination. Our collaborator J. Reinert carried out these experiments. He started with a pair of pure tones: the tone at 750 cycles per second was the positive stimulus and 500 cycles per second (three full notes lower in pitch) was the negative one. The sounds were produced electronically through a loudspeaker. To make the elephant's learning behavior more easily observable she was taught to "stand at attention" at the beginning of each series of trials: she had to grasp the lower iron bar of her cage with her trunk. If the sound presented was the "wrong" one, she was supposed to remain in this position. If it was the right one, she was to knock on the lid of a switch box in front of her cage with her trunk: this caused an electrical gadget to bring a food reward within reach of her trunk. The experimenter sat behind a screen watching the animal by means of a mirror system.

The elephant learned to discriminate six pairs of sounds, one of which differed by only a single full note. In tests on all of them in irregular rotation she was able to distinguish all 12 tones and to know their positive or negative meaning. From these results one may conclude that the elephant possesses an excellent memory of absolute pitch. Again in this case she demonstrated remarkably long retention: after a lapse of a year and a half, during which she went on to other acoustic learning, she was able to get nine out of 12 of the pitch discriminations correct on a return to the test.

In the meantime we had examined the elephant's ability to learn short melodies. The positive sound pattern was a melody consisting of three tones—low, high and low. The negative melody also had three tones, but the pattern was reversed: the second tone was lower than the first and the third higher than the second. After the elephant had fully learned these two melodies, they were altered by all possible means: shifted toward higher or lower frequencies, changed in intensity, rhythm or timing, played on various instruments that varied their timbre. In

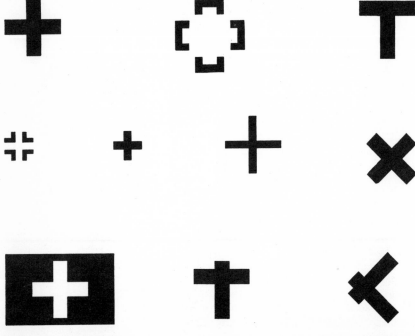

VARIATIONS OF A CROSS were presented to the elephant to determine whether she would respond to the abstract idea of a cross. The elephant had been trained to recognize the cross at upper left as a positive signal. She chose all the other figures as positive except the ones in the middle of the top row, at the left in the middle row and at lower left.

spite of all these alterations the elephant was able to recognize the positive and negative melodies (*i.e.*, the relations of notes) in the overwhelming majority of the trials.

To what extent are the elephant's remarkable learning ability and memory attributable to its big brain? For any meaningful answer to this question, we would have to compare its performance with that of a proboscid (trunk-bearing) relative of smaller body size. Unfortunately the elephant has no closely related, small-sized cousins. The best we could do was to compare it with horse-like animals.

Recently one of our collaborators attempted to teach the patterns that had been learned by the elephant to a horse, an ass and a zebra in the Münster Zoo. Some minor alterations had to be made in the experiments, of course, to suit them to the new animals. As we had more or less expected, the ass and the zebra could not compete with the elephant in the number of stimulus pairs learned. The ass could master only 13, the zebra only 10. But the horse, surprisingly enough, learned all the 20 pairs that the elephant had mastered. This seems to indicate that the horse possesses a very efficient visual learning capacity. We have not yet had time to compare its memory span with that of the elephant. but in a retest after three months it performed well.

These experiments and our earlier studies of other animals permit us to advance a few general hypotheses about brain size. Size quite evidently is a decisive factor in the brain's learning capacity. Of course this applies not only to the size of the forebrain as a whole but also to the relative size of the various brain regions, especially that of the seven-layered cerebral cortex. The density of brain cells (number per unit volume) also seems to be an important factor. Another significant fact is that the larger animals have bigger ganglion (gray-matter) cells than their smaller cousins. These larger cells have more branching fibers, and therefore probably allow more complicated associations for learning. Moreover the nerve fibers from large cells are bigger in diameter, and it seems reasonable to suppose that this may be responsible for good retention and long memory: the larger the fibers, the more stable and lasting connections can be established between cells.

How much truth there is in these hypotheses will have to be determined by further experiments.

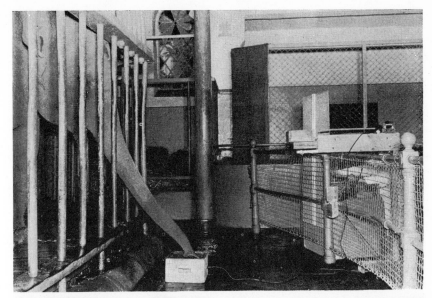

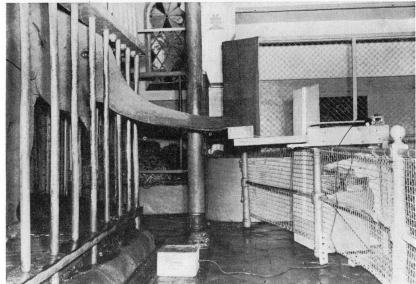

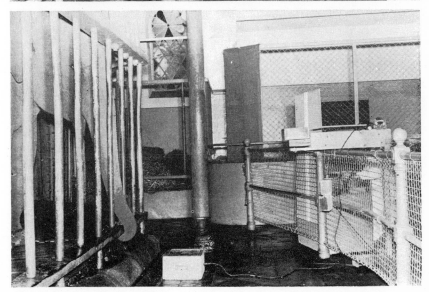

DISCRIMINATION BETWEEN SOUNDS was also tested. When the elephant heard a positive tone, she knocked on a box with her trunk (*top picture*). This closed an electrical circuit and moved another box containing a piece of bread toward the elephant (*middle*). At a negative tone she wrapped her trunk around a horizontal bar of her cage (*bottom*).

# 21

# LEARNING TO THINK

HARRY F. AND MARGARET KUENNE HARLOW

August 1949

HOW does an infant, born with only a few simple reactions, develop into an adult capable of rapid learning and the almost incredibly complex mental processes known as thinking? This is one of psychology's unsolved problems. Most modern explanations are not much more enlightening than those offered by 18th-century French and English philosophers, who suggested that the mind developed merely by the process of associating ideas or experiences with one another. Even the early philosophers realized that this was not a completely adequate explanation.

The speed and complexity of a human being's mental processes, and the intricacy of the nerve mechanisms that presumably underlie them, suggest that the brain is not simply a passive network of communications but develops some kind of organization that facilitates learning and thinking. Whether such organizing principles exist has been a matter of considerable dispute. At one extreme, some modern psychologists deny that they do and describe learning as a mere trial-and-error process—a blind fumbling about until a solution accidentally appears. At the other extreme, there are psychologists who hold that people learn through an innate insight that reveals relationships to them.

To investigate, and to reconcile if possible, these seemingly antagonistic positions, a series of studies of the learning process has been carried out at the University of Wisconsin. Some of these have been made with young children, but most of the research has been on monkeys.

For two basic reasons animals are particularly good subjects for the investigation of learning at a fundamental level. One is that it is possible to control their entire learning history: the psychologist knows the problems to which they have been exposed, the amount of training they have had on each, and the record of their performance. The other reason is that the animals' adaptive processes are more simple than those of human beings, especially during the first stages of the attack on a problem. Often the animal's reactions throw into clear relief certain mechanisms that operate more

obscurely in man. Of course this is only a relative simplicity. All the higher mammals possess intricate nervous systems and can solve complex problems. Indeed, it is doubtful that man possesses any fundamental intellectual process, except true language, that is not also present in his more lowly biological brethren.

Tests of animal learning of the trial-and-error type have been made in innumerable laboratories. In the special tests devised for our experiments, we set out to determine whether monkeys could progress from trial-and-error learning to the ability to solve a problem immediately by insight.

One of the first experiments was a simple discrimination test. The monkeys were confronted with a small board on which lay two objects different in color, size and shape. If a monkey picked up the correct object, it was rewarded by finding raisins or peanuts underneath. The position of the objects was shifted on the board in an irregular manner from trial to trial, and the trials were continued until the monkey learned to choose the correct object. The unusual feature of the experiment was that the test was repeated many times, with several hundred different pairs of objects. In other words, instead of training a monkey to solve a single problem, as had been done in most previous psychological work of this kind, we trained the animal on many problems, all of the same general type, but with varying kinds of objects.

When the monkeys first faced this test, they learned by the slow, laborious, fumble-and-find process. But as a monkey solved problem after problem of the same basic kind, its behavior changed in a most dramatic way. It learned each new problem with progressively greater efficiency, until eventually the monkey showed perfect insight when faced with this particular kind of situation—it solved the problem in one trial. If it chose the correct object on the first trial, it rarely made an error on subsequent trials. If it chose the incorrect object on the first trial, it immediately shifted to the correct object, and subsequently responded almost perfectly.

Thus the test appeared to demonstrate that trial-and-error and insight are but

two different phases of one long continuous process. They are not different capacities, but merely represent the orderly development of a learning and thinking process.

A LONG series of these discrimination problems was also run on a group of nursery-school children two to five years of age. Young children were chosen because they have a minimum of previous experience. The conditions in the children's tests were only slightly different from those for the monkeys: they were rewarded by finding brightly colored macaroni beads instead of raisins and peanuts. Most of the children, like the monkeys, made many errors in the early stages of the tests and only gradually learned to solve a problem in one trial. As a group the children learned more rapidly than the monkeys, but they made the same types of errors. And the "smartest" monkeys learned faster than the "dullest" children.

We have called this process of progressive learning the formation of a "learning set." The subject learns an organized set of habits that enables him to meet effectively each new problem of this particular kind. A single set would provide only limited aid in enabling an animal to adapt to an ever-changing environment. But a host of different learning sets may supply the raw material for human thinking.

We have trained monkeys and children to solve problems much more complex than the ones thus far described. For instance, a deliberate attempt is made to confuse the subjects by reversing the conditions of the discrimination test. The previously correct object is no longer rewarded, and the previously incorrect object is always rewarded. When monkeys and children face this switch-over for the first time, they make many errors, persistently choosing the objects they had previously been trained to choose. Gradually, from problem to problem, the number of such errors decreases until finally the first reversal trial is followed by perfect performance. A single failure becomes the cue to the subject to shift his choice from the object which has been rewarded many times to the object

**MONKEY EXPERIMENTS** at the University of Wisconsin illustrate the process of learning. In the drawing at the upper right a monkey is confronted with two different objects. Under one of them is always a raisin or a peanut. In the drawing at the right the monkey has learned consistently to pick the same object. In the drawing above the monkey has learned consistently to choose one object which differs from two others. In the two drawings below the monkey has learned a much more complicated process. In the drawing at the lower left it has learned that when the board is of a certain color it must choose the object that is odd in shape. In the drawing at the lower right it has learned that when the board is of another color it must choose the object that is odd in color. In all these problems the monkey first learned to solve the problem by trial and error. Later it solved them immediately by understanding.

which has never been rewarded before. In this type of test children learn much more rapidly than monkeys.

A group of monkeys that had formed the discrimination-reversal learning set was later trained on a further refinement of the problem. This time the reward value of the objects was reversed for only one trial, and was then shifted back to the original relationship. After many problems, the monkeys learned to ignore the single reversal and treated it as if the experimenter had made an error!

The problem was made more complicated, in another test, by offering the subjects a choice among three objects instead of two. There is a tray containing three food wells. Two are covered by one kind of object, and the third is covered by another kind. The animal must choose the odd object. Suppose the objects are building blocks and funnels. In half the trials, there are two blocks and a funnel, and the correct object is the funnel. Then a switch is made to two funnels and one block. Now the correct object is the block. The animal must learn a subtle distinction here: it is not the shape of the object that is important, but its relation to the other two. The meaning of a specific object may change from trial to trial. This problem is something like the one a child faces in trying to learn to use the words "I," "you," and "he" properly. The meaning of the words changes according to the speaker. When the child is speaking, "I" refers to himself, "you" to the person addressed, and "he" to some third person. When the child is addressed, the child is no longer "I" but "you." And when others speak of him, the terms shift again.

Monkeys and children were trained on a series of these oddity problems, 24 trials being allowed for the solution of each problem. At first they floundered, but they improved from problem to problem until they learned to respond to each new problem with perfect or nearly perfect scores. And on this complex type of problem the monkeys did better than most of the children!

ONE of the most striking findings from these tests was that once the monkeys have formed these learning sets, they retain them for long periods and can use them appropriately as the occasion demands. After a lapse of a year or more, a monkey regains top efficiency, in a few minutes or hours of practice, on a problem that it may have taken many weeks to master originally.

All our studies indicate that the ability to solve problems without fumbling is not inborn but is acquired gradually. So we must re-examine the evidence offered in support of the theory that animals possess some innate insight that has nothing to do with learning.

The cornerstone of this theory is the work of the famous Gestalt psychologist Wolfgang Köhler on the behavior of chimpanzees. In a series of brilliant studies he clearly showed that these apes can use sticks to help them obtain bananas beyond their reach. They employed the sticks to knock the bananas down, to rake them in, to climb and to vault. The animals sometimes assembled short sticks to make a pole long enough to reach the food, and even used sticks in combination with stacked boxes to knock down high-dangling bait. That the chimpanzees frequently solved these problems suddenly, as if by a flash of insight, impressed Köhler as evidence of an ability to reason independently of learning. He even suggested that this ability might differentiate apes and men from other animals.

Unfortunately, since Köhler's animals had been captured in the jungle, he had no record of their previous learning. Recent studies on chimpanzees born in captivity at the Yerkes Laboratory of Primate Biology at Orange Park, Fla., throw doubt on the validity of Köhler's interpretations. Herbert Birch of the Yerkes Laboratory reported that when he gave sticks to four-year-old chimps in their cages, they showed little sign at first of ability to use them as tools. Gradually, in the course of three days, they learned to use the sticks to touch objects beyond their reach. Later the animals solved very simple stick problems fairly well, but they had difficulty with more complex problems.

Extending Birch's investigations, the late Paul Schiller presented a series of stick tasks to a group of chimpanzees from two to over eight years of age. The younger the animal, the more slowly it mastered the problems. Some young subjects took hundreds of trials to perform efficiently on even the simplest problems, while old, experienced animals solved them with little practice. None of the apes solved the tasks initially with sudden insight.

Even at the human level there is no evidence that children possess any innate endowment that enables them to solve tool problems with insight. Augusta Alpert of Columbia University tried some of Köhler's simple chimpanzee tests on bright nursery-school children. The younger children typically went through a trial-and-error process before solving the problems. Some of them failed to solve the easiest problem in the series in five experimental sessions.

Eunice Mathieson presented more difficult Köhler-type tasks to a group of University of Minnesota nursery-school children. The results were even more overwhelmingly against the notion that tool problems are solved by flashes of natural insight. The children rarely solved a problem without making many mistakes.

This research, then, supports our findings. In all clear-cut tests—that is, whenever the animals' entire learning history is known—monkeys, apes and children at first solve problems by trial and error. Only gradually does such behavior give way to immediate solutions.

WE began by pointing out that psychologists have sought to find in the higher mental processes some organizing mechanism or principle that would explain learning and thinking. We can now suggest such a mechanism: the learning set. Suppose we picture mental activity as a continuous structure built up, step by step, by the solution of increasingly difficult problems, from the simplest problem in learning to the most complex one in thinking. At each level the individual tries out various responses to solve each given task. At the lowest level he selects from unlearned responses or previously learned habits. As his experience increases, habits that do not help in the solution drop out and useful habits become established. After solving many problems of a certain kind, he develops organized patterns of responses that meet the demands of this type of situation. These patterns, or learning sets, can also be applied to the solution of still more complex problems. Eventually the individual may organize simple learning sets into more complex patterns of learning sets, which in turn are available for transfer as units to new situations.

Thus the individual learns to cope with more and more difficult problems. At the highest stage in this progression, the intelligent human adult selects from innumerable, previously acquired learning sets the raw material for thinking. His many years of education in school and outside have been devoted to building up these complex learning sets, and he comes to manipulate them with such ease that he and his observers may easily lose sight of their origin and development.

The fundamental role that language plays in the thinking process may be deduced easily from our experiments. They suggest that words are stimuli or signs that call forth the particular learning sets most appropriate for solving a given problem. If you listen to yourself "talk" while you are thinking, you will find that this is exactly what is happening. You review the different ways of solving a problem, and decide which is the best. When you ask a friend for advice, you are asking him to give you a word stimulus which will tell you the appropriate learning set or sets for the solution of your problem.

This principle is particularly well illustrated by some of our monkey experiments. Though monkeys do not talk, they can learn to identify symbols with appropriate learning sets. We have trained our monkeys to respond to signs in the form of differently colored trays

on which the test objects appear. In one test the monkeys were presented with three different objects—a red U-shaped block, a green U-shaped block and a red cross-shaped block. Thus two of the objects were alike in form and two alike in color. When the objects were shown on an orange tray, the monkeys had to choose the green block, that is, the object that was odd in color. When they were shown on a cream-colored tray, the animals had to choose the cross-shaped block, that is, the object odd in form. After the monkeys had formed these two learning sets, the color cue of the tray enabled them to make the proper choice, trial after trial, without error. In a sense, the animals responded to a simple sign language. The difficulty of this test may be judged by the fact that the German neurologist Kurt Goldstein, using similar tests for human beings, found that people with organic brain disorders could not solve such tasks efficiently.

At the Wisconsin laboratories, Benjamin Winsten devised an even more difficult test for the monkeys. This problem tested the animals' ability to recognize similarities and differences, a kind of task frequently used on children's intelligence tests. Nine objects were placed on a tray and the monkey was handed one of them as a sample. The animal's problem was to pick out all identical objects, leaving all the rest on the tray. In the most complicated form of this test the monkey was given a sample which was not identical with the objects to be selected but was only a symbol for them. The animal was handed an unpainted triangle as a sign to pick out all red objects, and an unpainted circle as a sign to select all blue objects. One monkey learned to respond almost perfectly. Given a triangle, he would pick every object with any red on it; given a circle, he selected only the objects with blue on them.

All these data indicate that animals, human and subhuman, must learn to think. Thinking does not develop spontaneously as an expression of innate abilities; it is the end result of a long learning process. Years ago the British biologist, Thomas Henry Huxley, suggested that "the brain secretes thought as the liver secretes bile." Nothing could be further from the truth. The brain is essential to thought, but the untutored brain is not enough, no matter how good a brain it may be. An untrained brain is sufficient for trial-and-error, fumble-through behavior, but only training enables an individual to think in terms of ideas and concepts.

**MORE COMPLICATED TEST** involves teaching a monkey to choose certain objects not by matching but by response to a symbol. In the pair of drawings at the top of this page the monkey is shown a triangular object and pushes forward all the red objects. In drawings at bottom the monkey, shown a round object, pushes forward blue objects, here indicated by gray tone.

# Part VI

# SENSORY STIMULATION, MOTIVATION, AND EMOTION

# VI

## SENSORY STIMULATION, MOTIVATION, AND EMOTION

*Introduction*    Behavior is influenced to a considerable extent by the consequences of previous behavior. Animals learn to make responses that are rewarded and learn to stop making responses that are punished. Studies of learning and memory in animals, as we have seen, make extensive use of rewards and punishments. In most experiments that use rewards as a procedure for training animals, the animals are made hungry or thirsty and are rewarded with food or water. The effectiveness of such procedures as a means of training animals has caused some investigators to consider rewards as substances that reduce biological drives such as hunger and thirst. Evidence from common experience, however, as well as laboratory experiments, indicate quite clearly that animals (human as well as infrahuman) will work to obtain rewards that do not reduce any known biological drives—or that at least do not satisfy any nutritional need.

In the first article in this section, "Curiosity in Monkeys" (page 173), R. A. Butler describes the results of a series of experiments in which monkeys were rewarded only with opportunities to solve puzzles or to engage in visual exploration. The results clearly indicate that monkeys will solve puzzles with no reward other than that of working on puzzles and will learn problems when rewarded only with an opportunity to watch the activity occurring in the laboratory. Although the basis of "curiosity" is not well understood, curiosity appears to be an important regulator of behavior—even in infrahuman subjects. Findings such as these have had a considerable influence in the development of current theories of motivation.

The importance of varied sensory stimulation is revealed perhaps even more strikingly in "The Pathology of Boredom" (page 178), Woodburn Heron's report of the effects of restricted sensory stimulation on the experiences and behavior of human subjects. Monotonous environments are not merely unpleasant. Severe reduction of variation and sensory stimulation produces a variety of deleterious effects, including impairment of thinking and occurrence of hallucinations. As Heron points out, variation in sensory stimulation seems to be essential if human beings are to function efficiently.

In "Pleasure Centers in the Brain" (page 183) James Olds discusses his experimental work, which shows that electrical stimulation of certain brain structures is highly rewarding to animals. Although the basis of the rewarding effect of electrical stimulation of the brain is not yet understood, the hypothesis that the stimulation is rewarding because it excites nerve cells involved in motivational states—such as hunger, thirst, or sex—

has received support from subsequent research. In the past decade techniques of electrical stimulation have been used with considerable success in attempts to localize brain structures involved in motivation and emotion.

The last two articles in this section are concerned with physiological aspects of emotional states. Although it is generally known that worries, fears, and conflicts tend to produce ulcers, little is known about the specific conditions under which emotional stress produces ulcers. Ulcers are generally considered to be the occupational disease of executives. J. V. Brady in "Ulcers in 'Executive' Monkeys" (page 189), summarizes evidence that ulcers can be experimentally produced in animals by subjecting them to various kinds of conflict.

In the final article in this section, "The Physiology of Fear and Anger" (page 193), D. H. Funkenstein reports evidence that different emotional states are accompanied by different physiological reactions. All the papers in this section indicate that progress is being made toward discovering the nature and biological bases of motivation and emotion.

# 22

# CURIOSITY IN MONKEYS

ROBERT A. BUTLER                    February 1954

Curiosity is certainly one of the strongest motives in human behavior. Children begin very early to explore the world around them: they are excited by new sights and sounds, continually manipulate and investigate their toys or other small objects, and in general are extremely responsive to new things and events in their environment. Indeed, severe deprivation of environmental stimulation may permanently retard a child's development.

Until recently little or no research has been conducted on the curiosity motives, for reasons which are not hard to discover. A current theory in psychology has reduced human motivations to the biological drives of hunger, thirst and sex and the conditioned drive to avoid pain, and it has maintained that all learning is based on these drives. Curiosity was dismissed by the behaviorists as an "instinct," beyond the scope of experimental investigation. But in recent years psychologists have found a great deal of experimental evidence that the behavior of human beings and other primates cannot be explained adequately in terms of biological or pain-avoidance drives. Some experimental study has been given to the curiosity motives in monkeys, and this article will review those studies.

The everyday behavior of monkeys seems plainly to be motivated in considerable part by something akin to curiosity. Monkeys, not unlike children, persist in examining things in their immediate environment by close inspection and manipulation. Every object presented to a monkey is at one time or another handled, fondled, scratched, rubbed, bent, picked at, bitten and pulled apart before finally being discarded. A monkey will tamper with the lock on his cage door and will invariably confiscate any objects left on accessible shelves. In short, a monkey spends a considerable portion of his life "monkeying around" with anything he can get his hands on.

To prove that monkeys have a fundamental curiosity drive, or drive to manipulate, we must demonstrate three things: (1) that they will work for long periods with the manipulatory behavior itself as the sole reward; (2) that the manipulation drive will produce learning, in the same way as the hunger or pain-avoidance drives, and (3) that no drives other than curiosity are significantly influencing the experimental results.

Harry F. Harlow and his associates at the University of Wisconsin were the first to investigate manipulatory behavior in monkeys. Their experiments were designed to determine whether monkeys can learn how to solve a me-

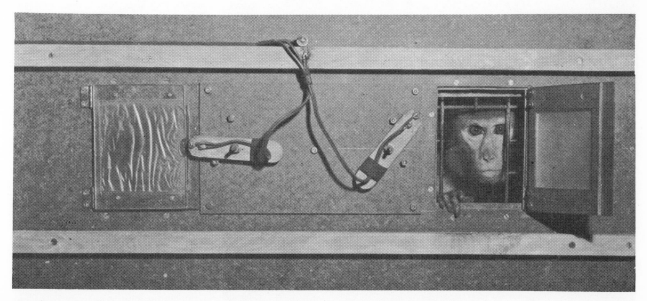

**CURIOUS MONKEY** stares out into the busy laboratory. Tirelessly the monkey in this experiment would push open the door with the blue card on its back when it learned that this and not the adjacent yellow door afforded a glimpse from its cage.

chanical puzzle with no reward other than the working of it. The puzzle consisted of three interlocking devices—a metal pin, a hook-and-eye and a hasp. The three items could be disengaged if the monkey first removed the pin, then took the hook out of the eye and finally lifted the hasp. If the monkey touched any of the items out of order, it was counted as an error. After a few training sessions the monkeys' score was nearly perfect. Then the puzzle was made harder by adding more devices, but it was just as readily solved. Another study investigated the persistence of this behavior. Every six minutes the puzzle was reset. The monkeys went on disassembling it repeatedly for 10 hours, at which point the experimenters, rather than the subjects, had had enough.

Recently Wisconsin's Primate Laboratory devised a puzzle that involves learning to discriminate between stimuli. The usual procedure in such a test is to give a reward, such as food, for the correct response in a choice between two different stimuli. But in this experiment the only reward was the opportunity to manipulate objects. Ten screw eyes were mounted in two vertical rows on a metal panel. Five of them, colored red, were removable; the other five, colored green, were firmly fixed. The screw eyes were randomly placed so that the only clue to whether they were removable was color. The monkeys soon learned that the red screw eyes could be removed to play with, and they almost unerringly touched only those.

These experiments yielded two important findings: that the opportunity to manipulate objects is reward enough to motivate monkeys to learn, and that an external stimulus, like an internal, biological one, can evoke a drive. The curiosity motives apparently are initiated by external stimuli.

What kinds of stimuli are most effective in eliciting the manipulation drive? Wallace Welker of the Yerkes Laboratories of Primate Biology has just completed experiments on chimpanzees which bear directly on this problem. On a table before the chimp's cage he placed a pair of objects. One of the pair would be movable and the other fixed, or the handling of one would produce a sound and the other not. Like monkeys, the chimpanzees showed a strong preference for movable objects over fixed ones and for objects that produced a sound or triggered a light over those that yielded no change in the environment. After 30 minutes with a pair of objects the animals became bored and stopped han-

**EAGER** to peer out of its cage, the monkey shown from without on page 173 is about to open the blue door. All these photographs were made at the University of Wisconsin.

dling them, but their interest could be maintained if new stimuli were introduced periodically. Young chimpanzees consistently displayed more manipulatory behavior than older ones.

Monkeys and apes watch closely everything that goes on around them. Perhaps this expression of curiosity in monkeys accounts for their popularity with man. At the zoo or in the laboratory, man and monkey seem to observe each other with great interest. Which one derives more information from the experience remains an enigma. It is as if man as an observer meets his first real competitor in the monkey. Sometimes this competition becomes rather unnerving. I had such an experience during the course of a series of experiments at the Wisconsin laboratories. I was testing monkeys on a food-rewarded problem. The monkey worked behind a screen where it could not see the experimenter. By the same token, the experimenter could not see the monkey, and there was a great temptation to peek to find out what the animal was doing. I first made a small peephole in the panel, but the monkey quickly discovered it and thereafter spied on me as often as I did on him. I next tried placing a small mirror in a position that enabled me to watch the animal constantly. The monkey turned the tables by dropping its work and watching me through the mirror!

Taking advantage of this lead, we designed an experiment to investigate monkeys' visual exploratory behavior. The apparatus was essentially an enclosure with a built-in color discrimination problem. Monkeys were rewarded by a view of the surroundings outside the enclosure, provided they responded correctly on the problem. The monkey was placed in a large box with two doors. The animal was given preliminary training to familiarize it with the apparatus: first it was given a look through the open doors into the laboratory, where considerable activity was going on, and then the experimenter closed the doors. Soon the monkey learned to open the doors within a few seconds.

Then the main part of the experiment began. One door was locked, and it was identifiable by a yellow card on the inside. The other door, marked by a blue card, was unlocked. The experimenter raised a screen that had been lowered between the monkey and the doors, exposing the two doors with their differently colored cards. If the monkey pushed against the door with the blue card, the door opened and it could look outside. After 30 seconds the experi-

**PUZZLE SOLVING** indicates the extent of the curiosity drive in monkeys. Learning to discriminate, monkey pulls only red, removable screw eyes (*left*). In another test with no reward other than doing it, monkey repeatedly works puzzle of pin, hook and eye, hasp.

TOY TRAIN proved to be a strong visual incentive for monkeys to open the door repeatedly in order to be able to view it. An even stronger one was the sight of another monkey.

BOWL OF FRUIT turned out to be less of a stimulus for the monkeys than either the toy train or another monkey as an inducement to push open the door of its cage to view it.

menter lowered the screen and the trial was over. If the animal pushed against the door holding the yellow card, it automatically flashed on a light which signaled its error; the experimenter immediately lowered the screen, denying the subject a glimpse of the outside world. Twenty trials a day were given for 20 days, and each test session lasted from 25 to 45 minutes. The experimenter recorded the number of correct responses and the length of time that elapsed between the raising of the screen and the monkey's attack on one of the doors. The speed of response provided a measure of the strength of the monkey's motivation to look outside.

The results of the experiment left no doubt about the strength of the monkeys' curiosity or its power in promoting learning. Throughout the 20 days of testing the animals worked away eagerly at the problem (the colored cards were shifted at random from door to door). Without tiring of the game, they went on pushing the doors enthusiastically to get a look at the people working in the laboratory outside the box. In a second study that ran for 57 days and presented various color-discrimination problems, the subjects worked just as unflaggingly.

These data strongly suggest that the drive to explore visually is indeed a fundamental drive in monkeys. To measure its strength and persistence further, two monkeys were tested for four continuous hours each day for five days. The animals worked as fast on Day Five as they did on Day One. A second experiment yielded still more surprising results. Three monkeys were put to the door-opening test hour after hour, with 30 seconds between trials, until they quit. One monkey performed for nine continuous hours, another worked for 11 and the third for more than 19 hours! The response time of this marathon performer was actually shortest during the final hour of the test.

That monkeys would work as long and as persistently for a food reward is highly unlikely. The tenacity and rapidity with which these subjects performed on the task of opening a door in order to see outside clearly indicated that the activities in the laboratory were extremely effective in exciting their curiosity.

To find out what specific kinds of visual stimuli excited them, we presented to the monkeys three different sights: a fellow monkey, an operating toy electric train and an array of fresh fruit and monkey chow. As a standard for comparison the test was arranged so that the monkeys would sometimes see nothing but an empty room. The apparatus was the same as before except that this time the box had only one door. Upon opening the door, the monkey saw a large chamber which contained a monkey, the running train, the array of food or nothing at all. The monkeys were allowed a five-second view, and the trials were repeated at 10-second intervals. Eight monkeys were tested 30 minutes a day, five days a week for a period of four weeks. Each week the visual incentive was changed. The strongest incentive turned out to be, not surprisingly, the sight of another monkey; the electric train ran a close second.

We next investigated the relative effectiveness of different sounds. A highly vocal monkey and the noise of the electric train were the incentives. Sometimes the subjects, after opening the door, could see the source of the sound, sometimes not. Ten of the youngest monkeys in the colony participated in the study. All of them opened the door frequently and rapidly, through five weeks of testing, irrespective of which sound they heard or whether they were rewarded with the sight of the sound-maker. Although the experiment failed to show any clear-cut differences among the incentives, it provided valuable evidence on the strength of the curiosity drive in young monkeys.

These researches with monkeys and apes are the beginnings of what promises to be a most fascinating and important area of investigation. The strong tendency of monkeys and apes to explore all things and situations provides an extremely serviceable mechanism for acquainting these animals with the intricacies of their environment. That this tendency is most marked in the younger animals suggests that the curiosity motives are largely responsible for the early and extensive learning which unquestionably contributes to the biological success of the primates.

# 23

# THE PATHOLOGY OF BOREDOM

WOODBURN HERON                                          January 1957

If you shake the surface on which a snail is resting, it withdraws into its shell. If you shake it repeatedly, the snail after a while fails to react. In the same way a sea anemone which is disturbed by a drop of water falling on the water surface above it ceases to be disturbed if drops continue to fall; a bird stops flying away from a rustling motion if the motion is steadily repeated. Most organisms stop responding to a stimulus repeated over and over again (unless the response is reinforced by reward or avoidance of punishment). Indeed, the higher organisms actively avoid a completely monotonous environment. A rat in a maze will use different routes to food, if they are available, rather than the same one all the time. It will tend to avoid areas in which it has spent considerable time and to explore the less familiar areas.

Monotony is an important and enduring human problem. Persons who have to work for long periods at repetitive tasks often complain of being bored and dissatisfied with their jobs, and frequently their performance declines. During the last war N. H. Mackworth of England made a series of researches for the Royal Air Force to find out why radar operators on antisubmarine patrol sometimes failed to detect U-boats. The operators usually worked in isolation, watching a radar screen hour after hour. Mackworth set up a comparable laboratory situation, requiring subjects to watch a pointer moving around a graduated dial and to press a button whenever the pointer made a double jump. The subjects' efficiency declined in the surprisingly short time of half an hour. As a result of this and other research the radar operators' tour of duty was shortened.

In this age of semi-automation, when not only military personnel but also many industrial workers have little to do but keep a constant watch on instruments, the problem of human behavior in monotonous situations is becoming acute. In 1951 the McGill University psychologist D. O. Hebb obtained a grant from the Defence Research Board of Canada to make a systematic study of the effects of exposure for prolonged periods to a rigidly monotonous environment. Hebb's collaborators in the project were B. K. Doane, T. H. Scott, W. H. Bexton and the writer of this article.

The aim of the project was to obtain basic information on how human beings would react in situations where

**EXPERIMENTAL CUBICLE** constructed at McGill University in Montreal to study the effects of perceptual isolation is at the right in this semischematic drawing from above. The subject lies on a bed 24 hours a day, with time out for meals and going to the bathroom. The room is always lighted. The visual perception of the subject is restricted by a translu-

nothing at all was happening. The purpose was not to cut individuals off from any sensory stimulation whatever, but to remove all patterned or perceptual stimulation, so far as we could arrange it.

The subjects were male college students, paid $20 a day to participate. They lay on a comfortable bed in a lighted cubicle 24 hours a day for as long as they cared to stay, with time out only for meals (which they usually ate sitting on the edge of the bed) and going to the toilet. They wore translucent plastic visors which transmitted diffuse light but prevented pattern vision. Cotton gloves and cardboard cuffs extending beyond the fingertips restricted perception by touch. Their auditory perception was limited by a U-shaped foam rubber pillow on which their heads lay and by a continuous hum of air-conditioning equipment which masked small sounds.

When we started the research we were not at all sure what aspects of behavior it would be most profitable to investigate. Accordingly we began with a preliminary run in which we merely

observed the subjects' behavior and interviewed them afterward. Most of these subjects had planned to think about their work: some intended to review their studies, some to plan term papers, and one thought that he would organize a lecture he had to deliver. Nearly all of them reported that the most striking thing about the experience was that they were unable to think clearly about anything for any length of time and that their thought processes seemed to be affected in other ways. We therefore decided that the first thing to do was to test effects on mental performance.

We used three main methods of investigating this. One was a battery of oral tests involving simple arithmetic, anagrams, word association and so on. This battery was given before the experiment, at 12, 24 and 48 hours during the isolation and finally three days afterward. Another battery of tests, given two days before and immediately after the isolation period, included copying a design with blocks, speed of copying a prose paragraph, substituting symbols for numbers, picking out what was odd

in each of a series of pictures (for instance, one picture showed a man in a canoe using a broom instead of a paddle) and recognizing patterns embedded in a complex background. The third test used a recording of a talk arguing for the reality of ghosts, poltergeists and other supernatural phenomena. It was played to each subject during his isolation. We examined the individual's attitude toward supernatural phenomena before he entered isolation and after he had emerged.

On almost every test the subjects' performance was impaired by their isolation in the monotonous environment (and was poorer than that of a control group of students). The isolation experience also tended to make the subjects susceptible to the argument for the existence of supernatural phenomena. Some of them reported that for several days after the experiment they were afraid that they were going to see ghosts.

As the subjects lay in isolation, cut off from stimulation, the content of their thought gradually changed. At first

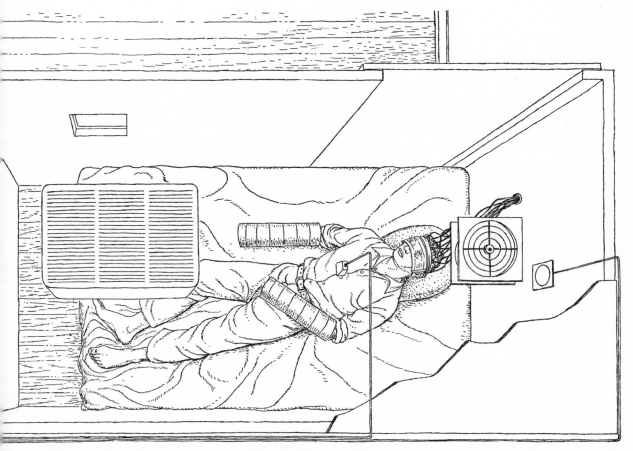

cent plastic visor; his auditory perception, by a U-shaped pillow covering his ears and by the noise of an air conditioner and a fan (*ceiling of cubicle*). In the experiment depicted here a flat pillow is used to leave room for the wires attached to the subject's scalp, which are connected to an electroencephalograph in an adjacent room. The subject's sense of touch is restricted by cotton gloves and long cardboard cuffs. The experimenter and the subject can communicate by means of a system of microphones and loud speakers.

they tended to think about their studies, about the experiment, about their personal problems. After a while they began to reminisce about past incidents, their families, their friends and so on. To pass the time some tried to remember in detail a motion picture they had seen; others thought about traveling from one familiar place to another and would try to imagine all the events of the journey; some counted numbers steadily into the thousands. (Incidentally, such experiences are commonly reported by persons who have been in solitary confinement for long periods.) Eventually some subjects reached a state in which it took too much effort to concentrate, and they became "content to let the mind drift," as one subject put it. Others said: "My mind just became full of sounds and colors, and I could not control it"; "I just ran out of things to think of"; "I couldn't think of anything to think about." Several subjects experienced "blank periods" when they did not seem to be thinking at all.

Not surprisingly, the subjects became markedly irritable as time went on and often expressed their irritation. Yet they also had spells when they were easily amused. In the interview afterward many of the subjects expressed surprise that their feelings could have oscillated so much, and that they could have behaved in such a childish way. They also said that they seemed to lose their "sense of perspective" while in the cubicle, and some subjects mentioned that at times they felt that the experimenters were against them, and were trying to make things exceptionally tough for them.

The subjects reported something else to which we at first paid no particular attention, but which was to emerge as the most striking result of the experiments. Many of them, after long isolation, began to see "images." One man repeatedly saw a vision of a rock shaded by a tree; another kept on seeing pictures of babies and could not get rid of them. Several subjects seemed to be "having dreams" while they were awake. Not until one of the experimenters himself went through the isolation experience for a long period did we realize the power and strangeness of the phenomenon. His report, and a review of the literature on other experiments in monotony, made clear that the experimental situation induced hallucinations.

The visual phenomena were similar to those experienced after taking the intoxicating drug of the mescal plant (mescal buttons), which is a ceremonial practice of some Indian tribes in the Southwest. They have also been reported in experiments in which subjects were exposed for long periods to blank visual fields or flickering light.

Our subjects' hallucinations usually began with simple forms. They might start to "see" dots of light, lines or simple geometrical patterns. Then the visions became more complex, with abstract patterns repeated like a design on wallpaper, or recognizable figures, such as rows of little yellow men with black caps on and their mouths open. Finally there were integrated scenes: e.g., a procession of squirrels with sacks over their shoulders marching "purposefully" across the visual field, prehistoric animals walking about in a jungle, processions of eyeglasses marching down a street. These scenes were frequently distorted, and were described as being like animated movie cartoons. Usually the subjects were at first surprised and amused by these phenomena, looked forward eagerly to see what was going to happen next and found that the "pictures" alleviated their boredom. But after a while the pictures became disturbing, and so vivid that they interfered with sleep. Some of the subjects complained that their eyes became tired from "focusing" on the pictures. They found sometimes that they could even scan the "scene," taking in new parts as they moved their eyes, as if they were looking at real pictures.

The subjects had little control over the content of the hallucinations. Some kept seeing the same type of picture no matter how hard they tried to change it. One man could see nothing but dogs, another nothing but eyeglasses of various types, and so on. Some subjects were able to realize visions of objects suggested by the experimenter, but not always in the way they were instructed. One man, trying to "get" a pen, saw first an inkblot on a white tablecloth, then a pencil, then a green horse, finally a pen.

The hallucinations were not confined to vision. Occasionally a subject heard people in the "scene" talking, and one man repeatedly heard a music box playing. Another saw the sun rising over a church and heard a choir singing "in full stereophonic sound." Several subjects reported sensations of movement or touch. One had a feeling of being hit in the arm by pellets fired from a miniature rocket ship he saw; another, reaching out to touch a doorknob in his vision, felt an electric shock. Some subjects reported that they felt as if another body were lying beside them in the cubicle; in one case the two bodies overlapped, partly occupying the same space. Some reported feelings of "otherness" or "bodily strangeness"; trying to describe their sensations, they said, "my mind seemed to be a ball of cotton wool floating above my body," or "something seemed to be sucking my mind out through my eyes."

After emerging from isolation, our subjects frequently reported that "things looked curved," "near things looked large and far things looked small," "things seemed to move," and so on. We therefore made some systematic tests of their visual perception. The most striking finding was that when subjects emerged after several days of isolation, the whole room appeared to be in motion. In addition there was a tendency for surfaces to appear curved, and for objects to appear to be changing their size and shape. Asked to match a disk that was handed to them to one in a row of disks of various sizes 12 feet away, the subjects consistently chose a larger disk than did control subjects.

We recorded changes in the electrical activity of the brain in these subjects by means of electroencephalograms made before, during and after the isolation period. There was a tendency for some slow waves, which are normally present in sleep but not when an adult is awake, to appear after a period of isolation. In addition, the frequencies in the region of the principal brain rhythm slowed down [see charts on opposite page].

The overt behavior of the subjects during the experiment was, of course, carefully recorded. Most of the subjects went to sleep fairly soon after they had been placed in the cubicle. After waking they showed increasing signs of restlessness. This restlessness was not continuous but came in more and more intense spells, which were described as being very unpleasant. The subjects appeared eager for stimulation, and would talk to themselves, whistle, sing or recite poetry. When they came out for meals, they tended to be garrulous and attempted to draw the experimenters into conversation. In moving about, as when they were led to the toilet, they appeared dazed and confused, and had increasing difficulty in finding their way about the washroom.

As an outgrowth of the general experiment, we have begun some tests to find out the effects of restriction of just one sense. We tested six subjects who wore the frosted visors constantly but who otherwise were allowed to pursue

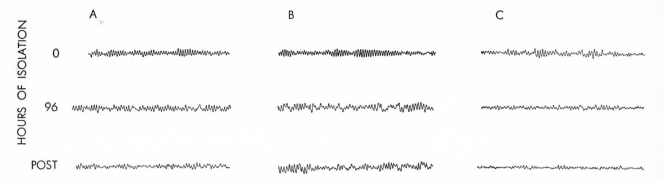

BRAIN WAVES from the occipital region of three subjects of the McGill University experiments (*above*) showed some change after 96 hours of isolation and three hours after the subject had emerged from isolation (POST). Similar changes in three other subjects are reflected in the bar charts (*bottom*). Below each bar is the number of waves counted in each one-second interval over a period of 300 seconds. The height of each bar is the percentage of all the waves during that period. Thus it indicates wave frequencies.

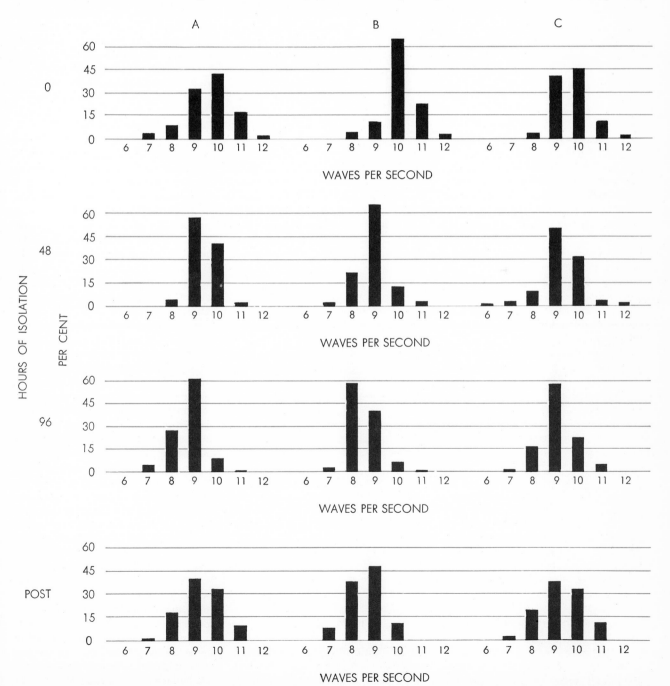

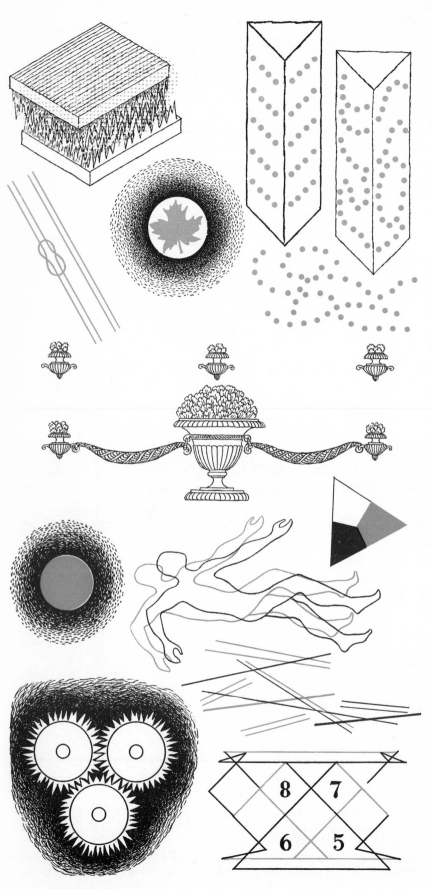

comparatively "normal" activities. Unfortunately the results of this experiment are not "pure," because the restriction of vision greatly restricted their movements and opportunity for other stimulation. These subjects developed visual hallucinations and also experienced some disorders of visual perception when the visors were removed.

Prolonged exposure to a monotonous environment, then, has definitely deleterious effects. The individual's thinking is impaired; he shows childish emotional responses; his visual perception becomes disturbed; he suffers from hallucinations; his brain-wave pattern changes. These findings are in line with recent studies of the brain, especially of the reticular formation in the midbrain [see the next article in this volume, "Pleasure Centers in the Brain" by James Olds]. In some way the reticular formation regulates the brain's activity. The recent studies indicate that normal functioning of the brain depends on a continuing arousal reaction generated in the reticular formation, which in turn depends on constant sensory bombardment. It appears that, aside from their specific functions, sensory stimuli have the general function of maintaining this arousal, and they rapidly lose their power to do so if they are restricted to the monotonously repeated stimulation of an unchanging environment. Under these circumstances the activity of the cortex may be impaired so that the brain behaves abnormally.

The results of our experiments seem to throw light on a number of practical problems. For instance, studies in France and at Harvard University have indicated that hallucinations are fairly common among long-distance truck drivers. After many hours on the road they may begin to see apparitions such as giant red spiders on the windshield and nonexistent animals running across the road, which frequently cause accidents. Similar phenomena have been reported by aviators on long flights: Charles Lindbergh described some in his autobiography. It is not improbable that some unexplained airplane and railroad accidents have been occasioned by effects of prolonged monotonous stimulation.

A changing sensory environment seems essential for human beings. Without it, the brain ceases to function in an adequate way, and abnormalities of behavior develop. In fact, as Christopher Burney observed in his remarkable account of his stay in solitary confinement: "Variety is not the spice of life; it is the very stuff of it."

**HALLUCINATIONS** of isolated subjects are depicted. The drawings are based on descriptions by the subjects during the experiment and on sketches made after isolation period.

# 24

# PLEASURE CENTERS IN THE BRAIN

JAMES OLDS                                    October 1956

The brain has been mapped in various ways by modern physiologists. They have located the sensory and motor systems and the seats of many kinds of behavior—centers where messages of sight, sound, touch and action are received and interpreted. Where, then, dwell the "higher feelings," such as love, fear, pain and pleasure? Up to three years ago the notion that the emotions had specific seats in the brain might have been dismissed as naive—

akin perhaps to medieval anatomy or phrenology. But recent research has brought a surprising turn of affairs. The brain does seem to have definite loci of pleasure and pain, and we shall review here the experiments which have led to this conclusion.

The classical mapping exploration of the brain ranged mainly over its broad, fissured roof—the cortex—and there localized the sensory and motor systems and other areas which seemed to control

most overt behavior. Other areas of the brain remained mostly unexplored, and comparatively little was known about their functions. Particularly mysterious was the series of structures lying along the mid-line of the brain from the roof down to the spinal cord, structures which include the hypothalamus and parts of the thalamus [see diagram on page 185]. It was believed that general functions of the brain might reside in these structures. But they were difficult

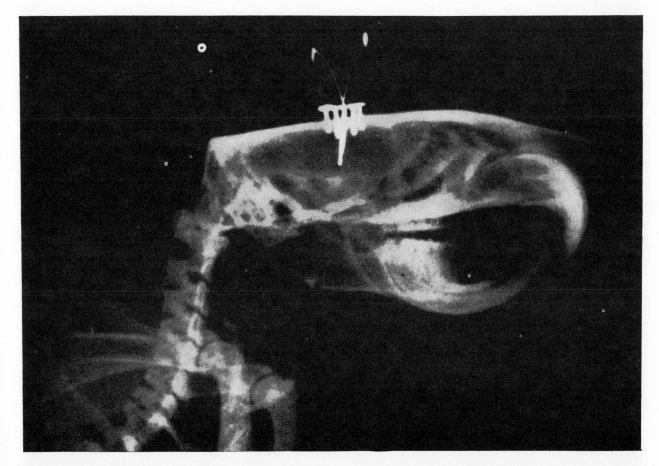

**IMPLANTED ELECTRODES** in the brain of a rat are shown in this X-ray photograph. The electrodes are held in a plastic carrier screwed to the skull. They can be used to give an electrical stimulus to the brain or to record electrical impulses generated by the brain.

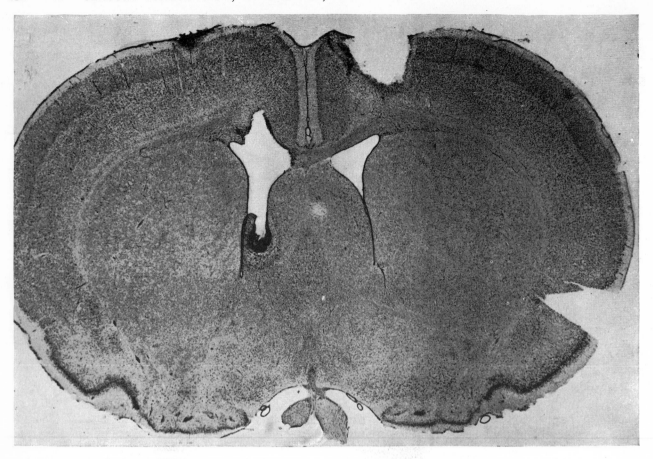

RAT'S BRAIN in a photomicrographic cross section shows a black spot to left of center, marking the point where electrical stimulus was applied. Such cross sections make it possible to tell exactly which center in the brain was involved in the animal's response.

to investigate, for two reasons. First, the structures were hard to get at. Most of them lie deep in the brain and could not be reached without damaging the brain, whereas the cortex could be explored by electrical stimulators and recording instruments touching the surface. Secondly, there was a lack of psychological tools for measuring the more general responses of an animal. It is easy to test an animal's reaction to stimulation of a motor center in the brain, for it takes the simple form of flexing a muscle, but how is one to measure an animal's feeling of pleasure?

The first difficulty was overcome by the development of an instrument for probing the brain. Basically the instrument is a very fine needle electrode which can be inserted to any point of the brain without damage. In the early experiments the brain of an animal could be probed only with some of its skull removed and while it was under anesthesia. But W. R. Hess in Zurich developed a method of studying the brain for longer periods and under more normal circumstances. The electrodes were inserted through the skull, fixed in position

and left there; after the skin healed over the wound, the animal could be studied in its ordinary activities.

Using the earlier technique, H. W. Magoun and his collaborators at Northwestern University explored the region known as the "reticular system" in the lower part of the mid-brain [see page 185]. They showed that this system controls the sleep and wakefulness of animals. Stimulation of the system produced an "alert" electrical pattern, even from an anesthetized animal, and injury to nerve cells there produced more or less continuous sleep.

Hess, with his new technique, examined the hypothalamus and the region around the septum (the dividing membrane at the mid-line), which lie forward of the reticular system. He found that these parts of the brain play an important part in an animal's automatic protective behavior. In the rear section of the hypothalamus is a system which controls emergency responses that prepare the animal for fight or flight. Another system in the front part of the hypothalamus and in the septal area apparently controls rest, recovery, diges-

tion and elimination. In short, these studies seemed to localize the animal's brain responses in situations provoking fear, rage, escape or certain needs.

There remained an important part of the mid-line region of the brain which had not been explored and whose functions were still almost completely unknown. This area, comprising the upper portion of the middle system, seemed to be connected with smell, and to this day it is called the rhinencephalon, or "smell-brain." But the area appeared to receive messages from many organs of the body, and there were various other reasons to believe it was not concerned exclusively or even primarily with smell. As early as 1937 James W. Papez of Cornell University suggested that the rhinencephalon might control emotional experience and behavior. He based this speculation partly on the observation that rabies, which produces profound emotional upset, seems to attack parts of the rhinencephalon.

Such observations, then, constituted our knowledge of the areas of the brain until recently. Certain areas had

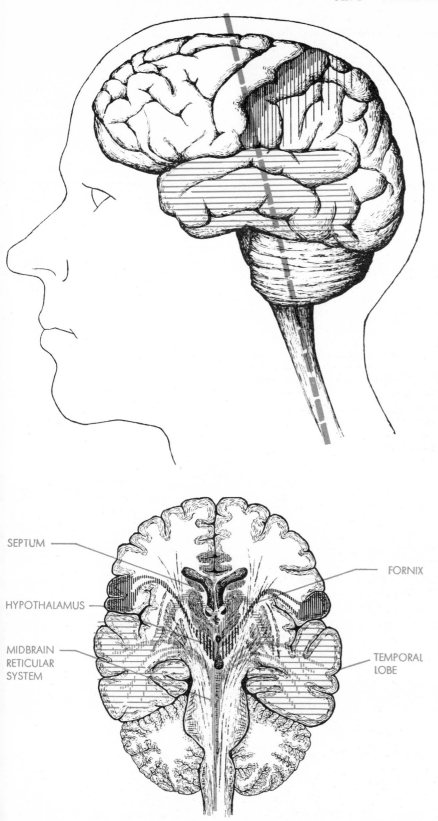

LOCATIONS OF FUNCTION in the human brain are mapped in these two diagrams. The white areas in both diagrams comprise the motor system; the black crosshatched areas, the sensory system. Crosshatched in color are the "nonspecific" regions now found to be involved in motivation of behavior. The diagram at bottom shows the brain from behind, dissected along the heavy dashed line at top. The labels here identify the centers which correspond to those investigated in the rat. The fornix and parts of the temporal lobes, plus associated structures not labeled, together constitute the rhinencephalon or "smell-brain."

been found to be involved in various kinds of emotional behavior, but the evidence was only of a general nature. The prevailing view still held that the basic motivations—pain, pleasure and so on—probably involved excitation or activity of the whole brain.

Investigation of these matters in more detail became possible only after psychologists had developed methods for detecting and measuring positive emotional behavior—pleasure and the satisfaction of specific "wants." It was B. F. Skinner, the Harvard University experimental psychologist, who produced the needed refinement. He worked out a technique for measuring the rewarding effect of a stimulus (or the degree of satisfaction) in terms of the frequency with which an animal would perform an act which led to the reward. For example, the animal was placed in a bare box containing a lever it could manipulate. If it received no reward when it pressed the lever, the animal might perform this act perhaps five to 10 times an hour. But if it was rewarded with a pellet of food every time it worked the lever, then its rate of performing the act would rise to 100 or more times per hour. This increase in response frequency from five or 10 to 100 per hour provided a measure of the rewarding effect of the food. Other stimuli produce different response rates, and in each case the rise in rate seems to be a quite accurate measure of the reward value of the given stimulus.

With the help of Hess's technique for probing the brain and Skinner's for measuring motivation, we have been engaged in a series of experiments which began three years ago under the guidance of the psychologist D. O. Hebb at McGill University. At the beginning we planned to explore particularly the midbrain reticular system—the sleep-control area that had been investigated by Magoun.

Just before we began our own work, H. R. Delgado, W. W. Roberts and N. E. Miller at Yale University had undertaken a similar study. They had located an area in the lower part of the mid-line system where stimulation caused the animal to avoid the behavior that provoked the electrical stimulus. We wished to investigate positive as well as negative effects—that is, to learn whether stimulation of some areas might be sought rather than avoided by the animal.

We were not at first concerned to hit very specific points in the brain, and in fact in our early tests the electrodes did not always go to the particular areas in the mid-line system at which they were aimed. Our lack of aim turned out to be a fortunate happening for us. In one animal the electrode missed its target and landed not in the mid-brain reticular system but in a nerve pathway from the rhinencephalon. This led to an unexpected discovery.

In the test experiment we were using, the animal was placed in a large box with corners labeled A, B, C and D. Whenever the animal went to corner A, its brain was given a mild electric shock by the experimenter. When the test was performed on the animal with the electrode in the rhinencephalic nerve, it kept returning to corner A. After several such returns on the first day, it finally went to a different place and fell asleep. The next day, however, it seemed even more interested in corner A.

At this point we assumed that the stimulus must provoke curiosity; we did not yet think of it as a reward. Further experimentation on the same animal soon indicated, to our surprise, that its response to the stimulus was more than curiosity. On the second day, after the animal had acquired the habit of returning to corner A to be stimulated, we began trying to draw it away to corner B, giving it an electric shock whenever it took a step in that direction. Within a matter of five minutes the animal was in corner B. After this, the animal could be directed to almost any spot in the box at the will of the experimenter. Every step in the right direction was paid with a small shock; on arrival at the appointed place the animal received a longer series of shocks.

Next the animal was put on a T-shaped platform and stimulated if it turned right at the crossing of the T but not if it turned left. It soon learned to turn right every time. At this point we reversed the procedure, and the animal had to turn left in order to get a shock. With some guidance from the experimenter it eventually switched from the right to the left. We followed up with a test of the animal's response when it was hungry. Food was withheld for 24 hours. Then the animal was placed in a T both arms of which were baited with mash. The animal would receive the electric stimulus at a point halfway down the right arm. It learned to go there, and it always stopped at this point, never going on to the food at all!

After confirming this powerful effect of stimulation of brain areas by experiments with a series of animals, we set out to map the places in the brain where

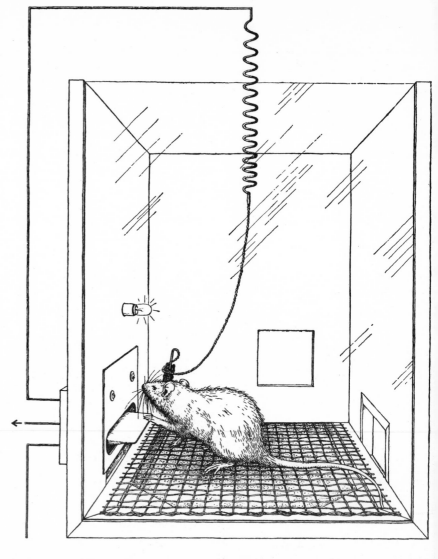

SELF-STIMULATION CIRCUIT is diagrammed here. When the rat presses on treadle it triggers an electric stimulus to its brain and simultaneously records action via wire at left.

such an effect could be obtained. We wanted to measure the strength of the effect in each place. Here Skinner's technique provided the means. By putting the animal in the "do-it-yourself" situation (i.e., pressing a lever to stimulate its own brain) we could translate the animal's strength of "desire" into response frequency, which can be seen and measured.

The first animal in the Skinner box ended all doubts in our minds that electric stimulation applied to some parts of the brain could indeed provide reward for behavior. The test displayed the phenomenon in bold relief where anyone who wanted to look could see it. Left to itself in the apparatus, the animal (after about two to five minutes of learning) stimulated its own brain regularly about once every five seconds, taking a

stimulus of a second or so every time. After 30 minutes the experimenter turned off the current, so that the animal's pressing of the lever no longer stimulated the brain. Under these conditions the animal pressed it about seven times and then went to sleep. We found that the test was repeatable as often as we cared to apply it. When the current was turned on and the animal was given one shock as an *hors d'oeuvre*, it would begin stimulating its brain again. When the electricity was turned off, it would try a few times and then go to sleep.

The current used to stimulate was ordinary house current reduced by a small transformer and then regulated between one and five volts by means of a potentiometer (a radio volume control). As the resistance in the brain was approximately 12,000 ohms, the current ranged from about .000083 to .000420 of an ampere. The shock lasted up to about a second, and the animal had to release the lever and press again to get more.

We now started to localize and quantify the rewarding effect in the brain by planting electrodes in all parts of the brain in large numbers of rats. Each rat had a pair of electrodes consisting of insulated silver wires a hundredth of an inch in diameter. The two stimulating tips were only about one 500th of an inch apart. During a test the animal was placed in a Skinner box designed to produce a chance response rate of about 10 to 25 bar-presses per hour. Each animal was given about six hours of testing with the electric current turned on and one hour with the current off. All responses were recorded automatically, and the

animal was given a score on the basis of the amount of time it spent stimulating its brain.

When electrodes were implanted in the classical sensory and motor systems, response rates stayed at the chance level of 10 to 25 an hour. In most parts of the mid-line system, the response rates rose to levels of from 200 to 5,000 an hour, definitely indicative of a rewarding effect of the electric stimulus. But in some of the lower parts of the mid-line system there was an opposite effect: the animal would press the lever once and never go back. This indicated a punishing effect in those areas. They appeared to be the same areas where Delgado, Roberts and Miller at Yale also had discovered the avoidance effect—and where Hess and others had found responses of rage and escape.

The animals seemed to experience the strongest reward, or pleasure, from stimulation of areas of the hypothalamus and certain mid-brain nuclei—regions which Hess and others had found to be centers for control of digestive, sexual, excretory and similar processes. Animals with electrodes in these areas would stimulate themselves from 500 to 5,000 times per hour. In the rhinencephalon the effects were milder, producing self-stimulation at rates around 200 times per hour.

Electric stimulation in some of these regions actually appeared to be far more rewarding to the animals than an ordinary satisfier such as food. For example, hungry rats ran faster to reach an electric stimulator than they did to reach food. Indeed, a hungry animal often ignored available food in favor of the pleasure of stimulating itself electrically. Some rats with electrodes in these places stimulated their brains more than 2,000 times per hour for 24 consecutive hours!

Why is the electric stimulation so rewarding? We are currently exploring this question, working on the hypothesis that brain stimulation in these regions must excite some of the nerve cells that would be excited by satisfaction of the basic drives—hunger, sex, thirst and so forth. We have looked to see whether some parts of the "reward system" of the brain are specialized; that is, there may be one part for the hunger drive, another for the sex drive, etc.

In experiments on hunger, we have found that an animal's appetite for electric stimulation in some brain regions increases as hunger increases: the animal will respond much faster when hungry than when full. We are performing similar tests in other places in the brain with variations of thirst and sex hormones. We have already found that there are areas where the rewarding effects of a brain stimulus can be abolished by castration and restored by injections of testosterone.

Our present tentative conclusion is that emotional and motivational mechanisms can indeed be localized in the brain; that certain portions of the brain are sensitive to each of the basic drives. Strong electrical stimulation of these areas seems to be even more satisfying than the usual rewards of food, etc. This finding contradicts the long-held theory that strong excitation in the brain means punishment. In some areas of the brain it means reward.

The main question for future research is to determine how the excited "reward" cells act upon the specific sensory-motor systems to intensify the rewarded

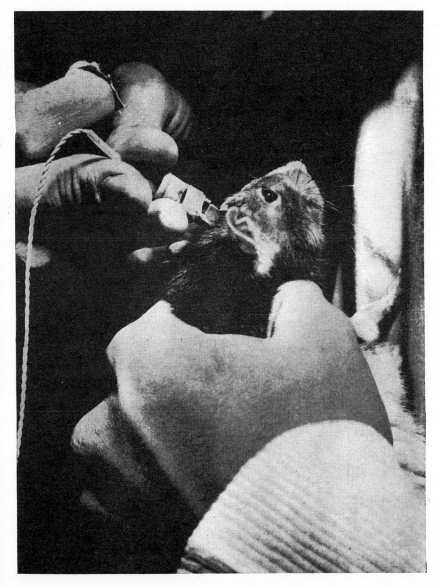

**RAT IS CONNECTED** to electrical circuit by a plug which can be disconnected to free the animal during rest periods. Presence of electrodes does not pain or discommode the rat.

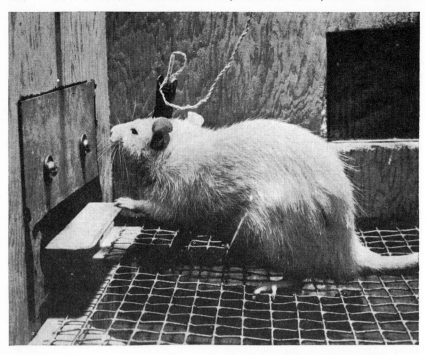

**RAT SEEKS STIMULUS** as it places its paw on the treadle. Some of the animals have been seen to stimulate themselves for 24 hours without rest and as often as 5,000 times an hour.

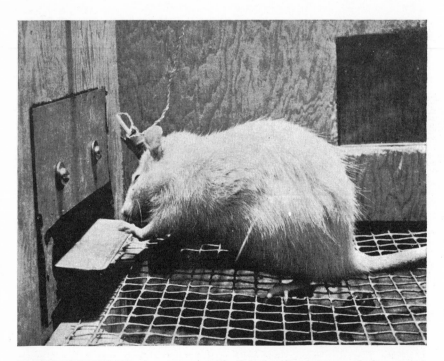

**RAT FEELS STIMULUS** as it presses on treadle. Pulse lasts less than a second; the current is less than .0005 ampere. The animal must release lever and press again to renew the stimulus.

behavior.

At the moment we are using the self-stimulating technique to learn whether drugs will selectively affect the various motivational centers of the brain. We hope, for example, that we may eventually find one drug that will raise or lower thresholds in the hunger system, another for the sex-drive system, and so forth. Such drugs would allow control of psy-chological disorders caused by surfeits or deficits in motivational conditions.

Enough of the brain-stimulating work has been repeated on monkeys by J. V. Brady and J. C. Lilly (who work in different laboratories in Washington, D. C.) to indicate that our general con-clusions can very likely be generalized eventually to human beings—with modi-fications, of course.

# 25

# ULCERS IN "EXECUTIVE" MONKEYS

JOSEPH V. BRADY                                    October 1958

Physicians and laymen alike have long recognized that emotional stress can produce bodily disease. Psychic disturbances can induce certain skin and respiratory disorders, can set off attacks of allergic asthma and may even play a part in some forms of heart disease. Of all the body's systems, however, the gastrointestinal tract is perhaps

the most vulnerable to emotional stress. The worries, fears, conflicts and anxieties of daily life can produce gastrointestinal disorders ranging from the "nervous stomach," which most of us know at first hand, to the painful and often disabling ulcers which are the traditional occupational disease of business executives.

Emotional stress appears to produce

ulcers by increasing the flow of the stomach's acid juices. The connection between emotional disturbance, stomach secretion and ulcers is well documented. A recent study of 2,000 Army draftees, for example, found that those who showed emotional disturbance and excessive gastric secretion during their initial physical examination developed

CONDITIONING EXPERIMENT involves training monkeys in "restraining chairs." Both animals receive brief electric shocks at regular intervals. The "executive" monkey (left) has learned

to press the lever in its left hand, which prevents shocks to both animals. The control monkey (right) has lost interest in its lever, which is a dummy. Only executive monkeys developed ulcers.

ulcers later on under the strains of military life.

But not every kind of emotional stress produces ulcers, and the same kind of stress will do so in one person and not in another. Experimental investigation of the problem is difficult. Animals obviously cannot provide wholly satisfactory experimental models of human mind-body interactions. They can, however, be studied under controlled conditions, and it is through animal experiments that we are finding leads to the cause of ulcers as well as to the effect of emotional stress on the organism in general.

Various investigators have succeeded in inducing ulcers in experimental animals by subjecting them to physical stress. But the role of the emotional processes in such experiments has been uncertain. Experiments on dogs by George F. Mahl of Yale University Medical School indicate that a "fear producing" situation lasting many hours increases the animals' gastric secretions, but these animals do not develop ulcers. William L. Sawrey and John D. Weisz of the University of Colorado produced ulcers in rats by subjecting them to a conflict situation: keeping them in a box where

they could obtain food and water only by standing on a grid which gave them a mild electric shock. But this experiment, as Sawrey and Weisz themselves pointed out, did not prove conclusively that emotional stress was the crucial factor in producing the ulcers.

Our studies of ulcers in monkeys at the Walter Reed Army Institute of Research developed somewhat fortuitously. For several years we had been investigating the emotional behavior of these animals. In some of our experiments we had been keeping monkeys in "restraining chairs" (in which they could move their heads and limbs but not their bodies) while we conditioned them in various ways. Since these procedures seemed to impose considerable emotional stress on the animals, we decided that we ought to know something about their physiological reactions. Preliminary investigation showed that stress brought about dramatic alterations in the hormone content of the animals' blood, but a more extensive study of 19 monkeys was brought to a halt when many of them died.

At first we considered this merely a

stroke of bad luck, but the post-mortem findings showed that more than bad luck was involved. Many of the dead monkeys had developed ulcers as well as other extensive gastrointestinal damage. Such pathological conditions are normally rare in laboratory animals, and previous experiments with monkeys kept in restraining chairs up to six months convinced us that restraint alone did not produce the ulcers. Evidently the conditioning procedures were to blame.

One of the procedures which showed a high correlation with ulcers involved training the monkey to avoid an electric shock by pressing a lever. The animal received a brief shock on the feet at regular intervals, say, every 20 seconds. It could avoid the shock if it learned to press the lever at least once in every 20-second interval. It does not take a monkey very long to master this problem; within a short time it is pressing the lever far oftener than once in 20 seconds. Only occasionally does it slow down enough to receive a shock as a reminder.

One possibility, of course, was that the monkeys which had developed ulcers under this procedure had done so not because of the psychological stress in-

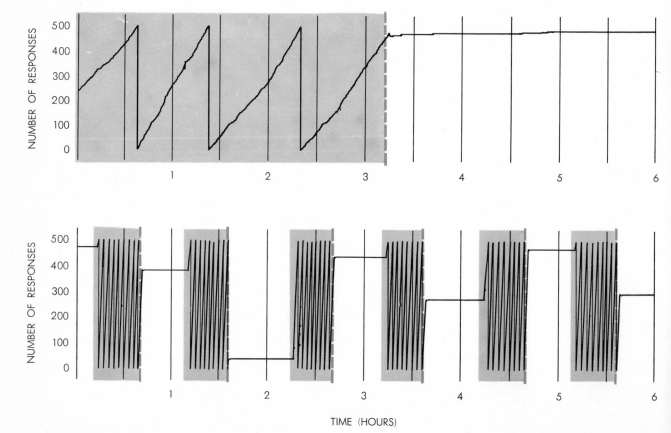

RESPONSES OF MONKEYS were recorded automatically. Slope of the lines shows the rate of lever-pressing (*vertical lines indicate resetting of stylus*). Upper chart shows responses of an executive monkey during the last half of a six-hour avoidance session (*colored area*) and the first half of a six-hour rest period; shocks were programmed every 20 seconds. Monkeys kept on this schedule developed ulcers. Lower chart shows responses during a 30-minutes-on, 30-minutes-off schedule with shocks programmed every two seconds. Monkeys on this schedule failed to develop ulcers, despite more intense activity and presumably greater psychic stress.

volved but rather as a cumulative result of the shocks. To test this possibility we set up a controlled experiment, using two monkeys in "yoked chairs" in which both monkeys received shocks but only one monkey could prevent them. The experimental or "executive" monkey could prevent shocks to himself and his partner by pressing the lever; the control monkey's lever was a dummy. Thus both animals were subjected to the same physical stress (*i.e.*, both received the same number of shocks at the same time), but only the "executive" monkey was under the psychological stress of having to press the lever.

We placed the monkeys on a continuous schedule of alternate periods of shock-avoidance and rest, arbitrarily choosing an interval of six hours for each period. As a cue for the executive monkey we provided a red light which was turned on during the avoidance periods and turned off during the "off" hours. The animal soon learned to press its lever at a rate averaging between 15 and 20 times a minute during the avoidance periods, and to stop pressing the lever when the red light was turned off. These responses showed no change throughout the experiment. The control monkey at first pressed the lever sporadically during both the avoidance and rest sessions, but lost interest in the lever within a few days.

After 23 days of a continuous six-hours-on, six-hours-off schedule the executive monkey died during one of the avoidance sessions. Our only advance warning had been the animal's failure to eat on the preceding day. It had lost no weight during the experiment, and it pressed the lever at an unflagging rate through the first two hours of its last avoidance session. Then it suddenly collapsed and had to be sacrificed. An autopsy revealed a large perforation in the wall of the duodenum—the upper part of the small intestine near its junction with the stomach, and a common site of ulcers in man. Microscopic analysis revealed both acute and chronic inflammation around this lesion. The control monkey, sacrificed in good health a few hours later, showed no gastrointestinal abnormalities. A second experiment using precisely the same procedure produced much the same results. This time the executive monkey developed ulcers in both the stomach and the duodenum; the control animal was again unaffected.

In a series of follow-up experiments which is still in progress we have tried to isolate the physiological and

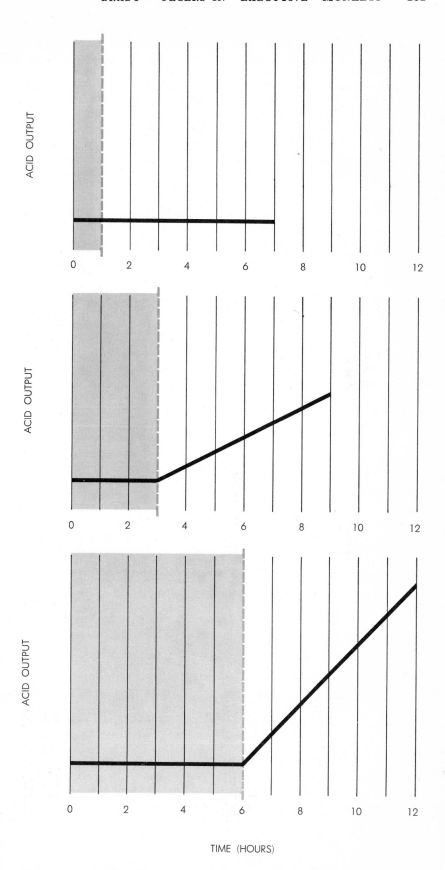

STOMACH ACIDITY of executive monkeys, as shown in these highly simplified charts, did not increase during avoidance sessions (*color*) but rather during the subsequent rest periods. The greatest increase followed a six-hour session; no rise followed a one-hour session.

psychological factors which produce the "laboratory ulcers." For example, one of our groups suggested that the "social" interaction between the two monkeys might be important. Certainly the most casual observation showed that considerable "communication" was going on between the two animals, who were seated within easy chattering distance of each other. We therefore studied several pairs of animals isolated from each other in soundproof "telephone booths." Unfortunately isolation failed to protect the executive monkeys, for they continued to develop ulcers.

More recently, however, we have found a factor or group of factors which does seem to be critical in producing ulcers. What we have learned seems to pivot on our chance selection of six hours as the interval for shock-avoidance and for rest in the conditioning procedure. We made this discovery when we sought to improve on the results of our experiments. Though laboratory animals can rarely be made to develop ulcers, we had come upon a procedure that seemed to produce ulcers "to order." The only uncertainty was the length of exposure required. This varied greatly among individual monkeys; some came down with ulcers in 18 days, others took as long as six weeks. If we could develop a technique guaranteed to produce ulcers in, say, 10 days, we could stop the shock-avoidance sessions on the eighth or ninth day, apply various therapeutic measures and study the monkey's response to them.

It seemed reasonable to assume that we might induce ulcers more rapidly and dependably by simply increasing the stress on the animals. We therefore put several monkeys on an 18-hours-on, six-hours-off schedule. After a few weeks one of the animals died, but of tuberculosis, not ulcers. The rest continued to press their levers week after week with no apparent ill effects. Finally, when it began to seem as if we might have to wait for the animals to die of old age, we sacrificed them—and found no gastrointestinal abnormalities whatever!

We put another group on an even more strenuous schedule: 30 minutes on and 30 minutes off, with the shocks programmed for every two seconds rather than every 20. Again one of the animals died, this time of a generalized virus infection unrelated to ulcers. The others, after weeks of frantic lever pressing, showed no gastrointestinal changes.

We had to conclude that the crucial factor was not the degree or even the frequency of stress but was to be sought in the relationship between the length of the stress period and that of the rest period. The six-hours-on, six-hours-off schedule had produced ulcers (and occasionally other somatic disorders) despite individual differences in monkeys, variations in diet and maintenance routines and gross alterations in preliminary physiological tests. No other schedule we had tried produced ulcers at all.

This unexpected finding suggested that we should investigate what was going on in the monkeys' stomachs during the conditioning procedure. A standard technique for investigating gastric processes in experimental animals makes use of an artificial opening, or fistula, in the animal's abdominal and stomach walls through which the contents of its stomach can be sampled. Such fistulas have played an important role in expanding our knowledge of the gastrointestinal system. In the early 19th century the famous U. S. Army surgeon William Beaumont made the first systematic study of the digestive process with the cooperation of a young Canadian who had a fistula due to an imperfectly healed gunshot wound. More than a century later Stewart G. Wolf, Jr., and Harold G. Wolff at the Cornell University Medical College, with the help of a man who had a similar injury, conducted a pioneer investigation of the relationship between emotional stress and ulcers. They found that situations which produced feelings of anxiety or aggression in their subject stepped up his gastric secretions and engorged his stomach wall with blood. Physiological changes of this sort, they believed, are the precursors of ulcers.

Edwin Polish of our department of neuroendocrinology has been studying the stomach acidity of some of our executive monkeys by means of artificial fistulas. His measurements, though far from complete, seem to provide one possible explanation of the results of our experiments.

The stomach secretions of the executive monkeys do indeed become considerably more acid, but not (as one might expect) during the avoidance periods. When the animals are actually pressing the levers the acidity of their stomachs rises little. The significant increase in acidity begins at the end of the avoidance session and reaches a peak several hours later, while the animal is presumably resting. This finding suggests a close relationship between the formation of ulcers and the cyclic character of the six-hours-on, six-hours-off procedure. Emotional stress, it appears, must be intermittent—turning the animal's system on and off, so to speak—if it is to cause ulcers. Continuous emotional stress seems to permit a stable adjustment (at least for a while) under which ulcers do not develop. It is tempting to consider the analogy of the vacuum tube or light bulb which seems to last much longer under conditions of continuous current than when it is subjected to frequent heating and cooling.

Like most analogies, this one limps badly and has its limitations. For example, our experiments show that periodic stress does not always bring on ulcers, and Polish's findings are consistent with this. His measurements indicate that the greatest increase in acidity occurs after a six-hour avoidance session. After a three-hour session acidity rises, but less sharply; after a one-hour session it does not rise at all [see illustration on page 191]. Periodic emotional stress apparently causes ulcers only if its period coincides with that of some natural rhythm of the gastrointestinal system.

Obviously our knowledge of the physiological and psychological processes which produce ulcers is far from complete. Our understanding of even the relatively well-controlled experiments I have described is just beginning to progress beyond the primitive level. We have yet to discover why emotional stress steps up the stomach's acidity later rather than immediately. We are still looking for a method of producing ulcers at will, in days rather than weeks. Eventually we hope to learn to detect an incipient ulcer before the animal collapses, by examining the subject's blood, urine and other secretions, thus making post-mortem examinations unnecessary.

There are many other questions about the effects of emotional stress which we have not yet begun to investigate. Really thorough examination of the experimental animals might well show other types of damage of which we are at present unaware. The two monkeys which died of causes unrelated to ulcers, for example, may have succumbed because their resistance had been lowered in some way by psychological stress. It would be surprising to find physical processes wholly unimpaired in monkeys who have been on a 30-minutes-on, 30-minutes-off schedule for several weeks. The opportunity to bring psychosomatic relationships under experimental scrutiny in the laboratory seems to open broad horizons for research into the causes and alleviation of this poorly understood class of ills.

# 26

# THE PHYSIOLOGY OF FEAR AND ANGER

DANIEL H. FUNKENSTEIN                    May 1955

When the late Walter B. Cannon, by his historic experiments nearly half a century ago, showed a connection between emotions and certain physiological changes in the body, he opened a new frontier for psychology and medicine. His work, coupled with that of Sigmund Freud, led to psychosomatic medicine. It also made the emotions accessible to laboratory measurement and analysis. Within the last few years there has been a keen revival of interest in this research, because of some important new discoveries which have sharpened our understanding of specific emotions and their bodily expressions. It has been learned, for instance, that anger and fear produce different physiological reactions and can be distinguished from each other. The findings have given us a fresh outlook from which to study mental illnesses.

The best way to begin the account of this recent work is to start with Cannon's own summary of what he learned. Cannon found that when an animal was confronted with a situation which evoked pain, rage or fear, it responded with a set of physiological reactions which prepared it to meet the threat with "fight" or "flight." These reactions, said Cannon, were mobilized by the secretion of adrenalin: when the cortex of the brain perceived the threat, it sent a stimulus down the sympathetic branch of the autonomic nervous system to the adrenal glands and they secreted the hormone. Cannon graphically described the results as follows:

"Respiration deepens; the heart beats more rapidly; the arterial pressure rises; the blood is shifted away from the stomach and intestines to the heart and central nervous system and the muscles; the processes in the alimentary canal cease; sugar is freed from the reserves in the liver; the spleen contracts and discharges its content of concentrated corpuscles, and adrenin is secreted from the adrenal medulla. The key to these marvelous transformations in the body is found in relating them to the natural accompaniments of fear and rage—running away in order to escape from danger, and attacking in order to be dominant. Whichever the action, a life-or-death struggle may ensue. *Stop*

"The emotional responses just listed may reasonably be regarded as preparatory for struggle. They are adjustments which, so far as possible, put the organism in readiness for meeting the demands which will be made upon it. The secreted adrenin cooperates with sympathetic nerve impulses in calling forth stored glycogen from the liver, thus flooding the blood with sugar for the use of laboring muscles; it helps in distributing the blood in abundance to the heart, the brain, and the limbs (i.e., to the parts essential for intense physical effort) while taking it away from the inhibited organs in the abdomen; it quickly abolishes the effects of muscular fatigue so that the organism which can muster adrenin in the blood can restore to its tired muscles the same readiness to act which they had when fresh; and it renders the blood more rapidly coagulable. The increased respiration, the redistributed blood running at high pressure, and the more numerous red corpuscles set free from the spleen provide for essential oxygen and for riddance of acid waste, and make a setting for instantaneous and supreme action. In short, all these changes are directly serviceable in rendering the organism more effective in the violent display of energy which fear or rage may involve."

Cannon recognized that among all these physiological changes there were a few which could not be ascribed directly to the action of adrenalin. He therefore postulated that the hormone was supplemented by two additional substances from the sympathetic nerves. An active agent, distinguishable from adrenalin, was eventually identified in 1948, when B. F. Tullar and M. L. Tainter at length succeeded in preparing the optically active form of the substance. It proved to be a second hormone secreted by the adrenal medulla. Called nor-adrenalin, it differs markedly from adrenalin in its physiological effects. Whereas adrenalin elicits profound physiological changes in almost every system in the body, nor-adrenalin apparently has only one important primary effect: namely, it stimulates the contraction of small blood vessels and increases the resistance to the flow of blood. *Start*

An animal exhibits only two major emotions in response to a threatening situation: namely, rage and fear. A man, however, may experience three: anger directed outward (the counterpart of rage), anger directed toward himself (depression) and anxiety, or fear. In studies of physiological changes accompanying various emotional states among patients at the New York Hospital, H. G. Wolff and his co-workers noticed that anger produced effects quite different from those of depression or fear. For example, when a subject was angry, the stomach lining became red and there was an increase in its rhythmic contractions and in the secretion of hydrochloric acid. When the same subject was depressed or frightened, the stomach lining was pale in color and there was a decrease in peristaltic movements and in the hydrochloric acid secretion.

The experiments of Wolff, the evidence that the adrenal medulla secreted two substances rather than one and certain clinical observations led our group at the Harvard Medical School to investigate whether adrenalin and nor-adrenalin might be specific indicators which distinguished one emotion from another. The clinical observations had to do with the effects of a drug, mecholyl, on psychotic patients. We had been studying their blood-pressure responses to injections of adrenalin, which acts on the sympathetic nervous system, and mecholyl, which stimulates the parasympathetic system. On the basis of their blood-pressure reactions, psychotic patients could be classified into seven groups [*see charts on next page*]. This test had proved of value in predicting patients' responses to psychiatric treatments, such as electric shock and insulin: certain groups responded better to the treatments than others. But more interesting was the fact that psychotic patients with high blood pressure reacted to the injection of mecholyl in two distinctly different ways. In one group there was only a small drop in the blood pressure after the injection, and the pressure returned to the usually high level within three to eight minutes. In the other group the blood pressure dropped markedly after the injection and remained below the pre-injection level even after 25 minutes. Not only were the physiological reactions quite different, but the two groups of patients also differed in personality and in response to treatment. Thirty-nine of 42 patients whose blood pressure was sharply lowered by mecholyl improved with electric shock treatment, whereas only three of 21 in the other group improved with the same treatment. Further, the two groups showed distinctly different results in projective psychological tests such as the Rorschach.

All this suggested that the two groups of patients might be differentiated on the basis of emotions. Most psychotic patients in emotional turmoil express the same emotion constantly over a period of days, weeks or months. Psychiatrists determined the predominant emotion expressed by each of 63 patients who had been tested with mecholyl, without knowing in which physiological group they had been classified. When the subjects' emotional and physiological ratings were compared, it turned out that almost all of the patients who were generally angry at other people fell in Group N (a small, temporary reduction of blood pressure by mecholyl), while almost all those who were usually depressed or frightened were in Group E (sharp re-

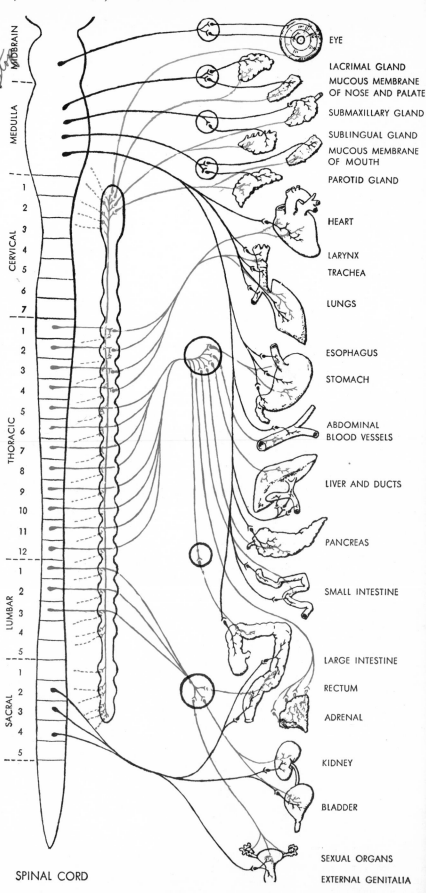

THE AUTONOMIC NERVOUS SYSTEM is represented by this diagram. The parasympathetic branches, arising from the brain and sacral vertebrae, are indicated in black; the sympathetic branches, arising from the thoracic and lumbar vertebrae, are in color.

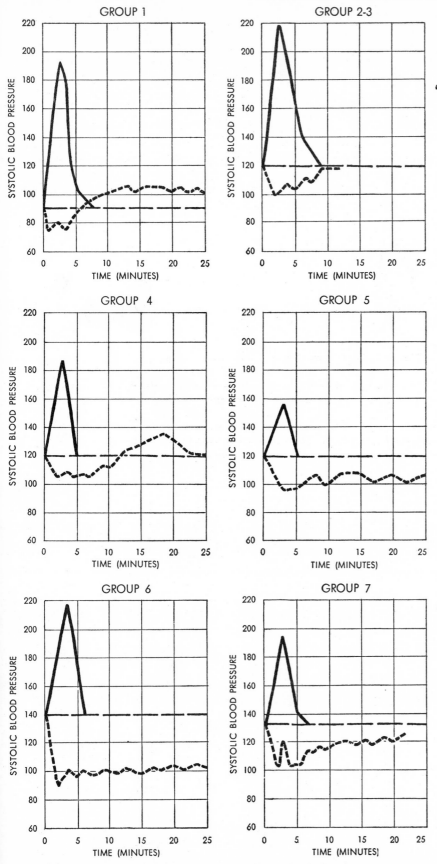

**SEVEN GROUPS of psychotic patients were distinguished on the basis of their blood pressure after injection with adrenalin or mecholyl. In these six charts the basal systolic blood pressure of the patients is indicated by the broken horizontal line. The solid curve shows their response to adrenalin; the broken curve, their response to mecholyl. Groups 2 and 3 are combined because the difference between them is too slight to show in the graph. The mecholyl response for Group 7 is incomplete because of experimental difficulties.**

sponse to mecholyl). In other words, the physiological reactions were significantly related to the emotional content of the patients' psychoses.

The next step was to find out whether the same test could distinguish emotions in normal, healthy people, using medical students as subjects. They were studied at a time when they were under stress—while they were awaiting the decisions of hospitals on their applications for internships. As the competition among the students for the hospitals of their choice is keen, the period just prior to such announcements is a time of emotional turmoil for the men. A group of students who responded to this situation with elevated blood pressure was given the standard dose of mecholyl. The results were the same as for the psychotic patients: students who were angry at others for the situation in which they found themselves had a Type N physiological reaction; those who felt depressed (angry at themselves) or anxious showed a Type E physiological reaction. The reaction was related only to their temporary emotional state; after the internships were settled and their blood pressures had returned to pre-stress levels, all the students reacted the same way to the injection of mecholyl.

It was at this point that we undertook to investigate the comparative effects of adrenalin and nor-adrenalin. A group of workers at the Presbyterian Hospital in New York had shown that injections of nor-adrenalin and adrenalin produced two different types of rise in blood pressure, one due to contraction of blood vessels and the other to faster pumping by the heart. Upon learning of this work, we designed experiments to test the hypothesis that the two types of elevated blood pressure, differentiated by us on the basis of mecholyl tests, indicated in one instance excessive secretion of nor-adrenalin and in the other excessive secretion of adrenalin. Healthy college students were first given a series of intravenous injections of salt water to accustom them to the procedure so that it would not disturb them. Then each subject was tested in the following way. He was given an injection of nor-adrenalin sufficient to raise his blood pressure by 25 per cent. Then, while his blood pressure was elevated, he received the standard dose of mecholyl, and its effects on the blood pressure were noted. The next day the subject was put through the same procedure except that adrenalin was given instead of nor-adrenalin to raise the blood pressure.

Ten students were studied in this way, and in every instance the effect of nor-adrenalin was different from that of adrenalin [*see charts on page 197*]. When the blood pressure was elevated by nor-adrenalin, mecholyl produced only a small drop in pressure, with a return to the previous level in seven to 10 minutes. This reaction was similar to the Type N response in psychotic patients and healthy students under stress. In contrast, when the blood pressure was elevated by adrenalin, mecholyl produced the Type E response: the pressure dropped markedly and did not return to the previous level during the 25-minute observation period.

These results suggested, in the light of the earlier experiments, that anger directed outward was associated with secretion of nor-adrenalin, while depression and anxiety were associated with secretion of adrenalin. To check this hypothesis, another series of experiments was carried out.

A group of 125 college students were subjected to stress-inducing situations in the laboratory. The situations, involving frustration, were contrived to bring out each student's habitual reaction to stresses in real life; that the reactions actually were characteristic of the subjects' usual responses was confirmed by interviews with their college roommates. While the subjects were under stress, observers recorded their emotional reactions and certain physiological changes—in the blood pressure, the pulse and the so-called IJ waves stemming from the action of the heart. This test showed that students who responded to the stress with anger directed outward had physiological reactions similar to those produced by injection of nor-adrenalin, while students who responded with depression or anxiety had physiological reactions like those to adrenalin.

There remained the question: Does the same individual secrete unusual amounts of nor-adrenalin when angry and of adrenalin when frightened? Albert F. Ax, working in another laboratory in our hospital, designed experiments to study this question. He contrived laboratory stressful situations which were successful in producing on one occasion anger and on another occasion fear in the same subjects. His results showed that when a subject was angry at others, the physiological reactions were like those induced by the injection of nor-adrenalin; when the same subject was frightened, the reactions were like those to adrenalin. This indicated that the physiology was specific for the emotion rather than for the person.

In all these experiments the evidence

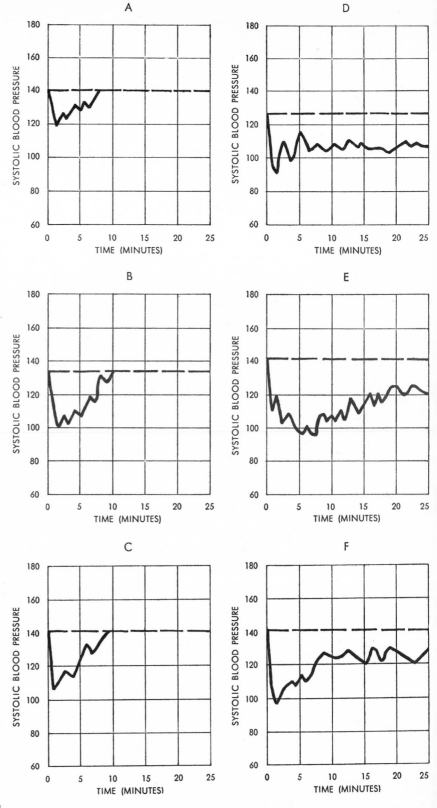

TYPE N RESPONSE to the injection of mecholyl is traced by the heavy line. The broken line represents the basal blood pressure. The response is shown for three kinds of subject: (A) healthy individuals under stress who respond with anger toward others, (B) healthy individuals whose blood pressure has been elevated with nor-adrenalin and (C) psychotic individuals with elevated blood pressure and anger toward others.

TYPE E RESPONSE to the injection of mecholyl is similarly traced by the heavy line. In these charts the response is shown for three different kinds of subject: (D) healthy individuals under stress who respond with anger directed inward, or depression, (E) healthy individuals whose blood pressure has been elevated with adrenalin and (C) psychotic individuals with elevated blood pressure and depression.

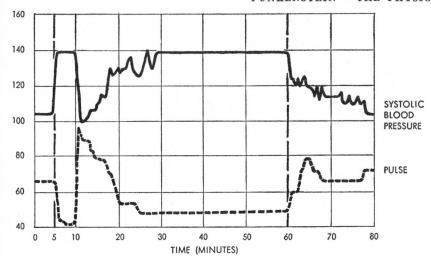

**EFFECT OF NOR-ADRENALIN** was observed by administering an infusion of the hormone for 60 minutes. After 5 minutes the blood pressure of the subject rose. After 10 minutes mecholyl was injected and the blood pressure fell. Then it rose in a Type N response.

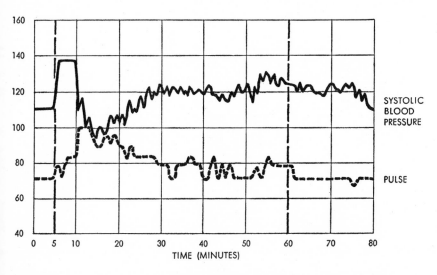

**EFFECT OF ADRENALIN** was observed by the same procedure. After the injection of mecholyl the systolic blood pressure of the subject remained depressed in a Type E response.

for excessive secretion of nor-adrenalin and adrenalin was based on the physiological changes being similar to those which can be produced by the intravenous injection of nor-adrenalin and adrenalin. Since the substances involved have not been identified chemically, and the evidence is entirely physiological, at the present time we prefer to limit ourselves to the statement that the reactions are *like* those to the two hormones. However, nothing in our experiments would contradict the hypothesis that these substances are actually adrenalin and nor-adrenalin.

What is the neurophysiological mechanism whereby different emotions evoke different adrenal secretions? Although no conclusive work in this area

is yet available, some recent investigations suggest a possible answer. U. S. von Euler in Sweden found that stimulation of certain areas of the hypothalamus caused the adrenal gland to secrete nor-adrenalin, whereas stimulation of other areas caused it to secrete adrenalin. These areas may correspond to those which the Nobel prize winner W. R. Hess of Zurich stimulated to produce aggressive behavior and flight, respectively, in animals. The experiments suggest that anger and fear may activate different areas in the hypothalamus, leading to production of nor-adrenalin in the first case and adrenalin in the second. Until more experiments are made, these possibilities must remain suppositions.

Some of the most intriguing work in this field was recently reported by von

Euler. He compared adrenal secretions found in a number of different animals. The research material was supplied by a friend who flew to Africa to obtain the adrenal medullae of wild animals. Interpreting his findings, J. Ruesch pointed out that aggressive animals such as the lion had a relatively high amount of nor-adrenalin, while in animals such as the rabbit, which depend for survival primarily on flight, adrenalin predominated. Domestic animals, and wild animals that live very social lives (*e.g.*, the baboon), also have a high ratio of adrenalin to nor-adrenalin.

These provocative findings suggest the theory that man is born with the capacity to react with a variety of emotions (has within him the lion and the rabbit), and that his early childhood experiences largely determine in which of these ways he will react under stress. Stated in another way, the evolutional process of man's emotional development is completed in the bosom of the family. We have found in other studies that individuals' habitual emotional reactions have a high correlation with their perceptions of psychological factors in their families.

This entire series of experiments yielded data which can be understood in the frame of reference of psychoanalytical observations. According to theory, anger directed outward is characteristic of an earlier stage of childhood than is anger directed toward the self or anxiety (conflicts over hostility). The latter two emotions are the result of the acculturation of the child. If the physiological development of the child parallels its psychological development, then we should expect to find that the ratio of nor-adrenalin to adrenalin is higher in infants than in older children. Bernt Hokfelt and G. B. West established that this is indeed the case: at an early age the adrenal medulla has more nor-adrenalin, but later adrenalin becomes dominant.

Paranoid patients show a greater degree of regression to infantile behavior than do patients with depression or anxiety neurosis. And it will be recalled that in our tests paranoid patients showed signs of excessive secretion of nor-adrenalin, while depressed and anxious patients exhibited symptoms of adrenalin secretion.

These parallels between psychological and physiological development suggest further studies and some theories for testing. Standing on the shoulders of Cannon and Freud, we have extended our view of human behavior and discovered fertile new fields for exploration.

# Part VII

# NEURAL SYSTEMS
# AND BEHAVIOR

# VII

## NEURAL SYSTEMS AND BEHAVIOR

*Introduction*    Previous sections have dealt with the variegated behavior of animals. We come now to a more detailed consideration of the mechanisms underlying behavior. This analysis necessarily concerns a study of the nervous system, and especially that most complex of organs, the brain. All phyla—with the exception of Protozoa (such as Amoeba or Paramecium), Mesozoa (for example Dicyema), and Porifera (such as Sponges)—possess a system of neurons. Neurons are cells specialized for the reception, conduction, and transmission of signals to other neurons and to effectors (muscles and glands). These signals or nerve impulses are in the form of electrical energy. One of the major findings of investigations of neuron physiology is that despite the almost incredible diversity of body form across phyla, there is little essential difference in basic neuronal functioning. Animals as relatively simplified in structure and behavior as the Platyhelminthes (flatworms) possess the same basic neuronal mechanisms as the Chordates (for example frogs or humans). Although there exist certain evolutionary modifications in neuron structure, the major differences appear to concern the complexity of neuron organization: "higher" organisms possess nervous systems that permit vastly greater degrees of integration and information storage, and thus greater plasticity of behavior.

At the present time we have a very poor understanding of how information is stored in the brain. Much progress has been made, however, in delineating the mechanisms underlying the reception, conduction, and transmission of information in the nervous system. The need to receive valid information from the environment is perhaps too obvious to require additional comment. Less well known is the fact that the brain is constantly being bombarded by information that originates from within the body. Receptors located throughout the body report such things as the gaseous content of the blood, degree of stretch of each muscle, position of each joint, and extent of stomach distention. These diverse types of data, together with information derived from the more commonly known sensory systems (visual, auditory, tactile, olfactory, or gustatory), must be converted into signals which can be handled by neurons. In "How Cells Receive Stimuli" (page 205), W. H. Miller, F. Ratliff, and H. K. Hartline describe some of the specialized sensory neurons which are able to convert or transduce various types of energy into the electrical signals that can then be processed by other neurons. Receptors are specialized to respond predominantly to one form of energy: radiant, mechanical, or chemical. Despite great differences in structure and type of energy transduced, all receptors operate on the common principle of producing receptor or generator potentials when appropriately stimulated. These potentials comprise the initial coding of sensory information. If they are of sufficient amplitude, generator potentials in turn produce nerve impulses, which are then relayed toward the brain for further processing.

Most neurons are not specialized for sensory functions. Rather, they receive excitation from other neurons, conduct this excitation down their axons, and then transmit the excitation to still other neurons. Neurons are not organized in simple chains, however, for one nerve cell may receive input from thousands of other neurons and project to a like number. Each neuron must be capable of (1) conducting nerve impulses from its receptive regions (the cell body and dendrites) along its axon toward other neurons, and (2) transmitting these signals to additional nerve cells or muscle fibers. These functions are discussed by Bernhard Katz in "How Cells Communicate" (page 215). Conduction is seen to depend upon the special properties of the neuronal axon—in particular, upon its selective permeability to various ions. Transmission is ordinarily accomplished by the release of minute quantities of chemicals from the terminal processes of the axon, across an exceedingly small intercellular space called the "synaptic cleft." These chemicals in turn impinge upon the receptive regions of other cells, causing the production of synaptic potentials, which may then produce nerve impulses in these cells. This process is similar in many ways to the action of the sensory neurons discussed above. Thus, while sensory neurons are differentially sensitive to one form of energy, it is probable that other neurons are differentially sensitive to various chemical transmitter substances (see pages 222–223). Attempts to identify neural transmitters constitute a very active area of nervous system investigation at the present time.

Progress in understanding brain mechanisms has not been limited to neuronal physiology. One of the most rewarding areas of research has concerned the neural bases of sleep and wakefulness. Although sleep and waking may seem to be rather prosaic sorts of behavior, it should be remembered that the degree of arousal that characterizes an organism at any given moment largely determines its responsiveness to and interaction with its environment. Thus, learning and motivational and perceptual processes are closely bound up with levels of arousal and attention. In addition, sleep and waking behavior present problems of interest and intrigue in their own right. Nathaniel Kleitman, a pioneer worker in sleep processes, discusses one of these in "Patterns of Dreaming" (page 225). One of the major findings in research on brain and behavior concerns the close relationship between behavioral level of arousal and patterns of brainwave (electroencephalographic) activity. These findings are summarized by Kleitman, as are more recent discoveries linking patterns of brain and muscular activity to dreaming. As a whole, these findings demonstrate that objective techniques can be successfully utilized in studying the neural bases of "mind" and "mental activity," thus removing these concepts from the aura of mysticism that usually surrounds them.

In 1949, G. Moruzzi and H. W. Magoun were able to produce the brain-wave patterns characteristic of the natural transition from sleep to waking by stimulating certain regions of the brain stem. This experiment initiated a new era in research in the neural bases of sleep, waking, and attention. These and related findings are discussed by J. D. French in "The Reticular Formation" (page 232). This region, which occupies the midportions of the brain stem, is seen to have a profound influence on a wide variety of bodily activities in addition to its control of arousal level. More recent studies have demonstrated that the reticular formation is comprised of a number of subareas, some of which are especially concerned with the onset of sleep, and others to the production of somatic and cerebral activites that accompany dreaming.

Like many other structures of the body, the brain is bilaterally symmetrical. Bands of neuron axons (commissures) join many symmetrical cerebral areas. In "The Great Cerebral Commissure" (page 240) R. W. Sperry details the results of experiments which have elucidated the functions of commissural systems. The ingenious studies of Sperry and his colleagues have demonstrated the importance of these systems for the coordination of the halves of the brain and for the transfer of memory from one side to the other. Their work has also revealed some of the capabilities and limitations of the brain in adapting to neural insult.

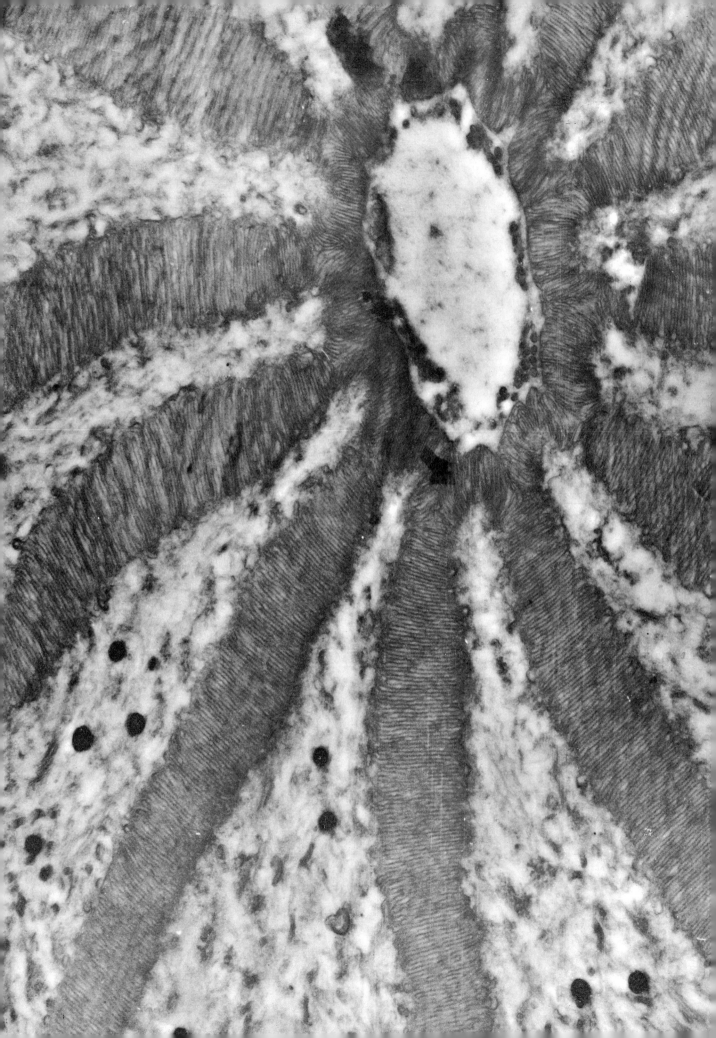

# 27

# HOW CELLS
# RECEIVE STIMULI

WILLIAM H. MILLER, FLOYD RATLIFF
AND H. K. HARTLINE        September 1961

The survival of every living thing depends ultimately on its ability to respond to the world around it and to regulate its own internal environment. In most multicellular animals this response and regulation is made possible by specialized receptor cells that are sensitive to a wide variety of physical, chemical and mechanical stimuli.

In many animals, including man, these receptors provide information that far exceeds that furnished by the traditional five senses (sight, hearing, smell, taste and touch). Sense organs of which we are less aware include equally important receptors that monitor the internal environment. Receptor organs in the muscles, called muscle spindles, provide a continuous measure of muscle stretch, and other receptors sense the movement of joints. Without such receptors it would be difficult to move or talk. Receptor cells in the hypothalamus, a part of the brain, are sensitive to the temperature of the blood; pressure-sensitive cells in the carotid sinus measure the blood pressure. Still other internal receptors monitor carbon dioxide in special regions of the large arteries. Pain receptors, widely distributed through-

out the body, respond to noxious stimuli of almost any nature that are likely to cause tissue damage.

Receptor cells not only have diverse functions and structures but also connect in various ways with the nerve fibers channeling into the central nervous system. Some receptor cells give rise directly to nerve fibers of their own; others make contact with nerve fibers originating elsewhere. All receptors, however, share a common function: the generation of nerve impulses. This does not imply that impulses necessarily occur in the receptor cells themselves. For example, in the eyes of vertebrates no one has yet been able to detect impulses in the photoreceptor cells: the rods and cones. Nevertheless, the rods and cones, when struck by light, set up the physicochemical conditions that trigger impulses in nerve cells lying behind them. Typical nerve impulses are readily detected in the optic nerve itself, which is composed of fibers of ganglion cells separated from the rods and cones by at least one intervening group of nerve cells.

Eventually physiologists hope to unravel the detailed train of events by which a receptor cell gives rise to a discharge of nerve impulses following mechanical deformation, absorption of light or heat, or stimulation by a particular molecule. In no case have all the events been traced out. In our discussion we will begin with the one final event common to all sensory reception—the generation of nerve impulses. We will then examine in some detail the events occurring in one particular receptor: the photoreceptor of *Limulus*, the horseshoe crab. Finally, we will describe some characteristics of the output of receptors acting singly and in concert with others.

The nerve fiber, or axon, is a thread-

like extension of the nerve-cell body. The entire surface membrane of the cell, including that of the axon, is electrically polarized; the inside of the cell is some 70 millivolts negative with respect to the outside. This potential difference is called the membrane potential. In response to a suitable triggering event the membrane potential is momentarily and locally altered, giving rise to a nerve impulse, which is then propagated the whole length of the axon ["How Cells Communicate," by B. Katz, page 215].

In any particular nerve fiber the impulses are always of essentially the same magnitude and form and they travel with the same speed. This has been known for some 30 years, since the pioneering studies of E. D. Adrian at the University of Cambridge. He and his colleagues found that varying the intensity of the stimulus applied to a receptor cell affects not the size of the impulses but the frequency with which they are discharged; the greater the intensity, the greater the frequency of nerve impulses generated by the receptor. Thus all sensory messages—concerning light, sound, muscle position and so on—are conveyed in the same code of individual nerve impulses. The animal is able to decode the various messages because each type of receptor communicates to the higher nerve centers only through its own private set of nerve channels.

Adrian and others have investigated the problem of how the receptor cell triggers sensory nerve impulses. Adrian suggested that the receptor must somehow diminish the resting membrane potential of its nerve fiber; that is, it must locally depolarize the axon membrane. The existence of local potentials in the eye has been known since 1865, and much later similar potentials were recorded in other sense organs. But the

VISUAL RECEPTOR of the horseshoe crab (*Limulus*) is enlarged 19,000 diameters in the electron micrograph on the opposite page. Called an ommatidium, it is one of about 1,000 photoreceptor units in the compound eye of *Limulus*. Here the ommatidium is seen in cross section; the individual receptor cells are arranged radially like segments of a tangerine around a nerve filament (dendrite) arising from an associated nerve cell (*see illustration on page 209*). The dark ring around the dendrite and spokelike areas may contain photosensitive pigment. The electron micrograph was made by William H. Miller, one of the authors.

relationship of these gross electrical changes to the discharge of nerve impulses was not clear. For some simple eyes, however, the polarity of the local potential changes in the receptors is such that they appear to depolarize the sensory nerve fibers. This led Ragnar Granit of the Royal Caroline Institute in Stockholm to propose that they be called "generator" potentials. The present view is that stimulation of the receptor cell gives rise to a sustained local depolarization of the sensory nerve fiber, which thereupon generates a train of impulses.

Some of the first direct evidence for generator potentials at the cellular level was produced in 1935 by one of the authors of this article (Hartline), then working at the Johnson Research Foundation of the University of Pennsylvania. He found what appeared to be a generator potential when he recorded the activity of a single optic nerve fiber and its receptor in the compound eye of *Limulus*. Superimposed on the potential was a train of nerve impulses [*see illustration on page 210*].

In 1950 Bernhard Katz of University College London obtained unmistakable evidence for a generator potential in a somewhat simpler receptor: the vertebrate muscle spindle. When the spindle was stretched, a small, steady depolarization could be recorded in the nerve fiber coming from the spindle. As viewed on the oscilloscope, it appeared that the base line of the recorded signal had been shifted slightly upward. Superimposed on the shifted signal, or local potential, was a series of "spikes" representing individual nerve impulses. The stronger or the more rapid the stretch, the greater the magnitude of the potential shift and the greater the frequency of the impulses [*see illustration on page 208*]. Analysis of many such records showed that in the steady state the frequency of nerve impulses depends directly on the magnitude of the altered potential. If a local anesthetic is applied to the spindle, the impulses are abolished but the potential shift remains. Katz concluded that this potential shift is an essential link between the stretching of the spindle and the discharge of nerve impulses; indeed, that it is the generator potential. Moreover, the potential can be detected only very close to the spindle, showing that it is conducted passively—which is to say poorly—along the nerve fiber.

Important confirmation of the role of the generator potential was provided by the work of Stephen W. Kuffler and

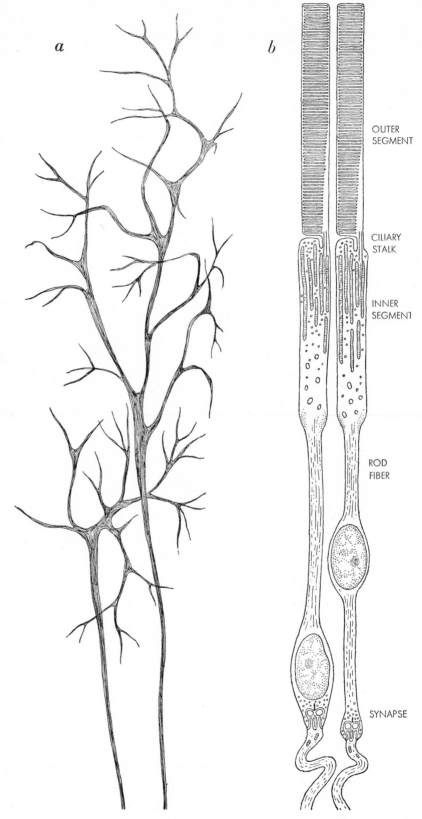

a    b

OUTER SEGMENT

CILIARY STALK

INNER SEGMENT

ROD FIBER

SYNAPSE

RECEPTOR CELLS, typical of those found in vertebrates, respond to a variety of stimuli: heat, light, chemicals and mechanical deformation. The "pit" on the head of the pit viper contains a network of free nerve endings (a) that are sensitive to heat and help the viper locate its prey. Rods (b) are light-sensitive cells in the retina of the eye; photosensitive pigment is in the laminar structure at top of drawing. Taste buds (c) are chemoreceptor cells embedded in the tongue. The cochlea, a spiral tube in the inner ear, contains thousands of

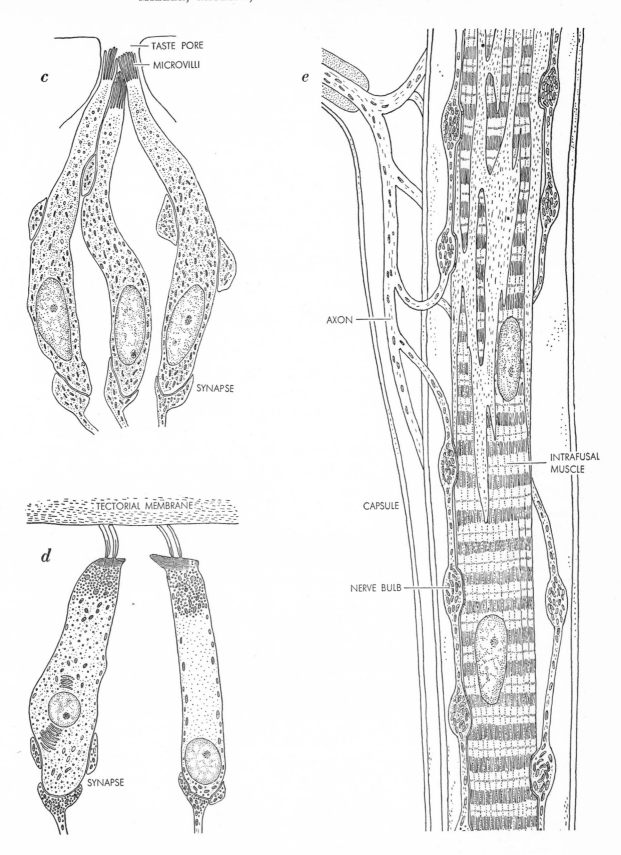

sensitive cells (*d*) in the so-called organs of Corti. When the hairlike bristles of these cells are mechanically deformed by sound vibrations, impulses are generated in the auditory nerve fibers leading to brain. Muscle spindle (*e*) contains a number of nerve endings that respond sensitively to stretching of muscle fibers surrounding them. These illustrations of receptor cells are based on the work

of the following investigators: Theodore H. Bullock of the University of California at Los Angeles (*a*), Fritiof Sjöstrand of the same institution (formerly of the Karolinska Institute, Stockholm) (*b*), A. J. de Lorenzo of the Johns Hopkins School of Medicine, Baltimore, Md. (*c*), Salvatore Iurato of the University of Milan (*d*) and Bernhard Katz of University College London (*e*).

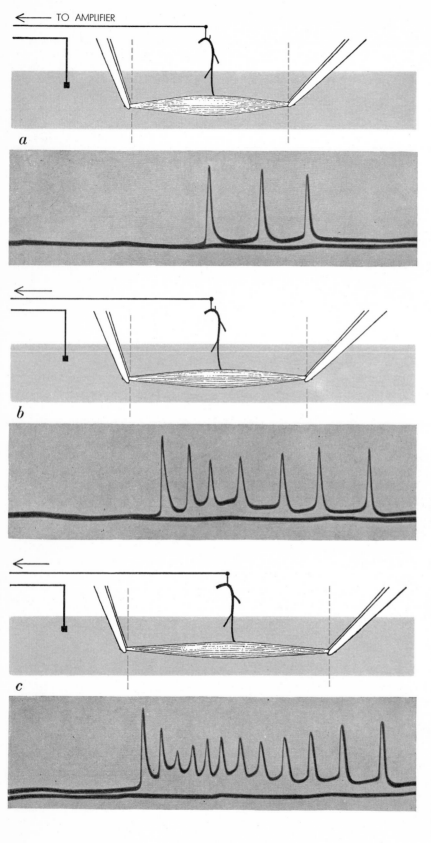

MUSCLE SPINDLE responds to stretch by firing nerve impulses at a rate proportional to the degree and speed of stretching. These recordings made by Bernhard Katz of University College London were the first to show that stretching causes depolarization of the nerve near the spindle (*base line shifted upward in the traces*) and that this depolarization is the precondition for the firing of nerve impulses. The shift is called the generator potential.

Carlos Eyzaguirre, then at Johns Hopkins University, using the so-called Alexandrowicz stretch-receptor cells in crustaceans. These are large single receptor cells with dendrites (short fibers) that are embedded in specialized receptor muscles. Kuffler was able to insert a microelectrode within the cell and record its membrane potential as well as the nerve impulses in its axon. He found that when he distorted the cell's dendrites by stretching the receptor muscle, the cell body became depolarized and the depolarization spread passively to the site of impulse generation, which is probably in the axon close to where it emerges from the cell body. When this generator potential reached a critical level, the cell fired a train of nerve impulses; the greater the depolarization of the axon above this critical level, the higher the frequency of the discharge.

There is now abundant evidence that a receptor cell triggers a train of nerve impulses by locally depolarizing the adjacent nerve fiber—either its own fiber or one provided by another cell. With few exceptions, a fiber of a nerve trunk will not respond repetitively if one passes a sustained depolarizing current through it; it responds only briefly with one to several impulses and then accommodates to the stimulus and responds no more. Evidently that part of the sensory nerve fiber close to the receptor must be specialized so that it does not speedily accommodate to the generator potential. It is nonetheless true that a certain amount of accommodation, or adaptation, almost always takes place when a receptor cell is exposed to a sustained stimulus. In any event, the initiation of nerve impulses in the axons of receptor cells by means of a generator potential appears to be a general phenomenon.

The question still remains: How does the external stimulus produce the generator potential? In most of the receptors studied there is no evidence whatever on this point. Only in the photoreceptor do we have precise knowledge of the first step in the excitation of the sense cell. Yet the study of the photoreceptor is beset by special difficulties. In most eyes the receptors are small and densely packed, and their associated neural structures are complex and highly organized. A fortunate exception is the compound eye of *Limulus*, which provided early evidence for the generator potential. In this eye the receptor cells are large and the neural organization is relatively simple.

The coarsely faceted compound eye

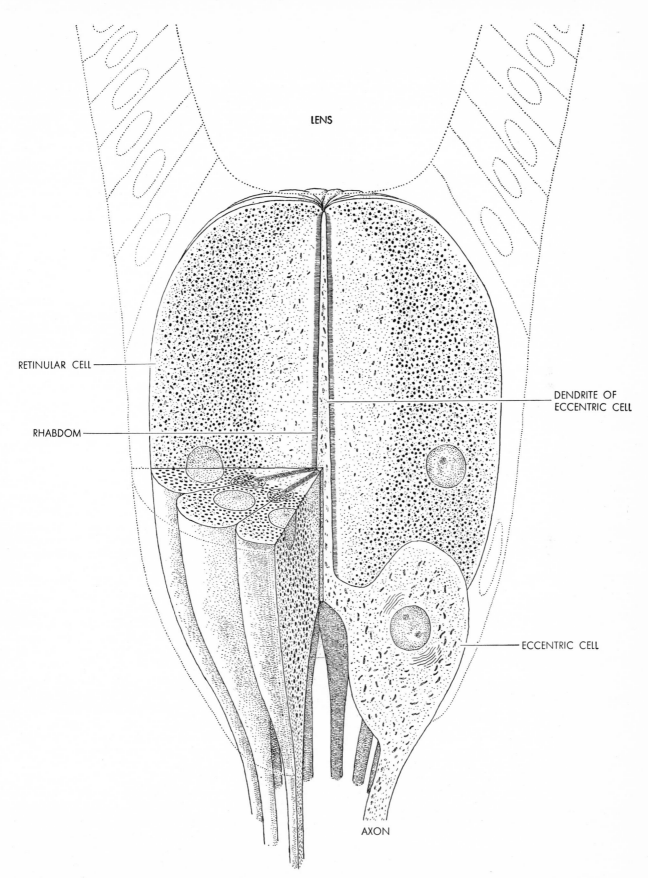

LENS

RETINULAR CELL

RHABDOM

DENDRITE OF
ECCENTRIC CELL

ECCENTRIC CELL

AXON

**OMMATIDIUM OF LIMULUS** is a remarkable structure roughly the size of a pencil lead. About 1,000 form the crab's compound eye. The ommatidium consists of about 12 wedge-shaped retinular cells clustered around a central fiber, which is the dendrite (sensitive process) of a nerve cell, the eccentric cell shown at lower right. When light strikes the ommatidium (*at the top*), the eccentric cell gives rise to nerve impulses (*see illustration on next page*). Photosensitive pigment rhodopsin is believed to be in the rhabdom.

of *Limulus* has some 1,000 ommatidia ("little eyes"), each of which contains about a dozen cells. The cells in each ommatidium have a regular arrangement. The retinular cells—the receptors—are arranged radially like the segments of a tangerine around the dendrite of an associated neuron: a single eccentric cell within each ommatidium [*see illustration on preceding page*].

Hartline, H. G. Wagner and E. F. MacNichol, Jr., working at Johns Hopkins University, found by the use of microelectrodes that the eccentric cell gives rise to the nerve impulses that can be recorded farther down in the nerve strand leaving the ommatidium. The microelectrode also records the generator potential of the ommatidium. Because of the anatomical complexity

of the ommatidium, the site of origin of the generator potential has not been identified with certainty. Nor has activity yet been detected in the axons of the retinular cells. As in the vertebrate and invertebrate stretch receptors, local anesthetics extinguish the nerve impulses without destroying the generator potential. Moreover, as in the stretch receptors, there is a proportional relationship between the degree of depolarization and the frequency of nerve impulses.

Recently M. G. F. Fuortes of the National Institute of Neurological Diseases and Blindness has shown that illumination increases the conductance of the eccentric cell. He postulates that the increase is produced by a chemical transmitter substance that is released by the action of light and acts on the eccentric cell's dendrite. Presumably the increased conductance of the dendrite results in a depolarization that spreads passively to the site of impulse generation, where it acts as the generator potential.

In photosensory cells—alone among all receptors—there exists direct experimental evidence of the initial molecular events in the receptor process. It has been known for about a century that visual receptor cells in both vertebrates and invertebrates have specially differentiated organelles containing a photosensitive pigment. In vertebrates this reddish pigment, called rhodopsin, can be clearly seen in the outer segments of rods. The absorption spectrum of human rhodopsin corresponds closely to the light-sensitivity curve for human vision under conditions of dim illumination, when only the rods of the retina are operative. This is strong evidence that rhodopsin brings about the first active event in rod vision: the absorption of light by the photoreceptor structure. (There is evidence for similar pigments in the outer segments of cones, but they have proved more difficult to isolate and study.)

The visual pigments are known to be complex proteins, but the light-absorbing part of the pigment, called the chromophore, has been found to be a relatively simple substance: vitamin A aldehyde. Because it contains a number of double chemical bonds in its make-up, vitamin A aldehyde can exist in various molecular configurations known as "*cis*" and "*trans*" isomers. We know from the work of Ruth Hubbard, George Wald and their colleagues at Harvard University that the absorption of light changes the chromophore from

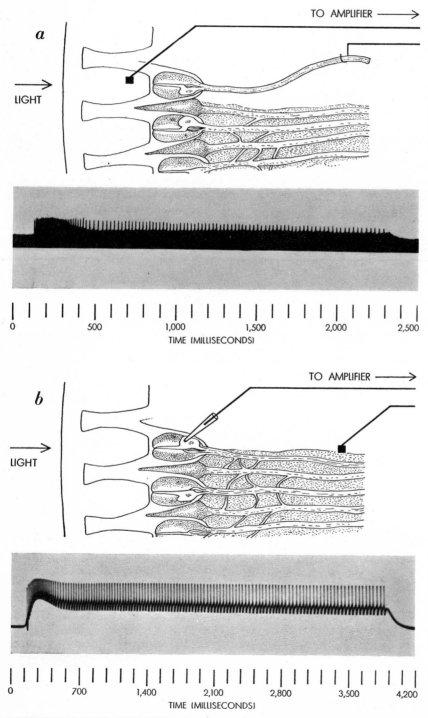

**RECORDINGS FROM OMMATIDIA** show trains of nerve impulses evoked by light. The upper recording from a nerve bundle (*a*) was made by one of the authors, H. K. Hartline, some 25 years ago. Shift of base line underlying nerve spikes is the generator potential. Lower recording, made with microelectrode (*b*), shows generator potential more clearly.

**NERVE IMPULSES TRIGGERED BY LIGHT** are directly related to intensity of steady light falling on the *Limulus* eye. Recordings were made from the optic nerve fiber arising from one ommatidium. At high light intensity (*top*) the nerve fires about 30 times per second. As intensity is reduced by factors of 10, firing is reduced in uniform steps, falling to a low of two or three impulses per second.

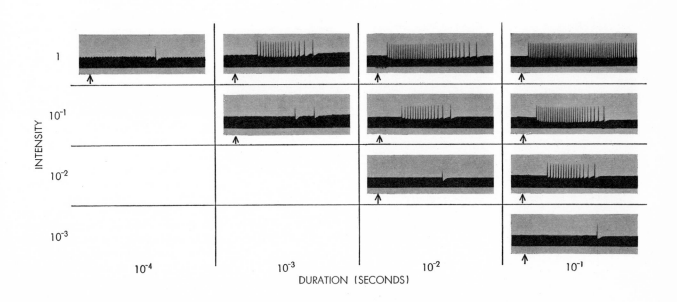

**DURATION AND INTENSITY OF LIGHT** have equivalent effect on the *Limulus* eye. Evidently the receptor responds to the total amount of energy received in a brief flash (*arrows*) regardless of how the energy is "packaged" in duration and intensity. Thus a brief intense flash (*top left*) evokes about the same response as a flash a 1,000th as bright lasting 1,000 times longer (*bottom right*).

11-*cis* vitamin A aldehyde to the *trans* configuration. This photochemical reaction is the first step that leads, through a chain of chemical and physical events as yet unknown, to the initiation of the generator potential of the receptor cell and finally to the discharge of impulses in the optic nerve. This is the only case in which the specific molecular mechanism is known whereby a receptor cell detects environmental conditions.

Supporting evidence that rhodopsin governs the response to a light stimulus can be found by comparing the absorption spectrum of *Limulus* rhodopsin with the sensitivity of the *Limulus* eye at various wavelengths. In 1935 Clarence H. Graham and Hartline measured the intensity of flashes at several wavelengths required to produce a fixed number of impulses in the *Limulus* optic nerve. When a sensitivity curve obtained from this experiment is superimposed on the absorption curve found by Hubbard and Wald for *Limulus* rhodopsin, the two match almost perfectly. At a wavelength of about 520 angstrom units, where rhodopsin absorbs light most strongly, the *Limulus* eye generates the highest number of impulses for a given quantity of light energy received. It turns out that the wavelength sensitivity of the *Limulus* eye is close to that of the human eye in dim light when rod vision dominates.

Many other familiar sensory experiences are manifestations of the properties of individual sense cells. Perhaps the most elementary experience is our ability to perceive when a stimulus has been increased in intensity. Under such circumstances we can be sure that the sensory fibers conveying information to the brain are firing more rapidly as the stimulus is increased. We are also familiar with the experience of sensory adaptation; for example, a strong odor usually seems to decrease in intensity after a time, although objective measurements would show that its intensity has remained constant.

We know from photography that shutter speed and lens opening can be interchanged to produce a constant exposure, which is the same as saying that intensity and duration of illumination can be interchanged (within limits) to produce a constant photochemical effect. The same equivalence holds for the human eye exposed to short flashes of light, and the equivalence can be demonstrated in the photoreceptor of *Limulus*. About the same number of nerve impulses are produced by exposing the ommatidium to a weak light for a 10th of a second as by exposing it to light 10 times as bright for a 100th of a second [*see bottom illustration on page 211*].

We also know from watching motion pictures or television that a light flickering at a high rate appears not to be flickering at all. A neural basis for this phenomenon can be seen in the generator potentials and nerve impulses recorded when a *Limulus* ommatidium is exposed to a light flickering at various rates [*see illustration at left*]. Flicker is detectable as fluctuations in the generator potential, which in turn gives rise to bursts of impulses. As the repetition rate increases, the rate of discharge becomes steadier and finally is indistinguishable from a response to continuous illumination. As can be seen from the records, this "flicker fusion" is directly attributable to the generator potential, which becomes smooth at the highest repetition rates.

The experiments described so far were carried out on single cells or single sensory units. In the eye, ear and other organs, however, receptor cells are grouped close together and usually act in concert. In fact, modern studies show that receptor cells of complex sense organs seldom act independently. In such organs the receptor cells are interconnected neurally and as a result of these connections new functional properties arise.

Although the compound eye of *Limu-*

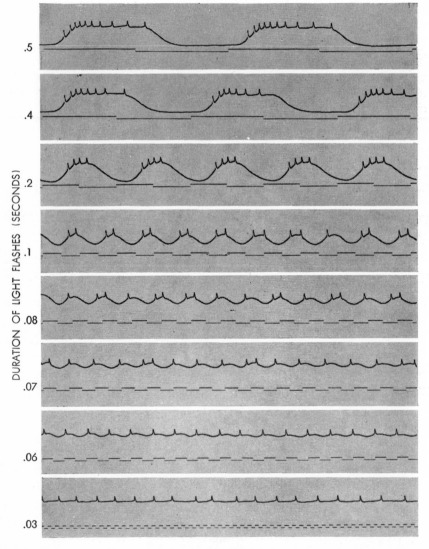

DURATION OF LIGHT FLASHES (SECONDS)

.5
.4
.2
.1
.08
.07
.06
.03

EFFECT OF FLICKERING LIGHT on the *Limulus* ommatidium provides a basis for explaining "flicker fusion": the inability to perceive a rapid flicker. The recordings show the response of the ommatidium to a light flickering at various rates; when the horizontal line is raised, the light is on. At low flicker rates the generator potential, indicated by a rise in base potential, rises and falls. As flicker rate increases, the generator potential no longer falls between flashes, and spacing between nerve impulses becomes more uniform.

*lus* is much less complex than the eyes of vertebrates, it still shows clearly the effects of neural interaction. In *Limulus* the activity of each photoreceptor unit is affected to some degree by the activity of adjacent ommatidia. The frequency of discharge of impulses in an optic nerve fiber from a particular ommatidium is decreased—that is, inhibited—when light falls on its neighbors. Since each ommatidium is a neighbor of its neighbors, mutual inhibition takes place. This inhibition is brought about by a branching array of nerve axons that make synaptic contact with each other in a feltwork of fine fibers behind the ommatidia. The inhibition probably results from a decrease in the magnitude of the generator potential at the site of origin of the nerve impulses, as a consequence of which the rate of firing is slowed down.

When two adjacent ommatidia are illuminated at the same time, each discharges fewer impulses than when it receives the same amount of light by itself [*see the illustrations on this page*]. The magnitude of the inhibition exerted on each ommatidium (in the steady state) depends only on the frequency of the response of the other. The more widely separated the ommatidia, the smaller the mutual inhibitory effect. When several ommatidia are illuminated at the same time, the inhibition of each is given by the sum of the inhibitory effects from all others.

Inhibitory interaction can produce important visual effects. The more intensely illuminated retinal regions exert a stronger inhibition on the less intensely illuminated ones than the latter do on the former. As a result differences in neural activity from differently lighted retinal regions are exaggerated. In this way contrast is heightened and certain significant features of the retinal image tend to be accentuated at the expense of fidelity of representation.

This has been shown by illuminating the *Limulus* compound eye with a "step" pattern: a bright rectangle next to a dimmer one [*see illustration on page 214*]. The eye was masked so that only one ommatidium "observed" the pattern, which was moved to various positions on the retinal mosaic. At each position the steady-state frequency of discharge was measured. The result was a faithful reproduction (in terms of frequency of impulses) of the form of the pattern. Then the eye was unmasked so that all the ommatidia observed the pattern, and a recording was again made from the single ommatidium. This time

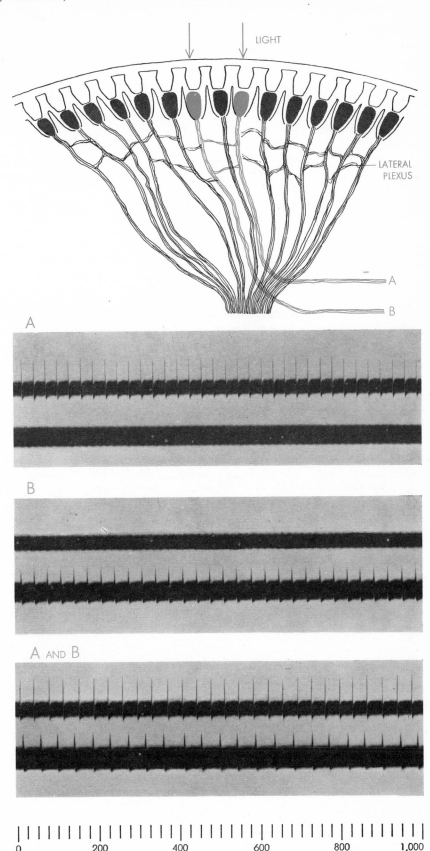

**MUTUAL INHIBITION** results when two neighboring ommatidia are illuminated at the same time (*top*). The inhibition is exerted by cross connections among nerve fibers. When ommatidia attached to fiber *A* and fiber *B* were illuminated separately, 34 and 30 impulses were recorded respectively in one second. Illuminated together, they fired less often.

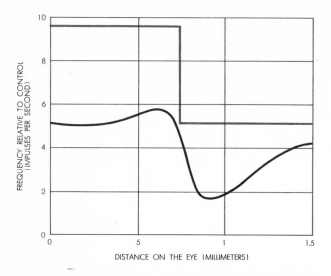

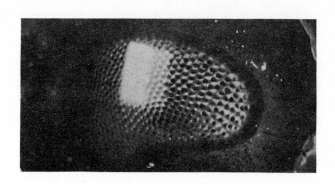

**CONTRAST HEIGHTENING AT CONTOURS** is demonstrated by letting "step" pattern of light, a bright area next to a darker one, fall on *Limulus* compound eye (*right*). If eye is masked so light strikes only one ommatidium, a recording of its output forms a simple step-shaped curve (*left*) as the pattern moved across the eye. If the eye is unmasked, the output of the single ommatidium is inhibited in varying degrees by the light striking its neighbors. The net effect (*lower curve*) is to heighten the contrast at light-dark boundaries.

the frequency increased on the bright side of the step and decreased near the dim side. This is expected because near the bright side of the step the neighboring ommatidia illuminated by the dim part of the step pattern have a low frequency of firing and therefore do not exert much inhibition. Consequently the frequency of discharge of the receptors on the bright side of the step is higher than its equally illuminated but more distant neighbors. Similar reasoning explains the decrease in frequency on the dim side of the step. The net effect of this pattern of response is to enhance contours, an effect we can easily demonstrate in our own vision by looking at a step pattern consisting of a series of uniform gray bands graded from white to black.

Artists are quite familiar with the existence of "border contrast" and may even heighten it in their paintings. And as we all know, significant information is conveyed by contours alone, as is demonstrated by cartoons and other line drawings. Georg von Békésy of Harvard University has suggested that a similar reciprocal inhibition in the auditory system would lead to a sharpening of the sense of pitch.

There is also evidence that in many sense organs the response can be modified by neural influences exerted back onto them by higher centers of the nervous system. Thus the sensitivity of the vertebrate stretch receptor or muscle spindle is established by variations in the length of the spindle fibers, and this length is dependent both on the output of the receptor and on its interaction with higher centers. The sensitivity of the vertebrate olfactory receptors can also be altered, in all probability, by the flow of impulses from above. Similar influences, not yet well understood, also seem to be at work in the retina of the eye.

It is evident, then, that the responses of complex sense organs are determined by the fundamental properties of the individual receptor cells, by the influences they exert on one another and by control exerted on them by other organs. In this way the activity of the receptor cells is integrated into complex patterns of nervous activity that enable organisms to survive in a world of endless variety and change.

# 28

# HOW CELLS COMMUNICATE

BERNHARD KATZ                                    September 1961

In the animal kingdom, the "higher" the organism, the more important becomes the system of cells set aside for co-ordinating its activities. Nature has developed two distinct co-ordinating mechanisms. One depends on the release and circulation of "chemical messengers," the hormones that are manufactured by certain specialized cells and that are capable of regulating the activity of cells in other parts of the body. The second mechanism, which is in general far superior in speed and selectivity, depends on a specialized system of nerve cells, or neurons, whose function is to receive and to give instructions by means of electrical impulses directed over specific pathways. Both co-ordinating mechanisms are ancient from the viewpoint of evolution, but it is the second—the nervous system—that has lent itself to the greater evolutionary development, culminating in that wonderful and mysterious structure, the human brain.

Man's understanding of the working of his millions of brain cells is still at a primitive stage. But our knowledge is reasonably adequate to a more restricted task, which is to describe and partially explain how individual cells—the neurons—generate and transmit the electrical impulses that form the basic code element of our internal communication system.

A large fraction of the neuronal cell population can be divided into two classes: sensory and motor. The sensory neurons collect and relay to higher centers in the nervous system the impulses that arise at special receptor sites [see "How Cells Receive Stimuli," on page

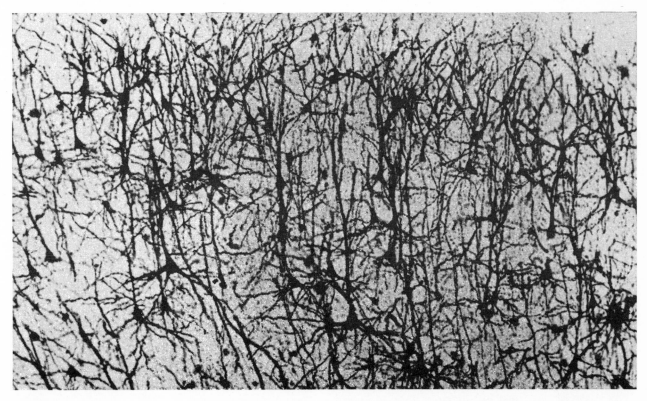

CEREBRAL CORTEX is densely packed with the bodies of nerve cells and the fibers called dendrites that branch from the cell body. This section through the sensory-motor cortex of a cat is enlarged some 150 diameters. Only about 1.5 per cent of the cells and den- drites actually present are stained and show here. The nerve axons, the fibers that carry impulses away from the cell body, are not usual- ly shown at all by this staining method. The photomicrograph was made by the late D. A. Scholl of University College London.

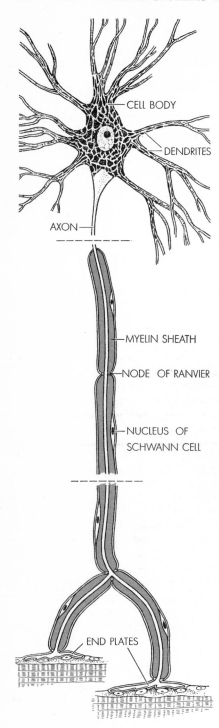

CELL BODY

DENDRITES

AXON

MYELIN SHEATH

NODE OF RANVIER

NUCLEUS OF SCHWANN CELL

END PLATES

**MOTOR NEURON** is the nerve cell that carries electrical impulses to activate muscle fibers. The cell body (*top*) fans out into a number of twigs, the dendrites, which make synaptic contact with other nerve fibers (*see top illustration on opposite page*). Nerve impulses arising at the cell body travel through the axon to the motor-plate endings, which are embedded in muscle fibers. Myelin sheath is formed by Schwann cells as shown at bottom of opposite page. By insulating the axon the myelin wrapping increases the speed of signal transmission.

205], whose function is to monitor the organism's external and internal environments. The motor neurons carry impulses from the higher centers to the "working" cells, usually muscle cells, which provide the organism's response to changes in the two environments. In simple reflex reactions the transfer of signals from sensory to motor neurons is automatic and involves relatively simple synaptic mechanisms, which are fairly well understood.

When a nerve cell, either motor or sensory, begins to differentiate in the embryo, the cell body sends out a long fiber—the axon—which in some unknown way grows toward its proper peripheral station to make contact with muscle or skin. In man the adult axon may be several feet long, although it is less than .001 inch thick. It forms a kind of miniature cable for conducting messages between the periphery and the central terminus, which lies protected together with the nerve-cell body inside the spinal canal or the skull. Isolated peripheral nerve fibers probably have been subjected to more intense experimental study than any other tissue, in spite of the fact that they are only fragments of cells severed from their central nuclei as well as their terminal connections. Even so, isolated axons are capable of conducting tens of thousands of impulses before they fail to work. This fact and other observations make it clear that the nucleated body of the nerve cell is concerned with long-term maintenance of the nerve fibers—with growth and repair rather than with the immediate signaling mechanism.

For years there was controversy as to whether or not our fundamental concept of the existence of individual cell units could be applied at all to the nervous system and to its functional connections. Some investigators believed that the developing nerve cell literally grows into the cytoplasm of all cells with which it establishes a functional relationship. The matter could not be settled convincingly until the advent of high-resolution electron microscopy. It turns out that most of the surface of a nerve cell, including all its extensions, is indeed closely invested and enveloped with other cells, but that the cytoplasm of adjacent cells remains separated by distinct membranes. Moreover, there is a small extracellular gap, usually of 100 to 200 angstrom units, between adjoining cell membranes.

A fraction of these cell contacts are functional synapses: the points at which signals are transferred from one cell to

the next link in the chain. But synapses are found only at and near the cell body of the neuron or at the terminals of the axon. Most of the investing cells, particularly those clinging to the axon, are not nerve cells at all. Their function is still a puzzle. Some of these satellite cells are called Schwann cells, others glia cells; they do not appear to take any part in the immediate process of impulse transmission except perhaps indirectly to modify the pathway of electric current flow around the axon. It is significant, for example, that very few scattered satellites are to be found on the exposed cell surfaces of muscle fibers, which closely resemble nerve fibers in their ability to conduct electrical impulses from one end to the other.

One of the known functions of the axon satellites is the formation of the so-called myelin sheath, a segmented insulating jacket that improves the signaling efficiency of peripheral nerve fibers in vertebrate animals. Thanks to the electron microscope studies of Betty Ben Geren-Uzman and Francis O. Schmitt of the Massachusetts Institute of Technology, we now know that each myelin segment is produced by a nucleated Schwann cell that winds its cytoplasm tightly around the surface of the axon, forming a spiral envelope of many turns [*see bottom illustration on opposite page*]. The segments are separated by gaps—the nodes of Ranvier—which mark the points along the axon where the electrical signal is regenerated.

There are other types of nerve fiber that do not have a myelin sheath, but even these are covered by simple layers of Schwann cells. Perhaps because the axon extends so far from the nucleus of the nerve cell it requires close association with nucleated satellite cells all along its length. Muscle fibers, unlike the isolated axons, are self-contained cells with nuclei distributed along their cytoplasm, which may explain why these fibers can manage to exist without an investing layer of satellite cells. Whatever the function of the satellites, they cannot maintain the life of an axon for long once it has been severed from the main cell body; after a number of days the peripheral segment of the nerve cell disintegrates. How the nerve cell nucleus acts as a lifelong center of repair and brings its influence to bear on the distant parts of the axon—which in terms of ordinary diffusion would be years away—remains a mystery.

The experimental methods of physiology have been much more successful in dealing with the immediate processes of nerve communication than with the equally important but much more intractable long-term events. We know very little about the chemical interactions between nerve and satellite, or about the forces that guide and attract growing nerves along specific pathways and that induce the formation of synaptic contacts with other cells. Nor do we know how cells store information and provide us with memory. The rest of this article will therefore be concerned almost solely with nerve signals and the method by which they pass across the narrow synaptic gaps separating one nerve cell from another.

Much of our knowledge of the nerve cell has been obtained from the giant axon of the squid, which is nearly a millimeter in diameter. It is fairly easy to probe this useful fiber with microelectrodes and to follow the movement of radioactively labeled substances into it and out of it. The axon membrane separates two aqueous solutions that are almost equally electroconductive and that contain approximately the same number of electrically charged particles, or ions. But the chemical composition of the two solutions is quite different. In the external solution more than 90 per cent of the charged particles are sodium ions (positively charged) and chloride ions (negatively charged). Inside the cell these ions together account for less than 10 per cent of the solutes; there the principal positive ion is potassium and the negative ions are a variety of organic particles (doubtless synthesized within the cell itself) that are too large to diffuse easily through the axon membrane. Therefore the concentration of sodium is about 10 times higher *outside* the axon, and the concentration of potassium is about 30 times higher *inside* the axon. Although the permeability of the membrane to ions is low, it is not indiscriminate; potassium and chloride ions can move through the membrane much more easily than sodium and the large organic ions can. This gives rise to a voltage drop of some 60 to 90 millivolts across the membrane, with the inside of the cell being negative with respect to the outside.

To maintain these differences in ion concentration the nerve cell contains a kind of pump that forces sodium ions "uphill" and outward through the cell membrane as fast as they leak into the cell in the direction of the electrochemical gradient [*see illustration on page 222*]. The permeability of the resting cell surface to sodium is normally so low that the rate of leakage remains very small, and the work required of the

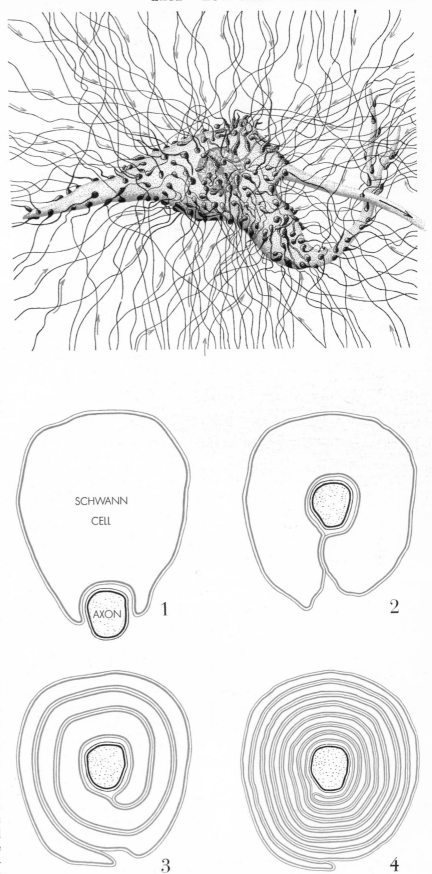

MYELIN SHEATH is created when a Schwann cell wraps itself around the nerve axon. After the enfolding is complete, the cytoplasm of the Schwann cell is expelled and the cell's folded membranes fuse into a tough, compact wrapping. Diagrams are based on studies of chick-embryo neurons by Betty Ben Geren-Uzman of Children's Medical Center in Boston.

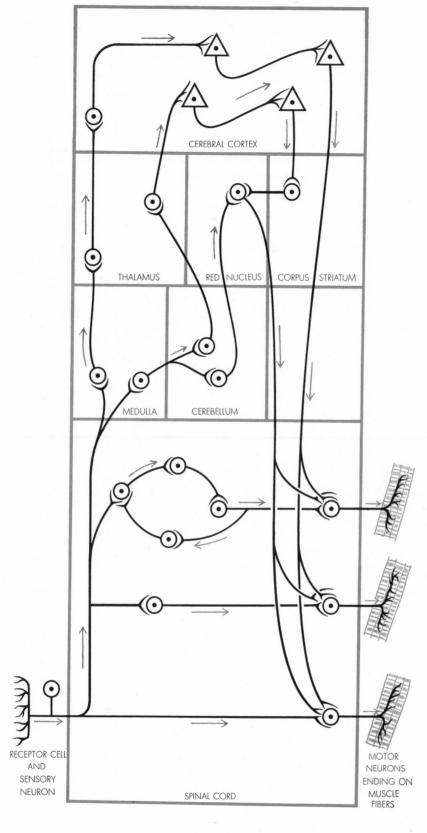

CEREBRAL CORTEX

THALAMUS   RED NUCLEUS   CORPUS STRIATUM

MEDULLA   CEREBELLUM

RECEPTOR CELL
AND
SENSORY
NEURON

SPINAL CORD

MOTOR
NEURONS
ENDING ON
MUSCLE
FIBERS

**SIMPLIFIED FLOW DIAGRAM OF NERVOUS SYSTEM** barely hints at the many possible pathways open to an impulse entering the spinal cord from a receptor cell and its sensory fiber. Rarely does the incoming signal directly activate a motor neuron leading to a muscle fiber. Typically it travels upward through the spinal cord and through several relay centers before arriving at the cerebral cortex. There (if not elsewhere) a "command" may be given (or withheld) that sends nerve impulses back down the spinal cord to fire a motor neuron.

pumping process amounts to only a fraction of the energy that is continuously being made available by the metabolism of the cell. We do not know in detail how this pump works, but it appears to trade sodium and potassium ions; that is, for each sodium ion ejected through the membrane it accepts one potassium ion. Once transported inside the axon the potassium ions move about as freely as the ions in any simple salt solution. When the cell is resting, they tend to leak "downhill" and outward through the membrane, but at a slow rate.

The axon membrane resembles the membrane of other cells. It is about 50 to 100 angstroms thick and incorporates a thin layer of fatty insulating material. Its specific resistance to the passage of an electric current is at least 10 million times greater than that of the salt solutions bathing it on each side. On the other hand, the axon would be quite worthless if it were employed simply as the equivalent of an electric cable. The electrical resistance of the axon's fluid core is about 100 million times greater than that of copper wire, and the axon membrane is about a million times leakier to electric current than the sheath of a good cable. If an electric pulse too weak to trigger a nerve impulse is fed into an axon, the pulse fades out and becomes badly blunted after traveling only a few millimeters.

How, then, can the axon transmit a nerve impulse for several feet without decrement and without distortion?

As one steps up the intensity of a voltage signal impressed on the membrane of a nerve cell a point is reached where the signal no longer fades and dies. Instead (if the voltage is of the right sign), a threshold is crossed and the cell becomes "excited" [*see illustrations on page 220*]. The axon of the cell no longer behaves like a passive cable but produces an extra current pulse of its own that amplifies the original input pulse. The amplified pulse, or "spike," regenerates itself from point to point without loss of amplitude and travels at constant speed down the whole length of the axon. The speed of transmission in vertebrate nerve fibers ranges from a few meters per second, for thin nonmyelinated fibers, to about 100 meters per second in the thickest myelinated fibers. The highest speeds, equivalent to some 200 miles per hour, are found in the sensory and motor fibers concerned with body balance and fast reflex movements. After transmitting an impulse the nerve is left briefly in a refractory, or inexcitable,

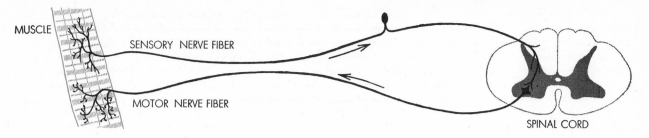

**REFLEX ARC** illustrates the minimum nerve circuit between stimulus and response. A sensory fiber arising in a muscle spindle enters the spinal cord, where it makes synaptic contact with a motor neuron whose axon returns to the muscle containing the spindle.

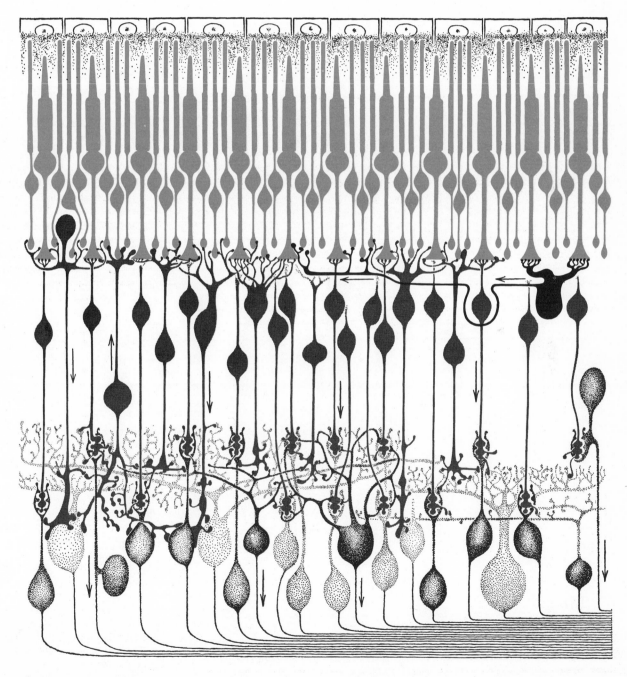

**NERVE-CELL NETWORK IN THE RETINA,** here magnified about 600 diameters, exemplifies the retinal complexity in man and apes. The photoreceptors are the densely packed cells shown in color; the thinner ones are rods, the thicker ones cones. To reach them the incoming light must traverse a dense but transparent layer of neurons *(dark shapes)* that have rich interconnections with the photoreceptors and with each other. The output of these neurons finally feeds into the optic nerve shown at the bottom of the diagram.

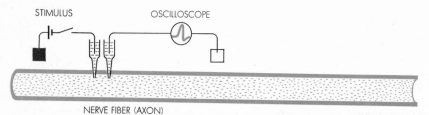

**INVESTIGATION OF NERVE FIBER** is carried out with two microelectrodes. One provides a stimulating pulse, the other measures changes in membrane potential (*see below*).

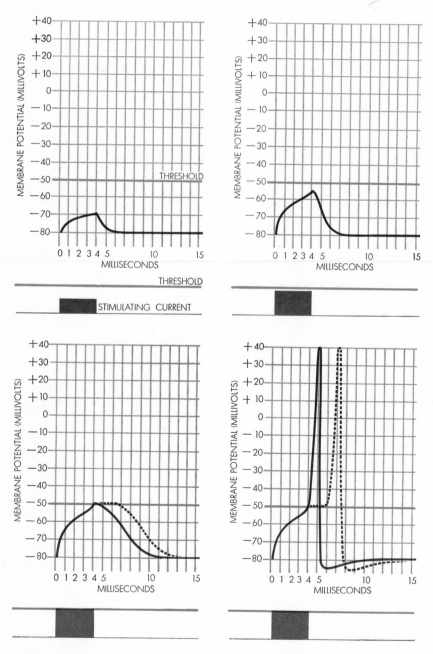

**ELECTRICAL PROPERTIES OF NERVE FIBER** are elucidated by measuring voltage changes across the axon membrane when stimulating pulses of varying size are applied. In the resting state the interior of the axon is about 80 millivolts negative. Subthreshold stimulating pulses (*top left and top right*) shift the potential upward momentarily. Larger pulses push the potential to its threshold, where it becomes unstable, either subsiding (*bottom left*) or flaring up into an "action potential" (*bottom right*) with a variable delay (*broken curve*).

state, but within one or two milliseconds it is ready to fire again.

The electrochemical events that underlie the nerve impulse—or action potential, as it is called—have been greatly clarified within the past 15 years. As we have seen, the voltage difference across the membrane is determined largely by the membrane's differential permeability to sodium and potassium ions. Many kinds of selective membrane, natural and artificial, show such differences. What makes the nerve membrane distinctive is that its permeability is in turn regulated by the voltage difference across the membrane, and this peculiar mutual influence is in fact the basis of the signaling process.

It was shown by A. L. Hodgkin and A. F. Huxley of the University of Cambridge that when the voltage difference across the membrane is artificially lowered, the immediate effect is to increase its sodium permeability. We do not know why the ionic insulation of the membrane is altered in this specific way, but the consequences are far-reaching. As sodium ions, with their positive charges, leak through the membrane they cancel out locally a portion of the excess negative charge inside the axon, thereby further reducing the voltage drop across the membrane. This is a regenerative process that leads to automatic self-reinforcement; the flow of some sodium ions through the membrane makes it easier for others to follow. When the voltage drop across the membrane has been reduced to the threshold level, sodium ions enter in such numbers that they change the internal potential of the membrane from negative to positive; the process "ignites" and flares up to create the nerve impulse, or action potential. The impulse, which shows up as a spike on the oscilloscope, changes the permeability of the axon membrane immediately ahead of it and sets up the conditions for sodium to flow into the axon, repeating the whole regenerative process in a progressive wave until the spike has traveled the length of the axon [*see illustration on opposite page*].

Immediately after the peak of the wave other events are taking place. The "sodium gates," which had opened during the rise of the spike, are closed again, and the "potassium gates" are opened briefly. This causes a rapid outflow of the positive potassium ions, which restores the original negative charge of the interior of the axon. For a few milliseconds after the membrane voltage has been driven toward its initial level it is difficult to displace the voltage and

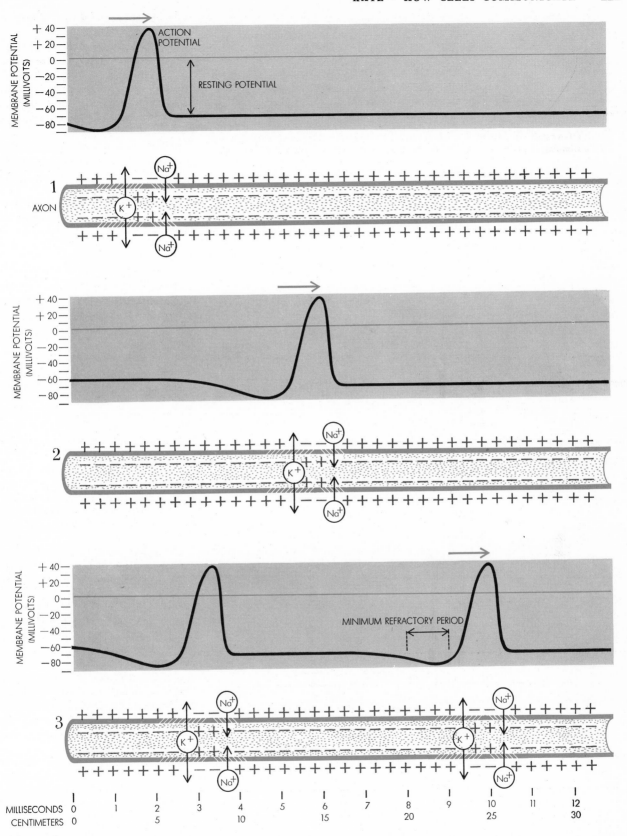

**PROPAGATION OF NERVE IMPULSE** coincides with changes in the permeability of the axon membrane. Normally the axon interior is rich in potassium ions and poor in sodium ions; the fluid outside has a reverse composition. When a nerve impulse arises, having been triggered in some fashion, a "gate" opens and lets sodium ions pour into the axon in advance of the impulse, making the axon interior locally positive. In the wake of the impulse the sodium gate closes and a potassium gate opens, allowing potassium ions to flow out, restoring the normal negative potential. As the nerve impulse moves along the axon (*1 and 2*) it leaves the axon in a refractory state briefly, after which a second impulse can follow (*3*). The impulse propagation speed is that of a squid axon.

set up another impulse. But the ionic permeabilities quickly return to their initial condition and the cell is ready to fire another impulse.

The inflow of sodium ions and subsequent outflow of potassium ions is so brief and involves so few particles that the over-all internal composition of the axon is scarcely affected. Even without replenishment the store of potassium ions inside the axon is sufficient to provide tens of thousands of impulses. In the living organism the cellular enzyme system that runs the sodium pump has no difficulty keeping nerves in continuous firing condition.

This intricate process—signal conduction through a leaky cable coupled with repeated automatic boosting along the transmission path—provides the long-distance communication needs of our nervous system. It imposes a certain stereotyped form of "coding" on our signaling channels: brief pulses of almost constant amplitude following each other at variable intervals, limited only by the refractory period of the nerve cell. To make up for the limitations of this simple coding system, large numbers of axon channels, each a separate nerve cell, are provided and arranged in parallel. For example, in the optic nerve trunk emerging from the eye there are more than a million channels running close together, all capable of transmitting separate signals to the higher centers of the brain.

Let us now turn to the question of what happens at a synapse, the point at which the impulse reaches the end of one cell and encounters another nerve cell. The self-amplifying cable process that serves within the borders of any one cell is not designed to jump automatically across the border to adjacent cells. Indeed, if there were such "cross talk" between adjacent channels, for instance among the fibers closely packed together in our nerve bundles, the system would become quite useless. It is true that at functional synaptic contacts the separation between the cell membranes is only 100 to a few hundred angstroms. But from what we know of the dimensions of the contact area, and of the insulating properties of cell membranes, it is unlikely that an effective cable connection could exist between the terminal of one nerve cell and the interior of its neighbor. This can easily be demonstrated by trying to pass a subthreshold pulse—that is, one that does not trigger a spike—across the synapse that separates a motor nerve from a muscle fiber. A recording probe located just inside the muscle detects no signal when a weak pulse is applied to the motor nerve close to the synapse. Clearly the cable linkage is broken at the synapse and some other process must take its place.

The nature of this process was discovered some 25 years ago by Sir Henry Dale and his collaborators at the National Institute for Medical Research in London. In some ways it resembles the hormonal mechanism mentioned at the beginning of this article. The motor nerve terminals act rather like glands secreting a chemical messenger. Upon arrival of an impulse, the terminals release a special substance, acetylcholine, that quickly and efficiently diffuses across the short synaptic gap. Acetylcholine molecules combine with receptor molecules in the contact area of the muscle fiber and somehow open its ionic gates, allowing sodium to flow in and trigger an impulse. The same result can be obtained by artificially applying ace-

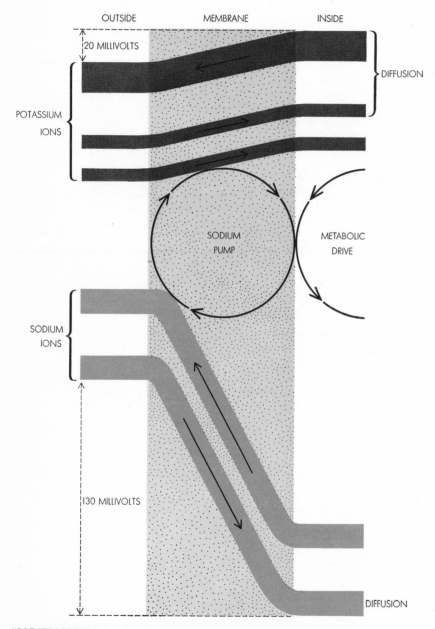

**"SODIUM PUMP,"** details unknown, is required to expel sodium ions from the interior of the nerve axon so that the interior sodium-ion concentration is held to about 10 per cent that of the exterior fluid. At the same time the pump drives potassium ions "uphill" from a low external concentration to a 30-times-higher internal concentration. The pumping rate must keep up with the "downhill" leakage of the two kinds of ion. Since both are positively charged, sodium ions have the higher leakage rate (expressed in terms of millivolts of driving force) because they are attracted to the negatively charged interior of the axon, whereas potassium ions tend to be retained. But there is still a net outward leakage of potassium.

tylcholine to the contact region of the muscle fiber. It is probable that similar processes of chemical mediation take place at the majority of cell contacts in our central nervous system. But it is most unlikely that acetylcholine is the universal mediator at all these points, and an intensive search is being made by many workers for other naturally occurring transmitter substances.

Synaptic transmission presents two quite distinct sets of problems. First, exactly how does a nerve impulse manage to cause the secretion of the chemical mediator? Second, what are the physicochemical factors that decide whether a mediator will stimulate the next cell to fire in some cases or inhibit it from firing in others? So far we have said nothing about inhibition, even though it occurs throughout the nervous system and is one of the most curious modes of nervous activity. Inhibition takes place when a nerve impulse acts as a brake on the next cell, preventing it from becoming activated by excitatory messages that may be arriving along other channels at the same time. The impulse that travels along an inhibitory axon cannot be distinguished electrically from an impulse traveling in an excitatory axon. But the physicochemical effect that it induces at a synapse must be different in kind. Presumably inhibition results from a process that in some way stabilizes the membrane potential (degree of electrification) of the receiving cell and prevents it from being driven to its unstable threshold, or "ignition" point.

There are several processes by which such a stabilization could be achieved. One of them has already been mentioned; it occurs in the refractory period immediately after a spike has been generated. In this period the membrane potential is driven to a high stable level (some 80 to 90 millivolts negative inside the membrane) because, to put it somewhat crudely, the potassium gates are wide open and the sodium gates are firmly shut. If the transmitter substance can produce one or both of these states of ionic permeability, it will undoubtedly act as an inhibitor. There are good reasons for believing that this is the way impulses from the vagus nerve slow down and inhibit the heartbeat; incidentally, the transmitter substance released from the vagus nerve is again acetylcholine, as was discovered by Otto Loewi 40 years ago. Similar effects occur at various inhibitory synapses in the spinal cord, but there the chemical nature of the transmitter has so far eluded identification.

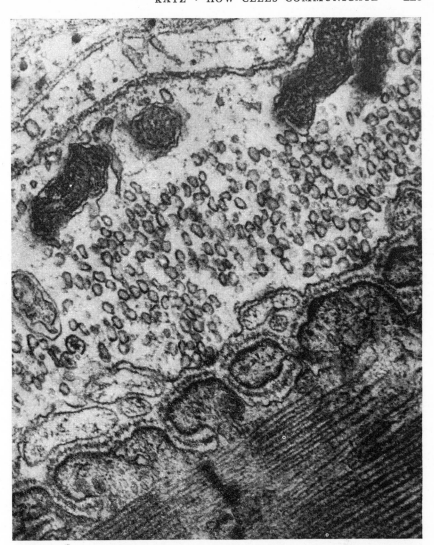

NERVE-MUSCLE SYNAPSE is the site at which a nerve impulse activates the contraction of a muscle fiber. In this electron micrograph (made by R. Birks, H. E. Huxley and the author) the region of the synapse is enlarged 53,000 diameters. Motor nerve terminal runs diagonally from lower left to upper right, being bounded at upper left by a Schwann cell. Muscle fiber is the dark striated area at lower right, with a folded membrane. Nerve terminal is populated with "synaptic vesicles" that may contain acetylcholine, which is released into the synaptic cleft by a nerve impulse and evokes electrical activity in the muscle.

Inhibition would also result if two "antagonistic" axons converged on the same spot of a third nerve cell and released chemically competing molecules. Although a natural example of this kind has not yet been demonstrated, the chemical and pharmacological use of competitive inhibitors is well established. (For example, the paralyzing effect of the drug curare arises from its competitive attachment to the region of the muscle fiber that is normally free to react with acetylcholine.) Alternatively, a substance released by an inhibitory nerve ending could act on the excitatory nerve terminal in such a way as to reduce its secretory power, thereby causing less of the excitatory transmitter substance to be released.

This brings us back to the question:

How does a nerve impulse lead to the secretion of transmitter substances? Recent experiments on the nerve-muscle junction have shown that the effect of the nerve impulse is not to initiate a process of secretion but rather, by altering the membrane potential, to change the rate of a secretory process that goes on all the time. Even in the absence of any form of stimulation, packets of acetylcholine are released from discrete spots of the nerve terminals at random intervals, each packet containing a large number—probably thousands—of molecules.

Each time one of these quanta of transmitter molecules is liberated spontaneously, it is possible to detect a sudden minute local response in the muscle fiber on the other side of the synapse.

Within a millisecond there is a drop of .5 millivolt in the potential of the muscle membrane, which takes about 20 milliseconds to recover. By systematically altering the potential of the membrane of the nerve ending it has been possible to work out the characteristic relation between the membrane potential of the axon terminal and the rate of secretion of transmitter packets. It appears that the rate of release increases by a factor of about 100 times for each 30-millivolt lowering of membrane potential. In the resting condition there is a random discharge of about one packet per second at each nerve-muscle junction. But during the brief 120-millivolt change associated with the nerve impulse the frequency rises momentarily by a factor of nearly a million, providing a synchronous release of a few hundred packets within a fraction of a millisecond.

It is significant that the transmitter is released not in independent molecular doses but always in multimolecular parcels of standard size. The explanation of this feature is probably to be found in the microstructural make-up of the nerve terminals. They contain a characteristic accumulation of so-called vesicles, each about 500 angstroms in diameter, which may contain the transmitter substance parceled and ready for release [see illustration on page 223]. Conceivably when the vesicles collide with the axon membrane, as they often must, the collision may sometimes cause the vesicular content to spill into the synaptic cleft. Such ideas have yet to be proved by direct evidence, but they provide a reasonable explanation of all that is known about the quantal spontaneous release of acetylcholine and its accelerated release under various natural and experimental conditions. At any rate, the ideas provide an interesting meeting point between the functional and structural approaches to a common problem.

Because of the sparseness of existing knowledge, we have left out of this discussion many fascinating problems of the long-term interactions and adaptive modifications that must certainly take place in nerve pathways. For handling such problems investigators will probably have to develop very different methods from those followed in the past. It may be that our preoccupation with the techniques that have been so successful in illuminating the brief reactions of excitable cells has prevented us from making inroads on the problems of learning, of memory, of conditioning and of the structural and operating relations between nerve cells and their neighbors.

# 29

# PATTERNS
# OF DREAMING

NATHANIEL KLEITMAN                    November 1960

Dreams have troubled the waking hours as well as the sleep of men since time immemorial. These hallucinatory experiences have inspired soothsayers and psychiatrists alike, and their bizarre contents, variously interpreted as prophetic insights and clues to personality, are the subject of a considerable body of literature. The scientific value of even the most recent contributions to this literature, however, is seriously qualified: The sole witness to the dream is the dreamer himself. The same limitation confronts the investigator who would inquire into the process of dreaming, as distinguished from the contents of dreams. Only the awakened sleeper can testify that he has dreamed. If he reports that he has not, it may be that he fails to recall his dreaming.

Nonetheless, in the course of our long-term investigation of sleep at the University of Chicago, we found ourselves venturing into research in the hitherto subjective realm of dreaming. We discovered an objective and apparently reliable way to determine whether a sleeper is dreaming—in the sense, of course, of his "reporting having dreamed" when he wakes up or is awakened. The objective indicator of dreaming makes it possible to chart the onset and duration of dreaming episodes throughout the night without disturbing the sleeper. One can also awaken and interrogate him at the beginning of a dream, in the middle, at the end, or at any measured interval after the end. By such means it has been determined that there is periodicity in dreaming, and the consequences of efforts to disturb this periodicity have been observed. The results indicate that dreaming as a fundamental physiological process is related to other rhythms of the body. As for the folklore that surrounds the process, this

work has answered such questions as: Does everyone dream? How often does one dream in the course of a night's sleep? Is the "plot" of a dream really compressed into a moment of dreaming? Do external and internal stimuli—light, noise, hunger or thirst—affect the content of dreams?

As so often happens in research, the objective indicator of dreaming was discovered by accident. During a study of the cyclic variations of sleep in infants, a graduate student named Eugene Aserinsky observed that the infant's eyes continued to move under its closed lids for some time after all major body movement had ceased with the onset of sleep. The eye movements would stop and then begin again from time to time, and were the first movements to be seen as the infant woke up. Aserinsky found that eye movements provided a more reliable means of distinguishing between the active and quiescent phases of sleep than did gross body movements.

These observations suggested that eye movements might be used to follow similar cycles in the depth of sleep in adults. Disturbance to the sleeper was minimized by monitoring the eye movements remotely with an electroencephalograph, a device that records the weak electrical signals generated continuously by the brain. A potential difference across the eyeball between the cornea and the retina makes it possible to detect movements of the eyes by means of electrodes taped to the skin above and below or on either side of one eye. Other channels of the electroencephalograph recorded the sleeper's brain waves, his pulse and respiration rates and the gross movements of his body.

The tracings of the electroencephalograph showed not only the slow move-

ments of the eyes that Aserinsky had observed in infants but also rapid eye-movements that came in clusters. Each individual eye-movement took a fraction of a second, but a cluster often lasted, with interruptions, as long as 50 minutes. The first rapid eye-movements usually began about an hour after the onset of sleep, and clusters appeared in cyclic fashion through the night [see illustration on page 229].

Coincident with this cycle of eye movement the electroencephalograph recorded a fluctuation in the brain-wave pattern. As each series of movements began, the brain waves changed from the pattern typical of deep sleep to one indicating lighter sleep. The pulse and respiration rates also increased, and the sleeper lay motionless.

Considered together, these observations suggested an emotionally charged cerebral activity—such as might occur in dreaming. This surmise was tested by the only possible means: arousing and questioning the sleepers. Those awakened in the midst of a cluster of rapid eye-movements testified they had been dreaming. Those awakened in the apparently deeper phases of sleep said they had not. Thus the objective indicator of dreaming came into use.

It is clear that such an indicator can reveal nothing about the content of dreams. But the process of dreaming is no more bound up with dream content than thinking is with what one is thinking about. The hallucinatory content of dreams would appear, in this light, to be nothing more than the expression of a crude type of activity carried on in the cerebral cortex during a certain phase of sleep. The contrast with the kind of cerebral activity that characterizes the waking state in healthy adults and older children is instructive. Responding to the impulses that stream in from the various receptor organs of the sensory system, the cortex first subjects them to analysis. It refers the present moment of experience to its memory of the past and projects past and present into the future, weighing the consequences of action not yet taken. A decision is reached, and the cortex generates an integrated response. This is manifested in the action of the effector organs (mostly muscles) or in the deliberate inhibition of action. (A great deal of civilized behavior consists in not doing what comes naturally.) In dreaming, the same kind of cortical activity proceeds at a lower level of per-

formance. The analysis of events is faulty; the dreamer recognizes a deceased friend but accepts his presence without surprise. The memory is full of gaps and brings the past to the surface in confusion. In consequence the integration of the cortical response is incomplete, and the dreamer is often led into the phantom commission of antisocial acts. Fortunately the impulses from the sleeping cortex die out on the way to the effector organs, and no harm is done.

Such protoplasmic poisons as alcohol may reduce cortical activity to an equally low level of performance. A markedly

intoxicated person misjudges the situation, assumes unwarranted risks in action and later does not recall what happened. Even when quite drunk, however, some persons stop short of foolish and dangerous extremes of behavior. So, also, a dreamer will accept absurdities in the imaginary series of events until they become too painful and ludicrous; he then wakes up to the comforting discovery that he was dreaming. The fantasizing of very young children, senile aged people and of persons suffering certain disorders of the central nervous system may also be likened to dreaming. After sudden awakening, even normal people may

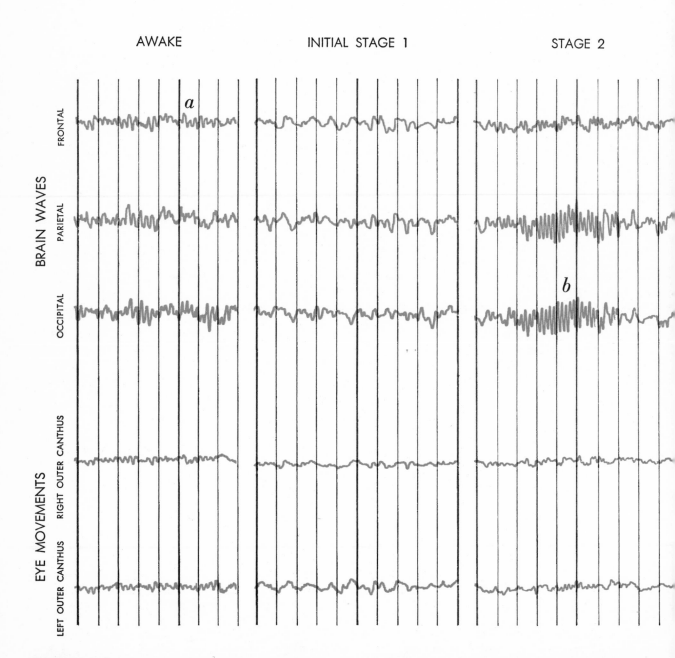

AWAKE    INITIAL STAGE 1    STAGE 2

BRAIN WAVES

FRONTAL

PARIETAL

OCCIPITAL

EYE MOVEMENTS

RIGHT OUTER CANTHUS

LEFT OUTER CANTHUS

**ELECTROENCEPHALOGRAMS** show the patterns of brain waves (*top three tracings*) and eye-movement potentials (*bottom two tracings*) that are characteristic of each level of sleep. Labels at left indicate region of head to which recording electrodes are at-    tached. Vertical lines are time-scale; 10 lines represent an interval of four seconds. A subject who is awake but resting with his eyes closed shows the brain-wave pattern known as alpha rhythm (*a*). As sleep begins, pattern known as Initial Stage 1 electroen-

be bewildered and act in a deranged manner for some time. The content of dreams, explicit or hidden, may indeed have inherent interest. But for the purpose of an investigation of dreaming, it is sufficient to recognize the dream itself as a manifestation of low-grade thinking.

The objective indicator that a sleeper is dreaming, it must be admitted, is not infallible. Some subjects reported they had been dreaming during periods when they showed no rapid eye-movements. Others moved their bodies restlessly when the records on the other channels of the electroencephalograph indicated they were dreaming. Sometimes the heart and respiration rate slowed down instead of speeding up. Occasionally a subject claimed to have been dreaming when his brain waves indicated a deeper phase of sleep. William Dement, another student in our laboratory who is now at Mount Sinai Hospital in New York City, showed that of the four criteria the most reliable is the brain-wave pattern.

A person who is awake but resting with his eyes closed shows the so-called alpha rhythm—brain waves with a relatively large amplitude and a frequency of eight to 13 cycles per second [see illustration on these two pages]. As he falls asleep, the amplitude of the waves decreases, and the rhythm slows to four to six cycles per second. Dement called this pattern the Stage 1 electroencephalogram (Stage 1 EEG). Deeper sleep is characterized by the appearance of "sleep spindles"—short bursts of waves that progressively increase and decrease in amplitude and have a frequency of 14 to 16 cycles per second; Dement divided this level of sleep into two stages (Stage 2 and Stage 3 EEG). The deepest level of sleep is characterized by the appearance of large, slow waves (Stage 4 EEG). During a typical night of sleep,

STAGE 3              STAGE 4              EMERGENT STAGE 1
                                          (DREAMING)

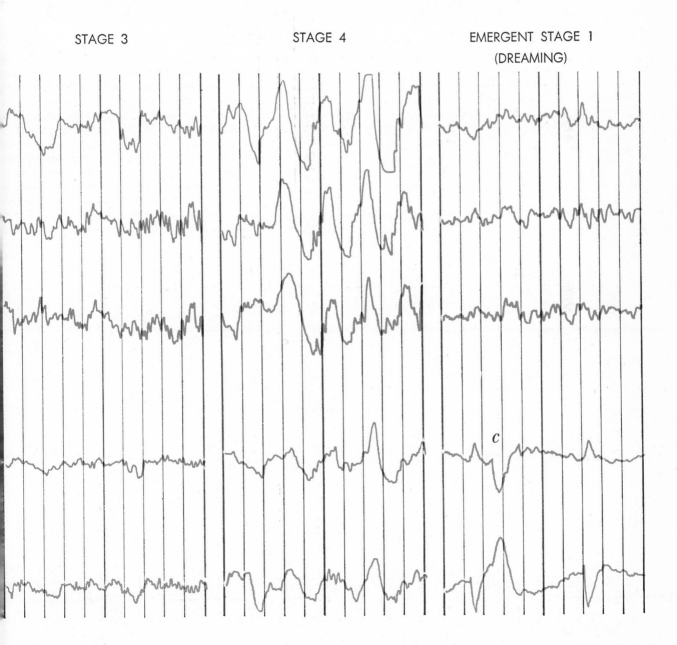

cephalogram (Initial Stage 1 EEG) appears. During deeper sleep subject shows short bursts of waves called sleep spindles (b). Deepest level of sleep (Stage 4 EEG) is characterized by the appearance of large, slow waves. EEG pattern changes from Stage 1 through Stage 4, then swings back to Stage 1. This "emergent" Stage 1 is accompanied by rapid eye-movements, as indicated by peaks in tracings of eye-movement potentials (c). Similar peaks during Stage 4 are not eye movements but brain waves that spread to eye electrodes.

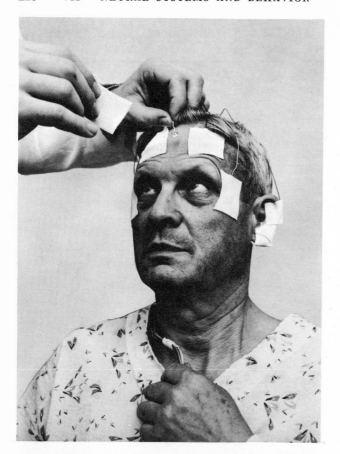

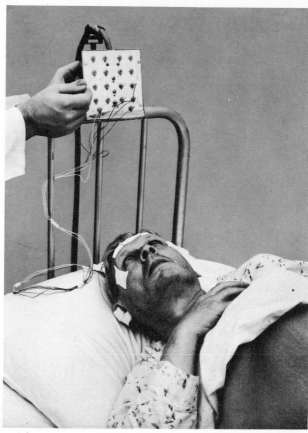

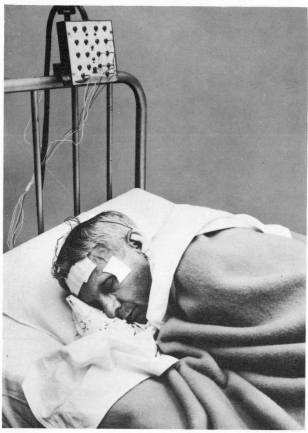

**DREAMING IS DETECTED** by attaching electrodes to the subject's scalp and to the skin at the corners of the eyes (*top left*). Leads are connected to cable (*top right*) that leads to electroencephalograph in another room. As the subject sleeps (*bottom left*), his brain waves and eye movements are recorded by pens of electroencephalograph (*bottom right*). The subject here is the author of this article.

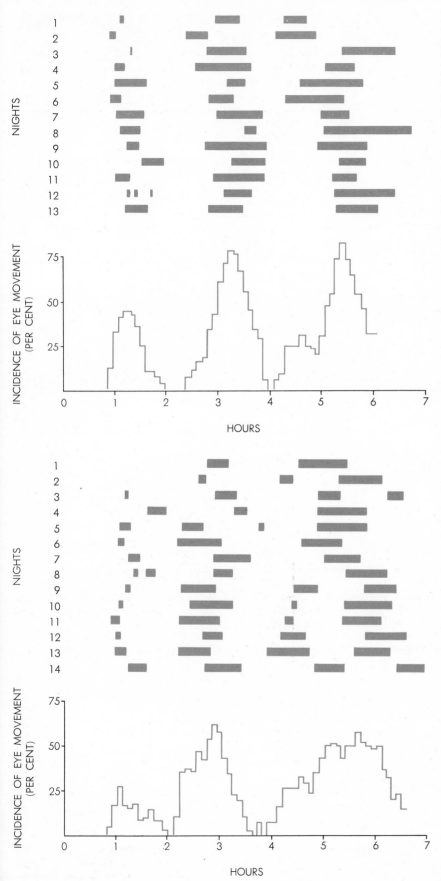

the depth of sleep fluctuates on a cycle lasting roughly 90 minutes. The EEG pattern passes from Stage 1 through Stage 4, then swings back to Stage 1. During later cycles the sleep may not be so deep; the EEG pattern may dip no farther than the intermediate stages before it returns to Stage 1 [*see illustration on page 230*].

Dement found that dreaming occurs during the Stage 1 EEG, but not when this brain-wave pattern first appears at the onset of sleep. Only when the cycle returns to the Stage 1 EEG from a deeper EEG level does it mark a dreaming episode. During this "emergent" Stage 1 it is much more difficult to awaken the sleeper than during the "initial" Stage 1 EEG.

The inconsistencies between the EEG record and the other criteria may be largely explained by the relationship of these other activities to the dream episode. For example, most of the rapid eye-movements are horizontal, and it is apparent that these movements represent a busy scanning of the scene of dream action. On the infrequent occasions when the rapid eye-movements were vertical, the sleepers reported dreams that involved the upward or downward motion of objects or persons. When the record showed few or no rapid eye-movements, and the EEG denoted dreaming, the subjects reported that they had been watching some distant point in their dreams. In other words, the amount and direction of the eye movements correspond to what the dreamer is looking at or following with his eyes. Moreover, rapid eye-movements seem to be related to the degree to which the dreamer participates in the events of the dream. An "active" dream, in which the dreamer is greatly involved, is more likely to be accompanied by rapid eye-movements than is a "passive" one.

The absence of gross body movements during dreaming seemed more difficult to explain. One would assume that a sleeper would begin to move about as his sleep lightens and that a good deal of activity would occur during dreaming. Actually the exact opposite was observed. Dreaming often began just after a series of body movements ceased. The sleeper usually remained almost motionless, showing only the telltale rapid eye-movements, and stirred again when the eye movements stopped. We were indebted to Georg Mann, a public-information officer at the University of Chicago, for the metaphor that captured the essence of this situation. He compared the dreamer to a spectator at a theater:

**RAPID EYE-MOVEMENTS** (*horizontal colored bars*) occur several times each night. Each horizontal row of bars represents a single night of sleep; one subject was studied for 13 nights (*top graph*), the other for 14 (*bottom graph*). Histograms at bottom of each graph show composite cycles of subject's eye movements during entire series of nights.

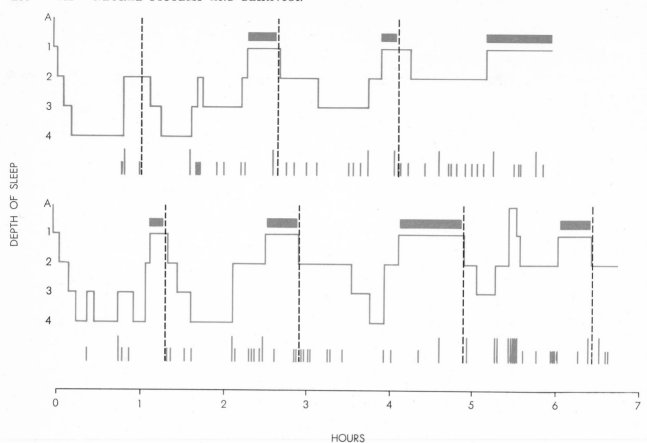

EEG STAGES of two subjects show a cyclic variation during typical night of sleep. Measured in terms of EEG stages, depth of sleep fluctuates on a 90-minute cycle. Cycle begins when subject who is awake (A) falls into light sleep (EEG Stage 1), then into successively deeper levels of sleep (EEG Stages 2, 3 and 4). Cycle ends with swing back to Stage 1. Periods of rapid eye-movement (*horizontal colored bars*) occur during this stage. Vertical broken lines indicate when next cycle begins. Vertical colored lines at bottom of each graph indicate when body movements occurred; longer lines represent major movements; shorter lines, minor ones.

fidgeting in his seat before the curtain goes up; then sitting quietly, often "spellbound" by the action, following the motions of the actors with his eyes; then stirring again when the curtain falls.

Some body movement may be related to dream content. Edward A. Wolpert of the University of Chicago attached electrodes to the limbs of sleeping subjects and recorded the electrical "action" potentials of the muscles. The record of one of his subjects showed a sequence of motor activity first in the right hand, then in the left, and finally in one leg (only one leg was wired for recording). When aroused immediately thereafter, the sleeper reported dreaming that he lifted a bucket with his right hand, transferred it to his left, and then started to walk. Sleepwalking may be an extreme expression of such motor outflow to extremities. Occasionally a subject would vocalize when he stirred, mumbling and even talking distinctly, but such activity usually occurred between episodes of dreaming.

Some people assert that they seldom or never dream. But all of the subjects— and all of those observed in other laboratories that employ the objective indicator—reported dreaming upon being awakened at appropriate times. It can be stated with some assurance, therefore, that everybody dreams repeatedly every night. Donald R. Goodenough and his associates at the Downstate Medical Center of the State University of New York compared one group of subjects who said they never dreamed with another group who said they always dreamed. Certain unexplained differences showed up in the EEG records of the two groups, and the "dreamers" were more likely to report dreaming in correspondence with rapid eye-movements than the "nondreamers." Rapid eye-movements were observed with the same frequency, however, in both groups. The evidence is overwhelming that the two groups should be classified as "recallers" and "nonrecallers."

These studies have also upset the notion that a long series of events can be compressed into a moment of dreaming. Whether the subject was loquacious or laconic in recounting his dream, the time-span of the narrative was consistent with dreaming time as indicated by our objective criteria. It appears that the course of time in dreaming is about the same as in the waking state.

It is often said that external events in the sleeper's immediate environment may suggest or affect the content of dreams. To test this idea Dement and Wolpert exposed a number of subjects to the stimuli of sound, light and drops of water during periods of dreaming. Elements suggestive of such stimuli appeared in only a minority of the dreams recounted thereafter. Drops of water, falling on the skin, proved to be the most suggestive. Falling water showed up in six dream reports out of 15 that followed arousal by this stimulus, and water had a place in 14 narratives out of 33 when the sleepers were subjected to the stimulus but not awakened by it. An electric bell used routinely to awaken the subjects found its way into 20 out of 204 dreams, most commonly as the ringing of a telephone or doorbell.

Internal stimuli from the viscera have

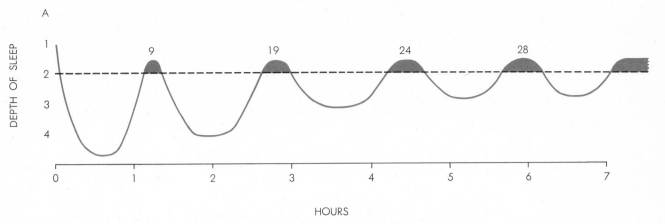

EPISODES OF DREAMING (*colored areas*) alternate with periods of deeper sleep. Dreaming and rapid eye-movements begin when sleeper emerges from deep sleep to level of EEG Stage 1. Numbers over colored areas show length of successive periods of dreaming.

been held to cause, or at least influence, dreams. Dreams about eating are said to be stimulated by contractions of an empty stomach. Dement and Wolpert had three subjects go without fluids for 24 hours on five occasions; only five of 15 dream narratives contained elements that could be related to thirst. In no case did the narrative involve an awareness of thirst or descriptions of drinking, although the subjects were very thirsty when they went to bed.

Most of the dream experience in normal sleep is never recalled. Recollection is best when the sleepers are awakened during the dreaming episode and becomes progressively poorer the longer they are permitted to sleep after a dream has ended. At the University of Chicago, Wolpert and Harry Trosman found that 25 out of 26 subjects had no memory of dreaming when they were roused for questioning more than 10 minutes after the Stage 2 EEG had superseded the Stage 1.

Once the objective indicator had shown itself to be a reliable measure of dreaming, it was employed to enact the pattern of dreaming through many nights of uninterrupted sleep. In a sampling of 71 nights of sleep, with 33 different subjects, the first emergent Stage 1 EEG—plus the accompanying rapid eye-movements and cardiac and respiratory changes—appeared a little over an hour after sleep had begun. This episode of dreaming lasted on the average less than 10 minutes. Three, four and even five dreaming periods followed at intervals of about 90 minutes. These lasted 20 to 35 minutes and added up to a total of one or two hours of dreaming for an average night's sleep. All of the subjects exhibited the cycle of alternate periods of dreaming and deeper sleep, some on

a more constant schedule than others.

The mechanism that spaces the episodes of dreaming is unknown, but it may be related to the cycle of rest and activity which Aserinsky found in infants. The mean length of that cycle is approximately an hour, and at the end of a cycle the infants stir, either to awaken fully or to go back to sleep for another cycle. In infants on a self-demand feeding schedule, the duration of the period between feedings tends to be roughly whole multiples of the length of this cycle. Apparently the cycle lengthens with age, extending to the 90-minute dreaming cycles observed in adults. A similar increase occurs in the length of the cardiac, respiratory and gastric cycles, indicating that the dream cycle is in line with the basic physiological rhythms of the body.

What happens if the dreaming cycle is disturbed? This interesting question has been taken up by Dement and his associates. Monitoring the subject's cycle, they awaken him as soon as he starts to dream and thus keep him from dreaming. Since one must be certain that dreaming has started before attempting to stop it, such interference cannot completely deprive the subject of his dreaming, but total dreaming time can be reduced by 75 to 80 per cent. Dement established that the mean normal dreaming time of his eight male subjects was 20 per cent, or about 82 minutes in about seven hours of sleep. Attempts to curtail their dreaming in the course of three to seven consecutive nights required in each case a progressively larger number of awakenings—in some cases three times as many. During the "recovery" period after this ordeal, the dreaming time of five of the subjects went up to 112 minutes, or 27 per cent of the sleeping time,

on the first night and gradually fell back to normal on succeeding nights. In six of the subjects arousal in the midst of nondreaming periods during "control" nights of sleep had no effect on dreaming during the recovery nights that followed. The curtailment of dreaming time produced anxiety, irritability, a greater appetite and a gain in body weight; the control awakenings had no such effects. As soon as the subjects of the experiment were allowed their usual dreaming time, they regained their emotional composure.

Dement tentatively interprets his findings as indicating that "a certain amount of dreaming is a necessity." Charles Fisher, a psychiatrist at Mount Sinai Hospital in New York, adds that "the dream is the normal psychosis and dreaming permits each and every one of us to be quietly and safely insane every night of our lives."

From the same evidence, however, one may equally well argue that the curtailment of dreaming engenders irritability and anxiety simply because it interferes with an acquired habit. Animals (and some people) that have acquired a "sweet tooth" may be similarly upset by deprivation of sugar. They will also consume excessive quantities of sugar after the supply is restored, just as Dement's subjects sought to make up for "missed" dreaming. In other words, the low-grade cerebral activity that is dreaming may serve no significant function whatever.

Further observation and experiment will have to decide which of these conflicting views is sound. The objective indicator is now available to help investigators find the answer to this and other questions about the nature and meaning of dreaming.

# 30

# THE RETICULAR FORMATION

J. D. FRENCH                                                          May 1957

The title "reticular formation" might suggest various things—a football line-up, a chess gambit, a geological structure or whatnot—but as readers of SCIENTIFIC AMERICAN well know, it is actually a part of the brain, a once mysterious part which has re-cently come in for a great deal of attention from biologists. The reticular formation is a tiny nerve network in the central part of the brain stem. Investigators have discovered that this bit of nerve tissue, no bigger than your little finger, is a far more important structure than anyone had dreamed. It underlies our awareness of the world and our ability to think, to learn and to act. Without it, an individual is reduced to a helpless, senseless, paralyzed blob of protoplasm.

The actual seat of the power to think,

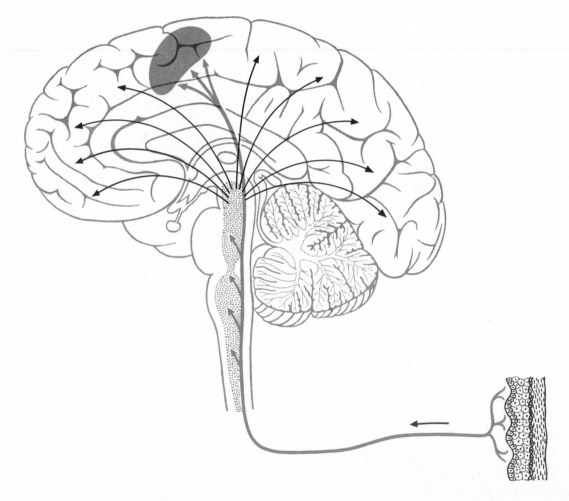

THE RETICULAR FORMATION is the area stippled with red in this cross section of the brain. A sense organ (*lower right*) is connected to a sensory area in the brain (*upper left*) by a path-way extending up the spinal cord. This pathway branches into the reticular formation. When a stimulus travels along the pathway, the reticular formation may "awaken" the entire brain (*black arrows*)

to perceive, indeed to respond to a stimulus with anything more than a reflex reaction, lies in the cortex of the brain. But the cortex cannot perceive or think unless it is "awake." Consider the alarm ring that awakens you in the morning: several seconds pass before you recognize the disturbance and can respond to stop the painful jangle. A sensory signal arriving at the cortex while it is asleep goes unrecognized. Experiments on anesthetized individuals have shown further that stimulation of the cortex alone is not sufficient to awaken the brain. Something else must arouse the cortex: that something is the reticular formation.

It was only about eight years ago that two eminent physiologists, H. W. Magoun of the U. S. and Giuseppe Moruzzi of Italy, working together at Northwestern University, discovered this fact. They were exploring the mystery of the reticular formation's functions by means of an electrode planted in this area in the brain of a cat. They found that stimulation of the area with a small electric current would awaken a drowsing cat as peacefully as a scratch on the head. The animal's behavior, and recordings of changes in its brain waves with the electroencephalograph, showed all the signs of a normal arousal from sleep. Magoun and Moruzzi decided that the reticular formation acted as a kind of sentinel which aroused the cortex, and they named it the RAS (reticular activating system).

Now mysteries began to clear—not only with regard to the function of the reticular formation but also as to some previously puzzling features of the nervous system's anatomy. All the great sensory nerve trunks in the body have brush-like branches which stream into the reticular formation. Sensory signals from all parts of the body go to the cortex by direct pathways, but on the way through the brain stem they also feed into the reticular formation. Evidently the reticular formation, when so stimulated, sends arousing signals to the cortex. The awakened cortex can then interpret the sensory signals it is receiving directly.

The RAS is a kind of general alarm: that is to say, it responds in the same way to any sensory stimulus, whether from the organs of hearing, seeing, touch or whatever. Its response is simply to arouse the brain, not to relay any specific message. Its signals spray the entire cortex rather than any one center of sensation. A noise, a flash of light, a pinch on the hand, the smell of burning wood, a

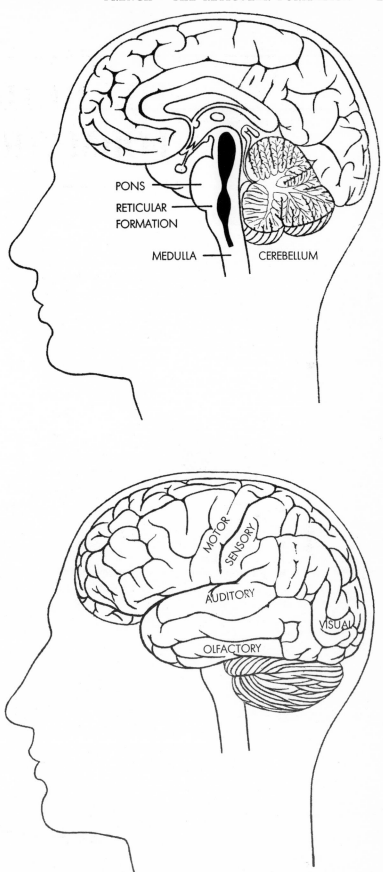

**RELATIONSHIP OF THE RETICULAR FORMATION** (*black area*) **to various parts of the brain is indicated at the top. The functional areas of the brain are outlined at bottom.**

pain in the stomach—any of these excites the reticular formation to alert the cortex to a state of wakefulness, so that when the specific stimulus arrives at the appropriate center in the cortex, the brain can identify it.

Apparently the RAS learns to be selective in its sensitivity to particular stimuli. A mother may be instantly awakened by the faintest whimper of her baby. Father, on the other hand, may sleep through baby's fiercest bellowings but be aroused by a faint smell of smoke. A city dweller may sleep peacefully in the midst of the riotous din of traffic while his visitor from the country spends a sleepless night wishing he were elsewhere. It is as if the RAS becomes endowed by experience with the ability to discriminate among stimuli, disregarding those it has found unimportant and responding to those that are helpful. Happily so. Imagine how unbearable life would be if you could not shut out most of the environment from consciousness and were at the mercy of the thousands of sights and sounds simultaneously clamoring for attention.

The RAS, like the starter in an automobile, starts the brain engine running, but this is by no means the end of its job. It goes on functioning to keep the individual in a conscious state. ("Consciousness" is a controversial word among psychologists, but for our purposes its meaning is clear enough.) If the RAS cannot function normally, consciousness is impossible. A person whose reticular formation has been permanently injured or destroyed falls into a coma from which he can never recover. He may live on for a year or more, but he remains as helpless and shut off from communication as a vegetable.

If uninjured, the RAS can maintain a wakeful state (but not consciousness) even in the absence of the cortex. In a newborn baby the cortex has not yet begun to function, but the infant nevertheless has short periods of wakefulness throughout the day. The same is true of the tragic creatures born without any cortex at all (called anencephalic monsters). Such a child (sometimes kept alive for three or four years) never achieves any understanding or real contact with its surroundings, but it has periods of wakefulness during which it swallows and digests food, smiles and coos when fondled and cries when treated roughly. We must conclude, therefore, that wakefulness of a very crude sort is possible without the cortex, so long as the RAS can function.

For sustained wakefulness, however,

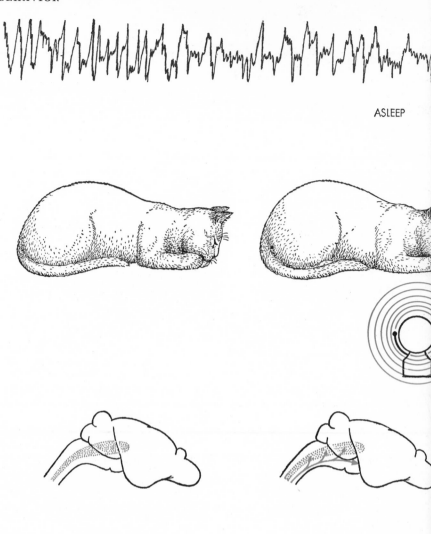

ASLEEP

CAT IS AWAKENED by the sound of a bell. The sound stimuli (*incoming red arrows*) reach the reticular activating system, or RAS, and the auditory area of the brain. The RAS acts (*black arrows*) to awaken the cortex so that it can "hear" signals arriving in the auditory

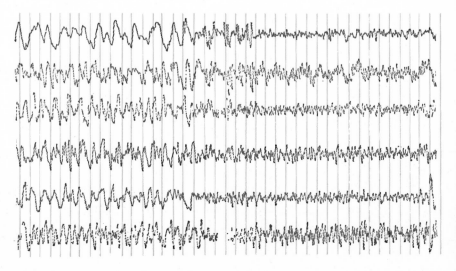

CORTEX IS STIMULATED by passing an electric current to the brain surface of a sleeping monkey. Six recording electrodes show the RAS has been activated to awaken the brain.

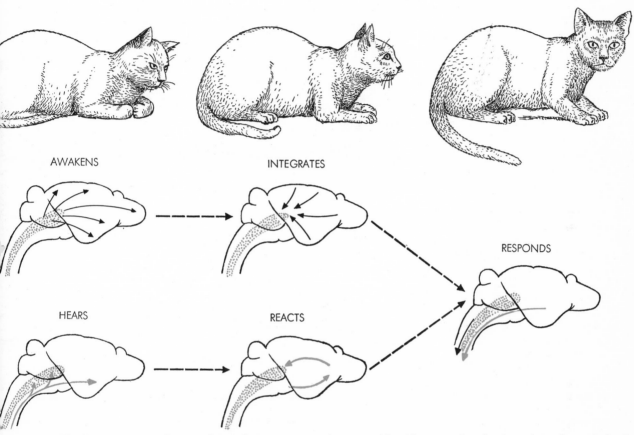

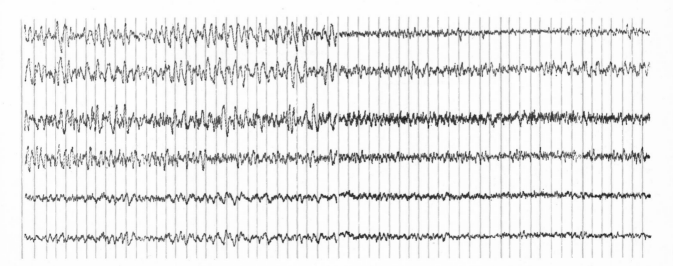

AKE

AWAKENS

INTEGRATES

RESPONDS

HEARS

REACTS

area. The brain waves at the top change from a pattern of sleep to one of wakefulness. The RAS then integrates the brain's activity so that the brain can react as a whole. The cat finally

responds with a motor impulse (*outgoing red arrow*) that is regulated by the RAS. The cat then jumps to its feet and runs away. The entire process takes place in a matter of a few seconds.

**RAS IS STIMULATED** by passing an electric current into the brain stem of a sleeping monkey. Recording electrodes show a more

abrupt transition from sleep to wakefulness. The waves become sharp, short and more frequent. This is a typical waking pattern.

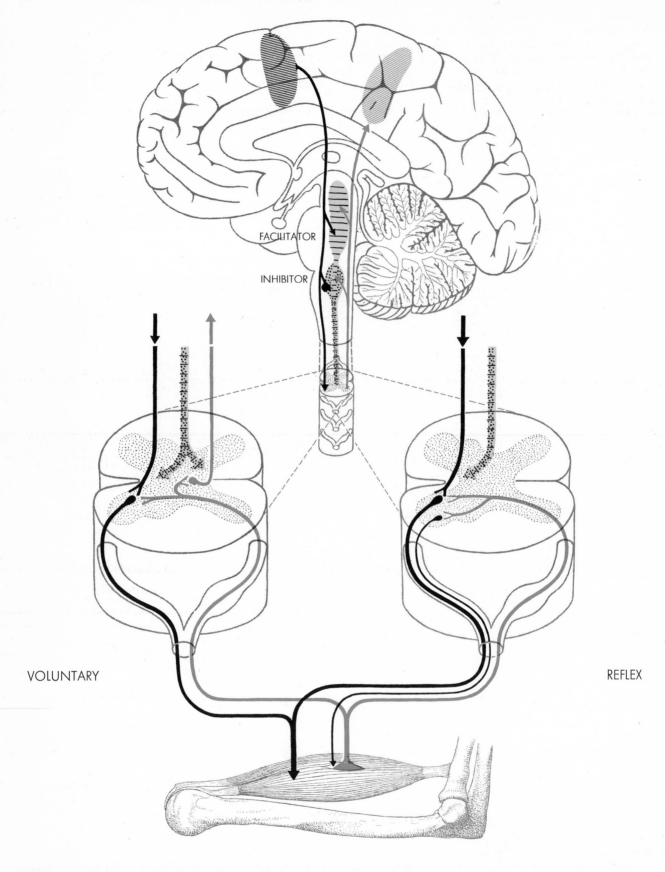

FACILITATOR

INHIBITOR

VOLUNTARY

REFLEX

**MOVEMENTS ARE MODIFIED** by the RAS. In voluntary movement sensory nerves (*red*) conduct impulses from the muscle spindle (*bottom*) to a sensory area in the brain (*red hatching*). Motor nerves (*black*) conduct impulses from the motor area (*black hatching*) to the muscle. Both nerve systems branch into the RAS.

The RAS sends down impulses (*heavy red arrows*) that facilitate or inhibit the response. In reflex movement sensory impulses are passed on immediately to motor nerves in the spinal cord. One nerve activates the muscle and maintains its "tone." The other (*thin black line*) sensitizes the spindle. The RAS controls both.

the cortex certainly is essential. The alert state seems to depend upon an interplay between the cortex and the RAS. The reticular formation is stimulated not only by the sensory nerves but also by impulses from some parts of the cortex. This has been demonstrated by electrical stimulation of certain areas of the cortex in monkeys: such stimulation will awaken a sleeping monkey. When the experiment is tried on a monkey that is awake, it evokes a dramatic response. The monkey instantly stops whatever it is doing and looks about intently and slightly puzzled, as if to say: "What was that?" It does not seem distressed or agitated—only warily alert. So it would seem that in the waking state the RAS plays a part, in combination with the cortex, in focusing attention and probably in many other mental processes.

All this raises the possibility that the RAS may be importantly involved in mental disorders. Investigations of this possibility have already begun by means of experiments with drugs. It is natural to start with anesthetic and sleep-inducing drugs, to see how they affect the RAS. The results of these experiments are illuminating but not surprising. They show that the drug blocks the flow of nerve impulses in the reticular formation but has little effect on the flow along the direct pathways from sense organs to the cortex. As the anesthesia wears off, the flow in the RAS returns to normal. A stimulating drug, on the other hand, has the opposite effect: it enhances the conduction of impulses in the RAS. It will be interesting to extend these experiments to the new tranquilizing drugs and the substances that produce experimental psychoses. Already there is evidence that these drugs do affect the functioning of the RAS.

Still another domain is under the control of this amazingly cogent bit of tissue in the brain. The RAS apparently has a hand in regulating all the motor activities of the body. It can modify muscle movements of both the voluntary type (controlled by the brain) and the reflex type (controlled in the spinal cord).

Just as the brain cortex has specific centers of sensation, it also has specific motor centers which generate muscle contractions. If one stimulates a motor center with an electric current, the appropriate muscles will respond, but the resulting body movements are jerky and uncontrolled. These powerful movements are normally controlled and polished by other motor centers of the

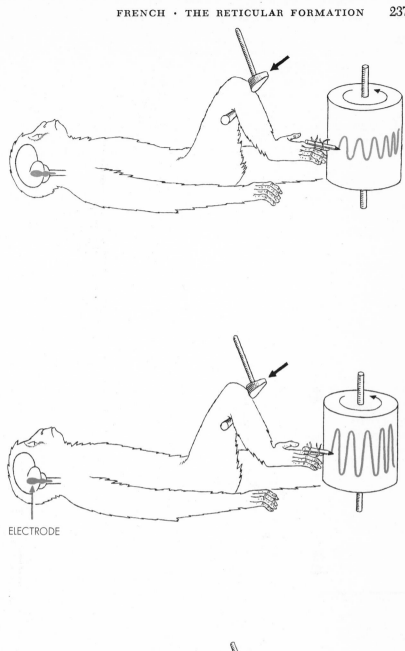

ELECTRODE

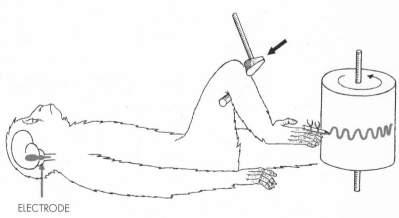

ELECTRODE

**CONTROL OF REFLEX MOTOR REACTIONS** by the reticular formation was demonstrated by this experiment on an anesthetized monkey. When the monkey's knee is tapped regularly, its knee jerks record a series of regular curves on a rotating drum (*top*). When the upper part of the monkey's reticular formation is stimulated, the jerks are larger (*middle*). When the lower part of the formation is stimulated, the jerks are smaller (*bottom*).

cortex, acting through the reticular formation. If the RAS is not stimulated or does not function properly, the movements will be jerky.

More surprising is the fact that the RAS can also act on the reflexes, centered in the spinal cord. The reflex apparatus has two functions. First, it generates automatic muscle movements. When signals from a sudden and alarming sensory stimulus (*e.g.,* touching something hot) arrive at the spinal cord, they are passed on immediately to an adjacent motor nerve and travel right back to the affected part of the body to jerk it away. In general, the automatic, reflex activities are protective—responses to danger or sudden challenges in the surroundings. But some of them can be tricked into action by suddenly stretching a muscle: for example, a tap on the knee elicits the well-known knee jerk.

The second function of the reflex system is to keep the muscles ready for action by maintaining "tone"—that is, a state of partial contraction. Just as a violin string must be stretched to a certain tension before it can emit music, so a muscle must be maintained at a certain tension to respond efficiently to a stimulus. The mechanism that regulates its resting tension, or "tone," is a small structure within the muscle called a "spindle." When a muscle contracts, it squeezes the spindle; when it relaxes, the pressure on the spindle loosens. Either departure from normal tone causes

the spindle to send signals by way of a sensory nerve to the spinal cord; there they excite a motor nerve to correct the contraction or relaxation of the muscle. This feedback system automatically keeps each muscle at precisely the right tone. And the appropriate tone itself is adjusted to suit the needs of the moment by nerve impulses which regulate the sensitivity of the spindle.

Now experiments have clearly demonstrated that the RAS exerts some control over voluntary and reflex motor reactions. Let us take for illustration an experiment on the reflex knee jerk, which is easy and convenient to perform. A monkey is anesthetized and a pen is tied to its toe to record the size of its knee kicks on a rotating drum. We keep tapping its knee and we get a uniform response, recorded as a nice series of regular curves on the drum. Then we suddenly stimulate the reticular formation electrically. The knee jerks immediately become larger: the RAS has enhanced them. When we stop stimulating it, the kicks return to normal size. Now in the course of exploratory experiments along the reticular formation a new fact emerges. If we stimulate the formation at a point toward its lower end in the brain stem, the kicks are not enhanced but instead are inhibited!

Following up this finding, we discover that these centers can enhance or inhibit sensory as well as motor impulses. In short, the RAS acts as a kind

of traffic control center, facilitating or inhibiting the flow of signals in the nervous system.

The astonishing generality of the RAS gives us a new outlook on the nervous system. Neurologists have tended to think of the nervous system as a collection of more or less separate circuits, each doing a particular job. It now appears that the system is much more closely integrated than had been thought. This should hardly surprise us. A simple organism such as the amoeba reacts with totality toward stimuli: the whole cell is occupied in the act of finding, engulfing and digesting food. Man, even with his 10 billion nerve cells, is not radically different. He must focus his sensory and motor systems on the problem in hand, and for this he obviously must be equipped with some integrating machine.

The RAS seems to be such a machine. It awakens the brain to consciousness and keeps it alert; it directs the traffic of messages in the nervous system; it monitors the myriads of stimuli that beat upon our senses, accepting what we need to perceive and rejecting what is irrelevant; it tempers and refines our muscular activity and bodily movements. We can go even further and say that it contributes in an important way to the highest mental processes– the focusing of attention, introspection and doubtless all forms of reasoning.

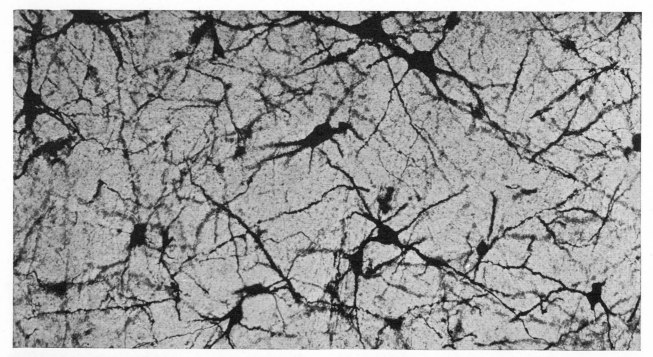

**EXTENSIVE BRANCHING OF CELLS** in the reticular formation is depicted by this photomicrograph of a section of the reticular formation in the brain of a dog. The dark areas in the photo- micrograph are cells of the formation which have been stained with silver. The section was lent by Drs. M. and A. Scheibel of the Medical School of the University of California at Los Angeles.

# 31

# THE GREAT
# CEREBRAL COMMISSURE

R. W. SPERRY                                      January 1964

The body plan of a mammal provides for two lungs, two kidneys and paired organs such as eyes, ears and limbs. In a sense it also provides for a paired brain. In structural detail and functional capacity the two halves of the mammalian brain are mirror twins, each with a full set of centers for the sensory and motor activities of the body: vision, hearing, muscular movement and so on. Each hemisphere of the brain is mainly associated with one side of the body, the right brain presiding over the left side and the left brain over the right side. Each hemisphere's influence is not, however, always restricted in this way: when an area in one hemisphere is damaged, the corresponding area in the other often can take over its work and so control the functions involved for both sides of the body. In short, either half of the brain can to a large extent serve as a whole brain.

Anatomically, of course, the two halves of the brain are linked together and normally function as one organ. They are united not only by the common stem that descends from the brain into the spinal cord but also by a number of cross bridges between the hemispheres. Especially striking is the system of connections between the two halves of the cerebrum: the upper part of the brain. The cerebral hemispheres are linked by discrete bundles of nerve fibers, called commissures, that form reciprocal connections between parallel centers in the two hemispheres. By far the most prominent of these bridges is a broad cable known as the great cerebral commissure or, more technically, as the corpus callosum [see illustration on pages 242–243]. This massive structure, which is particularly large in primates and largest in man, contains most of the millions of nerve fibers that connect the two halves of the cerebral cortex, which is the highest integrating organ of the brain.

The size and obviously important position of the corpus callosum suggest that it must be crucial for the proper performance of the brain's functions. Many years ago, however, brain surgeons discovered to their surprise that when the corpus callosum was cut into (as it sometimes had to be for medical reasons), this severing of fiber connections between the cerebral cortices produced little or no noticeable change in the patients' capacities. The same was true in the rare cases of individuals who lacked the corpus callosum because of a congenital failure in development. Experiments in severing the corpus callosum in monkeys tended to confirm the apparent harmlessness of the operation. Accordingly in the late 1930's surgeons tried cutting the entire corpus callosum in some cases of severe epilepsy as a measure to prevent the spread of epileptic seizures from one brain hemisphere to the other. Efforts to pinpoint losses of function in this series of cases were again unsuccessful.

Exactly what purpose the corpus callosum served became more and more a mystery. In 1940 the nerve physiologist Warren S. McCulloch, then working at the Yale University School of Medicine, summarized the situation with the remark that its only proved role seemed to be "to aid in the transmission of epileptic seizures from one to the other side of the body." As recently as 1951 the psychologist Karl S. Lashley, director of the Yerkes Laboratories of Primate Biology, was still offering his own jocular surmise that the corpus callosum's purpose "must be mainly mechanical . . . i.e., to keep the hemispheres from sagging." The curious capacity of the brain to carry on undisturbed after the destruction of what is by far its largest central fiber system came to be cited rather widely in support of some of the more mystical views in brain theory.

Intrigued by the problem of the great cerebral commissure and the theoretical implications of this problem, my colleagues and I began an intensive investigation of the matter, starting in the early 1950's at the University of Chicago and continuing after 1954 at the California Institute of Technology. This research, carried on by many workers at Cal Tech and elsewhere, has now largely resolved the mystery of the corpus callosum; today this bundle of fibers is probably the best understood of any of the large central association systems of the brain. The investigation has gone considerably beyond the question of the corpus callosum's functions. From it has emerged a new technique for analyzing the organization and operation of the brain; this approach has already yielded much interesting information and promises to open up for detailed study many heretofore inaccessible features of brain activity.

The technique essentially consists in the study or application, in various ways, of the split brain: a brain divided surgically so that the performance of each half can be tested separately. It has entailed a series of experiments with animals, starting with cats and continuing with monkeys and chimpanzees. The findings are not confined to animals; there has also been opportunity to study human patients who had been operated on for severe epilepsy and emerged from the operation with a split brain but freed of convulsive attacks and still in possession of most of their faculties.

The split-brain studies have borne out the earlier observation that the cutting of the entire corpus callosum causes little disturbance of ordinary behavior. This is generally true even when the operation severs not only the corpus callosum but also all the other connections between the right and left sides of the brain down through the upper part of the brain stem. Cats and monkeys with split brains can hardly be distinguished from normal animals in most of their activities. They show no noticeable disturbance of co-ordination, maintain their internal functions, are alert and active, respond to situations in the usual manner and perform just about as well as normal animals in standard tests of learning ability. Their individual traits of personality and temperament remain the same.

It required specially designed tests to show that the split brain is not, after all, entirely normal in its function. The first convincing demonstration was provided by Ronald E. Myers, in his doctoral research started in 1951 in our laboratory at the University of Chicago and continued at Cal Tech. Testing the performance of the two brain halves separately, he found that when the corpus callosum was cut, what was learned by one side of the brain was not transferred to the

other side. In fact, the two sides could learn diametrically opposed solutions to the same experimental problem, so that the animal's response in a given situation depended on which side of the brain was receiving the triggering stimulus. It was as though each hemisphere were a separate mental domain operating with complete disregard—indeed, with a complete lack of awareness—of what went on in the other. The split-brain animal behaved in the test situation as if it had two entirely separate brains.

The initial experiment involved segregating each eye with half of the brain as a separate system. This was accomplishing by cutting both the corpus callosum and the structure called the optic chiasm, in which half the nerve fibers from each eye cross over to the brain hemisphere on the opposite side of the head [*illustration on page 244*]. The effect of this combined operation is to leave each eye feeding its messages solely to the hemisphere on the same side of the head.

The animal was then trained to solve

a problem presented only to one eye, the other eye being covered with a patch. The problem might be, for example, to discriminate between a square and a circle; if the animal pushed a panel bearing the correct symbol, say the square, it got a reward of food. After it had learned to make the correct choice with one hemisphere, the problem was then presented to the other eye and hemisphere, the first eye now being blindfolded. When the subject used the second eye, it reacted as if it had never been faced with the problem before. The number of trials required to relearn the problem with the second eye showed that no benefit carried over from the earlier learning with the first eye. The transfer of learning and memory from one hemisphere to the other occurred readily in animals with the corpus callosum intact but failed completely in those with the corpus callosum cut. Each hemisphere, and its associated eye, was independent of the other.

This was again demonstrated when the two hemispheres were trained to make opposite choices. The animal was

EFFECT OF BRAIN DIVISION is tested on animals trained to perform a variety of tasks in response to visual or tactile cues. In this test designed by the author the monkey must pull one or the other of two levers with differently shaped handles.

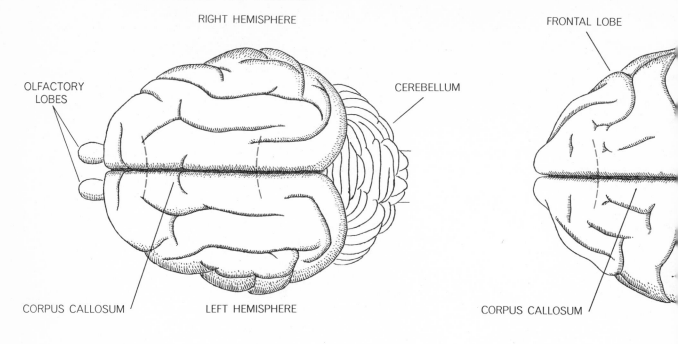

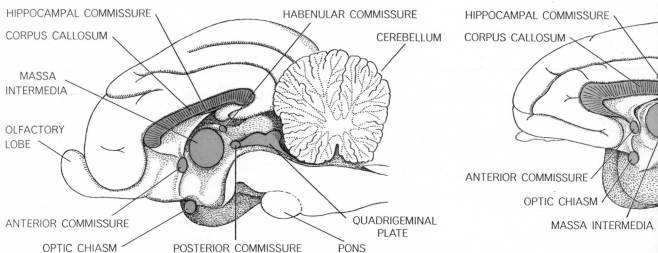
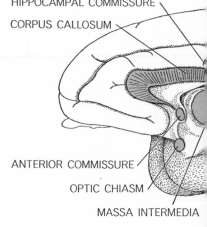

**CORPUS CALLOSUM and the other commissures connect the two halves of the mammalian brain. The drawings on these two pages** **show the brains of a cat (*left*), a monkey (*center*) and a human being (*right*). In each case the top drawing shows the top of the**

first trained to choose the square when the pair of symbols was seen through one eye. After learning was complete the eye patch was shifted and the animal was taught with the other eye to reject the square and pick the circle. This reversed training through the separate eyes gave rise to no sign of interference or conflict, as it does in an animal with an intact corpus callosum.

Subsequent studies, many dealing with forms of learning other than the visual—discrimination by touch, motor learning and so on—support the same conclusion. For example, in a special training box in which the animals could not see what their forepaws were doing,

John S. Stamm and I trained cats to get food by using a paw to choose correctly between a hard pedal and a soft one, or a rough pedal and a smooth one, or two pedals of different shapes [*see illustration on page 245*]. With the corpus callosum intact, an animal trained to use one paw is generally able to carry out the learned performance when it is made to use the untrained paw; normally the training transfers from one side to the other. But when the corpus callosum has been cut beforehand, the training of one paw does not help the other; on shifting from the first paw to the second the cat has to learn discrimination by touch all over again. The same applies to the

learning of a motor task, such as the pattern of finger or paw movements necessary to push a lever or open the hasp and cover of a food well. What is learned with one hand or paw fails, as a rule, to carry over to the other when the corpus callosum has been severed, be it in a cat, a monkey, a chimpanzee or a man.

In short, it appears from the accumulated evidence that learning in one hemisphere is usually inaccessible to the other hemisphere if the commissures between the hemispheres are missing. This means that the corpus callosum has the important function of allowing the two hemispheres to share learning and

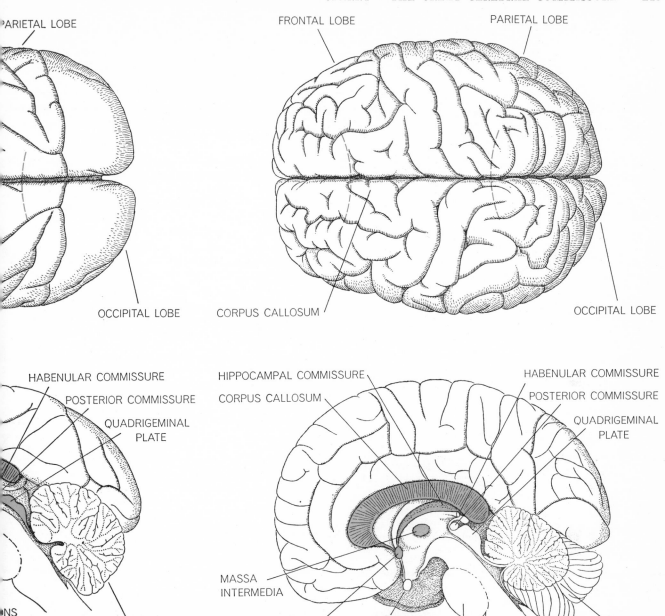

PARIETAL LOBE

FRONTAL LOBE

PARIETAL LOBE

OCCIPITAL LOBE

CORPUS CALLOSUM

OCCIPITAL LOBE

HABENULAR COMMISSURE

POSTERIOR COMMISSURE

QUADRIGEMINAL
PLATE

HIPPOCAMPAL COMMISSURE

CORPUS CALLOSUM

HABENULAR COMMISSURE

POSTERIOR COMMISSURE

QUADRIGEMINAL
PLATE

MASSA
INTERMEDIA

CEREBELLUM

ANTERIOR
COMMISSURE

OPTIC
CHIASM

PONS

CEREBELLUM

cerebral hemispheres, with the position of the corpus callosum indicated in color. The bottom drawings are sectional views of the right half of the brain as seen from the mid-line; the connecting structures cut in split-brain investigations are designated in color.

memory. It can do this in either of two ways: by transmitting the information at the time the learning takes place, or by supplying it on demand later. In the first case the engrams, or memory traces, of what is learned are laid down both in the directly trained hemisphere and, by way of the corpus callosum, in the other hemisphere as well. In other words, intercommunication via the corpus callosum at the time of learning results in the formation of a double set of memory traces, one in each half of the brain. In the second case a set of engrams is established only in the directly trained half, but this information is available to the other hemisphere, when it is re-

quired, by way of the corpus callosum.

By cutting the corpus callosum after learning, and by other methods of investigation, it is possible to determine which of these two memory systems is used in different learning situations and in different species. It appears from present evidence that the cat tends to form engrams in both hemispheres when it is learning something. In man, where one hemisphere is nearly always dominant, the single-engram system tends to prevail, particularly in all memory relating to language. The monkey seems to fall somewhere in between. It sometimes uses the double-engram system, but under other conditions it may lay down en-

grams in only one of its hemispheres.

Thanks to a wide variety of experiments with cats and monkeys, involving one-side training and testing of various eye-limb and other combinations, we are now beginning to get a fairly detailed picture of the functions of the corpus callosum. It is needed for correlating images in the left and right halves of the visual field; for integrating sensations from paired limbs, or for learning that requires motor co-ordination of the limbs; for unifying the cerebral processes of attention and awareness, and for a number of other specific activities that involve direct interaction of the hemispheres. Furthermore, the corpus callosum seems

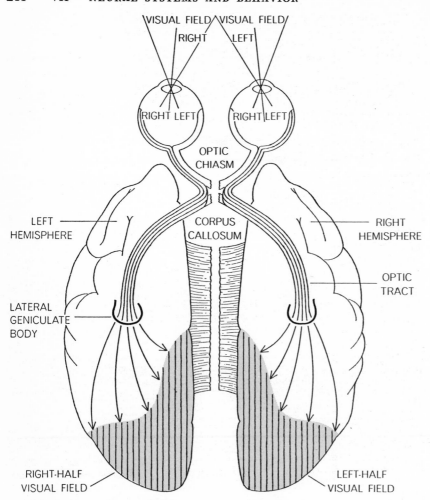

VISUAL FIELDS and the visual centers of the brain are related as shown in this diagram of the monkey brain. Cutting optic chiasm and corpus callosum leaves each eye feeding information to one side of the brain only and eliminates the normal overlap of visual fields.

to play important roles of a more general nature. Its absence slows down the rate of learning, at least in some situations. And, like other large nerve-fiber tracts, it has a general tonic effect on the brain cells to which it feeds impulses.

Many of these findings in animals have been checked and confirmed recently in studies conducted on a human patient in whom the hemispheres were surgically separated in an effort to control intractable epileptic convulsions. The seizures had been building up for 10 years in this man after a brain injury sustained in World War II. Philip J. Vogel and Joseph E. Bogen, surgeons at the Institute of Nervous Diseases of Loma Linda University in Los Angeles, cut through the corpus callosum and other commissures. The operation was remarkably successful in ending the attacks. Moreover, the patient, a 49-year-old man above average in intelligence, was left without any gross changes in his personality or level of intellect. In the months after the operation he comment-

ed repeatedly that he felt much better than he had in many years. In casual conversation over a cup of coffee and a cigarette one would hardly suspect that there was anything at all unusual about him.

With the collaboration of the patient and his physician, Michael S. Gazzaniga of our laboratory has carried out a series of careful tests probing the man's performances with one or both sides of the brain and body. Like most people, the patient is right-handed, and his dominant cerebral hemisphere is the left one. He is able to perform quite normally most activities involving only the left brain and right side of the body. For example, he can easily read material in the right half of his visual field, name and locate objects in that half, execute commands with his right hand or foot and so on. He does, however, have certain difficulties with activities on his left side.

Up to a point the left side of his body can function normally: he appears to see clearly in the left half of his visual field

and has good sensitivity to touch and good motor function on his left side. But in any task that requires judgment or interpretation based on language, which is stored only in his left cerebral hemisphere, he clearly shows the effects of the cerebral disconnection. He cannot read any material that falls in the left half of his visual field, so that when he reads with full vision he has difficulty and tires easily. Nor can he write anything at all meaningful with his left hand. As a rule he cannot carry out verbal commands with his left hand or left leg. When an object is presented solely in the left half of his visual field, he may react to it appropriately but he cannot name or describe it. The same is true of an object placed in his left hand when he is blindfolded. While blindfolded he is unable to say where he has been touched on the left side of the body or to describe the position or movements of his own left hand. In fact, if the dominant hemisphere of his brain is occupied with a task, anything happening to the left side of his body may go completely unnoticed. When his dominant left hemisphere is questioned about nonverbal activities that have just been carried out successfully by the left hand via the right hemisphere, it cannot recall them; this is often the case even when both of his eyes have been open and their visual fields unrestricted. Evidently the dominant hemisphere of the brain neither knows nor remembers anything about the experiences and activities of the other hemisphere.

The separation of the two hemispheres is further indicated by certain specific tests. For instance, when the skin on one side of the subject's body is lightly tapped with the point of a pencil, he can locate the point touched with the hand on that side but not with the other hand. When a spot of light is flashed on a screen in one half of the patient's visual field, he can point to it only with the hand on the same side. In generalized motor activities his left hand usually co-operates with the right, but not always. At times the left hand may go off in a distracted way on independent and even antagonistic activities of its own, which can be troublesome.

These findings are generally confirmed in work begun with a second patient who has more recently recovered from the same kind of brain operation. The results in this individual are not complicated by an earlier brain injury, and two months after the operation the overall recovery picture is even better than it was for the first patient. In particular, motor control of the left hand is not so markedly impaired.

It should be noted again that most of the impairments of brain function from such surgery do not show up in the common activities of daily life. They are detected only under special testing conditions, such as blindfolding the subject, restricting his movements to one or the other hand, using quick-flash projection to confine vision to half of the visual field and so on. One can hope that where the impairments do cause difficulty in ordinary activities, they will be correctible by re-education and other measures as further investigation adds to our understanding of the properties and capacities of the bisected brain.

In any case, it is now clear that the loss of the commissural connections between the two halves of the cerebrum does have important and well-marked effects on the functioning of the brain. If the corpus callosum fails to develop at all because of some congenital accident, centers for language and other functions may develop in compensation on both sides of the brain. This seems to have occurred in a nine-year-old boy lacking a corpus callosum, whom we recently tested. As in some earlier cases in the medical literature, he shows almost none of the impairments we observe in the two adult patients.

In other older cases distinct impairments were observed, but they were ascribed to damage in brain areas near the corpus callosum. In the light of present knowledge these cases reinforce the view that damage to the corpus callosum interferes with normal functioning in a number of clearly defined ways. For example, Norman Geschwind of the Veterans Administration Hospital in Boston has recently noted that a patient with a damaged corpus callosum, and similar individuals in the medical literature, have shown effects such as word-blindness, word-deafness and faulty communication between the right and left hands.

Once the enigma of the great cerebral commissure was cleared up and it was firmly established that the commissure really does serve important communication purposes, our interest shifted to more general questions that might be explored by investigation of the bisected brain. Such a brain offered an extraordinary opportunity to examine the many functions and interrelations of parts of the brain, structure by structure and control center by control center.

Bisection of the brain leaves each hemisphere virtually undisturbed. Each

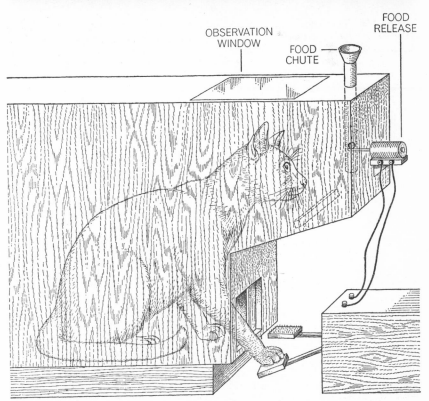

**TACTILE DISCRIMINATION** is tested with the apparatus shown in the photograph (*top*) and in the diagram (*bottom*). The animal is trained to distinguish between two pedals with different shapes or surface textures. In a normal cat, whatever is learned with one paw is transferred to the other one. But in a split-brain animal each side must learn a task anew.

half preserves intact its internal organization, the inflow of sensory messages and the outflow of motor commands. Each retains its full set of cerebral control centers and the potentiality for performing nearly all the functions of a whole brain. Even the human brain, in spite of the normal dominance of one side, can adapt itself to carry on fairly well when one hemisphere is eliminated early in life because of a tumor or an injury. A monkey with one cerebral hemisphere removed gets along better than a man in a comparable condition, and a cat does much better than a monkey.

Because of the independence of the two halves of the bisected brain, it is possible to study nearly all brain functions by concentrating on one half while the animal carries on normally with the other half. The situation affords certain uniquely helpful experimental conditions. Since the experiments are performed with one hemisphere, the identical opposite hemisphere can serve as a built-in control for comparison. Moreover, the fact that one half of the brain suffices to deal with the animal's needs makes it possible to remove or isolate parts of the experimental half, without disabling aftereffects to the animal, in order to identify the functions of each part.

A first question to arise in this connection is: How far can the brain be divided without grossly disrupting brain-mediated processes? We have already noted that cutting the cerebral commissures does not seriously interfere with the functioning of the two hemispheres. In monkeys the bisection has been carried down through the roof of the brain stem and completely through the cerebellum, leaving intact for cross communication only the tegmentum, or floor of the brain stem [*see illustration on opposite page*]. Such monkeys show some motor unsteadiness, weakness and uncertainty, but they eventually recover their strength and stability. Deeper splits through the tegmentum into the upper part of the pons have been made in the cat by Theodore Voneida of our laboratory. A curious blindness ensued, but it cleared up after several weeks and the animals made a good recovery. The effects on learning and perception of these deepest bisections have not yet been studied in detail. In general, however, it can be said that the two halves of the brain function well even when they are divided down into the upper regions of the brain stem, provided that only cross connections are cut.

The effect on behavior of severing the cross connections between the two halves of the brain is not always simple and unambiguous. An animal with a split brain sometimes behaves as if the two hemispheres were still in direct communication in one way or another. Some of these cases can be explained without difficulty; others are puzzling and call for further investigation.

One case involved the ability to respond to differences in the brightness of light. Thomas H. Meikle and Jeri A. Sechzer of the University of Pennsylvania School of Medicine trained cats to discriminate between brightness differences seen with one eye and then tested them with the other eye. With the corpus callosum severed the cats were able to transfer this learning from one hemisphere to the other when the brightness distinctions were easy to make, but not when they were fairly difficult. The transfer disappeared, however, when cross connections in the midbrain, as well as the corpus callosum, were cut. This case therefore appears to be explainable on the basis that in the cat the process involved is simple enough to occur at a level lower than the corpus callosum. In the monkey and in man, however, the corpus callosum seems to be required for the transfer of even the simplest brightness or color discrimination.

There are types of cross communication that can take place in a split brain because both sides of the brain are directly connected to the motor system or sensory organ involved. For example, each brain hemisphere receives sensory messages from both the right and the left sides of the face and other parts of the head; consequently the separation of the hemispheres does not interrupt the communication of sensations between the two sides of the head. Hearing in each ear is likewise extensively represented in both cerebral hemispheres. The same may apply in lesser degree to certain sensations in the limbs and the rest of the body; this may explain why learning involving hand and arm movements in monkeys

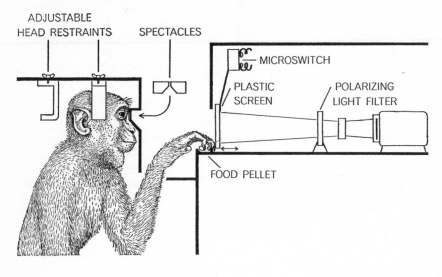

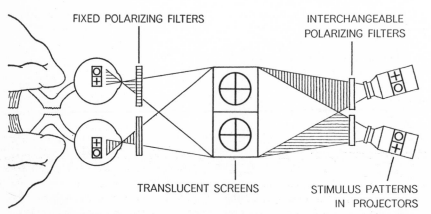

**PERCEPTUAL CONFLICT** in split-brain monkeys is tested with the apparatus shown in the top drawing. It presents a different image to each eye, as seen in the bottom diagram. While one of the animal's isolated eye-brain systems learns that pushing the panel with the cross is rewarded by food, the other eye-brain system learns to push the circle instead.

with split brains may on occasion transfer from one side to the other.

There is also the possibility of indirect communication between the split halves of the brain through feedback from activity in the body. A motor activity directed from one hemisphere may involve widespread bodily movements that will feed back messages to the opposite hemisphere as well as the active one. For instance, an action performed by one hand is likely to involve adjustments in posture and muscular activity that spread to the other side of the body and thus make themselves known to the other hemisphere. Unifying factors of this sort help to account for the fact that the two sides of the body do not act more independently in a split-brain situation. They do not, however, change the general inference that the two brain hemispheres are for the most part separate realms of knowledge and awareness.

A special case of cross transfer that was at first quite surprising was discovered recently in our laboratory by Joseph Bossom and Charles R. Hamilton. Their experiments dealt with the way in which the brain adjusts itself to overcome the distortions produced by looking through a wedge prism. Such a prism so displaces the visual scene that in reaching for an object the hand misses its mark. With a little practice, however, the eye-brain system soon achieves the necessary corrections to hit the target every time. Bossom and Hamilton trained split-brain monkeys to adapt themselves to the problem using one eye. After the monkeys had learned to correct for the displacement of the prism, they were switched to using the other eye. The learning was fully and immediately transferred—even in monkeys with a deep bisection through the brain-stem roof and cerebellum. This seemed to contradict the earlier experiments showing a lack of transfer of learning from one eye to the other. But when Hamilton followed up with repetitions of the experiments in which the monkey was made to practice the prism adaptation using only one hand, he found that corrective adjustments achieved through the one hand, in combination with either eye, do not transfer to the other hand. This suggested that the central adjustment to deflections of a target by a prism depends primarily on the brain centers concerned with motor activity and bodily sensations rather than on those involved in vision. This interpretation has now been supported in an extension of the study to human subjects. It is still not clear, however, how split-brain monkeys achieve this adjustment so easily when

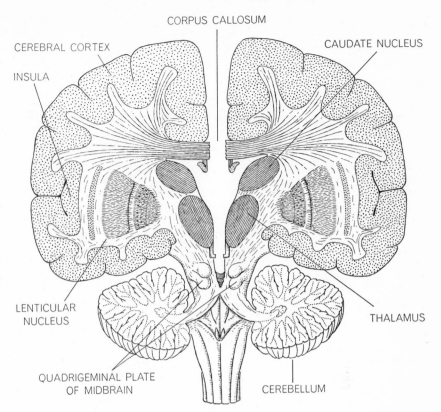

CORPUS CALLOSUM

CEREBRAL CORTEX

INSULA

CAUDATE NUCLEUS

LENTICULAR NUCLEUS

THALAMUS

QUADRIGEMINAL PLATE OF MIDBRAIN

CEREBELLUM

**DEGREE OF SEPARATION** among the higher brain centers that is produced by the surgical procedures discussed by the author is shown in this semisectional diagram of the brain.

the visual inflow is confined to one hemisphere and the only hand in use is the one governed primarily from the other hemisphere.

Certain other performances under study in our laboratory that appear to involve cross integration in the divided brain are even harder to explain. For example, Colwyn B. Trevarthen and I have found that a split-brain monkey can learn to select the larger (or smaller, as the case may be) of two circles of different sizes presented separately to the two brain hemispheres, the larger to one and the smaller to the other. To make the *relative* size count, the circles are selected from a series of five graded sizes. It would seem that to make the comparison successfully the two hemispheres, although cut apart, must collaborate in some way. Similarly, I have found that split-brain monkeys grasping two handles separately, one in each hand, can pick the larger or the rougher of the pair. Here again five different sizes and five degrees of roughness are paired in random right-left position.

Difficult as it is to avoid the conclusion that the two brain hemispheres are working together in these cases, the strong evidence of many experiments on the independence of the divided hemispheres suggests that one should seek other explanations. It is conceivable, for

example, that a combination of independent strategies used by the two hemispheres might have produced a high score without any real exchange of information. The discrimination of handles by touch might have been aided by cross communication through related sensations of movement or from motor feedback. It is also possible that the apparent communication between the hemispheres may have been achieved by way of interactions taking place in the lower brain stem or even in the spinal cord. These and other possibilities are being investigated.

Another group of observations revealed an interesting and significant difference between animal and human brains. The tests had to do with the ability of one side of the body to respond to visual cues received only by the cerebral hemisphere that directs the opposite side of the body. For example, with the corpus callosum divided and with vision restricted to one hemisphere, the animal is trained to reach out and pick by vision the correct one of two objects; can the subject do this when allowed to use only the hand or paw that normally is associated with the unseeing hemisphere? The cat proved to be able to use either forepaw under these conditions with about equal ease. The monkey does not

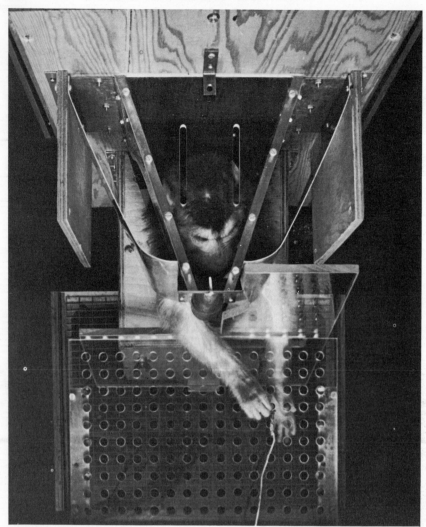

**HAND-TO-HAND CO-ORDINATION** is tested in this experiment. The split-brain monkey cannot see the plastic divider that prevents contact between its hands. By groping, it finds a peanut with its upper hand. It can retrieve the peanut only by poking it down through a hole and catching it with its lower hand. The only cues it has for placing the lower hand are based on a joint-and-muscle sense of the position and movement of the upper hand.

tion central controls are shifted from more primitive brain-stem areas to higher stations in the ballooning cerebral cortex, the role of the corpus callosum becomes more and more critical. So also do the phenomena of dominance and specialization in the hemispheres of the cerebrum. In cats and lower animals the two hemispheres seem to be essentially symmetrical, each learning equally and each capable of serving by itself almost as a whole brain. In the monkey the two hemispheres are apparently somewhat more specialized. As the accumulation of memories, or the storage of information, becomes more important in the higher animals, the duplication of memory files in the two brain hemispheres is given up for a more efficient system: the division of labor by the assignment of specialized files and functions to each hemisphere. This evolution has culminated in the human brain. Here a distinct separation of functions prevails: language is the task of the dominant hemisphere and lesser tasks are largely taken over by the other hemisphere.

The question of dominance is crucial for the effective functioning of the brain as the master control system. Bear in mind that the brain is composed of twin hemispheres, with a full set of control centers in each hemisphere that enables it to take command and govern the general behavior of the animal. What happens, then, if the two halves of an animal's split brain are taught to give completely conflicting responses to a given situation?

The devices developed in our laboratory allow a great variety of experiments, using all sorts of combinations of brain control centers with the sensory and motor organs of the body. They can restrict the animal to the use of one eye or the other with one hand or the other, to the tactile sense without vision, to vision in one brain hemisphere and the tactile sense in the other, and so on. A representative apparatus for the monkey, designed for experiments involving visual stimuli and responses with the hand, is shown in the illustration on page 241. The monkey stations itself behind a barrier that can be adjusted to let it see with both eyes or the right eye or the left eye or neither, and to let it use both hands or only the right or the left. By the use of light-polarizing filters, the visual stimulus (for example a circle) can be split and the two images projected separately to the two halves of its visual field in order to determine if the subject can integrate them. The monkey's responses consist in pressing buttons, pulling levers

do so well; sometimes it can co-ordinate its motor response with the visual message and sometimes not. In human patients, on the other hand, this ability is severely disrupted by the severing of the corpus callosum. As we have already noted, in the split-brain patient who was extensively tested the left hand generally is unable to respond correctly to commands or visual stimuli presented only to the left cerebral hemisphere. The patient without prior brain injury does somewhat better, but even so the performance is markedly poorer than that of the monkey.

The same applies to stimuli of other kinds. For instance, when the human patients are blindfolded and hold a pencil in one hand, the other hand is unable to find the end of the pencil if the hand holding the pencil shifts its angle or changes its position in some other way.

When monkeys whose corpus callosum had been cut were put to similar tests by Richard F. Mark and me, however, they performed almost normally [see illustration above]. And when all the cross connections down through the roof plate of the midbrain, with the exception of the corpus callosum, were cut, the performance also went well. Subsequent cutting of the corpus callosum in this last situation finally abolishes the performance, showing the participation of the corpus callosum. Even so, the difference between man and monkey in the expendability of the corpus callosum for such hand-to-hand activities remains striking.

Here we are probably seeing a reflection of the evolution of the brain. The appearance and development of the corpus callosum in evolution parallels the appearance and development of the cerebral cortex. As in the course of evolu-

and so forth; these responses are rewarded when they are correct. We can hook up to this apparatus automatic equipment that is programed to present any of a number of different problems to the animal. In that case the apparatus is attached to its home cage as a kind of porch where the monkey can station itself as the spirit moves it and work at its leisure.

With this apparatus a split-brain monkey can be trained, let us say, to choose between a triangle and a square as the rewarding stimulus. Looking through its left eye, it learns to select the triangle as the reward; through the right eye, the square. It is trained for a few trials with the left eye, then for a few trials with the right, and this alternation is continued until each eye comes to give a nearly perfect performance, even though the responses with the separate eyes are contradicting each other. As we have already noted, the animal usually evinces no conflict in this paradoxical situation: the left eye unhesitatingly chooses the triangle and

the right eye the square. Here the split-brain monkey learns, remembers and performs as if it were two different individuals, its identity depending on which hemisphere it happens to be using at the moment.

What if the two hemispheres are asked to learn these mutually contradictory answers simultaneously instead of one at a time alternately? Can each hemisphere attend to its own lesson and file one answer in its memory while the other is filing a conflicting answer in *its* memory?

Trevarthen found a way to investigate this question by introducing polarizing filters to present reversed pictures simultaneously to a monkey with both eyes open [*illustration on page 246*]. A pair of patterns (say a cross and a circle, but any pair of patterns or colors will do) is projected separately to the two eyes. To one eye it appears that the food reward is won by pushing the cross; to the other eye it seems that the circle is being pushed. In other words, for one hemisphere the correct answer

is "cross" and for the other it is "circle," but the panel that is pushed is the same in both cases. After the monkey, using both eyes, has learned to push the correct panel 90 per cent of the time, it is tested with each eye separately.

It turns out that there is a strong tendency for one hemisphere (usually the one governing the arm that is first used to push the panels) to learn the answer sooner and more fully than the other. This suggests that active attention by one hemisphere tends to weaken the attention of the second, although the activities of the two have no direct connection. Trevarthen has found, however, that sometimes both hemispheres learn their respective answers fully and simultaneously. That is, the split-brain monkey in these cases divides its attention between the two hemispheres, so that it masters the two contradictory problems in about the same time that a normal, single-minded monkey would be learning one problem.

This doubling of attention is also manifest in Gazzaniga's tests on the split-

**AUTOMATED EQUIPMENT is adapted to tabulating and recording the data from a number of trials conducted with several mon-** keys over a period of time. The animals work at their tasks at their leisure, moving to apparatus affixed to the rear of their cages.

brain human patient discussed earlier. The test consisted in asking the man to pick a certain figure out of a pair of figures flashed very briefly (for less than a tenth of a second) and simultaneously in each of his visual fields—one pair in the left field and one pair in the right. The subject abruptly points to the correct figure in the left field with his left hand (governed by the nondominant hemisphere) and at the same time indicates the correct figure in the right field verbally or by pointing (this act being governed by the dominant hemisphere, which controls language and speech). Discussing such responses afterward, the patient typically has no recollection of having pointed with his left hand; the dominant hemisphere seems completely ignorant of what went on in the other one.

These remarkable indications of a doubling of the psychic machinery in the brain raise a number of new questions about the roles played in the learning process by attention, perception and motivation. There are also many intriguing philosophical implications. When the brain is bisected, we see two separate "selves"—essentially a divided organism with two mental units, each with its own memories and its own will—competing for control over the organism. One is tempted to speculate on whether or not the normally intact brain is sometimes subject to conflicts that are attributable to the brain's double structure.

How does an animal with a split brain resolve the dilemma of being conditioned to two directly opposite answers to a given problem? Suppose it is confronted with a situation in which it must make a choice between two "correct" answers? Can it master the conflict or is it paralyzed like the proverbial donkey between a bag of oats and a bale of hay?

The kind of answer that is usually obtained is illustrated in an extension of the experiment with polarizing filters. After the split-brain monkey has been trained so that one hemisphere considers as correct the panel marked by a cross and the other hemisphere considers as correct the panel marked by a circle, one of the eye filters is turned 90 degrees. Now instead of the images being reversed in the two eyes, both eyes see the pair of symbols in the same way—say the cross on the left and the circle on the right. Will the animal, with both eyes open, choose the cross or the circle or waver in confusion between the two? In such tests the monkeys, after only a little indecision and hesitation, make a choice and adhere to it: they consistently select the cross or the circle for a series of trials. That is, one hemisphere or the other takes command and governs the monkey's behavior. This dominance may shift from time to time, each hemisphere taking its turn at control, but it would appear that no serious conflict disrupts any given movement.

Something more akin to conflict between the separated hemispheres is occasionally seen in tests given the human patients. Incorrect responses by the left hand may so exasperate the more sophisticated dominant hemisphere that it reaches across with the right hand to grab the left and force it to make the correct choice. Or conversely, when the literate hemisphere and right hand fail in a block-arrangement test—one of the few things that the left hand and nondominant hemisphere generally do better—impatient twitches and starts occur in the left arm, which may have to be restrained to keep it from intercepting the right. As in split-brain cats and monkeys, however, one hemisphere or the other generally prevails at any given time. Any incompatible messages coming down from the other hemisphere must be inhibited or disregarded.

The experiments discussed in this article are a sample of the large variety of studies with the split brain that are being carried on by our group at Cal Tech and by others in laboratories elsewhere. Work with the split brain has enabled us to pinpoint various centers of specific brain activity, has suggested new concepts and new lines of thought and has opened up a wealth of new possibilities for investigating the mysteries of the mind.

# Part VIII

PHYSIOLOGICAL BASES
OF SENSATION
AND PERCEPTION

# VIII

## PHYSIOLOGICAL BASES OF SENSATION AND PERCEPTION

*Introduction*    How is it that man and other creatures obtain a true representation of the world? This question, originally put forth by philosphers of long ago, has been partially answered by modern day neurophysiologists. We have already seen the manner in which information is originally coded by sensory neurons (Miller, Ratliff, and Hartline, "How Cells Receive Stimuli," page 205). The papers in this section deal with other details of the processes which form the physiological bases for sensation and perception. Great progress has been achieved in this area of sensory physiology. Some of this success has been due to detailed knowledge of sensory circuits and pathways, obtained by the painstaking analyses of neuroanatomists, past and present. The imaginative use of techniques for recording the electrical activity of the nervous system has been equally important, as the following papers adequately testify.

The first two papers are concerned with the functioning of the auditory system. In the first of these, "The Ear" (page 254), Georg von Békésy describes the mechanisms which translate sounds into nerve impulses. Appropriate stimulation of receptor hair cells in the Organ of Corti is seen to depend upon an almost unbelievably intricate series of preceding mechano-hydro-mechanical events. Minute movements of the hairlike processes of these cells produce receptor potentials, and ultimately nerve impulses in the auditory system. This system operates on the basis of a tonotopic organization: different neurons are maximally responsive to different frequencies, and neighboring neurons are maximally sensitive to adjacent frequencies. Von Békésy's experiments have shown how the basilar membrane serves to dissect sounds into their component frequencies, a process that is essential to tonotopic organization and thus to normal hearing.

Although von Békésy has elucidated mechanisms underlying the discrimination of pitch, we might ask how it is that animals can localize the source of sounds in a complex auditory environment—for animals are extremely accurate in localizing sound sources. Such accuracy is made possible because sound waves from a single source reach the two ears at different times and with different intensities. In "Auditory Localization" (page 264) Mark H. Rosenzweig explains how the nervous system utilizes such information in the localization of sound. Once again, we see that the nervous system performs exacting analyses, which dwarf by comparison any man-made devices.

The next two articles deal with some of the intricacies of the visual system. Early investigations of the operation of this sensory system generally employed flashes of light as stimuli. In recent years, the use of more complex and "natural" stimuli—contours, patterns, and moving figures—has revealed the existence of a rich neuronal language. O. H. Hubel, in "The Visual Cortex of the Brain" (page 270), describes how the analytical properties of neurons in the visual cortex of cats are dependent upon prior, more elementary analyses at lower levels of the visual system. One of the major implications of these studies is that the complex perceived visual world (with the exception of color perception) arises from merely two forms of relatively simple analysis in the retina.

The cerebral cortex is a relatively recent development in the evolution of nervous systems. Submammalian vertebrates lack a visual cortex of the type described by Hubel. In "Vision in Frogs" (page 279) W. R. A. Muntz describes how complex analyses are performed at more primitive levels of the visual system. One of the most fascinating findings is that certain neurons respond preferentially to stimuli that simulate living flies, a mechanism of specially adaptive significance to these animals. Muntz' own research provides both neurophysiological and behavioral evidence for color vision in frogs. His systematic studies illustrate the types of controls needed to establish the existence of true color vision.

Moving to a less well understood sensory system, Edward S. Hodgson discusses "Taste Receptors" (page 287). As he points out, the chemical senses (gustation and olfaction) developed early in evolution. The basis by which the taste system discriminates different substances is not yet well understood, but Hodgson presents evidence that supports the contention that molecular architecture is important. The finding that substances which cause extension of the blowfly's proboscis produce a nervous signal different from that produced by rejected substances is especially intriguing. Hodgson also discusses the process of sensory adaptation, common to all sensory systems but not discussed in previous articles. Although the blowfly may seem to have little in common with higher animals, there is no reason to suppose that the basic mode of coding in the taste system of this creature differs markedly from that of other animals.

# 32

# THE EAR

GEORG VON BÉKÉSY                                     August 1957

Even in our era of technological wonders, the performances of our most amazing machines are still put in the shade by the sense organs of the human body. Consider the accomplishments of the ear. It is so sensitive that it can almost hear the random rain of air molecules bouncing against the eardrum. Yet in spite of its extraordinary sensitivity the ear can withstand the pounding of sound waves strong enough to set the body vibrating. The ear is equipped, moreover, with a truly impressive selectivity. In a room crowded with people talking, it can suppress most of the noise and concentrate on one speaker. From the blended sounds of a symphony orchestra the ear of the conductor can single out the one instrument that is not performing to his satisfaction.

In structure and in operation the ear is extraordinarily delicate. One measure of its fineness is the tiny vibrations to which it will respond. At some sound frequencies the vibrations of the eardrum are as small as one billionth of a centimeter—about one tenth the diameter of the hydrogen atom! And the vibrations of the very fine membrane in the inner ear which transmits this stimulation to the auditory nerve are nearly 100 times smaller in amplitude. This fact alone is enough to explain why hearing has so long been one of the mysteries of physiology. Even today we do not know how these minute vibrations stimulate the nerve endings. But thanks to refined electro-acoustical instruments we do know quite a bit now about how the ear functions.

What are the ear's abilities? We can get a quick picture of the working condition of an ear by taking an audiogram, which is a measure of the threshold of hearing at the various sound frequencies. The hearing is tested with pure tones at various frequencies, and the audiogram tells how much sound pressure on the eardrum (*i.e.*, what intensity of sound) is necessary for the sound at each frequency to be just barely audible. Curiously, the audiogram curve often is very much the same for the various members of a family; possibly this is connected in some way with the similarity in the shape of the face.

The ear is least sensitive at the low frequencies: for instance, its sensitivity for a tone of 100 cycles per second is 1,000 times lower than for one at 1,000 cycles per second. This comparative insensitivity to the slower vibrations is an obvious physical necessity, because otherwise we would hear all the vibrations of our own bodies. If you stick a finger in each ear, closing it to air-borne sounds, you hear a very low, irregular tone, produced by the contractions of the muscles of the arm and finger. It is interesting that the ear is just insensitive enough to low frequencies to avoid the disturbing effect of the noises produced by muscles, bodily movements, etc. If it were any more sensitive to these frequencies than it is, we would even hear the vibrations of the head that are produced by the shock of every step we take when walking.

On the high-frequency side the range that the ear covers is remarkable. In childhood some of us can hear well at frequencies as high as 40,000 cycles per second. But with age our acuteness of hearing in the high-frequency range steadily falls. Normally the drop is almost as regular as clockwork: testing several persons in their 40s with tones at a fixed level of intensity, we found that over a period of five years their upper limit dropped about 80 cycles per second every six months. (The experiment was quite depressing to most of the partici-

pants.) The aging of the ear is not difficult to understand if we assume that the elasticity of the tissues in the inner ear declines in the same way as that of the skin: it is well known that the skin becomes less resilient as we grow old—a

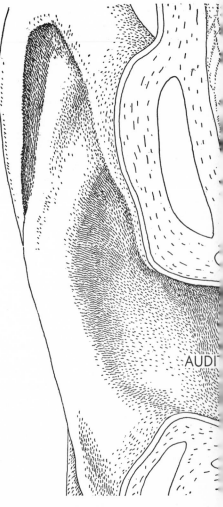

PARTS OF THE EAR are illustrated in somewhat simplified cross section. Be-

phenomenon anyone can test by lifting the skin on the back of his hand and measuring the time it takes to fall back.

However, the loss of hearing sensitivity with age may also be due to nerve deterioration. Damage to the auditory nervous system by extremely loud noises, by drugs or by inflammation of the inner ear can impair hearing. Sometimes after such damage the hearing improves with time; sometimes (*e.g.*, when the damaging agent is streptomycin) the loss is permanent. Unfortunately a physician cannot predict the prospects for recovery of hearing loss, because they vary from person to person.

Psychological factors seem to be involved. Occasionally, especially after an ear operation, a patient appears to improve in hearing only to relapse after a short time. Some reports have even suggested that operating on one ear has improved the unoperated ear as well. Since such an interaction between the two ears would be of considerable neuro-

logical interest, I have investigated the matter, but I have never found an improvement in the untreated ear that could be validated by an objective test.

## Structure of the Ear

To understand how the ear achieves its sensitivity, we must take a look at the anatomy of the middle and the inner ear. When sound waves start the eardrum (tympanic membrane) vibrating, the vibrations are transmitted via certain small bones (ossicles) to the fluid of the inner ear. One of the ossicles, the tiny stirrup (weighing only about 1.2 milligrams), acts on the fluid like a piston, driving it back and forth in the rhythm of the sound pressure. These movements of the fluid force into vibration a thin membrane, called the basilar membrane. The latter in turn finally transmits the stimulus to the organ of Corti, a complex structure which contains the endings of the auditory nerves. The question im-

mediately comes up: Why is this long and complicated chain of transmission necessary?

The reason is that we have a formidable mechanical problem if we are to extract the utmost energy from the sound waves striking the eardrum. Usually when a sound hits a solid surface, most of its energy is reflected away. The problem the ear has to solve is to absorb this energy. To do so it has to act as a kind of mechanical transformer, converting the large amplitude of the sound pressure waves in the air into more forceful vibrations of smaller amplitude. A hydraulic press is such a transformer: it multiplies the pressure acting on the surface of a piston by concentrating the force of the pressure upon a second piston of smaller area. The middle ear acts exactly like a hydraulic press: the tiny footplate of the stirrup transforms the small pressure on the surface of the eardrum into a 22-fold greater pressure on the fluid of the inner ear. In this way the

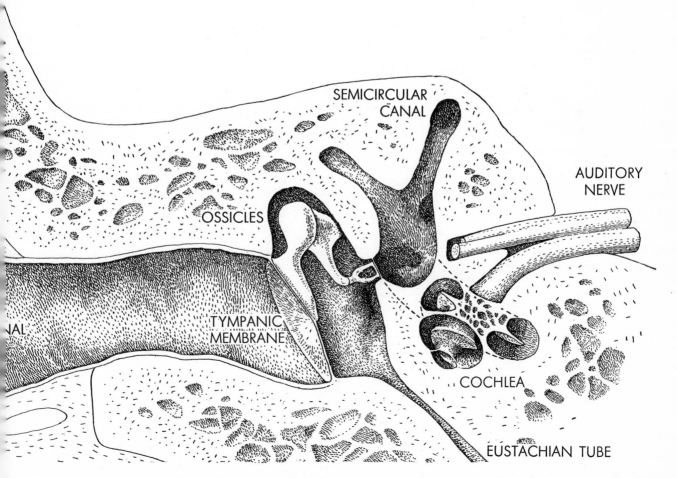

tween the eardrum (tympanic membrane) and the fluid-filled inner ear are the three small bones (ossicles) of the middle ear. The auditory nerve endings are in an organ (*not shown*) between the plate of bone which spirals up the cochlea and the outer wall of the cochlea.

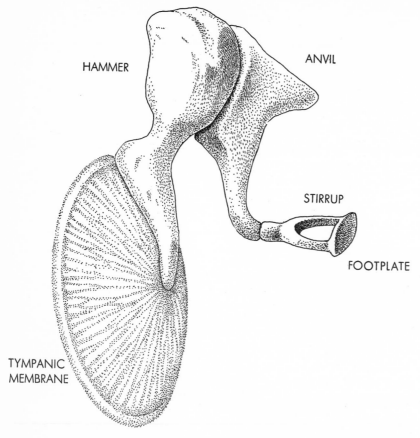

**THREE OSSICLES** transmit the vibrations of the tympanic membrane to the inner ear. The footplate of stirrup, surrounded by a narrow membrane, presses against inner-ear fluid.

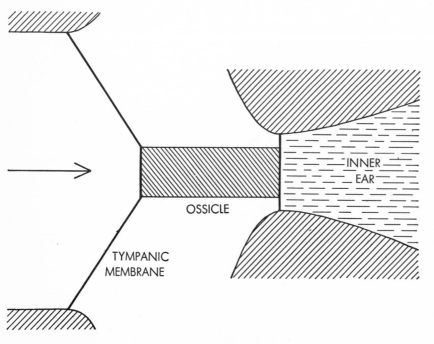

**HOW OSSICLES ACT** as a piston pressing against the fluid of the inner ear is indicated by this drawing. Pressure of the vibrations of tympanic membrane are amplified 22 times.

ear absorbs the greater part of the sound energy and transmits it to the inner ear without much loss.

But it needs another transformer to amplify the pressure of the fluid into a still larger force upon the tissues to which the nerves are attached. I think the ear's mechanism for this purpose is very ingenious indeed. It is based on the fact that a flat membrane, stretched to cover the opening of a tube, has a lateral tension along its surface. This tension can be increased tremendously if pressure is applied to one side of the membrane. And that is the function of the organ of Corti. It is constructed in such a way that pressure on the basilar membrane is transformed into shearing forces many times larger on the other side of the organ [*see diagram at bottom of opposite page*]. The enhanced shearing forces rub upon extremely sensitive cells attached to the nerve endings.

The eardrum is not by any means the only avenue through which we hear. We also hear through our skull, which is to say, by bone conduction. When we click our teeth or chew a cracker, the sounds come mainly by way of vibrations of the skull. Some of the vibrations are transmitted directly to the inner ear, by-passing the middle ear. This fact helps in the diagnosis of hearing difficulties. If a person can hear bone-conducted sounds but is comparatively deaf to air-borne sounds, we know that the trouble lies in the middle ear. But if he hears no sound by bone conduction, then his auditory nerves are gone, and there is no cure for his deafness. This is an old test, long used by deaf musicians. If a violin player cannot hear his violin even when he touches his teeth to the vibrating instrument, then he knows he suffers from nerve deafness, and there is no cure.

### Speaking and Hearing

Hearing by bone conduction plays an important role in the process of speaking. The vibrations of our vocal cords not only produce sounds which go to our ears via the air but also cause the body to vibrate, and the vibration of the jawbone is transmitted to the ear canal. When you hum with closed lips, the sounds you hear are to a large degree heard by bone conduction. (If you stop your ears with your fingers, the hum sounds much louder.) During speaking and singing, therefore, you hear two different sounds—one by bone conduction and the other by air conduction. Of course another listener hears only the air-conducted sounds. In these sounds

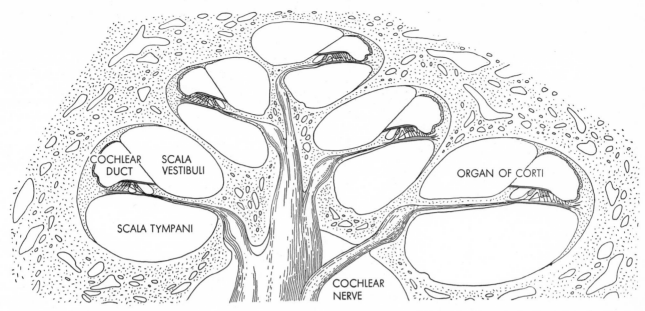

**TUBE OF THE COCHLEA,** coiled like the shell of a snail, is depicted in cross section. The plate of bone which appears in the cross section on pages 254–255 juts from the inside of the tube. Between it and the outside of the tube is the sensitive organ of Corti.

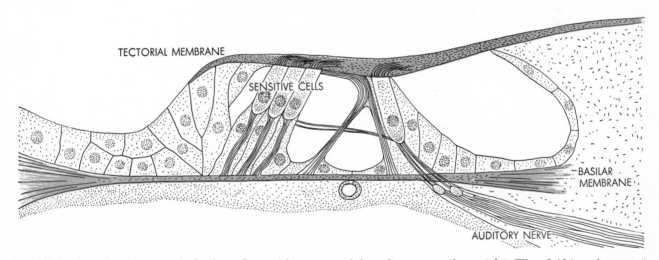

**ORGAN OF CORTI** lies between the basilar and tectorial membranes. Within it are sensitive cells which are attached to a branch of the auditory nerve (*lower right*). When fluid in scala tympani (*see drawing at top of page*) vibrates, these cells are stimulated.

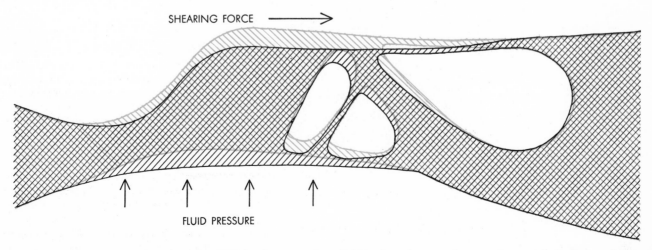

**HOW VIBRATION FORCES ARE AMPLIFIED** by the organ of Corti is indicated by this drawing. When the vibration of the fluid in the scala tympani exerts a force on the basilar membrane, a larger shearing force is brought to bear on tectorial membrane.

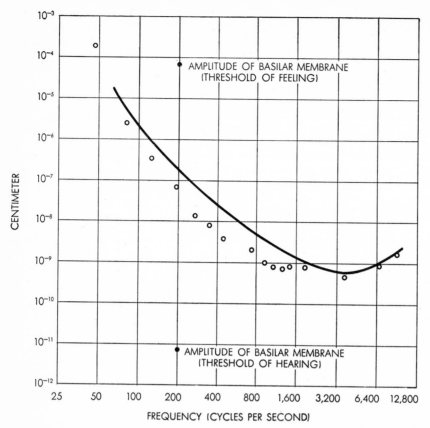

SENSITIVITY OF THE EAR is indicated by this curve, in which the amplitude of the vibrations of the tympanic membrane in fractions of a centimeter is plotted against the frequency of sound impinging on the membrane. Diameter of hydrogen atom is $10^{-8}$ centimeter.

cording of our voice may strike us as very thin and disappointing. From this point of view we have to admire the astonishing performance of an opera singer. The singer and the audience hear rather different sounds, and it is a miracle to me that they understand each other so well. Perhaps young singers would progress faster if during their training they spent more time studying recordings of their voices.

### Feedback to the Voice

The control of speaking and singing involves a complicated feedback system. Just as feedback between the eyes and the muscles guides the hand when it moves to pick up an object, so feedback continually adjusts and corrects the voice as we speak or sing. When we start to sing, the beginning of the sound tells us the pitch, and we immediately adjust the tension of the vocal cords if the pitch is wrong. This feedback requires an exceedingly elaborate and rapid mechanism. How it works is not yet entirely understood. But it is small wonder that it takes a child years to learn to speak, or that it is almost impossible for an adult to learn to speak a foreign language with the native accents.

Any disturbance in the feedback immediately disturbs the speech. For instance, if, while a person is speaking, his speech is fed back to him with a time delay by means of a microphone and receivers at his ears, his pronunciation and accent will change, and if the delay interval is made long enough, he will find it impossible to speak at all.

some of the low-frequency components of the vocal cords' vibrations are lost. This explains why one can hardly recognize his own voice when he listens to a recording of his speech. As we normally hear ourselves, the low-frequency vibrations of our vocal cords, conducted to our own ears by the bones, make our speech sound much more powerful and dynamic than the pure sound waves heard by a second person or through a recording system. Consequently the re-

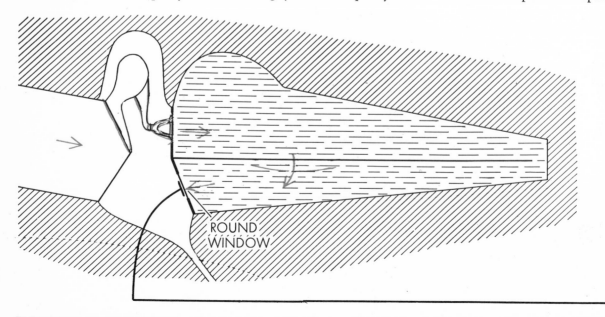

ELECTRICAL POTENTIALS of the microphonic type generated by the inner ear of an experimental animal can be detected by this arrangement. At left is a highly schematic diagram of the ear, the cochlea is represented in cross section by the fluid-filled chamber and the organ of Corti by the horizontal line in this chamber. When the vibrations of the eardrum are transmitted to the organ of Corti,

This phenomenon affords an easy test for exposing pretended deafness. If the subject can continue speaking normally in the face of a delayed feedback through the machine to his ears, we can be sure that he is really deaf.

The same technique can be used to assess the skill of a pianist. A piano player generally adjusts his touch to the acoustics of the room: if the room is very reverberant, so that the music sounds too loud, he uses a lighter touch; if the sound is damped by the walls, he strengthens his touch. We had a number of pianists play in a room where the damping could be varied, and recorded the amplitude of the vibrations of the piano's sounding board while the musicians played various pieces. When they played an easy piece, their adjustment to the acoustics was very clear: as the sound absorption of the room was increased, the pianist played more loudly, and when the damping on the walls was taken away, the pianist's touch became lighter. But when the piece was difficult, many of the pianists concentrated so hard on the problems of the music that they failed to adjust to the feedback of the room. A master musician, however, was not lost to the sound effects. Taking the technical difficulties of the music in stride, he was able to adjust the sound level to the damping of the room with the same accuracy as for an easy piece. Our rating of the pianists by this test closely matched their reputation among musical experts.

In connection with room acoustics, I should like to mention one of the ear's most amazing performances. How is it

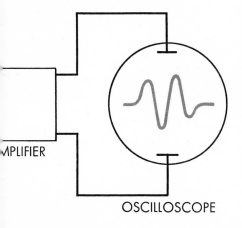

...IFFERENT ELECTRODE
...THE MUSCLE

**its microphonic potentials can be picked up at the round window of the cochlea and displayed on the face of an oscilloscope (*right*).**

that we can locate a speaker, even without seeing him, in a bare-walled room where reflections of his voice come at us from every side? This is an almost unbelievable performance by the ear. It is as if, looking into a room completely lined with mirrors, we saw only the real figure and none of the hundreds of reflected images. The eye cannot suppress the reflections, but the ear can. The ear is able to ignore all the sounds except the first that strikes it. It has a built-in inhibitory mechanism.

### Suppressed Sounds

One of the most important factors that subordinate the reflected sounds is the delay in their arrival; necessarily they come to the ear only after the sound that has traveled directly from the speaker to the listener. The reflected sounds reinforce the loudness and tone volume of the direct sound, and perhaps even modify its localization, but by and large, they are not distinguishable from it. Only when the delay is appreciable does a reflected sound appear as a separate unit—an echo. Echoes often are heard in a large church, where reflections may lag more than half a second behind the direct sound. They are apt to be a problem in a concert hall. Dead walls are not desirable, because the music would sound weak. For every size of concert room there is an optimal compromise on wall reflectivity which will give amplification to the music but prevent disturbing echoes.

In addition to time delay, there are other factors that act to inhibit some sounds and favor others. Strong sounds generally suppress weaker ones. Sounds in which we are interested take precedence over those that concern us less, as I pointed out in the examples of the speaker in a noisy room and the orchestra conductor detecting an errant instrument. This brings us to the intimate collaboration between the ear and the nervous system.

Any stimulation of the ear (*e.g.*, any change in pressure) is translated into electrical messages to the brain via the nerves. We can therefore draw information about the ear from an analysis of these electrical impulses, now made possible by electronic instruments. There are two principal types of electric potential that carry the messages. One is a continuous, wavelike potential which has been given the name microphonic. In experimental animals such as guinea pigs and cats the microphonics are large enough to be easily measured (they range up to about half a millivolt). It

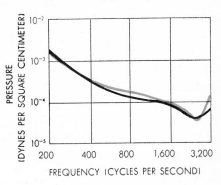

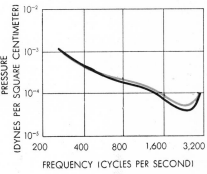

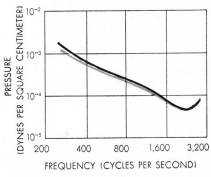

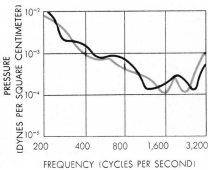

AUDIOGRAMS plot the threshold of hearing (in terms of pressure on the tympanic membrane) against the frequency of sound. The first three audiograms show the threshold for three members of the same family; the fourth, the threshold for an unrelated person. The black curves represent the threshold for one ear of the subject; the colored curves, for the other ear of the same subject. The audiogram curves indicate that in normal hearing the threshold in both ears, and the threshold in members of the same family, are remarkably similar.

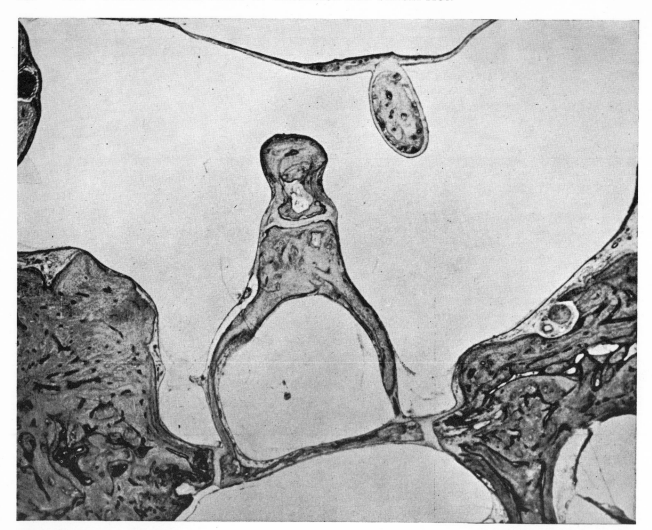

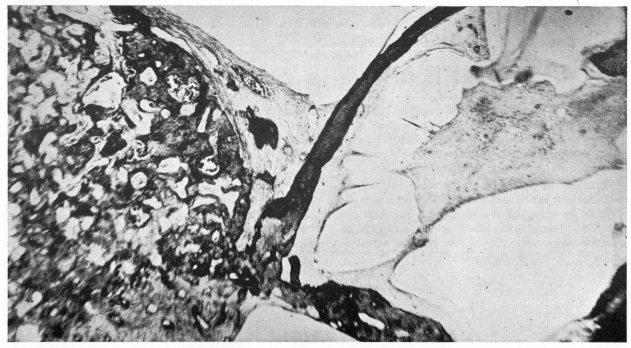

STIRRUP of the normal human ear is enlarged 19 times in the photograph at the top of this page. The thin line at the top of the photograph is the tympanic membrane seen in cross section. The hammer and anvil do not appear. The narrow membrane around the footplate of the stirrup may be seen as a translucent area between the footplate and the surrounding bone. The photograph at the bottom shows the immobilized footplate of an otosclerotic ear. In this photograph only the left side of the stirrup appears; the footplate is the dark area at the bottom center. The membrane around the footplate has been converted into a rigid bony growth.

has turned out that the magnitude of the microphonics produced in the inner ear is directly proportional to the displacements of the stirrup footplate that set the fluid in the inner ear in motion. The microphonics therefore permit us to determine directly to what extent the sound pressure applied to the eardrum is transmitted to the inner ear, and they have become one of the most useful tools for exploring sound transmission in the middle ear. For instance, there used to be endless discussion of the simple question: Just how much does perforation of the eardrum affect hearing? The question has now been answered with mathematical precision by experiments on animals. A hole of precisely measured size is drilled in the eardrum, and the amount of hearing loss is determined by the change in the microphonics. This type of observation on cats has shown that a perforation about one millimeter in diameter destroys hearing at the frequencies below 100 cycles per second but causes almost no impairment of hearing in the range of frequencies above 1,000 cycles per second. From studies of the physical properties of the human ear we can judge that the findings on animals apply fairly closely to man also.

The second type of electric potential takes the form of sharp pulses, which appear as spikes in the recording instrument. The sound of a sharp click produces a series of brief spikes; a pure tone generates volleys of spikes, generally in the rhythm of the period of the tone. We can follow the spikes along the nerve pathways all the way from the inner ear up to the cortex of the brain. And when we do, we find that stimulation of specific spots on the membrane of the inner ear seems to be projected to corresponding spots in the auditory area of the cortex. This is reminiscent of the projection of images on the retina of the eye to the visual area of the brain. But in the case of the ear the situation must be more complex, because there are nerve branches leading to the opposite ear and there seem to be several auditory projection areas on the surface of the brain. At the moment research is going on to find out how the secondary areas function and what their purpose is.

### Detecting Pitch

The orderly projection of the sensitive area of the inner ear onto the higher brain levels is probably connected with the resolution of pitch. The ear itself can analyze sounds and separate one tone from another. There are limits to this

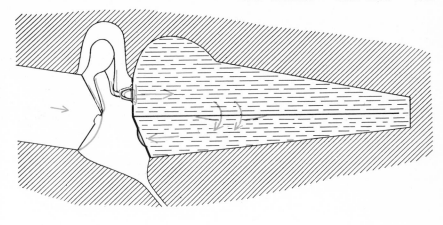

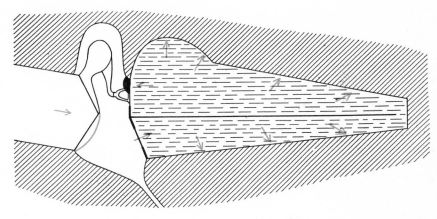

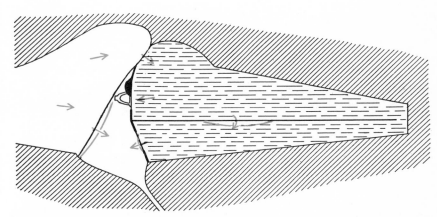

FENESTRATION OPERATION can alleviate the effects of otosclerosis. The drawing at the top schematically depicts the normal human ear as described in the caption for the illustration on pages 258–259. The pressure on the components of the ear is indicated by the colored arrows. The drawing in the middle shows an otosclerotic ear; the otosclerotic growth is represented as a black protuberance. Because the stirrup cannot move, the pressure on the tympanic membrane is transmitted to the organ of Corti only through the round window of the cochlea; and because the fluid in the cochlea is incompressible, the organ of Corti cannot vibrate. The drawing at the bottom shows how the fenestration operation makes a new window into the cochlea to permit the organ of Corti to vibrate freely.

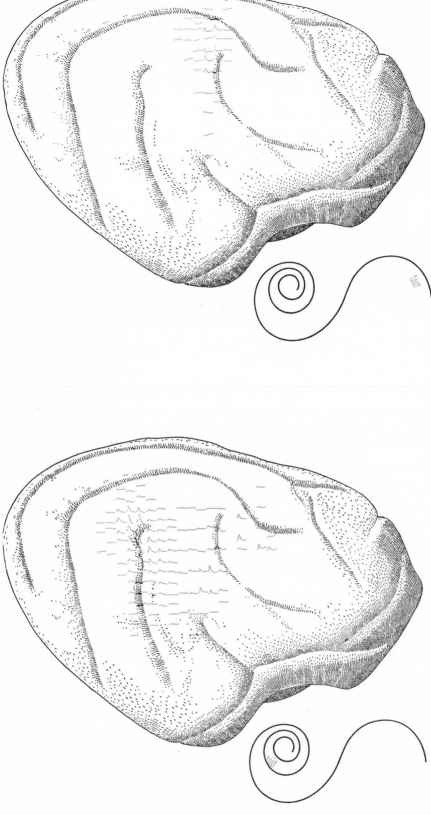

ability, but if the frequencies of the tones presented are not too close together, they are discriminated pretty well. Long ago this raised the question: How is the ear able to discriminate the pitch of a tone? Many theories have been argued, but only within the last decade has it been possible to plan pertinent experiments.

In the low-frequency range up to 60 cycles per second the vibration of the basilar membrane produces in the auditory nerve volleys of electric spikes synchronous with the rhythm of the sound. As the sound pressure increases, the number of spikes packed into each period increases. Thus two variables are transmitted to the cortex: (1) the number of spikes and (2) their rhythm. These two variables alone convey the loudness and the pitch of the sound.

Above 60 cycles per second a new phenomenon comes in. The basilar membrane now begins to vibrate unequally over its area: each tone produces a maximal vibration in a different area of the membrane. Gradually this selectivity takes over the determination of pitch, for the rhythm of the spikes, which indicates the pitch at low frequencies, becomes irregular at the higher ones. Above 4,000 cycles per second pitch is determined entirely by the location of the maximal vibration amplitude along the basilar membrane. Apparently there is an inhibitory mechanism which suppresses the weaker stimuli and thus sharpens considerably the sensation around the maximum. This type of inhibition can also operate in sense organs such as the skin and the eye. In order to see sharply we need not only a sharp image of the object on the retina but also an inhibitory system to suppress stray light entering the eye. Otherwise we would see the object surrounded by a halo. The ear is much the same. Without inhibitory effects a tone would sound like a noise of a certain pitch but not like a pure tone.

We can sum up by saying that the basilar membrane makes a rough, mechanical frequency analysis, and the auditory nervous system sharpens the analysis in some manner not yet understood. It is a part of the general functioning of the higher nerve centers, and it will be understood only when we know more about the functioning of these centers. If the answer is found for the ear, it will probably apply to the other sense organs as well.

## Deafness

Now let us run briefly over some of

NERVE IMPULSES due to the electrical stimulation of the organ of Corti were localized on the surface of the brain of a cat. The spirals below each of these drawings of a cat's brain represent the full length of the organ of Corti. The pairs of colored arrows on each spiral indicate the point at which the organ was stimulated. The colored peaks superimposed on the brains represent the electrical potentials detected by an electrode placed at that point.

the types of hearing disorders, which have become much more understandable as a result of recent experimental researches.

Infections of the ear used to be responsible for the overwhelming majority of the cases of deafness. Ten years ago in a large city hospital there was a death almost every day from such infections. Thanks to antibiotics, they can now be arrested, and, if treated in time, an ear infection is seldom either fatal or destructive of hearing, though occasionally an operation is necessary to scoop out the diseased part of the mastoid bone.

The two other principal types of deafness are those caused by destruction of the auditory nerves and by otosclerosis (a tumorous bone growth). Nerve deafness cannot be cured: no drug or mechanical manipulation or operation can restore the victim's hearing. But the impairment of hearing caused by otosclerosis can usually be repaired, at least in part.

Otosclerosis is an abnormal but painless growth in a temporal bone (*i.e.*, at the side of the skull, near the middle ear). If it does not invade a part of the ear that participates in the transmission of sound, no harm is done to the hearing. But if the growth happens to involve the stirrup footplate, it will reduce or even completely freeze the footplate's ability to make its piston-like movements; the vibrations of the eardrum then can no longer be transmitted to the inner ear. An otosclerotic growth can occur at any age, may slow down for many years, and may suddenly start up again. It is found more often in women than in men and seems to be accelerated by pregnancy.

Immobilization of the stirrup blocks the hearing of air-borne sound but leaves hearing by bone conduction unimpaired. This fact is used for diagnosis. A patient who has lost part of his hearing ability because of otosclerosis does not find noise disturbing to his understanding of speech; in fact, noise may even improve his discrimination of speech. There is an old story about a somewhat deaf English earl (in France it is a count) who trained his servant to beat a drum whenever someone else spoke, so that he could understand the speaker better. The noise of the drum made the speaker raise his voice to the earl's hearing range. For the hard-of-hearing earl the noise of the drum was tolerable, but for other listeners it masked what the speaker was saying, so that the earl enjoyed exclusive rights to his conversation.

Difficulty in hearing air-borne sound can be corrected by a hearing aid. Theoretically it should be possible to compensate almost any amount of such hearing loss, because techniques for amplifying sound are highly developed, particularly now with the help of the transistor. But there is a physiological limit to the amount of pressure amplification that the ear will stand. Heightening of the pressure eventually produces an unpleasant tickling sensation through its effect on skin tissue in the middle ear. The sensation can be avoided by using a bone-conduction earphone, pressed firmly against the surface of the skull, but this constant pressure is unpleasant to many people.

## Operations

As is widely known, there are now operations (*e.g.*, "fenestration") which can cure otosclerotic deafness. In the 19th century physicians realized that if they could somehow dislodge or loosen the immobilized stirrup footplate, they might restore hearing. Experimenters in France found that they could sometimes free the footplate sufficiently merely by pressing a blunt needle against the right spot on the stirrup. Although it works only occasionally, the procedure seems so simple that it has recently had a revival of popularity in the U. S. If the maneuver is successful (and I am told that 30 per cent of these operations are) the hearing improves immediately. But unfortunately the surgeon cannot get a clear look at the scene of the operation and must apply the pushing force at random. This makes the operation something of a gamble, and the patient's hearing may not only fail to be improved but may even be reduced. Moreover, the operation is bound to be ineffectual when a large portion of the footplate is fixed. There are other important objections to the operation. After all, it involves the breaking of bone, to free the adhering part of the stirrup. I do not think that bone-breaking can be improved to a standard procedure. In any case, precision cutting seems to me always superior to breaking, in surgery as in mechanics. This brings us to the operation called fenestration.

For many decades it has been known that drilling a small opening, even the size of a pinhead, in the bony wall of the inner ear on the footplate side can produce a remarkable improvement in hearing. The reason, now well understood, is quite simple. If a hole is made in the bone and then covered again with a flexible membrane, movements of the fluid in, for instance, the lateral canal of the vestibular organ can be transmitted to the fluid of the inner ear, and so vibrations are once again communicable from the middle to the inner ear. In the typical present fenestration operation the surgeon bores a small hole in the canal wall with a dental drill and then covers the hole with a flap of skin. The operation today is a straightforward surgical procedure, and all its steps are under accurate control.

## Hazards to Hearing

I want to conclude by mentioning the problem of nerve deafness. Many cases of nerve deafness are produced by intense noise, especially noise with high-frequency components. Since there is no cure, it behooves us to look out for such exposures. Nerve deafness creeps up on us slowly, and we are not as careful as we should be to avoid exposure to intense noise. We should also be more vigilant about other hazards capable of producing nerve deafness, notably certain drugs and certain diseases.

We could do much to ameliorate the tragedy of deafness if we changed some of our attitudes toward it. Blindness evokes our instant sympathy, and we go out of our way to help the blind person. But deafness often goes unrecognized. If a deaf person misunderstands what we say, we are apt to attribute it to lack of intelligence instead of to faulty hearing. Very few people have the patience to help the deafened. To a deaf man the outside world appears unfriendly. He tries to hide his deafness, and this only brings on more problems.

# 33

# AUDITORY LOCALIZATION

MARK R. ROSENZWEIG                    October 1961

Anyone who has ever gone temporarily deaf in one ear can testify to the advantages of binaural hearing. Sounds heard through one ear only are difficult or impossible to localize, and they lose their quality of depth. For human beings the ability to localize sound is more than a convenience; for some animals it is a necessity. Two ears are better than one if a person is trying to understand one voice against a background of other voices. (This is what acoustical engineers call the cocktail-party problem.) Two ears provide bats and certain night-flying birds with their fantastically sensitive location system.

That a pair of separated receivers should facilitate localization is reasonable enough. Each ear receives a slightly different sound pattern from a given source. The difference is somehow used by the brain to fix the position of the source. For more than 150 years investigators have been trying to find out how. Recently there has been considerable progress, but the process is still far from completely understood.

So far as the records show, the first person to look into the matter was the Italian physicist Giovanni Battista Venturi (1746–1822). Nowadays Venturi is remembered for his research in fluid dynamics. In fact, his name has become a common noun: the venturi, or venturi tube, is a standard device for measuring the flow of fluids. Venturi also turned his talents to many problems outside of physics. He studied visual and auditory perception, wrote on economics and history and was active in politics during the Napoleonic period.

In his work on auditory localization Venturi stationed a blindfolded subject in the middle of an unobstructed meadow. Circling around the subject at a distance of about 150 feet, the experimenter periodically sounded a note on a flute or rang a bell. When the sound came from a direction at right angles to "straight ahead," the listener could easily identify the direction. If he kept his head still, he often confused sounds coming from directly in front of him with sounds coming from behind him. When the source was diagonally in front of him or diagonally in back of him on the same side, the subject frequently was unable to distinguish front from back, but he never had any trouble with right and left. If the test sound was sustained for a few seconds and the listener was allowed to turn his head, he did not make these mistakes.

Venturi also found that a person with one deaf ear could localize sounds, but only if he turned his head while the sound continued. The subject simply turned until the sound was loudest, at which time his good ear directly faced the source. The experimenter noted that subjects with one deaf ear never localized brief sounds accurately.

Venturi concluded that a listener uses the relative intensities of the stimuli arriving at his ears to localize sound. He believed, furthermore, that the process involves judgment, and he denied the possibility of physiological interaction of the neural messages from the ears. "Since we distinguish the two simultaneous sensations of the two ears," he wrote, "and since their different intensities furnish us knowledge of the true direction of the sound, therefore one must conclude that the two sound impressions do not mix together inside the skull." This interpretation was to prevail for more than a century.

Notwithstanding the fact that Venturi published his findings no less than four times between 1796 and 1801—twice in German and once each in French and Italian—they made remarkably little impression. His observations and conclusions were occasionally mentioned in early 19th-century texts, but they were not credited to him. Later they were forgotten altogether. In the 1870's the British physicist Lord Rayleigh repeated essentially the same experiments, with the same results, apparently with no knowledge of Venturi's work. He believed that the observations supported the common view that localization is judged on the basis of the relative intensities of stimulation at the two ears.

Shortly after 1900 a German physician named Stenger devised an ingenious clinical hearing test that effectively demolished the ordinary view of localization, although no one seems to have realized it at the time. The test, which is still in use, was designed to expose people feigning deafness in one ear. Anyone who pretends to be deaf in his right ear, for example, will report hearing a tone if it is presented to his left ear through an earphone. What happens if the tone is now presented to the left ear and simultaneously but more intensely to the right ear? The listener hears the sound as coming from the right. The malingerer will therefore give himself away by saying that he does not hear any sound, in spite of the fact that it is just as intense as before at his admittedly good left ear. The effectiveness of this test makes it clear that the listener hears only a single localized sound and does not compare separate sensations arising at the two ears. Unfortunately the obvious meaning of the clinical discovery was ignored by students of auditory perception.

In 1911 there was published the first suggestion that a different mechanism—small differences in the time of arrival

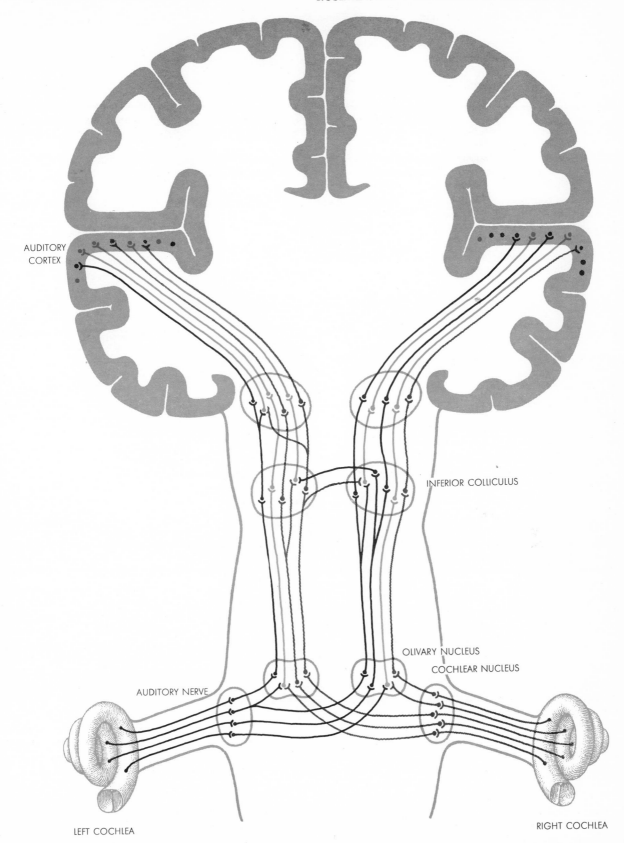

**AUDITORY-NERVE PATHWAYS** connect the cochlea of each ear with the auditory areas of the cerebral cortex. At the lowest level of the auditory system (the auditory nerves and cochlear nuclei) the pathways are completely separate. (In this greatly simplified diagram of the system the pathways from the left ear are shown in black; those from the right ear are shown in gray.) At the next level (the olivary nucleus in the medulla) some of the nerve fibers from the cochlear nuclei of both ears converge on the same nerve cells. These cells, which thus carry messages from both ears, are shown in color. At successively higher levels of the system there is increasing convergence, and increasing interaction, between messages from the two ears, as is indicated by the larger proportion of cells in color. The majority of nerve pathways starting in one cochlear nucleus cross to the opposite side of the brain.

of a sound at the two ears—might influence the apparent location of the source. A sound originating directly to the right side of the head reaches the right ear about .0005 second before it reaches the left ear. A sound originating five degrees to the right of straight ahead or straight back reaches the right ear only .00004 second earlier than the left ear. Could perception of location be based on such minute time differences? During World War I the question was investigated secretly, both in France and Germany, in connection with the development of sound locators to detect airplanes. The tests showed that time differences of the order of .0001 second (with no accompanying differences in intensity) do indeed serve to locate the

source of sound. Such intervals are far too small to allow the sound to be heard as separate stimuli by the two ears.

When the results were made public after the war, the judgment theory of localization was finally abandoned and a search was begun for the neural mechanisms underlying the process. During the 1920's there was a good deal of speculation about possible mechanisms. The 1930's saw the beginning of a mounting volume of experimentation on the electrical activity of the nervous system in response to auditory stimulation, as well as a revival of studies of the effect of brain damage on localization. The latter investigations had first been conducted in the 1880's.

Whenever a nerve conducts messages,

small changes in electrical potential travel along the fibers of its constituent cells. With suitable equipment experimenters can tap the electrical signals as they travel from each ear up the auditory pathways to the auditory cortex [*see illustration on preceding page*]. My colleagues and I have pursued this line of research for a number of years, first at Harvard University and later at the University of California.

Our subjects were anesthetized cats. As sources of stimuli we used independent earphones, one at each ear. Tiny electrodes inserted at various points in the auditory neural pathways fed signals into our amplifier and recorder.

Stimulating the cats' ears with a brief,

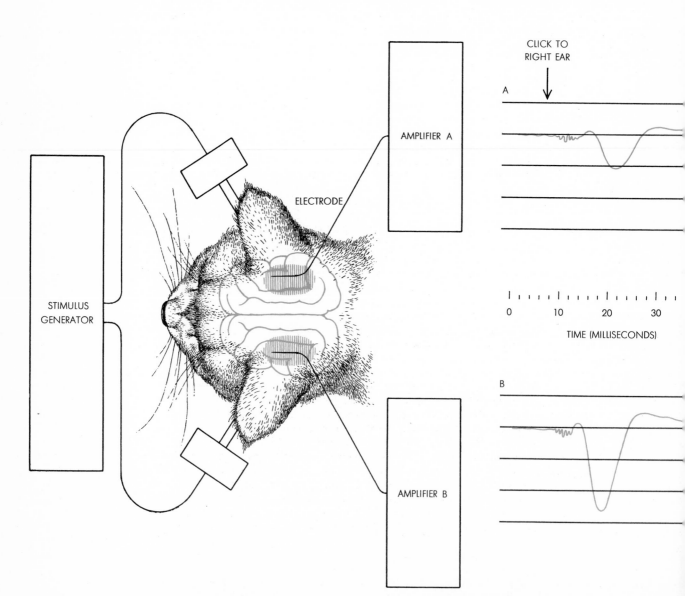

RESPONSES OF AUDITORY CORTEX, recorded through openings in the skull of an anesthetized cat, vary according to the stimulus conditions. Four electrical response curves for the cortex of the right hemisphere appear at top; those for the left cortex, at bottom. When only the right ear is stimulated, there are responses in the auditory cortex on both sides of the brain; response from the left

sharp click produced characteristically different electrical responses at each of the levels of the auditory system. Moreover, we found that, at every level in the neural pathways serving each half of the brain, an input to the ear on the opposite side of the body elicited a larger response than it did on the same side [see illustration on these two pages]. Most of the neural systems of the body run contralaterally in this way: from one side of the brain to the opposite side of the body. This asymmetry is less pronounced in the auditory system than in most others, but it is clearly present. Because of the asymmetry we could always tell which ear had been stimulated by comparing the responses at the two sides of the brain. A basis for an elementary localization—

discrimination of right from left—appeared clearly in the neural responses.

These first experiments corroborated some earlier findings, obtained in a different way. It has been known for many years that nerve cells can be stimulated to activity by small electric currents. In the 1870's physiologists began to map the functional regions of the brain by applying currents to portions of the exposed brain and observing the different bodily responses that were evoked. In this way the British neurologist Sir David Ferrier delimited several sensory regions of the cerebral cortex, including an area devoted to hearing. When Ferrier touched an electrode to the auditory cortex on one side of a monkey's brain, the ear on the other side of the head pricked up,

and the animal often turned its eyes or head to that side. In Ferrier's description it was as if a shrill note had been sounded in the ear. Moreover, the "sound" was always on the opposite side of the head from the stimulus.

In the past 25 years or so human testimony has confirmed Ferrier's observations. Patients whose cortex was being mapped in preparation for brain surgery have reported what they felt when electric current was applied to different regions of the brain. A great deal of such information has been obtained by Wilder Penfield and his associates at the Montreal Neurological Institute. When the auditory area is stimulated, patients say they hear sounds, even though no sound waves have reached

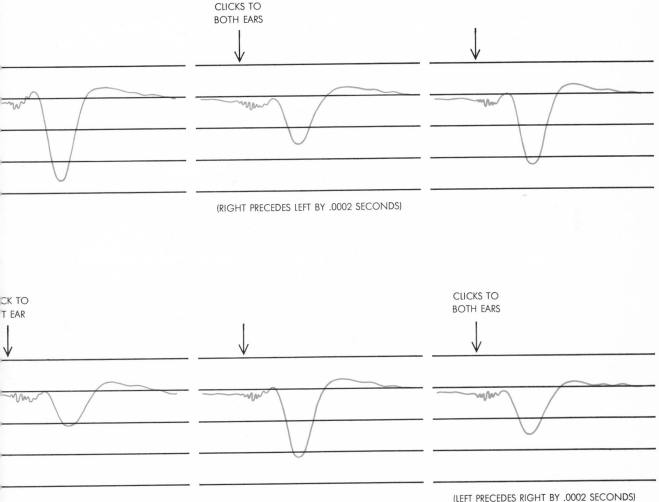

CLICKS TO BOTH EARS

(RIGHT PRECEDES LEFT BY .0002 SECONDS)

CK TO T EAR

CLICKS TO BOTH EARS

(LEFT PRECEDES RIGHT BY .0002 SECONDS)

side is larger. When only the left ear is stimulated, the response from the right side is greater. When both ears are stimulated with a small time interval between clicks, the response tends to resemble

the response to the prior stimulus alone. Thus when a click to the right ear precedes one to the left by .0002 second, the response from the left side is slightly larger than that from the right, and vice versa.

their ears. When the right side of the brain is stimulated, the patient usually hears the sound as coming from his left; when the left side is stimulated, he hears it as coming from his right. Occasionally the sound seems to come from both sides, but never only from the same side as that on which the brain is stimulated.

All the experiments point to the same conclusion: each ear is represented more strongly in the opposite side of the brain than in the same side, and a sound delivered to one ear alone excites more neural activity in the opposite side than in the same side.

Under normal hearing conditions, of course, both ears receive sound, not just one at a time. We extended our experiments with cats by stimulating both ears and recording the electrical activity along the auditory pathways. When we began, it was generally doubted that small differences in the time of arrival of a sound wave at the two ears could be preserved in the neural messages during the 10 milliseconds required for them to travel from the ear to the cerebral cortex. We soon discovered, however, that the electrical pattern does reflect such differences. If the interval was a few milliseconds, long enough so that the two electrical responses showed up separately, the response to the earlier stimulus partially inhibited the response to the later one. With shorter intervals the electrical responses fused into one, but the amplitude was chiefly determined by the first stimulus. Stimulating the ears in the order left-right produced a larger response on the right side of the brain; stimulating in the order right-left, a larger response on the left side. This remained true down to intervals of a tenth of a millisecond, although differences between responses became harder to detect as the interval grew smaller.

Differences in the intensity of stimulation at the two ears were found to produce comparable effects. Feeding a more intense sound to the right ear evoked larger responses on the left side of the brain, and the other way around. The patterns in the nervous system therefore reflect all the differences in the pattern of stimulation—temporal order of stimulation, time interval, and relative intensities of the stimuli at the two ears. (Under ordinary circumstances the temporal and intensity cues reinforce each other. The ear on the side opposite to the source of sound receives not only a later signal but also one of lower intensity, because of the shadowing effect of the head.)

We next carried our investigation down the auditory pathway from the cortex toward the ears. The interaction between the two sides was found to decrease steadily the lower we went. Some interaction can be traced, however, down as far as the olivary nucleus, a group of nerve cells in the medulla that is the next to the last station before each ear. In these nuclei the anatomist W. A. Stotler of the University of Oregon Medical School has found cells that receive connections from both ears [see *illustration on this page*]. At the Walter Reed Army Institute of Research, Robert Galambos and his associates have

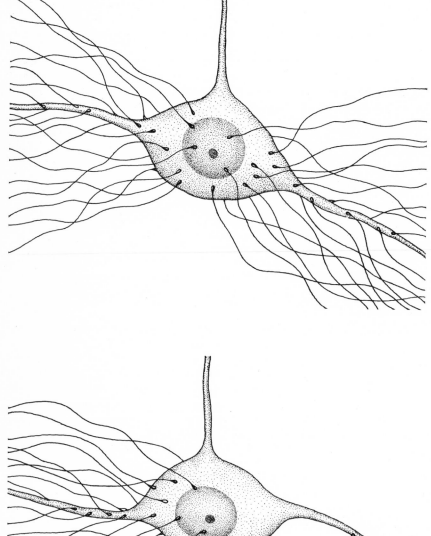

CELLS OF OLIVARY NUCLEUS normally receive connections from the cochlear nuclei of both ears (*see illustration on page 265*). In a normal cell (*drawing at top*) the incoming fibers (*thin black lines*) from the cochlear nuclei terminate on the dendritic "poles" of the cell. When the cochlear nucleus on one side of the brain stem is destroyed, the fibers leaving that nucleus degenerate; cells of the olivary nucleus lose almost all their connections on that side, demonstrating that each pole receives its connections from the ear on the same side.

recently been able to record the activity of single nerve cells in the olivary nucleus. They found that some of the cells respond differently according to which ear receives the earlier stimulus. At the last station before the ear—the cochlear nucleus—there is no indication of binaural interaction.

The picture of increasing interconnection of pathways as they go from lower to higher centers suggests that the higher brain centers may be required for auditory localization. The first direct attempt to test the matter goes back 80 years to the work of an Italian physiologist, Luigi Luciani. Experimenting on dogs, he removed the part of the brain then considered to constitute the auditory cortex. To test the effect on localization he blindfolded the animals and tossed small bits of food on the floor near them, observing how promptly and accurately they retrieved the food. When the operation was performed on only one cerebral hemisphere, the ability to localize was impaired, particularly in the case of sounds originating on the other side of the head. A bilateral operation disrupted localization completely. In the course of time Luciani's studies were generally forgotten. Seen from the vantage point of the present, his results lead to the right answer, but in themselves they are not conclusive. The dogs' ability to localize recovered somewhat several weeks after the operation, perhaps because Luciani never cut away all of what is now known to constitute the auditory cortex.

In the 1930's interest in Luciani's approach revived. Two independent groups reported that cats with the entire cerebral cortex removed could still localize sound. In both experiments, however, the test sound was sustained for several seconds, and the animals were allowed to move their heads. More recent studies by William D. Neff and his collaborators at the University of Chicago served to indicate that the cortex is necessary for auditory localization. From the design of the experiments, however, it was not clear whether the cats had actually lost the ability to localize or had merely lost the ability to keep their attention fixed on the task.

Finally, in 1959, Walter Riss of the State University of New York Downstate Medical Center reported a series of more conclusive experiments. Also working with cats, he removed the auditory cortex in some of the animals and other regions of the cortex in a group of control animals. Both groups were tested with two types of stimulus, one very brief and the other sustained. The brief noise was produced by dropping a food pellet on the platform on which the animal stood; the sustained noise, by rapping the pellet repeatedly against the edge of the platform. He compared the performance of the two groups, recording the accuracy with which the animals turned their heads to face the sound and also measuring the time that they took to reach the food.

In tests with the single brief stimulus the animals without an auditory cortex performed at a random level. The control cats, on the other hand, turned their heads promptly toward the sound every time. With the repetitive stimuli, the performance of the experimental cats was somewhat better. They seemed to sample the sound field by movements of the head and ears. Their first reaction was correct in half the trials. Throughout the tests the experimental animals showed no deficiency of attention, so their poor performance could not be attributed to impairment of this faculty. Riss came to the conclusion that the auditory cortex is necessary for localizing the instantaneous position of a sound—the performance that is characteristic of binaural perception.

What emerges from all the studies so far is a physiological picture—in the higher mammals at least—that partially accounts for the ability to locate a source of sound. Starting at each ear and leading to the cerebral cortex is a chain of neurons. There are several stations along the chain where some neurons end and others begin. At all but the very lowest of these stations the pathways from the two ears overlap to some extent, the degree of overlap increasing as the pathways ascend. Neural impulses from one ear consequently have an increasing probability of encountering impulses from the other as they approach the cortex. Depending on the conditions of stimulation, which in turn depend on the relative positions of the listener and the source of sound, the converging impulses make some groups of nerve cells become more active and others less so. The different patterns of activity that result in the auditory cortex are correlated with different locations of auditory stimuli.

Here, for the present, the story ends. Of course, the cortex in its turn must send neural impulses to further centers so that localization ultimately evokes different patterns of behavior. Exploring this part of the neural pathway is a job for the future.

# 34

# THE VISUAL CORTEX
# OF THE BRAIN

DAVID H. HUBEL                    November 1963

An image of the outside world striking the retina of the eye activates a most intricate process that results in vision: the transformation of the retinal image into a perception. The transformation occurs partly in the retina but mostly in the brain, and it is, as one can recognize instantly by considering how modest in comparison is the achievement of a camera, a task of impressive magnitude.

The process begins with the responses of some 130 million light-sensitive receptor cells in each retina. From these cells messages are transmitted to other retinal cells and then sent on to the brain, where they must be analyzed and interpreted. To get an idea of the magnitude of the task, think what is involved in watching a moving animal, such as a horse. At a glance one takes in its size, form, color and rate of movement. From tiny differences in the two retinal images there results a three-dimensional picture. Somehow the brain manages to compare this picture with previous impressions; recognition occurs and then any appropriate action can be taken.

The organization of the visual system —a large, intricately connected population of nerve cells in the retina and brain —is still poorly understood. In recent years, however, various studies have begun to reveal something of the arrangement and function of these cells. A decade ago Stephen W. Kuffler, working with cats at the Johns Hopkins Hospital, discovered that some analysis of visual patterns takes place outside the brain, in the nerve cells of the retina. My colleague Torsten N. Wiesel and I at the Harvard Medical School, exploring the first stages of the processing that occurs in the brain of the cat, have mapped the visual pathway a little further: to what appears to be the sixth step from the retina to the cortex of the cerebrum. This kind of

work falls far short of providing a full understanding of vision, but it does convey some idea of the mechanisms and circuitry of the visual system.

In broad outline the visual pathway is clearly defined [see bottom illustration on opposite page]. From the retina of each eye visual messages travel along the optic nerve, which consists of about a million nerve fibers. At the junction known as the chiasm about half of the nerves cross over into opposite hemispheres of the brain, the other nerves remaining on the same side. The optic nerve fibers lead to the first way stations in the brain: a pair of cell clusters called the lateral geniculate bodies. From here new fibers course back through the brain to the visual area of the cerebral cortex. It is convenient, although admittedly a gross oversimplification, to think of the pathway from retina to cortex as consisting of six types of nerve cells, of which three are in the retina, one is in the geniculate body and two are in the cortex.

Nerve cells, or neurons, transmit messages in the form of brief electrochemical impulses. These travel along the outer membrane of the cell, notably along the membrane of its long principal fiber, the axon. It is possible to obtain an electrical record of impulses of a single nerve cell by placing a fine electrode near the cell body or one of its fibers. Such measurements have shown that impulses travel along the nerves at velocities of between half a meter and 100 meters per second. The impulses in a given fiber all have about the same amplitude; the strength of the stimuli that give rise to them is reflected not in amplitude but in frequency.

At its terminus the fiber of a nerve cell makes contact with another nerve cell (or with a muscle cell or gland

cell), forming the junction called the synapse. At most synapses an impulse on reaching the end of a fiber causes the release of a small amount of a specific substance, which diffuses outward to the membrane of the next cell. There the substance either excites the cell or inhibits it. In excitation the substance acts to bring the cell into a state in which it is more likely to "fire"; in inhibition the substance acts to prevent firing. For most synapses the substances that act as transmitters are unknown. Moreover, there is no sure way to determine from microscopic appearances alone whether a synapse is excitatory or inhibitory.

It is at the synapses that the modification and analysis of nerve messages take place. The kind of analysis depends partly on the nature of the synapse: on how many nerve fibers converge on a single cell and on how the excitatory and inhibitory endings distribute themselves. In most parts of the nervous system the anatomy is too intricate to reveal much about function. One way to circumvent this difficulty is to record impulses with microelectrodes in anesthetized animals, first from the fibers coming into a structure of neurons and then from the neurons themselves, or from the fibers they send onward. Comparison of the behavior of incoming and outgoing fibers provides a basis for learning what the structure does. Through such exploration of the different parts of the brain concerned with vision one can hope to build up some idea of how the entire visual system works.

That is what Wiesel and I have undertaken, mainly through studies of the visual system of the cat. In our experiments the anesthetized animal faces a wide screen 1.5 meters away, and we shine various patterns of white light on the screen with a projector. Simultaneously we penetrate the visual portion of the cortex with microelectrodes. In that way we can record the responses of individual cells to the light patterns. Sometimes it takes many hours to find the region of the retina with which a particular visual cell is linked and to work out the optimum stimuli for that cell. The reader should bear in mind the relation between each visual cell—no matter how far along the visual pathway it may be—and the retina. It requires an image on the retina to evoke a meaningful response in any visual cell, however indirect and complex the linkage may be.

The retina is a complicated structure, in both its anatomy and its physiology, and the description I shall give is highly simplified. Light coming through the lens of the eye falls on the mosaic of receptor cells in the retina. The receptor cells do not send impulses directly through the optic nerve but instead connect with a set of retinal cells called bipolar cells. These in turn connect with retinal ganglion cells, and it is the latter set of cells, the third in the visual pathway, that sends its fibers—the optic nerve fibers—to the brain.

This series of cells and synapses is no simple bucket brigade for impulses: a receptor may send nerve endings to more than one bipolar cell, and several receptors may converge on one bipolar cell. The same holds for the synapses between the bipolar cells and the retinal ganglion cells. Stimulating a single receptor by light might therefore be expected to have an influence on many bipolar or ganglion cells; conversely, it should be possible to influence one bipolar or retinal ganglion cell from a number of receptors and hence from a substantial area of the retina.

The area of receptor mosaic in the retina feeding into a single visual cell is called the receptive field of the cell. This term is applied to any cell in the visual system to refer to the area of retina with which the cell is connected—the retinal area that on stimulation produces a response from the cell.

Any of the synapses with a particular cell may be excitatory or inhibitory, so that stimulation of a particular point on the retina may either increase or decrease the cell's firing rate. Moreover, a single cell may receive several excitatory and inhibitory impulses at once, with the result that it will respond according to the net effect of these inputs. In considering the behavior of a single cell an observer should remember that it is just one of a huge popu-

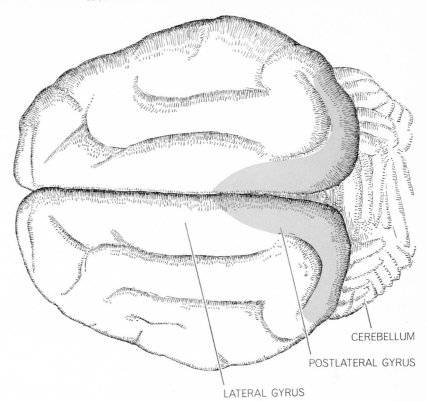

CORTEX OF CAT'S BRAIN is depicted as it would be seen from the top. The colored region indicates the cortical area that deals at least in a preliminary way with vision.

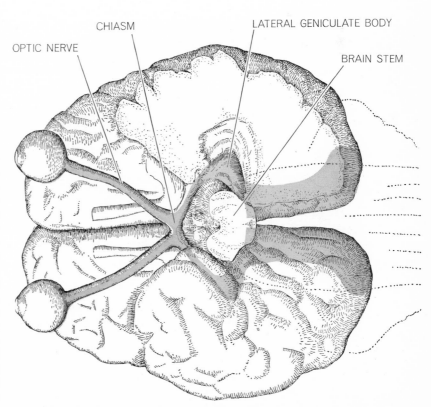

VISUAL SYSTEM appears in this representation of the human brain as viewed below. Visual pathway from retinas to cortex via the lateral geniculate body is shown in color.

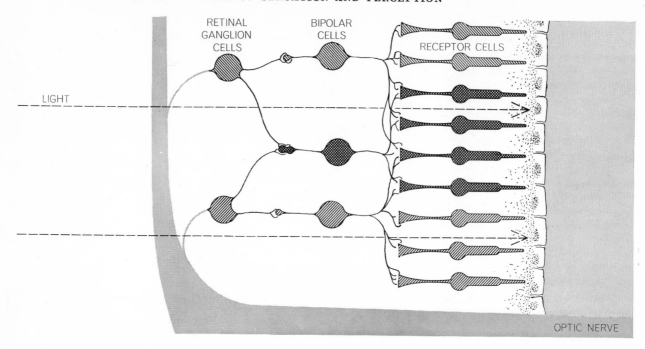

**STRUCTURE OF RETINA** is depicted schematically. Images fall on the receptor cells, of which there are about 130 million in each retina. Some analysis of an image occurs as the receptors transmit messages to the retinal ganglion cells via the bipolar cells. A group of receptors funnels into a particular ganglion cell, as indicated by the shading; that group forms the ganglion cell's receptive field. Inasmuch as the fields of several ganglion cells overlap, one receptor may send messages to several ganglion cells.

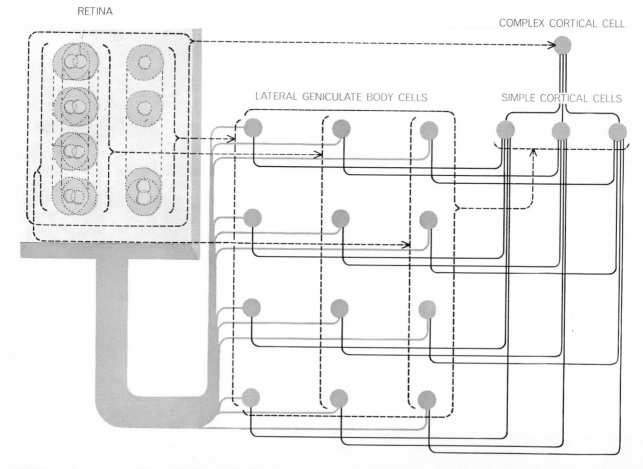

**VISUAL PROCESSING BY BRAIN** begins in the lateral geniculate body, which continues the analysis made by retinal cells. In the cortex "simple" cells respond strongly to line stimuli, provided that the position and orientation of the line are suitable for a particular cell. "Complex" cells respond well to line stimuli, but the position of the line is not critical and the cell continues to respond even if a properly oriented stimulus is moved, as long as it remains in the cell's receptive field. Broken lines indicate how receptive fields of all these cells overlap on the retina; solid lines, how several cells at one stage affect a single cell at the next stage.

lation of cells: a stimulus that excites one cell will undoubtedly excite many others, meanwhile inhibiting yet another array of cells and leaving others entirely unaffected.

For many years it has been known that retinal ganglion cells fire at a fairly steady rate even in the absence of any stimulation. Kuffler was the first to observe how the retinal ganglion cells of mammals are influenced by small spots of light. He found that the resting discharges of a cell were intensified or diminished by light in a small and more or less circular region of the retina. That region was of course the cell's receptive field. Depending on where in the field a spot of light fell, either of two responses could be produced. One was an "on" response, in which the cell's firing rate increased under the stimulus of light. The other was an "off" response, in which the stimulus of light decreased the cell's firing rate. Moreover, turning the light off usually evoked a burst of impulses from the cell. Kuffler called the retinal regions from which these responses could be evoked "on" regions and "off" regions.

On mapping the receptive fields of a large number of retinal ganglion cells into "on" and "off" regions, Kuffler discovered that there were two distinct cell types. In one the receptive field consisted of a small circular "on" area and a surrounding zone that gave "off" responses. Kuffler termed this an "on"-center cell. The second type, which he called "off"-center, had just the reverse form of field—an "off" center and an "on" periphery [see top illustration on this page]. For a given cell the effects of light varied markedly according to the place in which the light struck the receptive field. Two spots of light shone on separate parts of an "on" area produced a more vigorous "on" response than either spot alone, whereas if one spot was shone on an "on" area and the other on an "off" area, the two effects tended to neutralize each other, resulting in a very weak "on" or "off" response. In an "on"-center cell, illuminating the entire central "on" region evoked a maximum response; a smaller or larger spot of light was less effective.

Lighting up the whole retina diffusely, even though it may affect every receptor in the retina, does not affect a retinal ganglion cell nearly so strongly as a small circular spot of exactly the right size placed so as to cover precisely the receptive-field center. The main concern of these cells seems to be the contrast in illumination between one retinal region and surrounding regions.

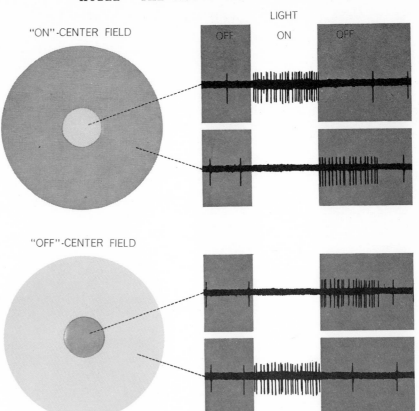

CONCENTRIC FIELDS are characteristic of retinal ganglion cells and of geniculate cells. At top an oscilloscope recording shows strong firing by an "on"-center type of cell when a spot of light strikes the field center; if the spot hits an "off" area, the firing is suppressed until the light goes off. At bottom are responses of another cell of the "off"-center type.

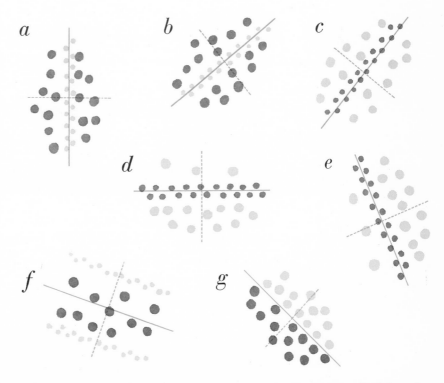

SIMPLE CORTICAL CELLS have receptive fields of various types. In all of them the "on" and "off" areas, represented by colored and gray dots respectively, are separated by straight boundaries. Orientations of fields vary, as indicated particularly at a and b. In the cat's visual system such fields are generally one millimeter or less in diameter.

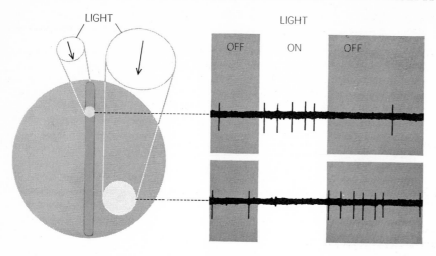

**RESPONSE IS WEAK** when a circular spot of light is shone on receptive field of a simple cortical cell. Such spots get a vigorous response from retinal and geniculate cells. This cell has a receptive field of type shown at *a* in bottom illustration on preceding page.

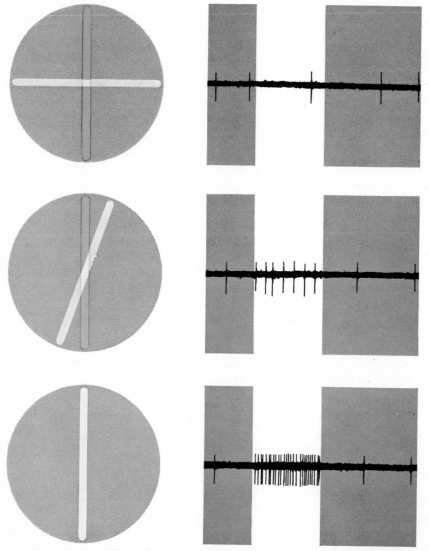

**IMPORTANCE OF ORIENTATION** to simple cortical cells is indicated by varying responses to a slit of light from a cell preferring a vertical orientation. Horizontal slit *(top)* produces no response, slight tilt a weak response, vertical slit a strong response.

Retinal ganglion cells differ greatly in the size of their receptive-field centers. Cells near the fovea (the part of the retina serving the center of gaze) are specialized for precise discrimination; in the monkey the field centers of these cells may be about the same size as a single cone—an area subtending a few minutes of arc at the cornea. On the other hand, some cells far out in the retinal periphery have field centers up to a millimeter or so in diameter. (In man one millimeter of retina corresponds to an arc of about three degrees in the 180-degree visual field.) Cells with such large receptive-field centers are probably specialized for work in very dim light, since they can sum up messages from a large number of receptors.

Given this knowledge of the kind of visual information brought to the brain by the optic nerve, our first problem was to learn how the messages were handled at the first central way station, the lateral geniculate body. Compared with the retina, the geniculate body is a relatively simple structure. In a sense there is only one synapse involved, since the incoming optic nerve fibers end in cells that send their fibers directly to the visual cortex. Yet in the cat many optic nerve fibers converge on each geniculate cell, and it is reasonable to expect some change in the visual messages from the optic nerve to the geniculate cells.

When we came to study the geniculate body, we found that the cells have many of the characteristics Kuffler described for retinal ganglion cells. Each geniculate cell is driven from a circumscribed retinal region (the receptive field) and has either an "on" center or an "off" center, with an opposing periphery. There are, however, differences between geniculate cells and retinal ganglion cells, the most important of which is the greatly enhanced capacity of the periphery of a geniculate cell's receptive field to cancel the effects of the center. This means that the lateral geniculate cells must be even more specialized than retinal ganglion cells in responding to spatial differences in retinal illumination rather than to the illumination itself. The lateral geniculate body, in short, has the function of increasing the disparity—already present in retinal ganglion cells—between responses to a small, centered spot and to diffuse light.

In contrast to the comparatively simple lateral geniculate body, the cerebral cortex is a structure of stupendous complexity. The cells of this great plate of

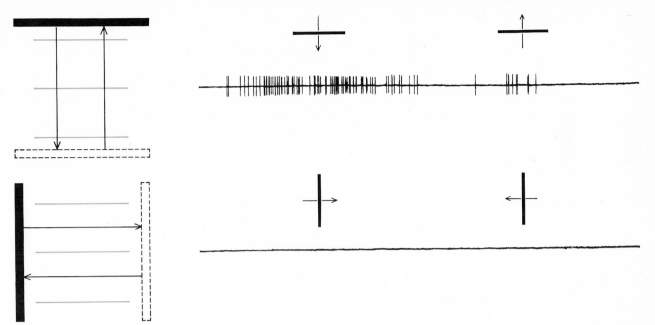

COMPLEX CORTICAL CELL responded vigorously to slow downward movement of a dark, horizontal bar. Upward movement of bar produced a weak response and horizontal movement of a vertical bar produced no response. For other shapes, orientations and movements there are other complex cells showing maximum response. Such cells may figure in perception of form and movement.

gray matter—a structure that would be about 20 square feet in area and a tenth of an inch thick if flattened out—are arranged in a number of more or less distinct layers. The millions of fibers that come in from the lateral geniculate body connect with cortical cells in the layer that is fourth from the top. From here the information is sooner or later disseminated to all layers of the cortex by rich interconnections between them. Many of the cells, particularly those of the third and fifth layers, send their fibers out of the cortex, projecting to centers deep in the brain or passing over to nearby cortical areas for further processing of the visual messages. Our problem was to learn how the information the visual cortex sends out differs from what it takes in.

Most connections between cortical cells are in a direction perpendicular to the surface; side-to-side connections are generally quite short. One might therefore predict that impulses arriving at a particular area of the cortex would exert their effects quite locally. Moreover, the retinas project to the visual cortex (via the lateral geniculate body) in a systematic topologic manner; that is, a given area of cortex gets its input ultimately from a circumscribed area of retina. These two observations suggest that a given cortical cell should have a small receptive field; it should be influenced from a circumscribed retinal region only, just as a geniculate or retinal ganglion cell is. Beyond this the anatomy provides no hint of what the cortex does

with the information it receives about an image on the retina.

In the face of the anatomical complexity of the cortex, it would have been surprising if the cells had proved to have the concentric receptive fields characteristic of cells in the retina and the lateral geniculate body. Indeed, in the cat we have observed no cortical cells with concentric receptive fields; instead there are many different cell types, with fields markedly different from anything seen in the retinal and geniculate cells.

The many varieties of cortical cells may, however, be classified by function into two large groups. One we have called "simple"; the function of these cells is to respond to line stimuli—such shapes as slits, which we define as light lines on a dark background; dark bars (dark lines on a light background), and edges (straight-line boundaries between light and dark regions). Whether or not a given cell responds depends on the orientation of the shape and its position on the cell's receptive field. A bar shone vertically on the screen may activate a given cell, whereas the same cell will fail to respond (but others will respond) if the bar is displaced to one side or moved appreciably out of the vertical. The second group of cortical cells we have called "complex"; they too respond best to bars, slits or edges, provided that, as with simple cells, the shape is suitably oriented for the particular cell under observation. Complex cells, how-

ever, are not so discriminating as to the exact position of the stimulus, provided that it is properly oriented. Moreover, unlike simple cells, they respond with sustained firing to moving lines.

From the preference of simple and complex cells for specific orientation of light stimuli, it follows that there must be a multiplicity of cell types to handle the great number of possible positions and orientations. Wiesel and I have found a large variety of cortical cell responses, even though the number of individual cells we have studied runs only into the hundreds compared with the millions that exist. Among simple cells, the retinal region over which a cell can be influenced—the receptive field—is, like the fields of retinal and geniculate cells, divided into "on" and "off" areas. In simple cells, however, these areas are far from being circularly symmetrical. In a typical example the receptive field consists of a very long and narrow "on" area, which is adjoined on each side by larger "off" regions. The magnitude of an "on" response depends, as with retinal and geniculate cells, on how much either type of region is covered by the stimulating light. A long, narrow slit that just fills the elongated "on" region produces a powerful "on" response. Stimulation with the slit in a different orientation produces a much weaker effect, because the slit is now no longer illuminating all the "on" region but instead includes some of the antagonistic "off" region. A slit at right angles to the optimum orientation for a

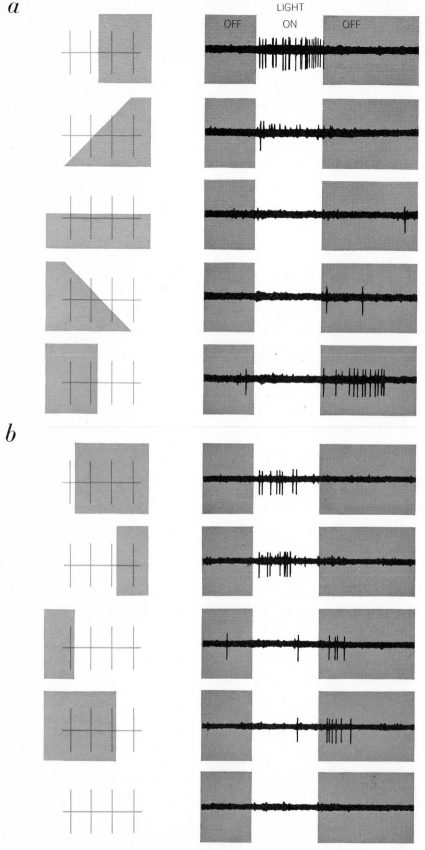

SINGLE COMPLEX CELL showed varying responses to an edge projected on the cell's receptive field in the retina. In group *a* the stimulus was presented in differing orientations. In group *b* all the edges were vertical and all but the last evoked responses regardless of where in the receptive field the light struck. When a large rectangle of light covered entire receptive field, however, as shown at bottom, cell failed to respond.

cell of this type is usually completely ineffective.

In the simple cortical cells the process of pitting these two antagonistic parts of a receptive field against each other is carried still further than it is in the lateral geniculate body. As a rule a large spot of light—or what amounts to the same thing, diffuse light covering the whole retina—evokes no response at all in simple cortical cells. Here the "on" and "off" effects apparently balance out with great precision.

Some other common types of simple receptive fields include an "on" center with a large "off" area to one side and a small one to the other; an "on" and an "off" area side by side; a narrow "off" center with "on" sides; a wide "on" center with narrow "off" sides. All these fields have in common that the border or borders separating "on" and "off" regions are straight and parallel rather than circular [*see bottom illustration on page 273*]. The most efficient stimuli—slits, edges or dark bars—all involve straight lines. Each cell responds best to a particular orientation of line; other orientations produce less vigorous responses, and usually the orientation perpendicular to the optimum evokes no response at all. A particular cell's optimum, which we term the receptive-field orientation, is thus a property built into the cell by its connections. In general the receptive-field orientation differs from one cell to the next, and it may be vertical, horizontal or oblique. We have no evidence that any one orientation, such as vertical or horizontal, is more common than any other.

How can one explain this specificity of simple cortical cells? We are inclined to think they receive their input directly from the incoming lateral geniculate fibers. We suppose a typical simple cell has for its input a large number of lateral geniculate cells whose "on" centers are arranged along a straight line; a spot of light shone anywhere along that line will activate some of the geniculate cells and lead to activation of the cortical cell. A light shone over the entire area will activate all the geniculate cells and have a tremendous final impact on the cortical cell [*see bottom illustration on page 272*].

One can now begin to grasp the significance of the great number of cells in the visual cortex. Each cell seems to have its own specific duties; it takes care of one restricted part of the retina, responds best to one particular shape of stimulus and to one particular orientation. To look at the problem from the opposite direction, for each stimulus—each area of the retina stimulated, each type of line (edge, slit or bar) and each orientation of stimulus—there is a particular set of simple cortical cells that will respond; changing any of the stimulus arrangements will cause a whole new population of cells to respond. The number of populations responding successively as the eye watches a slowly rotating propeller is scarcely imaginable.

Such a profound rearrangement and analysis of the incoming messages might seem enough of a task for a single structure, but it turns out to be only part of what happens in the cortex. The next major transformation involves the cortical cells that occupy what is probably the sixth step in the visual pathway: the complex cells, which are also present in this cortical region and to some extent intermixed with the simple cells.

Complex cells are like simple ones in several ways. A cell responds to a stimulus only within a restricted region of retina: the receptive field. It responds best to the line stimuli (slits, edges or dark bars) and the stimulus must be oriented to suit the cell. But complex fields, unlike the simple ones, cannot be mapped into antagonistic "on" and "off" regions.

A typical complex cell we studied happened to fire to a vertical edge, and it gave "on" or "off" responses depending on whether light was to the left or to the right. Other orientations were almost completely without effect [see illustration on opposite page]. These re-sponses are just what could be expected from a simple cell with a receptive field consisting of an excitatory area separated from an inhibitory one by a vertical boundary. In this case, however, the cell had an additional property that could not be explained by such an arrangement. A vertical edge evoked responses anywhere within the receptive field, "on" responses with light to the left, "off" responses with light to the right. Such behavior cannot be understood in terms of antagonistic "on" and "off" subdivisions of the receptive field, and when we explored the field with small spots we found no such regions. Instead the spot either produced responses at both "on" and "off" or evoked no responses at all.

Complex cells, then, respond like simple cells to one particular aspect of the stimulus, namely its orientation. But when the stimulus is moved, without changing the orientation, a complex cell differs from its simple counterpart chiefly in responding with sustained firing. The firing continues as the stimulus is moved over a substantial retinal area, usually the entire receptive field of the cell, whereas a simple cell will respond to movement only as the stimulus crosses a very narrow boundary separating "on" and "off" regions.

It is difficult to explain this behavior by any scheme in which geniculate cells project directly to complex cells. On the other hand, the findings can be explained fairly well by the supposition that a complex cell receives its input from a large number of simple cells. This supposition requires only that the simple cells have the same field orientation and be all of the same general type. A complex cell responding to vertical edges, for example, would thus receive fibers from simple cells that have vertically oriented receptive fields. All such a scheme needs to have added is the requirement that the retinal positions of these simple fields be arranged throughout the area occupied by the complex field.

The main difficulty with such a scheme is that it presupposes an enormous degree of cortical organization. What a vast network of connections must be needed if a single complex cell is to receive fibers from just the right simple cells, all with the appropriate field arrangements, tilts and positions! Yet there is unexpected and compelling evidence that such a system of connections exists. It comes from a study of what can be called the functional architecture of the cortex. By penetrating with a microelectrode through the cortex in many directions, perhaps many times in a single tiny region of the brain, we learned that the cells are arranged not in a haphazard manner but with a high degree of order. The physiological results show that functionally the cortex is subdivided like a beehive into tiny columns, or segments [see illustration on next page], each of which extends from the surface to the white matter lower in the brain. A column is de-

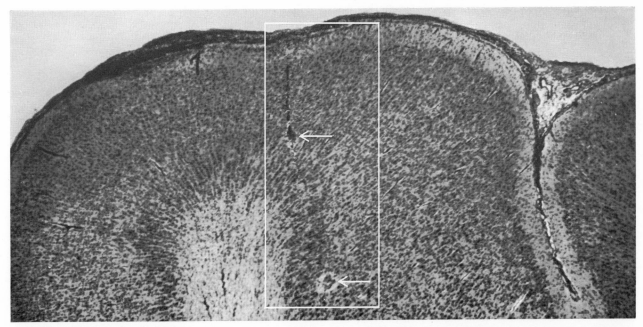

**SECTION OF CAT'S VISUAL CORTEX** shows track of microelectrode penetration and, at arrows, two points along the track where lesions were made so that it would be possible to ascertain later where the tip of the electrode was at certain times. This section of cortex is from a single gyrus, or fold of the brain; it was six millimeters wide and is shown here enlarged 30 diameters.

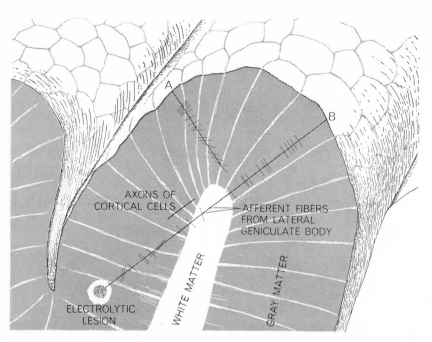

**FUNCTIONAL ARRANGEMENT** of cells in visual cortex resembled columns, although columnar structure is not apparent under a microscope. Lines *A* and *B* show paths of two microelectrode penetrations; colored lines show receptive-field orientations encountered. Cells in a single column had same orientation; change of orientation showed new column.

fined not by any anatomically obvious wall—no columns are visible under the microscope—but by the fact that the thousands of cells it contains all have the same receptive-field orientation. The evidence for this is that in a typical microelectrode penetration through the cortex the cells—recorded in sequence as the electrode is pushed ahead—all have the same field orientation, provided that the penetration is made in a direction perpendicular to the surface of the cortical segment. If the penetration is oblique, as we pass from column to column we record several cells with one field orientation, then a new sequence of cells with a new orientation, and then still another.

The columns are irregular in cross-sectional shape, and on the average they are about half a millimeter across. In respects other than receptive-field orientation the cells in a particular column tend to differ; some are simple, others complex; some respond to slits, others prefer dark bars or edges.

Returning to the proposed scheme for explaining the properties of complex cells, one sees that gathered together in a single column are the very cells one should expect to be interconnected: cells whose fields have the same orientation and the same general retinal position, although not the same position. Furthermore, it is known from

the anatomy that there are rich interconnections between neighboring cells, and the preponderance of these connections in a vertical direction fits well with the long, narrow, more or less cylindrical shape of the columns. This means that a column may be looked on as an independent functional unit of cortex, in which simple cells receive connections from lateral geniculate cells and send projections to complex cells.

It is possible to get an inkling of the part these different cell types play in vision by considering what must be happening in the brain when one looks at a form, such as, to take a relatively simple example, a black square on a white background. Suppose the eyes fix on some arbitrary point to the left of the square. On the reasonably safe assumption that the human visual cortex works something like the cat's and the monkey's, it can be predicted that the near edge of the square will activate a particular group of simple cells, namely cells that prefer edges with light to the left and dark to the right and whose fields are oriented vertically and are so placed on the retina that the boundary between "on" and "off" regions falls exactly along the image of the near edge of the square. Other populations of cells will obviously be called into action by the other three edges of the square. All the cell populations will change if the eye strays from the point fixed on, or if

the square is moved while the eye remains stationary, or if the square is rotated.

In the same way each edge will activate a population of complex cells, again cells that prefer edges in a specific orientation. But a given complex cell, unlike a simple cell, will continue to be activated when the eye moves or when the form moves, if the movement is not so large that the edge passes entirely outside the receptive field of the cell, and if there is no rotation. This means that the populations of complex cells affected by the whole square will be to some extent independent of the exact position of the image of the square on the retina.

Each of the cortical columns contains thousands of cells, some with simple fields and some with complex. Evidently the visual cortex analyzes an enormous amount of information, with each small region of visual field represented over and over again in column after column, first for one receptive-field orientation and then for another.

In sum, the visual cortex appears to have a rich assortment of functions. It rearranges the input from the lateral geniculate body in a way that makes lines and contours the most important stimuli. What appears to be a first step in perceptual generalization results from the response of cortical cells to the orientation of a stimulus, apart from its exact retinal position. Movement is also an important stimulus factor; its rate and direction must both be specified if a cell is to be effectively driven.

One cannot expect to "explain" vision, however, from a knowledge of the behavior of a single set of cells, geniculate or cortical, any more than one could understand a wood-pulp mill from an examination of the machine that cuts the logs into chips. We are now studying how still "higher" structures build on the information they receive from these cortical cells, rearranging it to produce an even greater complexity of response.

In all of this work we have been particularly encouraged to find that the areas we study can be understood in terms of comparatively simple concepts such as the nerve impulse, convergence of many nerves on a single cell, excitation and inhibition. Moreover, if the connections suggested by these studies are remotely close to reality, one can conclude that at least some parts of the brain can be followed relatively easily, without necessarily requiring higher mathematics, computers or a knowledge of network theories.

# 35

# VISION IN FROGS

W. R. A. MUNTZ                                    March 1964

The analogy between the eye and the camera has helped to clarify the process by which the lens of the eye, its aperture regulated by the iris, casts an image on the light-sensitive screen of the retina. On this basis the optic nerve connects the retina to the central nervous system in such a way that a map of the retina is formed on the surface of the brain. The analogy can be carried too far. Students of the visual system came to assume that the retina was like a photographic film, its individual receptor cells responding to light and its absence like the grains of silver salt in a photographic emulsion; that the whole function of the eye and the optic nerve was to form and then transmit a mosaic of the visual world to the brain, there to form the basis of visual perception.

Anatomical investigations have shown, however, that there are many more receptor cells in the retina than there are fibers in the optic nerve. It is thus impossible for every receptor cell to send a separate message to the brain, and the concept that the array of receptor cells is equivalent to the grain of a photographic emulsion must be abandoned. The very intricacy of the retina, the cells of which are variously specialized and richly interconnected, hints at a role more complex than the mere relaying of a visual map. The fact is that the retina is more filter than film. It discriminates: it sends on to the brain only the most useful information.

What is useful varies from animal to animal. Consider, for example, the frog. From the frog's point of view the most relevant objects are the insects on which it feeds. Any small moving object is therefore likely to be important and calls for a specific set of fast responses; no such responses are required by small

stationary objects such as pebbles. According to the earlier theories an image of the object—whether moving or stationary, important or unimportant—was sent to the brain, where the meaningful distinctions were made at some later stage.

It now appears that the retina itself makes the distinctions. Certain nerve fibers leaving the retina have been found to respond specifically to small moving objects and not to stationary objects or even to large moving ones. Such "bug-detectors" can be disadvan-

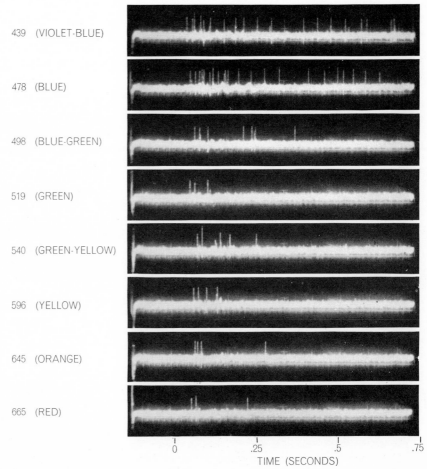

439 (VIOLET-BLUE)

478 (BLUE)

498 (BLUE-GREEN)

519 (GREEN)

540 (GREEN-YELLOW)

596 (YELLOW)

645 (ORANGE)

665 (RED)

0            .25           .5           .75
TIME (SECONDS)

IMPULSES from an "on" fiber are picked up by a microelectrode and recorded on an oscilloscope. Each spike represents response by fiber to stimulation by light of various wavelengths (*shown in millimicrons*). Fibers responded strongly to blue and weakly to green.

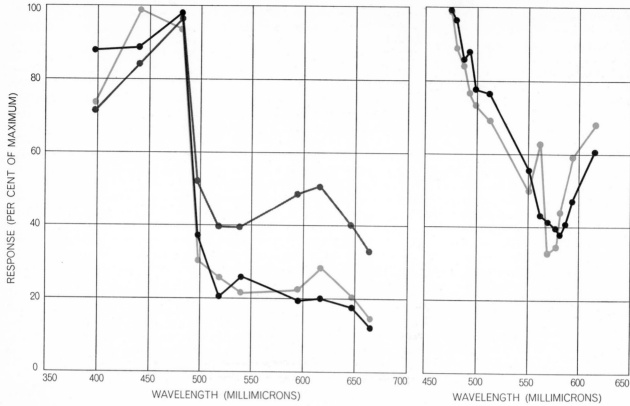

RESPONSES of three on-fibers to 10 different colored lights are compared in the curves at left. The "maximum response" was the largest number of spikes counted in a 1/2-second period. These colors, obtained from interference filters, were quite pure. Unsaturated, or impure, colors had about the same effect, however, as shown by the responses of two fibers to 14 colored papers (*right*).

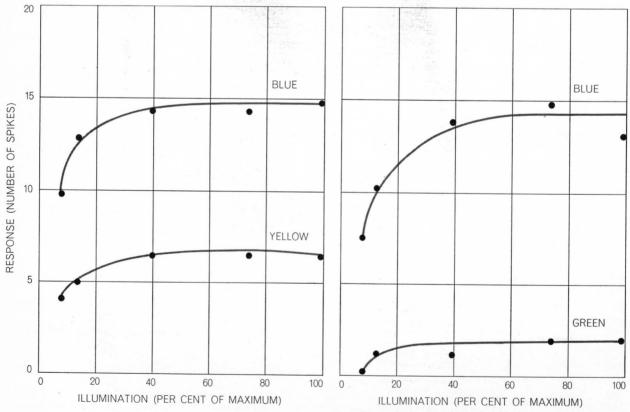

INTENSITY of the stimulating light was not a major factor. The curves at left are for light reflected from colored papers, those at right for filtered light. In both instances blue brought a greater response than yellow or green even when only a tenth as bright.

tageous under unusual conditions: a frog will starve to death surrounded by dead flies. In the ordinary circumstances of a frog's life, however, the early filtering of significant information by the retina makes for efficient utilization of the limited number of optic nerve fibers.

Each fiber, then, reports not whether illumination is present but whether some rather complex situation—such as the approach of a bug—exists in a given part of the visual field. The eye is not a physical instrument like a camera but a biological instrument adapted to meet the animal's needs; to understand the function of the frog's eye it is necessary to consider the frog's point of view. To this end several investigators have studied the nature of some of the messages sent by the frog's eye to the frog's brain and have undertaken to correlate the properties of individual optic nerve fibers with the behavior of the whole animal.

The first recordings of the activity of single optic nerve fibers in the retina of a vertebrate were made by H. K. Hartline at Johns Hopkins University in 1938. Under the microscope he teased a single fiber out of the inner surface of the retina of a frog, placed an electrode under the fiber and then amplified and displayed on an oscilloscope the nerve impulses that resulted when the eye was stimulated by various visual events. Hartline found three types of fiber in the frog's retina: those responding only to the onset of illumination, which he called "on" fibers, those responding only to the end of illumination ("off" fibers), and "on-off" fibers, which responded to both events. The subsequent perfection of microelectrodes made it possible to confirm and extend Hartline's findings without dissecting out the individual fibers; this was done by H. B. Barlow of the University of Cambridge and Ragnar A. Granit of the Royal Caroline Medico-Surgical Institute in Sweden. Their experiments, like Hartline's, were performed on the isolated retina of the frog and therefore demonstrated the retina's analytical capabilities.

From the retina most of the optic nerve fibers pass to the optic tectum, the chief visual center in the frog, where they project a map—not a one-to-one reproduction of the visual world as it appears on the retina but a selective map. At the Massachusetts Institute of Technology Jerome Y. Lettvin, Humberto R. Maturana, Warren S. McCul-

loch and W. H. Pitts were able to determine that four specific attributes of the visual field elicit responses in four specific types of fiber and are emphasized in the map projected on the optic tectum. Each fiber ends in a dense mass of small branches that makes contact with the cells of the tectum; Lettvin and his colleagues, recording nerve impulses in these "terminal arbors" with a special microelectrode, located each type of fiber at a different level.

Fibers ending in the surface layers of the tectum responded to the presence of any sharp edge in the visual field whether the edge was moving or stationary. Fibers ending slightly deeper proved to be the bug-detectors: they responded to small, dark moving objects but not to large or stationary objects. Neither of these groups reacted to a change in general illumination: switching a light on or off did not affect them. They had probably eluded discovery by earlier investigators of isolated retinas because they lack the fatty myelin sheathing of most nerve fibers and are hard to isolate by dissection.

Probing deeper into the optic tectum,

the investigators found the myelinated fibers detected earlier by Hartline. The first of these responded to either the onset or the end of illumination, and they fitted his category of on-off fibers. They responded even more markedly to the movement of a linear shape, however, and therefore they are called "moving-edge detectors." Deeper still Lettvin came on fibers that responded to the cessation of illumination: Hartline's off-fibers.

The M.I.T. workers, to sum up, identified in the tectum four different kinds of optic nerve fiber, each carrying information about an attribute of the visual world that the animal requires in its daily life. They did not find a tectal projection of Hartline's on-fibers. Anatomical studies had shown that not all the frog's optic nerve fibers pass to the tectum; some go instead to a secondary visual center in the dorsal thalamus. This thalamic system is of particular interest because it is the forerunner of the visual system in higher animals, including man. In the human brain the tectal network is small

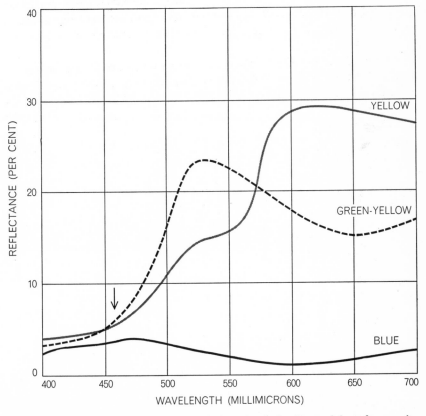

DIM BLUE LIGHT in an experiment such as the one graphed at bottom left on the opposite page had the characteristics of the bottom curve in this graph. It is compared with a green and a yellow light 10 times brighter and has less energy in the blue region (*arrow*) than either. It nevertheless stimulated a greater response. This demonstrates that the sensitivity of the thalamic fibers to blue cannot be due to any single visual pigment in the retina.

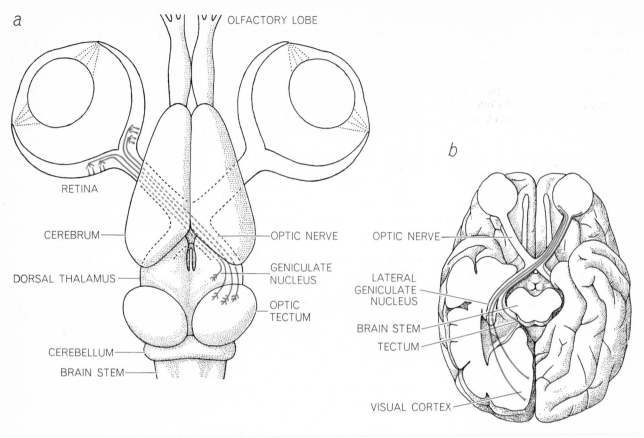

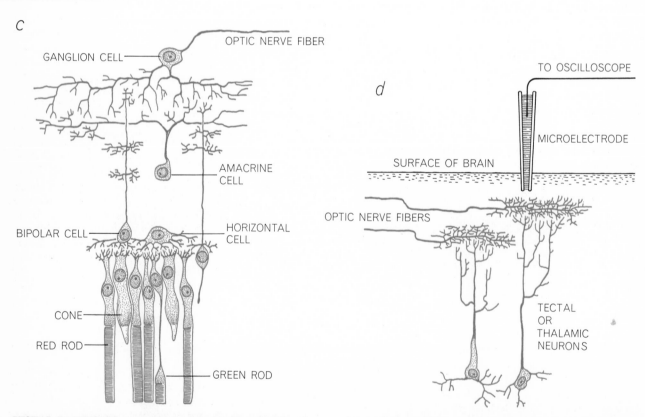

**VISUAL PATHWAYS** are traced in color in these drawings. In the frog (*a*) an image of the visual world formed on the retina is transmitted by optic nerve fibers to the optic tectum and, to a lesser extent, to the geniculate nucleus in the dorsal thalamus. In man (*b*) the tectum is unimportant; most of the fibers go, via the geniculate nucleus, to the visual cortex. The frog retina (*c*) contains about a million receptors (rods and cones), three million connecting cells (bipolar, amacrine and horizontal) and 500,000 ganglion cells leading to optic nerve fibers. In the brain (*d*) these fibers end as small branches that intermingle with the neurons of the optic tectum and dorsal thalamus. A microelectrode records impulses from these terminal arbors of the optic nerve fibers.

and relatively unimportant; most of the fibers carry signals from the retina, by way of the lateral geniculate nucleus in the dorsal thalamus, to the visual area of the cerebral cortex [see the preceding article, "The Visual Cortex of the Brain," by David H. Hubel, on page 270].

In Lettvin's laboratory at M.I.T. I applied his microelectrode methods to an exploration of the optic nerve endings in the dorsal thalamus of the frog. When I displayed various targets in the visual field of a frog, the record of responses showed that all the optic fibers running to the thalamus were sensitive to the onset of illumination and to no other stimulus; they are the on-fibers. Clearly the frog's eye transmits messages about objects primarily to the tectum and sends information from light-detectors primarily to the dorsal thalamus. The information does not become mixed, since four kinds of optic nerve fibers go only to the tectum and one kind only to the thalamus. There are opportunities for interaction at a subsequent stage, however, through a rich network of nerve fibers that con-

nects the optic tectum and the dorsal thalamus.

The light-detectors of the dorsal thalamus proved to be sensitive not only to the presence or absence of light but also to the color of the light. Every fiber I tested in this area responded much more strongly to blue light than to light of any other color. Exposure to blue light brought a rapid burst of nerve impulses that often lasted for several seconds, but in response to green, yellow or red light there was only a brief burst of a few impulses [see illustration on page 279].

In considering this selective response to blue the first question to be settled was whether it represented mere color-dependence or true color vision. Any visual receptor responds only to the light it absorbs, and receptors absorb different wavelengths depending on the visual pigment they contain. For example, the retinal cells called rods, which are responsible for vision in faint light, contain a pigment (rhodopsin, or visual purple) that strongly absorbs blue-green light. Consequently rod vision is much more sensitive to blue-green than to other colors; it is

color-dependent. The rods, however, are not capable of color vision, because they cannot distinguish between a low-intensity blue-green and, say, a high-intensity yellow. Although a blue-green barn may appear lighter than a red one in the moonlight, it will appear gray rather than blue-green. True color vision distinguishes among different wavelengths regardless of the intensity or the purity of the stimulating light.

What was manifested in the blue-sensitive system of the frog's dorsal thalamus: color-dependence ("spectral sensitivity") or color vision ("wavelength discrimination")? The question had an important biological aspect in view of the eminently useful nature of the information delivered to the optic tectum by the bug-detectors and similar fibers. The information about blue light supplied to the dorsal thalamus might be similarly significant, but not unless it was true color vision. That is, to be useful it must respond differentially not only to the pure colors I obtained from interference filters in my first experiments but also to the impure colors of nature. In addition it must also distinguish among colors regardless of their brightness, making the distinction, for example, between a dim blue and a bright green.

A series of experiments demonstrated that the on-fibers do indeed respond in just this manner, emitting a prolonged burst of impulses on exposure to anything that looks blue to the human eye. This was true, first of all, in the case of light transmitted by gelatin filters that passed a rather broad portion of the spectrum in contrast to the narrow band passed by the interference filters. Next the retina was exposed to light reflected from a series of colored papers. All of these were highly unsaturated—that is, they reflected light at all wavelengths with only a slight peak at the dominant wavelength of their apparent color—but they nevertheless stimulated the differential response to blue [see top illustration on page 280]. Finally, when I varied the intensity of the light reflected from these papers or passed by interference filters, there was a much stronger response to dim blue light than to bright yellow or green [see bottom illustration on page 280]. This was true even when the blue paper was illuminated only a tenth as brightly as the green, at which point the unsaturated green actually contained more blue than did the light from the blue paper [see the illustration shown on page 281]. This proved that the re-

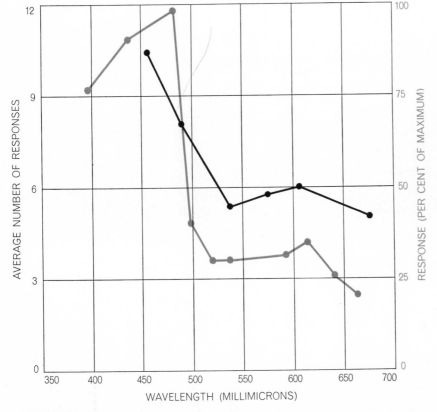

BEHAVIORAL EXPERIMENT showed that frogs preferred a blue light to other colors when they were tested in the apparatus illustrated on the opposite page. Six colors were displayed, each paired with one another and with darkness. Black curve shows average number of times frogs jumped toward each color out of a possible maximum of 12. The results are similar to those obtained in the earlier experiment on thalamic fibers (colored curve).

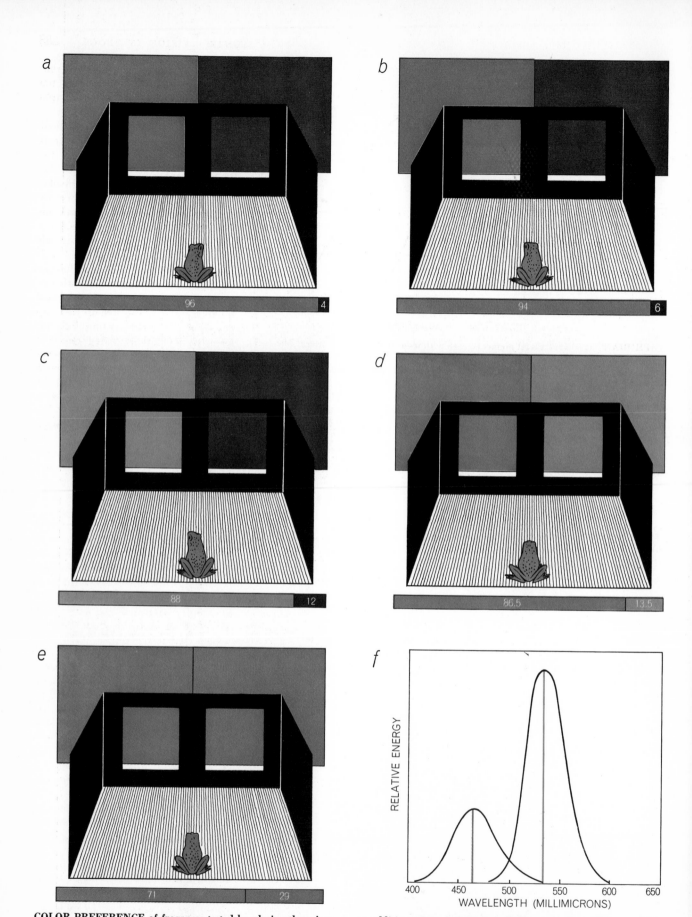

**COLOR PREFERENCE** of frogs was tested by placing them in a small box, drawn here with the top and back wall removed. The animals faced two windows backed by a screen. The part of the screen visible through each window was illuminated with a different color or left dark; the investigators recorded the number of times the frogs jumped toward each color. In the experiment illustrated here the colors were blue and green and an additive mixture of the two. The frogs preferred blue to darkness on 96 per cent of the occasions (a) and preferred blue-green and green to darkness as shown (b, c). They preferred blue to green (d) and even to the mixture of blue plus green (e). Ten frogs were tested several times on each pair of colors, which appeared at left or right at random. The wavelengths and relative intensities of the blue and green are shown by the two curves (f).

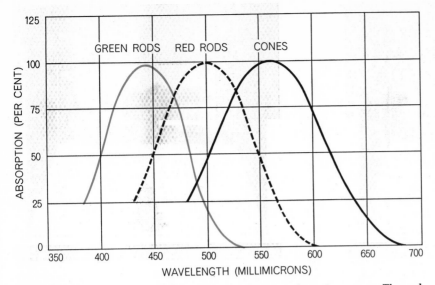

AMPHIBIANS have three visual pigments, each with its own absorption pattern. The peak sensitivity of the green rods is at 440 millimicrons, that of the red rods at 502. The cone pigment has not yet been extracted but is believed to have its peak sensitivity at about 560.

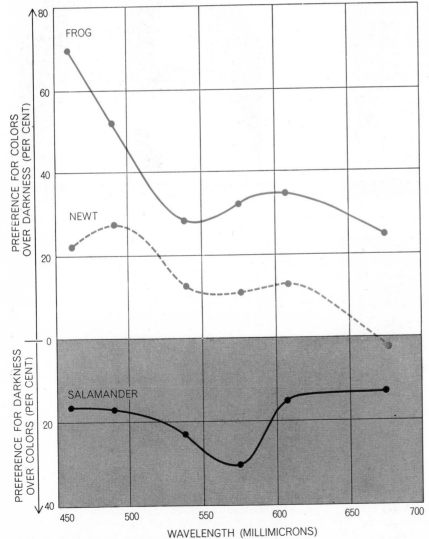

COLOR PREFERENCES of three amphibians are compared on the basis of jumping or swimming behavior. Scores for each color and darkness were converted to percentages. Frog and newt have green rods; they seek light and are most sensitive to blue. Salamander lacks green rods; it seeks darkness and is most sensitive to green light rather than to blue.

sponse to blue was genuine hue discrimination and that the on-fibers of the thalamus were indeed capable of true color vision.

Does the frog use this information? Zoologists have known for many years that frogs tend to jump toward the light and that this "phototactic" behavior is stimulated particularly by blue light. In my laboratory at the University of Oxford we undertook to confirm this blue-seeking behavior and to find out if it was caused by the retinal signals carried by on-fibers to the dorsal thalamus. To test frogs for color preference we built a simple black box with two windows through which the animal could jump. A screen behind the windows was illuminated in turn with different pairs of colors. A frog placed in the box invariably jumped (sometimes a gentle poke was required) through one of the windows; we recorded the number of times each frog chose a certain color or a dark window. The experiment confirmed the frog's reputed preference for blue, and the curve for the behavioral response was very similar to the one for the electrophysiological response of the thalamic fibers [see illustration on page 283].

Subsequent experiments demonstrated clearly that the animals' behavior involved genuine color vision. For one thing, the degree of preference for blue was largely unaffected by variations in the intensity of the stimulating lights. In another parallel to the earlier tests of individual fibers, the frogs preferred a blue light to other colors even when it contained only about a tenth as much energy. The most striking demonstration involved various paired combinations of a blue and a green light [see illustration on page 284]. The green was almost three times brighter than the blue, but when the two were opposed the green was chosen on only 13.5 per cent of the occasions. Furthermore, adding the green to the blue reduced the attractiveness of the blue. When the blue and the blue-green were opposed, the frogs chose the pure blue 71 per cent of the time in spite of the fact that the additive mixture of blue and green contained nearly four times more energy and just as much blue. Like the colored-paper experiment, this ruled out the possibility that mere sensitivity is involved, because no visual pigment can exist that will absorb more of a pure blue light than it will of the same blue light plus green.

The frog shows a simple type of color vision: it is capable of distinguishing blue from other colors. The parallelism between the blue-seeking behavior and the response of the fibers running to the dorsal thalamus is strong evidence that it is these thalamic fibers that underlie the behavior. Such a simple example of color vision merits close attention, because it should be possible to learn in detail how the retina performs the color analysis in the frog and perhaps to derive general principles that apply to other animals as well. We have made a small start in this direction by comparing the frog's color sensitivity with that of some other amphibians.

The spectral sensitivities of the visual pigments in the frog's receptor cells must account for at least the first stage of its color vision system. There are three pigments, each with a characteristic absorption curve [see top illustration on preceding page]. The pigment contained by the green rods is most sensitive at a wavelength of about 440 millimicrons and is therefore presumably implicated in the blue color vision. If it is, we reasoned, the blue-seeking behavior should not occur in certain amphibians that lack green rods. We tested two closely related amphibians: the European newt (Triturus cristatus), which has green rods, and the fire salamander (Salamandra salamandra), which does not. The testing apparatus differed from the frogs' jumping box in several respects, in particular in that it was filled with water and the animals swam toward the target screens.

When they were tested with the same colored lights that had been used with the frogs, the newts showed much the same behavior: they chose blue more often than other colors [see bottom illustration on preceding page]. (The newt's response curve, however, is shifted bodily toward the red end of the spectrum, probably because of a difference in the spectral sensitivity of the receptors; it is known that the rods of the newt have their maximum sensitivity at longer wavelengths than the peak sensitivity of the frog's rods, and it is likely that the same displacement toward the red occurs for the other receptors as well.) The salamander behaves quite differently, shunning light instead of seeking it. Our salamanders swam away from colors and toward a dark screen whenever they could. And the color to which they were apparently most sensitive—the one they most avoided—was green, not blue.

These results supported the finding that the green rod is a basic factor in blue color vision. It cannot, however, be the only receptor involved. Since no single visual pigment can be more sensitive to pure blue than to the same blue plus green, no one kind of receptor can underlie the blue-seeking behavior. There must be some inhibitory element at work to account for the fact that adding green light to blue renders the blue less effective. We are investigating the nature of this inhibitory receptor and have some preliminary evidence that it may be the red rod.

As was suggested earlier, an efficient color vision system should offer some biological advantage to the animal. Why should a frog need to distinguish blue? I think it is quite possible that the function of the blue-sensitive system is to direct the jump of a frightened frog in such a way that it will leap into the water to avoid its predators. Frogs normally live at the edges of ponds, in the grass or under trees. The predominant color around the frog will therefore be green. In the direction of the water, however, there is likely to be less vegetation, and there may also be more blue light from the open sky. Since blue light is effective in guiding the direction of the jump and green light is very ineffective—even less effective than yellow or red—when the frog is frightened it will tend to jump away from the vegetation toward the open space and thus into the water. On this view the important point is that green is particularly ineffective in stimulating the blue-sensitive system, so that light from any other source will be more effective than the green light from the vegetation. Although ponds are not necessarily blue and the sky may be overcast, still the light from the open sky over the pond will contain more blue and less green than the light reflected from the vegetation.

A number of studies in the past few years have demonstrated that the frog's retina responds selectively to various attributes of the visual world, filters out information significant to the animal and sends it along to different areas of the brain. What happens to the messages when they reach the brain, however, is still largely unknown. Even at the retinal level there is much to be learned about how the different cells are interconnected to perform their complex tasks of reception and analysis. What the retina of the frog does is fairly clear; how it does its work remains to be investigated.

# 36

# TASTE RECEPTORS

EDWARD S. HODGSON                                        May 1961

The severed head of a fly, a lump of wax and a minute glass tube filled with salt water were the novel ingredients of the experiment. The other items, including an amplifier, a cathode-ray oscilloscope and a motion-picture camera, were conventional tools for exploring the workings of the nervous system. When this improbable collection was appropriately hooked up, it provided the long-sought means of measuring directly the electrical impulses by which a single taste cell sends a taste sensation to the brain. At last the workings of one of the least understood types of sensory receptor cell could be subjected to direct observation.

Blowflies began losing their heads to such good purpose in 1955, when I collaborated in a study of taste mechanisms with Jerome Y. Lettvin of the Massachusetts Institute of Technology and Kenneth D. Roeder of Tufts University. In our experiments we fastened the fly's head upside down to the lump of wax and subjected the head to slight pressure, causing the proboscis to extend. Then, using a micromanipulator, we could slip the water-filled glass tube over one of the fine sensory hairs on the tip of the proboscis. A silver wire inserted into the other end of the tube connects it with the amplifier and the oscilloscope.

BLOWFLY PROBOSCIS with water-filled glass tube slipped over a single hair (right) is in position for experiment. The shiny horizontal object is a staple that keeps the proboscis extended. Part of one of the fly's eyes is just below the staple (right of center).

**ELECTRICAL CONNECTION** carries impulse from taste cells. Blowfly head is on lump of wax. Electrode at right is glass tube filled with salt water. Electrode at left, connected to amplifier, is implanted in severed head to complete the electrical circuit.

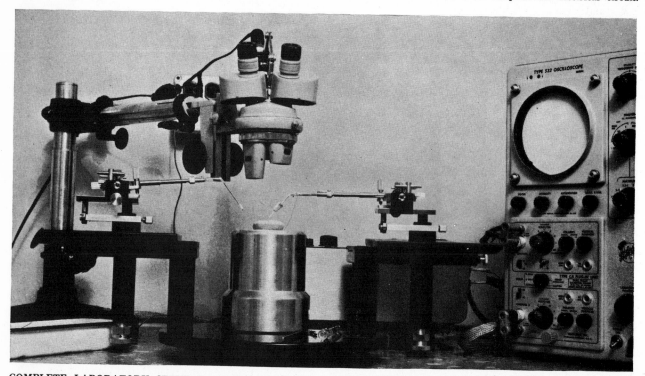

**COMPLETE LABORATORY SETUP** for measuring impulses from blowfly taste cells includes microscope, micromanipulators (*at left and right of center stand*) and oscilloscope (*right*). Electrodes that make contact with fly's head are just above lump of wax.

To complete the circuit, another wire from the amplifier is inserted into the fly's head. Contact between the sensory hair and the solution in the tube causes the taste nerve to produce a series of electrical impulses that register as a fleeting trace on the face of the oscilloscope tube. This visible image of the nerve impulse is recorded by the motion-picture camera.

Although the chemical senses—taste and smell—may seem less important than other sensory systems in man, they have always had a central role in the behavior of other animals. Cells particularly sensitive to the chemical environment were among the earliest to appear, no doubt because the murky aquatic environments that were the scene of so much evolutionary history made chemical perception essential for survival. Chemical detectors are found in one of the oldest of multicellular creatures: the jellyfish. In flatworms, the simplest bilaterally symmetrical animals, chemoreceptors on the sides of the head direct the search for food. Knowledge of the operation of these primitive receptors is so meager, however, that the concepts of "smell" and "taste" must be reserved for the animals that evolved later.

When animals emerged from the water, they continued to depend heavily on the chemical senses. In most insects and in many other land animals, taste and smell play a key part in detecting a suitable environment, finding sustenance and initiating reproductive behavior. The chemical senses do much more than provide pleasurable sensations for gourmets: they are essential to the survival of many animal species.

The study of taste and smell not only sheds light on one of the fundamental processes in nature; it also can be of help in combating insects and other pests that share with man a taste for certain foods. By understanding the mechanism of the chemical senses, man may be able to interfere with their operation, to anesthetize them or even to exploit them with chemicals that attract or repel pests.

Quantitative studies of the chemical senses largely awaited the development of equipment sensitive enough to measure nerve impulses. The first such study was made less than three decades ago by E. D. Adrian and C. Ludwig at the University of Cambridge. They recorded impulses from the olfactory stalk of a catfish brain while flushing the fish's nasal sac with fluid from decaying earthworms or from a putre-

fying alligator head. They found that the olfactory nerves carry some impulses even without stimulation. The fluid from decaying meat greatly increases the number of impulses, which signal the brain that food is nearby. Adrian and Ludwig also discovered that the olfactory stalk will not show a response to stimulation twice in quick succession: full sensitivity reappears only after a recovery period. (Nerve physiologists would say that the olfactory system is "slow-adapting.") Subsequent studies have shown that the chemoreceptor systems of most animals, including many only distantly related to the catfish, have the same general characteristics.

From the point of view of the investigator, however, the taste and smell receptors of vertebrate animals usually share certain drawbacks. The actual receptor cells are too small or too inconveniently located to be probed with electrodes; hence recordings of nerve impulses are customarily taken from nerve fibers connected to the receptor cells rather than from the receptors themselves. Since each nerve fiber is connected to several receptor cells, the original messages must be condensed and delayed by the time they reach the recording electrodes. The situation can be further complicated by a layer of mucus over the receptor cell; it is extremely difficult even to estimate the time it takes a stimulating chemical to penetrate the mucus or wash out of it.

The line of investigation that was eventually to lead to the making of direct and convenient contact with single receptor cells began even before the work of Adrian and Ludwig. In the 1920's D. E. Minnich of the University of Minnesota applied a sugar solution to the sensory hairs on the mouth parts of flies and on the feet of butterflies. When the solution touched even a single hair, the proboscis would extend as if the insect were trying to feed. Each hair seemed to be a taste receptor.

More recently V. G. Dethier, working at Johns Hopkins University, dipped the feet of blowflies into a variety of solutions. He observed which solutions caused extension of the proboscis and so was able to compile a long list of molecules that the fly apparently found tasty. By 1950, largely as a consequence of Dethier's work, more was known about the taste receptors of blowflies than about those of any other organism, including man.

The taste hairs of the fly are merely the inert housings of the living taste-receptor cells. By means of microscopic studies of thin sections of the hairs and the surrounding tissue, Dethier found that each sensory hair on the proboscis of the blowfly has three receptor cells at its base. Two of the cells send thin filaments through the hollow shaft of the hair to its tip. Dethier concluded that these two cells are the taste receptors because when he rolled a droplet

**LIVING AUSTRALIAN SHEEP BLOWFLY is shown here with proboscis (*between two front legs*) extended. The fly, which lays its eggs on sheep, is a serious pest in Australia.**

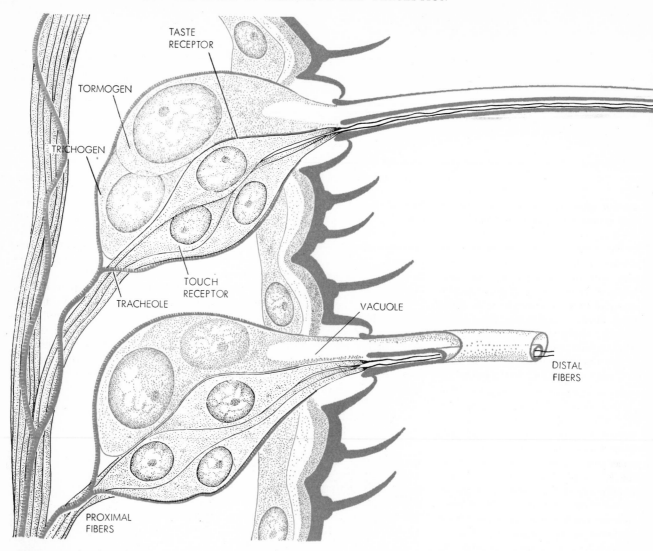

**SENSORY HAIR** of blowfly proboscis ends in papilla (*far right*) capable of detecting chemicals. A "bag" of cells (*left*) lies at base of each hair. The smaller cells in the bag are the two taste receptors, which send filaments ("*distal fibers*") through hollow hair, and between them is a touch receptor. The tormogen and trichogen are not receptors but give rise to the hair structure. The proximal fibers connect the taste and touch receptors directly with the brain. The entire chemoreception system is shown in black.

of sugar water along the shaft of the hair, the proboscis extended only after the solution had reached the tip. The third receptor cell, which sends no filament into the hair, was found by Myron L. Wolbarsht and Dethier to be a touch receptor, sensitive to the bending of the hair. From each of the three cells an extension goes directly to the brain.

The blowfly's two taste-receptor cells, made accessible to external stimuli by the extension of their sensitive filaments in hairs outside the body, seemed to offer an ideal opportunity for observing the chemoreceptor mechanism. No mucus or saliva flows over the cells. Moreover, the hairs on the end of the proboscis are so far apart that experiments on a single hair do not disturb neighboring hairs.

One important difficulty remained to be overcome: making an electrical connection to detect the nerve impulse. Near the tip of a sensory hair the filaments from each receptor are only about a ten-thousandth of a millimeter in diameter—too small to generate much voltage or withstand conventional techniques of making electrical connections with cells. At its largest the diameter of the receptor-cell body may be 22 thousandths of a millimeter, but this part of the cell lies buried at the base of the hair, shielded by the tough, nonconducting waxy cuticle of the hair wall and by the surrounding proboscis tissue.

A clue to the technique for making the electrical connection without injuring the delicate receptor cell came from a beautifully simple experiment performed by Eleanor H. Slifer at the State University of Iowa. By dipping hairs on the antenna of a grasshopper into water containing a dye she showed that aqueous solutions penetrate the tips of sensory hairs. These antenna hairs re-

semble in miniature the taste hairs of the blowfly proboscis. Lettvin, Roeder and I guessed that if water passes through the cuticle at the tip of a sensory hair, a solution that conducts electricity might pick up a nerve impulse through the same permeable spot. Perhaps the solution could both stimulate the taste-receptor cell and provide a workable connection between the receptors inside the fly hair and the electrical recording system outside. Thus it was that we performed the experiment described at the beginning of this article.

As we had hoped, the salt water in the tiny glass tube at once stimulated the receptors and conducted a current away from them. Now that we could record messages directly from the taste receptors, we were able to attack the more interesting problem of how the receptors work. Their reactions to various chemical stimuli would, we felt, provide im-

SENSORY PAPILLA

portant clues to the chemical events that generate the electrical impulses in the receptors.

We were especially curious to see if both of the taste receptors in a sensory hair are sensitive to the same kinds of chemical. It quickly became apparent that they are not. Salts, acids, most alcohols and most other compounds, except sugars, elicited electrical impulses with a constant amplitude of about 300 microvolts (300 millionths of a volt). Test solutions of sucrose and many other sugars, mixed with a trace of salt to provide electrical conductivity, elicited predominantly smaller impulses, about 200 microvolts in amplitude. Since a given nerve cell normally produces impulses of only one amplitude, the two distinct amplitudes from the taste hair provided a way to tell the response of one cell from that of the other. Actually the impulse amplitudes varied somewhat in recordings from different hairs, but the impulses of the two taste cells were usually distinguishable.

For easy reference we called the cell producing the larger impulses the "L" receptor and the cell producing the smaller impulses the "S" receptor. Our first generalization was that the S cell appears to be a sugar receptor and the L cell a less specific nonsugar receptor. Since blowflies feed on sugars and avoid most of the chemicals that stimulate the L receptor, the electrical activity of the nerves seemed to match the flies' feeding behavior.

Further work in my laboratory at Columbia University supported the idea that compounds "acceptable" to the fly stimulate the S receptor, whereas "unacceptable" compounds stimulate the L receptor. We found that the electrical recordings from L and S receptors in single hairs correlate well with the proboscis behavior that follows stimulation of single hairs with a droplet of each test solution. For example, fructose and glucose, both sugars that trigger proboscis extension, strongly stimulate S receptors, even when applied in relatively

low concentration. Two other sugars, cellobiose and mannose, must be applied in high concentration or to many sensory hairs in order to produce a proboscis response. Correspondingly, they evoke only a few S impulses when observed electrically.

The most striking correlation between taste-receptor activities and behavior occurs with four polyhydric alcohols. All these compounds are composed of exactly the same atoms; only the arrangement of the atoms differs. Sorbitol, dulcitol and mannitol stimulate the L re-

ceptor. Inositol, however, strongly stimulates the S receptor; it is also the only one of these alcohols that evokes the feeding response of the proboscis. These reactions indicate that the architecture of a stimulating molecule plays a part in the function of the S receptor, because inositol is the only polyhydric alcohol with a ring-shaped molecule, resembling the sugars we found to be most stimulating.

The selective response of the S receptor suggests that enzymes mediate the chemical reaction that triggers the impulse. These biological catalysts are

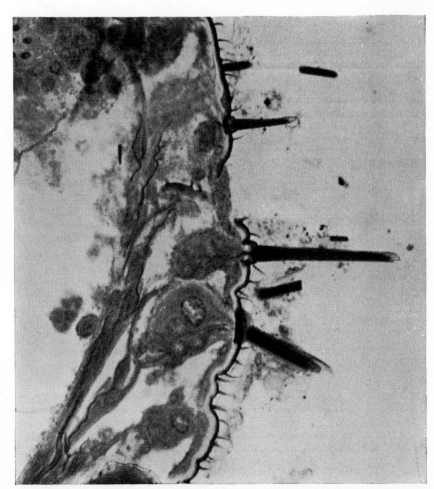

**SENSORY HAIRS AND CELLS** of blowfly proboscis are shown in section in photomicrograph by V. G. Dethier of University of Pennsylvania. Magnification is 600 diameters.

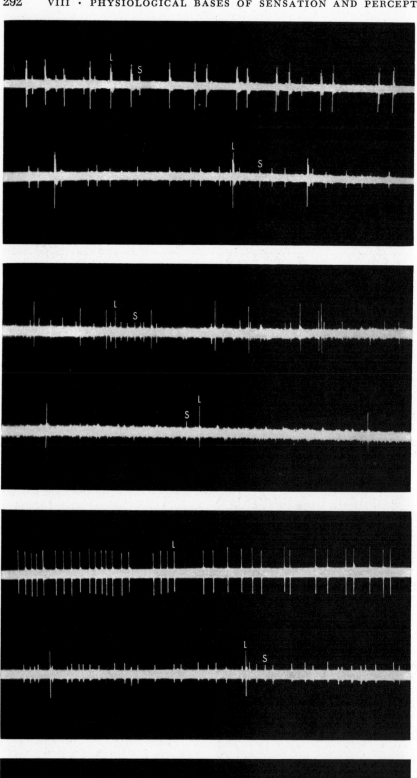

highly specific in their activity. The far less specific responses of the L receptor, which is stimulated by salts and a variety of other nonsugars, suggest that a different mechanism is involved here. It might be sufficient for ions of the stimulating compounds to become loosely bound to the surface of the L receptor. This possibility is particularly interesting, because the same mechanism has been postulated for the salt-taste receptors in mammals.

Further support for the idea of different mechanisms of S and L activity comes from experiments that Lindsay Barton-Browne and I performed on the Australian sheep blowfly at the Australian National University and at the Australian Commonwealth Scientific and Industrial Research Organization. We were able to measure the time interval between the applications of the stimulus and the first receptor impulse in 141 individual taste-receptor cells. It happens that the oscilloscope beam shows a slight deflection the instant our experimental circuit is closed by contact between the stimulating solution and the sensory hair [*see bottom illustration on opposite page*]. The deflection is followed by a brief interval before the taste cell fires the impulse that goes to the brain. We found that the impulses from the L receptors appear within as little as a millisecond (a thousandth of a second) after a salt solution is applied. With S receptors, however, the delay after contact with a sugar solution is always at least five milliseconds. (These speeds are only a fourth to a 20th as long as those generally observed in experiments with vertebrates, showing again the value of making recordings as close as possible to the site of receptor stimulation.) The sugar molecules would be expected to move slower than the salt ions to the receptor site. Only part of the difference in the response times of S and L receptors can, however, be explained on this basis alone, and some fundamental difference in their mechanism of operation again seems indicated.

Of course, a fly does not normally encounter chemicals in the pure forms employed in our experiments. In nature, feeding behavior may depend on the proportions of L and S impulses reaching the brain. Experiments at Columbia have shown that mixtures seldom produce impulses that are the simple sum of the impulses obtained when the chemicals are tried singly. The addition of sucrose to a solution of sodium chloride, for example, not only activates the S receptor; it also lowers the frequency

OSCILLOSCOPE TRACES show reactions of taste hairs to various chemicals. Each hair has two receptors, one giving an "L" (large amplitude) response on the oscilloscope, and one giving an "S" (small) response. In top picture top trace resulted from application of the sugar raffinose, which caused many L impulses, while bottom trace shows reaction of same hair to fructose, which caused more S than L impulses. Middle picture shows how another hair reacted to fructose (*top trace*) and to another sugar, ribose (*bottom trace*). Ribose stimulated scarcely any impulses. The bottom pair of traces was made by a third hair exposed to two polyhydric alcohols. The alcohol dulcitol (*top trace*) strongly stimulated L impulses, whereas inositol, made up of same atoms in a different arrangement, primarily stimulated S responses. At bottom is time scale for traces; it has 100 peaks a second.

of the L impulses caused by the salt. This may be due in part to interactions of the ions and molecules in solution. Whatever the mechanism, this effect tends to increase the discrepancy between frequencies of L and S impulses, enhancing the contrast between acceptable and unacceptable chemicals. Thus the fly's taste receptors would signal the brain that a substance is either "very acceptable" or "very unacceptable."

The individual sensory hairs on the fly's mouth parts exhibit further refinements that provide additional informa-

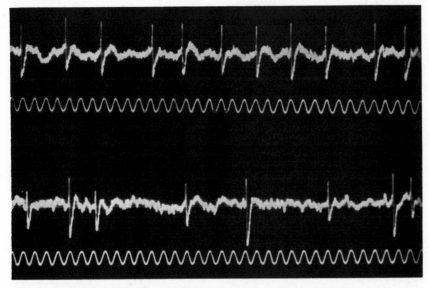

ONLY L FIBER RESPONDS when solution consists of sodium chloride alone (*top*). A much weaker salt solution plus the sugar sucrose causes five S and only three L impulses in same time period (*bottom*). The time scales here contain 100 peaks to the second.

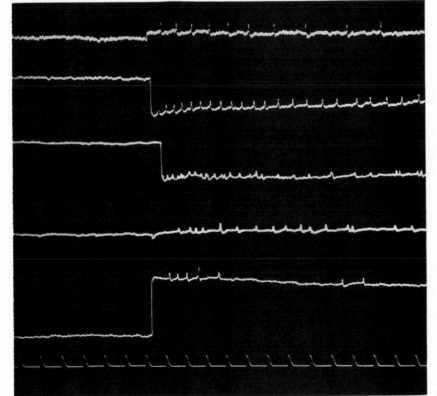

TIME OF RESPONSE after application of stimulus can be seen on these tracings. Each peak on time scale (*bottom*) marks passage of 10 one-thousandths of a second. First deflection of beam indicates application of stimulus. Second deflection is first receptor response. The three top traces show response of L receptors to salt. The two bottom traces, showing response of S receptors to sucrose, illustrate how the S receptor reacts slower.

tion to the brain. Barton-Browne and I found that the receptors in some hairs are slow in responding to stimuli and are relatively inexcitable, while those in other hairs always fire rapidly. Thus strong stimulation that would virtually inactivate the sensitive receptors would still be affecting the less active receptors. The reverse would be true of barely perceptible stimuli.

Temperature changes of less than a degree can also modulate the frequency of firing of some receptors during a period of otherwise regular discharge. This temperature effect is not produced at the tips of the hairs and apparently does not involve the chemosensory processes occurring there. Since the bending of a sensory hair can also provide information about tactile properties of the environment, the range of sensations provided by even a single sensory hair can be wide indeed.

It is amusing to imagine the sensations experienced by the living fly when a taste receptor hair is stimulated in various ways. In contact with heated sirup a single hair might signal not only a strong and acceptable taste but the temperature and stickiness of the sirup as well. Other situations and the sensations they excite are not too difficult to imagine. The wire tapping that brings the nerve impulse to the oscilloscope has probably provided far more accurate information about the fly's taste sensations than could be obtained if the insect could talk.

Although microelectrodes attached to the tip of a fly's taste hairs have revealed a great deal about nerve cells sensitive to chemicals, they have failed to detect one of the very first steps that was expected to occur in the process of tasting: the initial electrical changes that trigger the fly's taste cell to send an impulse to the brain. Recently two Japanese investigators, Hiromichi Morita and Satoru Yamashita of Kyushu University, reached this objective. Through an opening in the side wall of a fly's sensory hair they managed to connect a microelectrode to the filaments inside. Before being stimulated, the receptor-cell filaments registered some spontaneous activity like that found by Adrian and Ludwig in the catfish olfactory stalk. More important, Morita and Yamashita have demonstrated that, upon stimulation, a relatively slow change in electrical potential in the filament precedes and leads to the generation of the brief but much stronger impulse going to the brain. These slow electrical changes occur only in the filaments that lie within

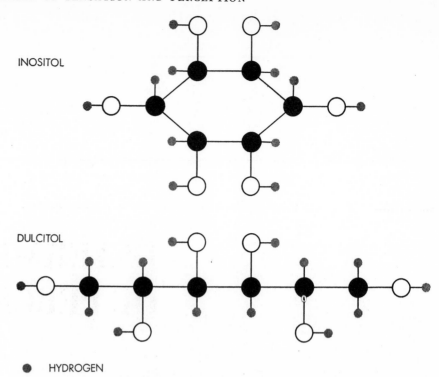

**POLYHYDRIC ALCOHOL MOLECULES** are made of same atoms in different arrangements. Because of its ring structure, which resembles that of stimulating sugars, inositol evokes feeding response in blowflies. Dulcitol, which has no ring, tends instead to repel the fly.

the shaft of the sensory hair and are elicited by chemical reaction with the stimulating chemical. They correspond to the "generator" potentials observed in other receptor cells, which cause the main bodies of the cells to fire impulses into the central nervous system [see "Biological Transducers, by Werner R. Loewenstein, for further details; Offprint #70]. Further study of these generator potentials in taste-receptor cells will undoubtedly lead to a more complete description of the mechanisms of the chemical senses.

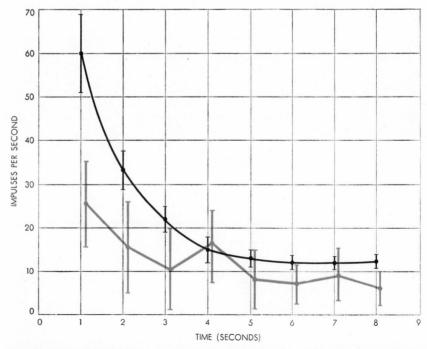

**TASTE CELLS "ADAPT"** to stimulus by decreasing number of impulses sent to brain. L receptor (*black line*) sends more impulses than S receptor (*color*) and rate decreases faster. The vertical lines indicate the range of impulses found in repeated tests on one hair.

# Part IX

---

# DETERMINANTS OF PERCEPTION

# IX

## DETERMINANTS OF PERCEPTION

*Introduction*  As has been shown in some of the preceding papers, research in recent years has provided a great deal of insight into the mechanisms responsible for the faithful coding of stimuli into nerve impulses. Perception, however, is not always valid. The misread sign and the apparent movement of lights on a marquee are only two of many instances which attest to this fact. This section examines some of the variables which influence perception, and thus may control behavior dependent upon that perception. Perception, however, should not be considered merely as a unitary subject, because different variables influence perceptions concerned with different sensory systems (such as the auditory or visual) and even different perceptions within a given system (form, color, depth, or motion). Space permits us to consider only a few of the factors which determine perception, but these factors represent widely disparate types of influences and so serve to point out that perception is a product of several complex structural, functional, and experiential interactions. Perception, then, is some product of sensory system interaction with brain mechanisms concerned with the storage and retrieval of information.

The first article in this section concerns a topic which could almost as easily have been discussed in the preceding section. The subject of pain has always been somewhat elusive and difficult to classify. Even at the present time, there is dispute regarding the existence of pain receptors. Furthermore, complete elucidation of neural "pain" pathways has not yet been accomplished. R. Melzack's discussion in "The Perception of Pain" (page 299) leaves no doubt, however, that the reaction to noxious stimulation may be modified by a variety of environmental influences. One of the more interesting neurophysiological findings of recent years is the existence of central cerebral mechanisms which can alter sensory transmission from the periphery to the brain. We still lack definitive neurobehavioral information concerning their role in the perception of pain. Melzack's article also points out how objective procedures can be applied to study so elusive a subject. Further experiments employing both neural techniques and careful behavioral analyses should yield additional insights into this very important and perplexing subject.

Historically, the topic of perception has been involved in philosophical considerations of the origins of man's knowledge. Arguments have centered around whether perceptions are solely inborn or acquired. In "The Origin of Form Perception" (page 308) Robert L. Fantz discusses experiments which shift this problem from the arena of the philosopher to that of the scientist. The evidence that Fantz presents indicates that neonates—whether chicks, chimpanzees, or humans—exhibit certain perceptual preferences. These findings support the contention that some perceptual capacities are innate. Furthermore, perceptual preferences present at birth appear to have adaptive significance for the particular organism: small grainlike objects for chicks, and facial patterns for human babies. However, innate capacity cannot account for all of perception, and Fantz proposes an interesting hypothesis regarding the interrelationships among innate capacity, maturation, and learning as factors in perception. Evaluation of such proposals naturally awaits additional experimental investigations.

As we have previously seen, the visual system has received the most extensive scrutiny of any of the sensory systems. Its organ, the eye, is an exceedingly complex organ. Yet all of its focusing powers and receptive properties would be insufficient for normal perception were it not for its constant miniscule movements. Roy M. Pritchard, in "Stabilized Images on the Retina" (page 315) discusses the alterations in perception that occur when visual receptors receive constant, rather than continually changing stimulation. The neural bases for these strange and intriguing effects are not yet known, but they may be related to receptor adaptation —that is, decreased neuronal output with constant stimulus intensity. Such adaptation is known for other sensory systems, and was previously discussed by Hodgson in "Taste Receptors" (page 287). Even adaptation cannot provide the complete answer, for Pritchard notes that the disintegration of forms during stabilization of the retinal image is not random but is in some way related to their meaning or organization. We see again in this article the two-headed theoretical monster of innate versus acquired determinants of perception. Pritchard, like Fantz, attempts to reconcile the two, but is unable to do so on the basis of the particular evidence presented.

In "Plasticity in Sensory-Motor Systems" (page 322) Richard Held discusses the consequences of experimentally induced visual distortions. This method is exceptionally useful because it permits the study of the brain's adjustment to controlled changes in sensory input without involving damage to the nervous system itself. Although not generally recognized by the layman, all behavior has sensory consequences which feed back into the brain. As was discussed in the Introduction to "Neural Systems and Behavior" (page 200), the brain receives sensory information not simply from the external environment, but also from receptors located throughout the body. Held's studies show that the brain requires sensory feedback resulting from active (rather than passive) movements in order to adjust to prismatically induced distortions. These findings indicate that the brain accomplishes adjustment to the new situation by comparing its "commands" with the feedback from these command-produced movements. Other experiments involving the auditory system have also revealed the dependence of normal behavior upon normal feedback to the brain; for example, speech is impaired when the subject hears his own words delayed a few seconds. The nervous system is often likened to a telephone switchboard or digital computer, but studies of the type discussed by Held illustrate particularly the dynamic qualities of the brain, which clearly limit the value of such analogies.

Even under circumstances of normal receptor-organ functioning, sensory system development, and cerebral feedback, perception may not correspond to reality. In "Experiments in Perception" (page 330) W. H. Ittelson and F. P. Kilpatrick point out the dependence of certain aspects of visual perception upon various environmental cues and prior experience. One of the major findings of such studies is that perceptions are based upon certain assumptions (such as parallelism of floors and ceilings) formed from prior experience, even though the actual stimulation of the receptor organ is valid for the particular stimuli present.

# 37

# THE PERCEPTION OF PAIN

RONALD MELZACK                                   February 1961

Even though pain is a private and personal experience, we rarely pause to define it in ordinary conversation. Indeed, no one who has worked on the problem of pain has ever been able to define pain to the satisfaction of all his colleagues. When compared with vision or hearing, for example, the perception of pain seems simple, urgent and primitive. We expect the nerve signals evoked by injury to "get through," unless we are unconscious or anesthetized. But experiments show that pain is not always perceived after injury even when we are fully conscious and alert. Thus a knowledge of pain perception goes beyond the problem of pain itself: it helps us to understand the enormous plasticity of the nervous system and how each of us responds to the world in a unique fashion.

A vast amount of study has been devoted to the perception of pain, especially in the last decade, and from it is emerging a concept of pain quite different from the classical view. Research shows that pain is much more variable and modifiable than many people have believed in the past. Moreover, direct recordings of nerve signals are helping us to see, in physiological detail, why pain is such a complex experience.

Anyone who has suffered prolonged, severe pain comes to regard it as an evil, punishing affliction that is harmful in its own right. Yet everyone recognizes the positive aspect of pain. It warns us that something biologically harmful is happening. The occasional reports of people who are born without the ability to feel pain provide convincing testimony on the value of pain. Such a person sustains extensive burns and bruises during childhood, frequently bites deep into his tongue while chewing food, and learns only with difficulty to avoid inflicting severe wounds on himself.

It is the obvious biological significance of pain that leads most of us to expect that it must always occur after injury and that the intensity of pain we feel is proportional to the amount and extent of the damage. Actually, in higher species at least, there is much evidence that pain is not simply a function of the amount of bodily damage alone. Rather, the amount and quality of pain we feel are also determined by our previous experiences and how well we remember them, by our ability to understand the cause of the pain and to grasp its consequences. Even the significance pain has in the culture in which we have been brought up plays an essential role in how we feel and respond to it.

In our culture, for example, childbirth is widely regarded as a painful experience. Yet anthropologists have observed cultures in which the women show virtually no distress during childbirth. In some of these cultures a woman who is going to have a baby continues to work in the fields until the child is about to be born. Her husband then gets into bed and groans as though he were in great pain while she bears the child. The husband stays in bed with the baby to recover from the terrible ordeal he has just gone through, and the mother almost immediately returns to attend the crops.

Can this mean that all women in our culture are making up their pain? Not at all. It happens to be part of our culture to recognize childbirth as possibly endangering the life of the mother, and young girls learn to fear it in the course of growing up. Books on "natural childbirth" ("childbirth without fear") stress the extent to which fear increases the amount of pain felt during labor and birth and point out how difficult it is to dispel it.

The influence of early experience on the perception of pain was demonstrated a few years ago in experiments my colleagues and I conducted at McGill University [our results were summarized in "Early Environment," by William R. Thompson and Ronald Melzack, Offprint #469]. We raised Scottish terriers in isolation from infancy to maturity so that they were deprived of normal environmental stimuli, including the bodily knocks and scrapes that young animals get in the course of growing up. We were surprised to find that when these dogs grew up they failed to respond normally to a flaming match. Some of them repeatedly poked their noses into the flame and sniffed at it as long as it was present. If they snuffed it out, they reacted similarly to a second flaming match and even to a third. Others did not sniff at the match but made no effort to get away when we touched their noses with the flame repeatedly. These dogs also endured pinpricks with little or no evidence of pain. In contrast, littermates that had been reared in a normal environment recognized potential harm so quickly that we were usually unable to touch them with the flame or pin more than once.

This astonishing behavior of dogs reared in isolation cannot be attributed to a general failure of the sensory conducting systems. Intense electric shock elicited violent excitement. Moreover, reflex movements made by the dogs during contact with fire and pinprick indicate that they may have felt something during stimulation; but the lack of any observable emotional disturbance, apart from reflex movements, suggests that

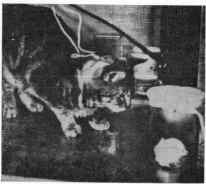

ATTENTIVE CAT (*middle*) watching mouse in a jar presumably does not hear a click as loudly as when it is in repose (*top and bottom*). Assumption is based on shape of nerve-signal recordings picked up by electrode implanted in auditory pathway. Clicks were sounded at the dots. This experiment was performed at the School of Medicine of the University of California at Los Angeles by Raúl Hernández-Peon and his associates.

their perception of actual damage to the skin was highly abnormal.

We have considerable evidence to show that people too attach variable meanings to pain-producing situations and that these meanings greatly influence the degree and quality of pain they feel. During World War II Henry K. Beecher of the Harvard Medical School observed the behavior of soldiers severely wounded in battle. He was astonished to find that when the wounded were carried into combat hospitals, only one out of three complained of enough pain to require morphine. Most of the soldiers either denied having pain from their extensive wounds or had so little that they did not want any medication to relieve it. These men, Beecher points out, were not in a state of shock, nor were they totally unable to feel pain, for they complained as vigorously as normal men at an inept vein puncture. When Beecher returned to clinical practice as an anesthesiologist, he asked a group of civilians who had just undergone major surgery and who had incisions similar to the wounds received by the soldiers whether they wanted morphine to alleviate their pain. In contrast with the wounded soldiers, four out of five claimed they were in severe pain and pleaded for a morphine injection.

Beecher concluded from his study that "the common belief that wounds are inevitably associated with pain, that the more extensive the wound the worse the pain, was not supported by observations made as carefully as possible in the combat zone." He goes on to say: "The data state in numerical terms what is known to all thoughtful clinical observers: There is no simple direct relationship between the wound per se and the pain experienced. The pain is in very large part determined by other factors, and of great importance here is the significance of the wound.... In the wounded soldier [the response to injury] was relief, thankfulness at his escape alive from the battlefield, even euphoria; to the civilian, his major surgery was a depressing, calamitous event."

The importance of the meaning associated with a pain-producing situation is made particularly clear in conditioning experiments carried out by the Russian physiologist Ivan Pavlov. Dogs normally react violently when they are given strong electric shocks to a paw. Pavlov found, however, that if he consistently presented food to a dog after each shock, the dog developed an entirely new response. Immediately after a shock the dog would salivate, wag its tail and turn

eagerly toward the food dish. The electric shock now failed to evoke any responses indicative of pain and became instead a signal meaning that food was on the way. The dog's conditioned behavior persisted when Pavlov increased the intensity of the electric shocks and even when he supplemented them by burning and wounding the dog's skin. Jules H. Masserman of Northwestern University carried the experiment still further. After cats had been taught to respond to electric shock as a signal for feeding, they were trained to administer the shock themselves by walking up to a switch and closing it.

It is well known that prize fighters, football players and other athletes can sustain severe injuries without being aware that they have been hurt. In fact, almost any situation that attracts intense, prolonged attention may diminish or abolish pain perception. Formal recognition of this fact has led to increasing medical interest in hypnosis. Like pain itself, the hypnotic state eludes precise definition. But loosely speaking hypnosis

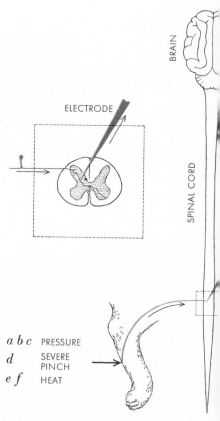

NEURON-FIRING PATTERNS, recorded from single cells in the spinal cord of a cat, show the initial response in the central nervous system to various stimuli applied to the cat's leg. Pattern *a* was caused by

is a trance state in which the subject's attention is focused intensely on the hypnotist while attention to other stimuli is markedly diminished. Evidently a small percentage of people can be hypnotized deeply enough to undergo surgery entirely without anesthesia. For a larger number of people hypnosis reduces the amount of pain-killing drug required to produce successful analgesia.

If, however, the subject's attention is focused on a potentially painful experience, he will tend to perceive pain more intensely than he would normally. K. R. L. Hall and E. Stride in England found that the simple appearance of the word "pain" in a set of instructions made anxious subjects report as painful a level of electric shock they did not regard as painful when the word was absent from the instructions. Thus the mere anticipation of pain is sufficient to raise the level of anxiety and thereby the intensity of perceived pain. Similarly, experiments carried out by Harris E. Hill and his colleagues at the U. S. Public Health Service Hospital in Lexington, Ky., have shown that if anxiety is dispelled (by re-

assuring a subject that he has control over the pain-producing stimulus), a given level of electric shock or burning heat is perceived as significantly less painful than the same stimulus under conditions of high anxiety. Hill was also able to show that morphine diminishes pain if the anxiety level is high but has no demonstrable effect if the subject's anxiety has been dispelled.

The influence of psychological processes such as anxiety, attention and suggestion on the intensity of perceived pain is further demonstrated by studies of the effectiveness of placebos. Clinical investigators have found that severe pain (such as postsurgical pain) can be relieved in some patients by giving them a placebo, such as sugar solution or saline solution, in place of morphine or other analgesic drugs. About 35 per cent of the patients report marked relief from pain after being given a placebo. Since morphine, even in large doses, will relieve severe pain in only some 75 per cent of patients, one can conclude that nearly half of the drug's effectiveness is really a placebo effect. This is not to imply that

people who are helped by a placebo do not have real pain; no one will deny the reality of postsurgical pain. Rather, it illustrates the powerful contribution of psychological processes to the perception of pain.

Taken together, the observations described so far indicate that the same injury can have different effects on different people or even on the same person at different times. A stimulus may be painful in one situation and not in another. How can we account for such variability in terms of what we know about the nervous system? First, we must recast the psychological facts into physiological terms. We must assume that psychological processes such as memories of previous experiences, thoughts, emotions and the focusing of attention are in some way functions of the higher areas of the brain—that they represent the actual activities of nerve impulses. What the psychological data suggest, then, is that these higher brain functions are able to modify the patterns of nerve impulses produced by an injury. Re-

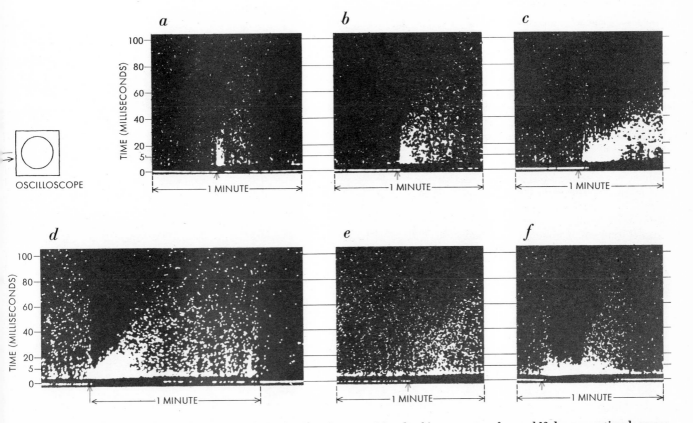

hanging a two-gram weight on a single hair; *b* shows effect of a 20-gram weight; *c* is effect of a mild pinch. All three stimuli start at arrows and continue for duration of the recording. In *d* the skin was severely pinched for one minute. In *e* and *f* a heat lamp was directed at the skin for 15 seconds after the arrows, raising the skin temperature four and 12 degrees centigrade respectively. Each dot in the recordings represents a single nerve impulse; height above base line represents time interval between recorded impulse and preceding one. These experiments were performed by Patrick D. Wall at Massachusetts Institute of Technology.

markable evidence for such complex neural interplay has recently been observed in physiological laboratories.

When energy from the environment stimulates the skin, a message is transmitted along nerve bundles to the spinal cord of the central nervous system. Until recently it was believed that the message, once fed in, was relayed without interference direct to a particular area of the brain cortex; the arrival of the message at this cortical area produced the sensation of pain, touch, warmth or cold, depending entirely on the physical characteristics of the initial stimulus. We now know that this is only a part of the picture. Investigators in a number of countries have recently demonstrated the presence of systems of nerve fibers that run from the higher areas of the brain downward to make connection with the message-carrying nerve pathways in the spinal cord. Electrical activity induced in these higher brain areas is capable of suppressing or modifying the message; it may never get beyond the lower levels of the central nervous system or an entirely different message may reach the brain [see illustration on opposite page].

There is no longer any doubt that these message-modifying fibers exist; it has been found that electrical stimulation of widespread regions of the brain is able to modify the messages transmitted through every major sensory system. The origins and terminations of these message-controlling fibers have not yet been fully established. But even at this stage it is reasonable to speculate that the fibers provide the mechanism whereby higher brain activities such as memories, thoughts and emotions can modify the sensory messages after injury. We can assume, moreover, that this modification can occur throughout the entire axis of the central nervous system, at every junction at which nerve messages are relayed from one neuron to the next in the course of their ascent to the highest areas of the brain. If this view is right, we have a conceptual physiological model to account for the fact that psychological events play an essential role in determining the quality and intensity of the ultimate perceptual experience.

We may ask at this point: What is the nature of the sensory nerve signals or messages traveling to the brain after injury that permits them to be modified in the course of their transmission? Let us say we have burned a finger; what is the sequence of events that follows in the nervous system? To begin with, the intense heat energy is converted into a code of electrical nerve impulses. These

energy conversions occur in nerve endings in the skin called receptors, of which there are many different types. It was once popular to identify one of these types as the specific "pain receptor." We now believe that receptor mechanisms are more complicated. There is general agreement that the receptors that respond to noxious stimulation are widely branching, bushy networks of fibers that penetrate the layers of the skin in such a way their receptive fields heavily overlap with one another. Thus damage at any point on the skin will activate at least two or more of these networks and initiate the transmission of trains of nerve impulses along bundles of sensory nerve fibers that run from the finger into the spinal cord. What enters the spinal cord of the central nervous system is a coded pattern of nerve impulses, traveling along many fibers and moving at different speeds and with different frequencies [see illustration on preceding page].

Before the nerve-impulse pattern can begin its ascent to the brain, a portion of it must first pass through a pool of short, densely packed nerve fibers that are dif-

fusely interconnected. The fibers comprising these pools, found throughout the length of the spinal cord, are called internuncial neurons. It is in the course of transmission from the sensory fibers to the ascending spinal cord neurons that the pattern of signals may be modified. Patrick D. Wall of the Massachusetts Institute of Technology has been able to insert microelectrodes into single spinal cord neurons in cats and record the patterns of neural firing evoked when painful stimuli are applied to the skin. He has shown that these patterns of firing can be altered and limited in duration by subjecting the surrounding skin to a vibratory stimulus [see illustration below]. Wall has directly confirmed with human subjects that normally painful electric shocks and pinpricks are not perceived as painful when the surrounding skin is stimulated with a rapidly vibrating device.

Once the sensory patterns or signals have entered the spinal cord neurons they are transmitted to the brain along nerve bundles that occupy the anterolateral (front and side) portions of the spinal cord. Many fibers belonging to

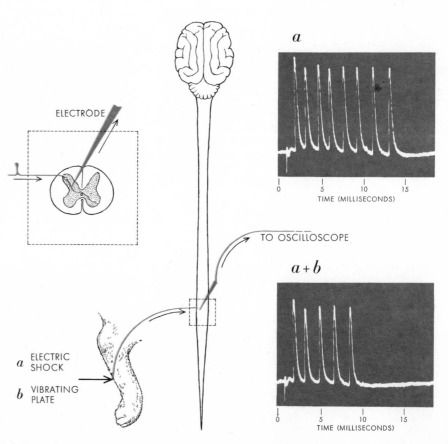

MODIFICATION OF SENSORY MESSAGES can take place within the spinal cord under certain conditions. In experiment at left, performed by Wall, the long train of nerve impulses following a single shock (a) is shortened when the skin around the shocked region is simultaneously vibrated by a metal plate (b). In experiment at right an afferent nerve

these bundles continue to the thalamus, forming the spinothalamic tract. The majority of the fibers, however, penetrate a tangled thicket of short, diffusely interconnected nerve fibers that form the central core of the lower part of the brain. Out of this formation of "reticulated" cells there emerges a series of pathways, so that the sensory patterns now stream along multiple routes to the higher regions of the brain.

When I was working with W. K. Livingston at the University of Oregon Medical School, our group found that electrical impulses evoked by painful stimuli are transmitted through the lower part of the brain along five distinct routes [*see illustrations on next two pages*]. Three of them—the spinothalamic tract, the central tegmental tract and the central gray pathway—appear to represent major conduction systems for sensory pain patterns since their electrical activity is significantly depressed by analgesic agents (such as nitrous oxide) that are capable of abolishing the awareness of pain in human patients without similarly affecting vision and hear-

ing. Analgesic drugs also produce a striking reduction in the electrical activity in the fourth region, the central core of reticulated cells, which has been shown by other investigators to have the role of arousing the whole brain into alert activity. The final pathway, a major sensory system called the lemniscal tract, plays an undetermined role in the total pain process since its transmission capacity is unaffected by anesthetic or analgesic drugs.

In order to determine the role played by these various ascending pathways in the perception of pain, we studied the behavior of cats in which some of the pathways had been selectively destroyed [*see illustration, page 307*]. We found that cats with lesions of the spinothalamic tract often failed to respond to normally painful stimuli, confirming earlier evidence that had demonstrated the importance of this pathway in the sensory pain process. But we found that it is not the only pathway involved. Cats with lesions in the central gray pathway also failed to respond to the stimuli. In contrast, cats with the lemniscal tract made inactive responded immediately to the stimuli.

To our surprise, the picture turned out to be even more complex than this. Lesions of the central tegmental tract had the opposite effect of making the cats excessively responsive to some kinds of painful stimuli, and many of these cats showed behavior suggesting "spontaneous pain" in the absence of external stimulation.

A recent development in the surgical control of pain in human patients lends striking confirmation to the results obtained in the cat study. Frank R. Ervin and Vernon H. Mark of the departments of psychiatry and neurosurgery at the Massachusetts General Hospital have found that patients suffering unbearable pain from cancer and other pathological sources may obtain excellent relief from pain after a small surgical lesion is made in that part of the human thalamus which receives fibers from the spinothalamic tract as well as from the pathways that stem from the reticular formation. If, however, the lesion is made just a few millimeters in front of this area, destroying the thalamic fibers of the lemniscal pathway, the experience of pain remains unchanged. Direct obser-

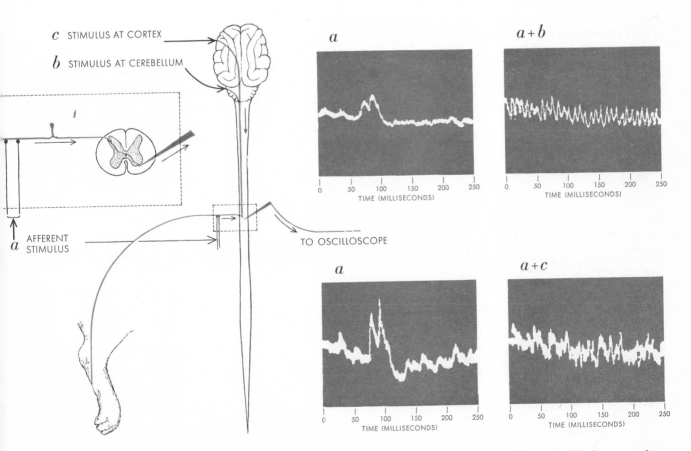

fiber entering the spinal cord is electrically stimulated directly (*a*). The signal passes through a pool of neurons and is recorded on the other side of the cord (whence it ascends to the brain), producing tracing *a*. If the cerebellum (*b*) or cortex (*c*) is stimulated simultaneously, the afferent signal is almost completely suppressed, as shown in tracings *a* + *b* and *a* + *c*. These experiments were performed at the School of Medicine of the University of California at Los Angeles by K.-E. Hagbarth and D. I. B. Kerr.

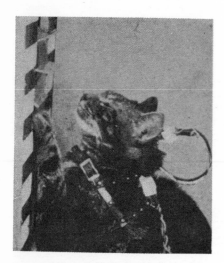

**STIMULATION OF BRAIN STEM** impels a cat to rotate a paddle wheel that turns off the weak electric stimulus. The stimulus was turned on between top and middle photographs. The cat's quickly learned behavior has all the characteristics of pain avoidance. These are frames from a motion picture made **by Neal E. Miller of Yale University.**

vations such as these on the sensory mechanisms of the pain process have provided us with valuable information on the nature of pain.

But we still cannot account for the complexity of many pain phenomena, especially bizarre pain syndromes sometimes encountered in hospital clinics. One in particular—phantom-limb pain— is both fascinating and terrible. In 1552 Ambroise Paré described it thus: "Verily it is a thing wondrous strange and prodigious, and which will scarce be credited, unless by such as have seen with their eyes, and heard with their ears, the patients who have many months after the cutting away of the leg, grievously complained that they yet felt exceeding great pain of that leg so cut off."

The majority of amputees report feeling a phantom limb soon after amputation and it may remain for years without bothering them. About 30 per cent, however, have the misfortune to develop pains in their phantom limbs, and in about 5 per cent the pain is severe. These pains may be occasional or continuous, but they are felt in definite parts of the phantom limb. W. K. Livingston reports the case of a young woman who described her phantom hand as being clenched, fingers bent over the thumb and digging into the palm of her hand, so that the whole hand became tired and painful. When she was able to open her phantom hand as a result of her physician's treatment, the pain vanished.

Phantom-limb pain tends to decrease and eventually disappear in most amputees. There are a few, however, for whom the pain increases in severity over the years. In addition, the disturbance spreads and other regions of the body may become so sensitized that merely touching them will evoke spasms of severe pain in the phantom limb. Even emotional upsets such as seeing a disturbing film may sharply increase the pain. Still worse, the conventional surgical procedures, such as cutting the spinothalamic tract, usually fail to bring permanent relief, so that these patients may undergo a series of such operations without any decrease in the severity of the pain. Phenomena such as these defy explanation in terms of our present physiological knowledge. A few psychiatrists have been tempted simply to label these amputees as neurotic, but the evidence argues against such an explanation for all cases.

So far we can only speculate on the nature of phantom-limb pain. We know that irritation of the nerves of the remaining part of the limb contributes to the pain process, since stimulation of

these nerves can trigger severe pain. But the spread of the trigger sites and the frequent failure of conventional surgical procedures make it clear that this is not the whole story. All the evidence suggests that the primary focus of physiological disturbance lies in the central nervous system itself. Livingston believes that the initial damage to the limb, or perhaps the trauma associated with its removal, disturbs the patterning of neural activity in the internuncial pools of the spinal cord, creating reverberating, abnormally patterned activity. Even minor irritations to the skin or nerves near the site of the operation can then feed into these active pools of neurons and keep them in an abnormal, disturbed state over periods of years. Im-

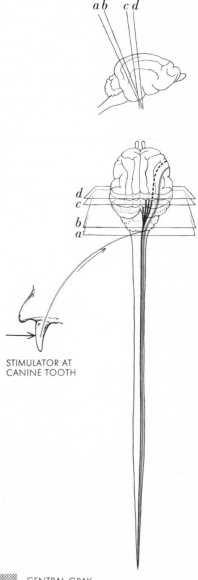

STIMULATOR AT CANINE TOOTH

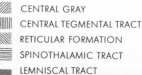

CENTRAL GRAY
CENTRAL TEGMENTAL TRACT
RETICULAR FORMATION
SPINOTHALAMIC TRACT
LEMNISCAL TRACT

pulse patterns that would normally be interpreted as touch may now trigger these neuron pools into greater activity, thereby sending volleys of abnormal patterns of impulses to the higher areas of the brain and bringing about the perception of pain. Although there is no direct evidence that the internuncial pools play this role in phantom-limb pain, the concept helps us to understand facts that are otherwise difficult to explain.

So far we have been discussing pain primarily as a sensory experience somewhat similar to sight or hearing. But there is something missing. Pain has a unique, distinctly unpleasant quality that wells up in consciousness and obliterates anything we may have been

thinking or doing at the time. It becomes overwhelming and demands immediate attention. Pain has a strong emotional quality that drives us into doing something about it. We seek desperately to stop the pain as quickly as we can by whatever means we can.

Introspectionist psychologists at the turn of the century made a sharp distinction between the sensory and the emotional, or affective, dimensions of pain. The psychologist Edward B. Titchener was convinced that there is a continuum of *feeling* in conscious experience, distinctly different from sensation, that ranges through all the degrees of pleasantness and unpleasantness. "The pain of a toothache," Titchener wrote, "is localized at a particular place, 'in the

tooth'; but the unpleasantness of it suffuses the whole of present experience, is as wide as consciousness. The word 'pain'... often means the whole toothache experience."

These two dimensions, the sensory and the affective, are brought clearly into focus by clinical studies on prefrontal lobotomy, a neurosurgical operation for intense pain in which the connections between the prefrontal lobes and the rest of the brain are severed. Typically, these patients report after the operation that they still have pain but it does not bother them; they simply no longer care about the pain and often forget it is there. When they are questioned more closely, they frequently say that they still have the "little" pain, but the "big" pain, the

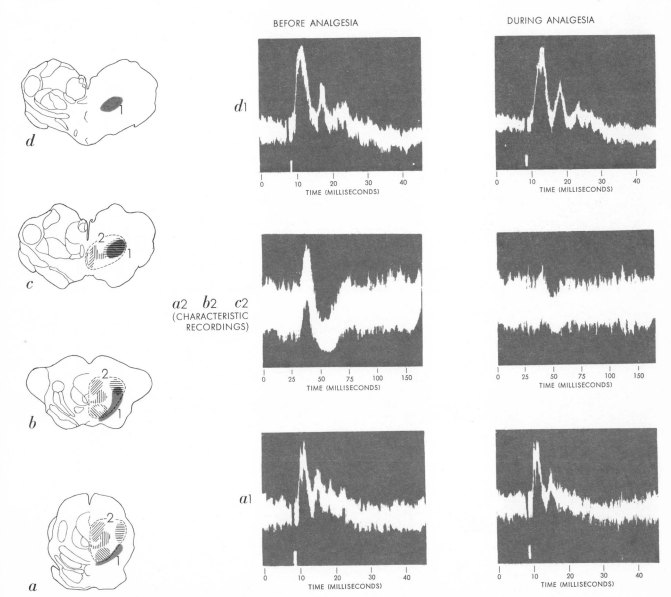

BEFORE ANALGESIA    DURING ANALGESIA

FIVE PATHWAYS in the brain stem transmit signals evoked by stimulating the nerve of a cat's tooth. The sections *a*, *b*, *c* and *d* show how the pathways progress through the midbrain and thalamus; two of the pathways, the spinothalamic and lemniscal, send projections to the cortex [see also illustration on next page]. An analgesic mixture of nitrous oxide and oxygen largely blocks the signals in four (2) of the five pathways. The signal is not blocked, however, in the lemniscal pathway (1), which projects to the cortex. These experiments were performed by D. I. B. Kerr, Frederick P. Haugen and the author at the University of Oregon Medical School.

suffering, the anguish are gone. Yet they complain vociferously about pinprick and mild burn. It is certain that the operation does not stop pain perception entirely, since the sensory component is still present. Its predominant effect appears to be on the emotional coloring of the total pain experience; the terribly unpleasant quality of the pain has been abolished.

How are we to account for these effects? It is known that prefrontal lobotomy lowers the anxiety associated with pain to a striking degree: the fear of death is greatly diminished as well as the patient's preoccupation with his painful disease. It is often suggested that the reduction of anxiety brings about a concomitant reduction of pain intensity; specifically that the brain's prefrontal lobes, which are presumably involved in higher psychological processes, fail to elaborate the sensory nerve patterns as they ascend from the source of the pain. Such an explanation is consistent with the perceptual approach to pain that we have been discussing.

But is it only this? The emotional quality of the pain experience and its remarkable capacity for acting as a drive are both so different from touch, warmth or cold that to explain its psychological and neural basis seems to require something more than different patterns of nerve impulses arriving at the higher sensory areas of the brain. We might infer that distinctly different parts of the brain are involved in addition to the sensory areas.

Where, then, do the streams of sensory nerve impulses go after they are transmitted through the lower portions of the brain? We know that the spinothalamic tract has a relay station in the thalamus and there is good evidence that at least a portion of its impulse patterns is transmitted upward to the sensory cortex. The central gray neurons and the central tegmental tract, however, make connection with other neural systems, so that impulse patterns produced by painful stimuli have access to large areas of the brain that lie beneath the cortex.

Various experiments suggest that some of these subcortical areas are particularly concerned with the "driving" or motivating aspects of behavior. Neal E. Miller and other investigators at Yale University have used implanted electrodes to make a systematic exploration of areas deep within the brains of cats and other animals. When certain areas are stimulated, the animals cry out and behave exactly as if they were in pain [see illustration, page 304]. To call these areas "pain centers" would be misleading, since the evidence we have been discussing points to a complex interaction of sensory and cognitive processes involving other major portions of the brain. But there can be little doubt that these subcortical areas make a major contribution to the total pain process. Is it possible that the activities in these areas provide the neural substrate for the affective, "driving" component of pain perception? There is great temptation to speculate that they do—but in fact we do not know. All we can say for the present is that the ascending sensory patterns arouse activities in the brain that somehow subserve the broad category

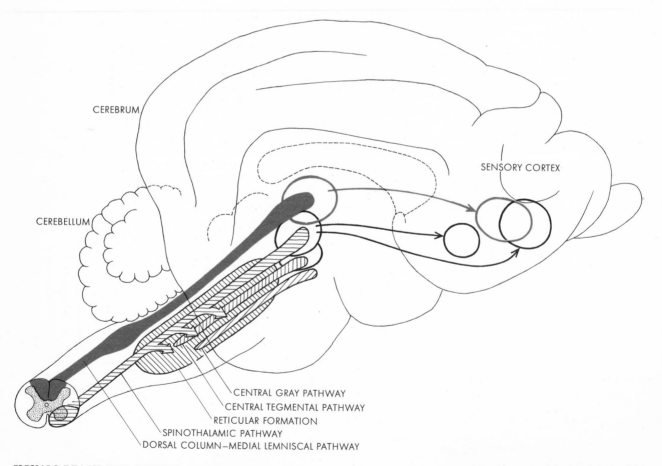

CEREBRUM

SENSORY CORTEX

CEREBELLUM

CENTRAL GRAY PATHWAY
CENTRAL TEGMENTAL PATHWAY
RETICULAR FORMATION
SPINOTHALAMIC PATHWAY
DORSAL COLUMN–MEDIAL LEMNISCAL PATHWAY

**SIGNALS REACH THE CORTEX** via projections from at least two of the five pathways ascending through the brain stem: the spinothalamic and the dorsal column–medial lemniscal pathways. Fibers from the former also penetrate the brain stem reticular formation, which is capable of arousing the whole cortex into activity. Surgical experiments [see illustration on opposite page] and analgesia experiments, suggest that pain perception is associated least with signals reaching cortex from lemniscal pathway.

of perceptions we describe as "pain."

It is now almost eight years since W. K. Livingston attempted to answer in these pages the question "What Is Pain?" [presently available as the Offprint #407]. He argued against the classical conception that the intensity of pain sensation is always proportional to the stimulus. He proposed instead that pain, like all perceptions, is "subjective, individual and modified by degrees of attention, emotional states and the conditioning influence of past experience." Since that time we have moved still further away from the classical assumptions of specific "pain receptors," "pain pathways" and a "pain center" in the brain, all of which implied that stimulation of a "pain receptor" will invariably produce pain, that the pain will have only one specific quality and that it can vary only in intensity.

Pain, we now believe, refers to a category of complex experiences, not to a single sensation produced by a specific stimulus. In her essay "On Being Ill" Virginia Woolf touches on precisely this point. "English," she writes, "which can express the thoughts of Hamlet and the tragedy of Lear, has no words for the shiver and the headache.... The merest schoolgirl, when she falls in love, has Shakespeare and Keats to speak for her; but let a sufferer try to describe a pain in his head to a doctor and language at once runs dry."

We are beginning to recognize the poverty of language for describing the many different qualities of sensory and affective experience that we simply categorize under the broad heading of "pain." We are more and more aware of the plasticity and modifiability of events occurring in the central nervous system. We are aware that in the lower part of the brain, at least, the patterns of impulses produced by painful stimuli travel over multiple pathways going to widespread regions of the brain and not along a single path going to a "pain center." The psychological evidence strongly supports the view of pain as a perceptual experience whose quality and intensity is influenced by the unique past history of the individual, by the meaning he gives to the pain-producing situation and by his "state of mind" at the moment. We believe that all these factors play a role in determining the actual patterns of nerve impulses ascending to the brain and traveling within the brain itself. In this way pain becomes a function of the whole individual, including his present thoughts and fears as well as his hopes for the future.

HEAT            PINPRICK

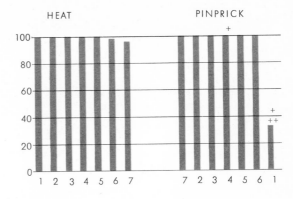

PATHWAY INACTIVATED

LEMNISCAL

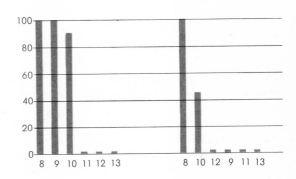

SPINOTHALAMIC

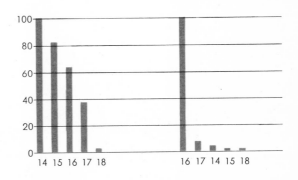

CENTRAL GRAY

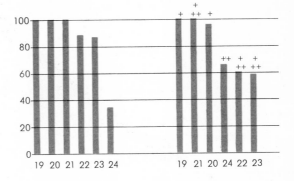

CENTRAL TEGMENTAL

SURGICAL INACTIVATION OF BRAIN STEM PATHWAYS gives added evidence of complexity of pain perception. The surgery was performed on cats that had been trained to jump out of a box to avoid having their paws pricked or burned. Brain sections at left indicate the pathways inactivated in various animals. After surgery the animals were retested. The code number of each animal appears at the bottom of the bar graphs. Height of bar indicates percentage of avoidance responses when paws were pricked or heated. The marks + and ++ indicate, respectively, animals that became hyperresponsive to pain or that gave evidence of "spontaneous" pain. Inactivation of the spinothalamic and central gray pathways reduced the behavioral evidence of pain; inactivation of the lemniscal path had little or no effect. Inactivation of the central tegmental pathway seemed to heighten pain sensitivity.

# 38

# THE ORIGIN OF FORM PERCEPTION

ROBERT L. FANTZ                                      May 1961

Long before an infant can explore his surroundings with hands and feet he is busy exploring it with his eyes. What goes on in the infant's mind as he stares, blinks, looks this way and that? Does he sense only a chaotic patchwork of color and brightness or does he perceive and differentiate among distinctive forms? The question has always fascinated philosophers and scientists, for it bears on the nature and origin of knowledge. At issue is the perennial question of nature v. nurture. On one side is the nativist, who believes that the infant has a wide range of innate visual capacities and predilections, which have evolved in animals over millions of years, and that these give a primitive order and meaning to the world from the "first look." On the other side is the extreme empiricist, who holds that the infant learns to see and to use what he sees only by trial and error or association, starting, as John Locke put it, with a mind like a blank slate.

It has long been known that very young infants can see light, color and movement. But it is often argued that they cannot respond to such stimuli as shape, pattern, size or solidity; in short, that they cannot perceive form. This position is the last stronghold of the empiricist, and it has been a hard one to attack. How is one to know what an infant sees? My colleagues and I have recently developed an experimental method of finding out. We have already disposed of the basic question, that of whether babies can perceive form at all. They can, at least to some degree, although it appears that neither the view of the simple nativist nor that of the simple empiricist tells the whole story. Now we are investigating the further question of how and when infants use their capacity to perceive form to confer order and meaning on their environment.

The technique grew out of studies with lower animals, which are of importance in themselves. They were undertaken in 1951 at the University of Chicago with newly hatched chicks. Paradoxically, chicks can "tell" more directly what they see than higher animals can. Soon after they break out of the shell they go about the business of finding things to peck at and eat. Their purposeful, visually dominated behavior is ideally suited for observation and experiment.

We presented the chicks with a number of small objects of different shapes.

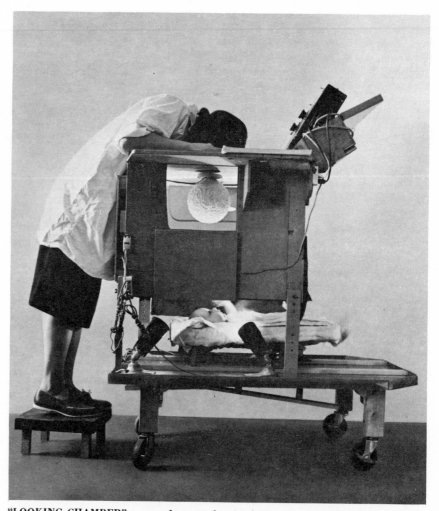

"LOOKING CHAMBER" was used to test the visual interests of chimpanzee and human infants. Here a human infant lies on a crib in the chamber, looking at objects hung from the ceiling. The observer, watching through a peephole, records the attention given each object.

Each object was enclosed in a clear plastic container to eliminate the possible influence of touch, smell or taste, but this did not prevent the chicks from pecking at preferred forms for hours on end. An electrical circuit attached to each container recorded the number of pecks at it.

More than 1,000 chicks were tested on some 100 objects. To exclude any opportunity for learning, the chicks were hatched in darkness and tested on their first exposure to light, before they had had any experience with real food. Presented with eight objects of graded angularity, from a sphere to a pyramid, the subjects pecked 10 times oftener at the sphere than they did at the pyramid. Among the flat forms, circles were preferred to triangles regardless of comparative size; among circles, those of ⅛-inch diameter drew the most attention. In a test of the effect of three-dimensionality the chicks consistently selected a sphere over a flat disk.

The results provided conclusive evidence that the chick has an innate ability to perceive shape, three-dimensionality and size. Furthermore, the chick uses the ability in a "meaningful" way by selecting, without learning, those objects most likely to be edible: round, three-dimensional shapes about the size of grain or seeds. Other birds exhibit similar visual capacity. For example, N. Tinbergen of the University of Oxford found selective pecking by newly hatched herring gulls. These chicks prefer shapes resembling that of the bill of the parent bird, from which they are fed [see "The Evolution of Behavior in Gulls," by N. Tinbergen, Offprint #456, for an account of his work].

Of course, what holds true for birds does not necessarily apply to human beings. The inherent capacity for form perception that has developed in birds may have been lost somewhere along the evolutionary branch leading to the primates, unlikely as it seems. Or, more plausibly, the primate infant may require a period of postnatal development to reach the level of function of the comparatively precocious chick.

When we set out to determine the visual abilities of helpless infants, the only indicator we could find was the activity of the eyes themselves. If an infant consistently turns its gaze toward some forms more often than toward others, it must be able to perceive form. Working on this premise, we developed a visual-interest test, using as our first subjects infant chimpanzees at the Yerkes Laboratories of Primate Biology in Orange Park, Fla.

A young chimpanzee lay on its back in a comfortable crib inside a "looking chamber" of uniform color and illumination. We attached to the ceiling of the chamber pairs of test objects, slightly separated from each other. They were exposed to view, alternately at right and left, in a series of short periods. Through a peephole in the ceiling we could see tiny images of the objects mirrored in the subjects' eyes. When the image of

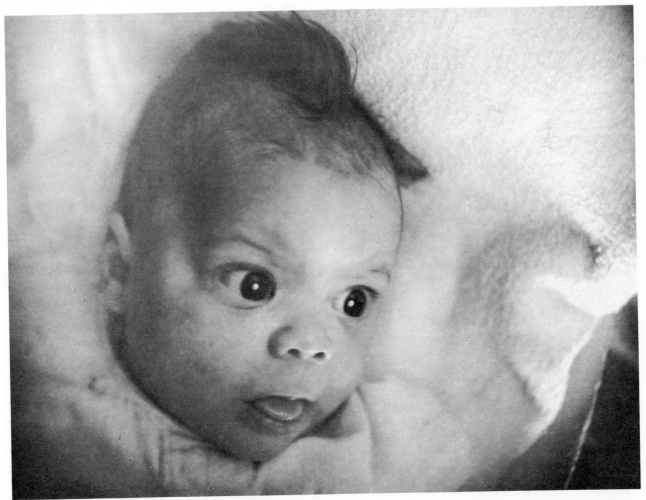

VISUAL INTEREST in various shapes was determined by noting reflections in the subject's eyes. In this case, with the reflection over the center of the infant's eye, the reflected object is being fixated, or looked at directly. (Because this young infant's binocular coordination is poor, only the right eye is fixating the object.) The length of each such fixation was recorded electrically.

**PATTERN PREFERENCE** of newly hatched chicks is studied by recording their pecks at each of a number of different shapes in plastic containers set into the wall of a test box.

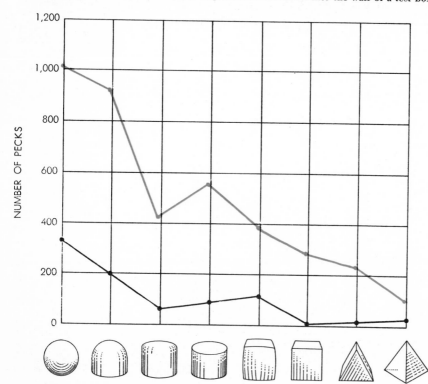

**PREFERENCE FOR ROUNDNESS** is shown by this record of total pecks by 112 chicks at the eight test objects shown across the bottom of the chart. The results are for the chicks' first 10 minutes (*black line*) and first 40 minutes (*colored line*) of visual experience.

one of the objects was at the center of the eye, over the pupil, we knew the chimpanzee was looking directly at it. The experimenter recorded on an electric timer the amount of attention given each target. The results were then analyzed to determine their statistical significance. Our first subject was a five-month-old chimpanzee. Later we followed a chimpanzee from birth, keeping it in darkness except during the tests. In both cases we found a definite preference for certain objects, indicating an inborn ability to distinguish among them.

Turning to human infants, we made no major change in our procedure except that we did not tamper with their everyday environment. The experiments did not disturb the infants but they did demand great patience of the investigators. Human infants are more rapidly bored than chimpanzees and they tend to go to sleep.

In the first experiment we tested 30 infants, aged one to 15 weeks, at weekly intervals. Four pairs of test patterns were presented in random sequence. In decreasing order of complexity they were: horizontal stripes and a bull's-eye design, a checkerboard and two sizes of plain square, a cross and a circle, and two identical triangles. The total time spent looking at the various pairs differed sharply, the more complex pairs drawing the greater attention. Moreover, the relative attractiveness of the two members of a pair depended on the presence of a pattern difference. There were strong preferences between stripes and bull's-eye and between checkerboard and square. Neither the cross and circle nor the two triangles aroused a significant differential interest. The differential response to pattern was shown at all ages tested, indicating that it was not the result of a learning process. The direction of preference between stripes and bull's-eye, on the other hand, changed at two months of age, due either to learning or to maturation.

Later we learned that a Swiss pediatrician, F. Stirnimann, had obtained similar results with still younger infants. He held cards up to the eyes of infants one to 14 days old and found that patterned cards were of more interest than those with plain colors.

Clearly some degree of form perception is innate. This, however, does not dispose of the role of physiological growth or of learning in the further development of visual behavior. Accordingly we turned our attention to the influence of these factors.

By demonstrating the existence of form perception in very young infants we had already disproved the widely held notion that they are anatomically incapable of seeing anything but blobs of light and dark. Nevertheless, it seems to be true that the eye, the visual nerve-pathways and the visual part of the brain are poorly developed at birth. If this is so, then the acuteness of vision—the ability to distinguish detail in patterns—should increase as the infant matures.

To measure the change in visual acuity we presented infants in the looking chamber with a series of patterns composed of black and white stripes, each pattern paired with a gray square of equal brightness. The width of the stripes was decreased in graded steps from one pattern to the next. Since we already knew that infants tend to look longer and more frequently at a patterned object than at a plain one, the width of the stripes of the finest pattern that was preferred to gray would provide an index to visual acuity. In this modified version the visual-interest test again solved the difficulties involved in getting infants to reveal what they see.

The width of the finest stripes that could be distinguished turned out to decrease steadily with increasing age during the first half-year of life. By six months babies could see stripes 1/64 inch wide at a distance of 10 inches—a visual angle of five minutes of arc, or 1/12 degree. (The adult standard is one minute of arc.) Even when still less than a month old, infants were able to perceive ⅛-inch stripes at 10 inches, corresponding to a visual angle of a little less than one degree. This is poor performance compared to that of an adult, but it is a far cry from a complete lack of ability to perceive pattern.

The effects of maturation on visual acuity are relatively clear and not too hard to measure. The problem of learning is more subtle. Other investigators have shown that depriving animals of patterned visual stimuli for a period after birth impairs their later visual performance, especially in form perception [see "Arrested Vision," by Austin H. Riesen, for further details; Offprint #408]. Learned behavior is particularly vulnerable, but even innate responses are affected. For example, chicks kept in darkness for several weeks after hatching lose the ability to peck at food.

Research is now under way at Western Reserve University on this perplexing problem. We have raised monkeys in darkness for periods varying from one to 11 weeks. In general, the longer the period of deprivation, the poorer the performance when the animals were finally exposed to light and the more time they required to achieve normal responses. When first brought into the light, the older infant monkeys bumped into things, fell off tables, could not locate objects visually—for all practical purposes they were blind. It sometimes took weeks for them to "learn to see."

Monkeys kept a shorter time in the dark usually showed good spatial orientation in a few hours or days. Moreover, they showed normal interest in patterned objects, whereas the animals deprived of light for longer periods seemed more interested in color, brightness and size.

These results cannot be explained by innate capacity, maturation or learning alone. If form perception were wholly innate, it would be evident without experience at any age, and visual deprivation would have no effect. If maturation were the controlling factor, younger infant animals would be inferior rather than superior to older ones with or without visual experience. If form perception were entirely learned, the same period of experience would be required regardless of age and length of deprivation.

Instead there appears to be a complex interplay of innate ability, maturation

**TEST OBJECTS** included smooth and textured disks and spheres (*upper left*) to check interest in solidity. Attention to faces was tested with three patterns at lower left. The six round patterns at the right included (*top to bottom, left to right*) a face, a piece of printed matter, a bull's-eye, yellow, white and red disks. Round objects are six inches in diameter; "faces," nine inches long.

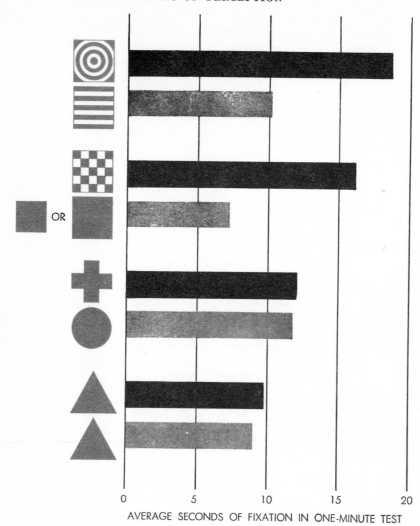

AVERAGE SECONDS OF FIXATION IN ONE-MINUTE TEST

**INTEREST IN FORM** was proved by infants' reactions to various pairs of patterns (*left*) presented together. (The small and large plain squares were used alternately.) The more complex pairs received the most attention, and within each of these pairs differential interest was based on pattern differences. These results are for 22 infants in 10 weekly tests.

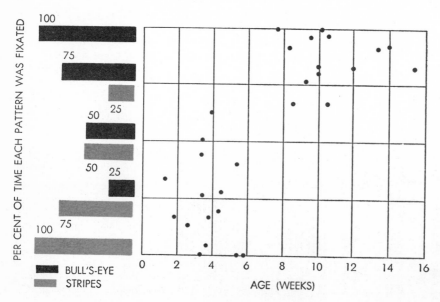

**REVERSAL OF INTEREST** from the striped pattern to the bull's-eye was apparent at two months of age. Each dot is for a single infant's first test session. It shows the time spent looking at the bull's-eye and at the stripes as a per cent of the time spent looking at both.

and learning in the molding of visual behavior, operating in this manner: there is a critical age for the development of a given visual response when the visual, mental and motor capacities are ready to be used and under normal circumstances will be used together. At that time the animal will either show the response without experience or will learn it readily. If the response is not "imprinted" at the critical age for want of visual stimulus, development proceeds abnormally, without the visual component. Presented with the stimulus later on, the animal learns to respond, if it responds at all, only with extensive experience and training. This explanation, if verified by further studies, would help to reconcile the conflicting claims of the nativist and the empiricist on the origin of visual perception.

To return to human infants, the work described so far does not answer the second question posed earlier in this article: whether or not the infant's innate capacity for form perception introduces a measure of order and meaning into what would otherwise be a chaotic jumble of sensations. An active selection process is necessary to sort out these sensations and make use of them in behavior. In the case of chicks such a process is apparent in the selection of forms likely to be edible.

In the world of the infant, people have an importance that is perhaps comparable to the importance of grain in the chick's world. Facial pattern is the most distinctive aspect of a person, the most reliable for distinguishing a human being from other objects and for identifying him. So a facelike pattern might be expected to bring out selective perception in an infant if anything could.

We tested infants with three flat objects the size and shape of a head. On one we painted a stylized face in black on a pink background, on the second we rearranged the features in a scrambled pattern, and on the third we painted a solid patch of black at one end with an area equal to that covered by all the features. We made the features large enough to be perceived by the youngest baby, so acuity of vision was not a factor. The three objects, paired in all possible combinations, were shown to 49 infants from four days to six months old.

The results were about the same for all age levels: the infants looked mostly at the "real" face, somewhat less often at the scrambled face, and largely ignored the control pattern. The degree of preference for the "real" face to the other one was not large, but it was

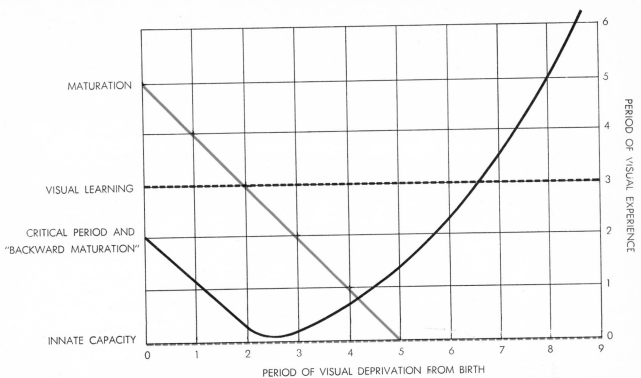

**HYPOTHETICAL RESULTS** that might be expected if any one developmental factor operated alone are plotted. The horizontal axis shows the period of rearing without visual experience; the vertical axis, the time subsequently required in the light until a given response is shown. Units of time are arbitrary. If innate capacity alone were effective, the response would always come without any experience (*broken colored line*). If maturation were necessary, the response would not be shown before a certain age, in this case five units, regardless of deprivation (*solid colored line*). If learning alone were operative, the required amount of experience would be constant (*broken black line*). Actually tests with chicks and monkey infants suggest the result shown by the solid black curve: after a short period of maturation, a "critical period" is reached when innate capacity can be manifested; more deprivation brings on "backward maturation," in which more and more experience is required before a response is shown.

consistent among individual infants, especially the younger ones. The experiment suggested that there is an unlearned, primitive meaning in the form perception of infants as well as of chicks.

Further support for the idea was obtained when we offered our infant subjects a choice between a solid sphere and a flat circle of the same diameter. When the texture and shading clearly differentiated the sphere from the circle —in other words, when there was a noticeable difference in pattern—the solid form was the more interesting to infants from one to six months old. This unlearned selection of a pattern associated with a solid object gives the infant a basis for perceiving depth.

The last experiment to be considered is a dramatic demonstration of the interest in pattern in comparison to color and brightness. This time there were six test objects: flat disks six inches in diameter. Three were patterned—a face, a bull's-eye and a patch of printed matter. Three were plain—red, fluorescent yellow and white. We presented them, against a blue background, one at a time in varied sequence and timed the length of the first glance at each.

The face pattern was overwhelmingly the most interesting, followed by the printing and the bull's-eye. The three brightly colored plain circles trailed far behind and received no first choices. There was no indication that the interest in pattern was secondary or acquired.

What makes pattern so intrinsically interesting to young infants? It seems to me that the answer must lie in the uses of vision for the child and adult.

One of these functions is the recognition of objects under various conditions. The color and brightness of objects

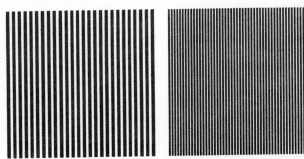

**VISUAL ACUITY** was tested with these stripes: 1/8, 1/16, 1/32 and 1/64 inch wide. Each pattern was displayed with a gray square of equal brightness 10 inches from the infants' eyes. The finest pattern consistently preferred to gray showed how narrow a stripe the infant could perceive. Infants under a month old could see the 1/8-inch stripes and the six-month-olds could see 1/64-inch stripes.

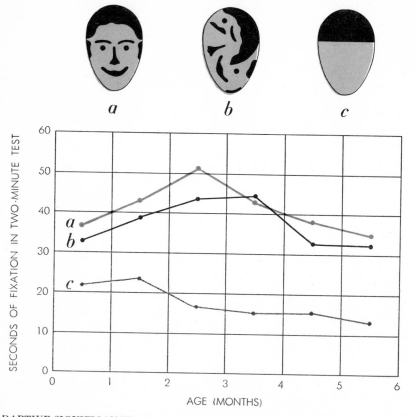

change with illumination; apparent size changes with distance; outline changes with point of view; binocular depth perception is helpful only at short range. But the pattern of an object—the texture, the arrangement of details, the complexity of contours—can be relied on for identification under diverse conditions.

A good example is social perception. As noted earlier, the general configuration of a face identifies a human being to an infant. At a later age a specific person is recognized primarily by more precise perception of facial pattern. Still later, subtle details of facial expression tell the child whether a person is happy or sad, pleased or displeased, friendly or unfriendly.

Another important function of vision is to provide orientation in space. For this purpose James J. Gibson of Cornell University has shown clearly the importance of a specific type of pattern: surface texture. For example, texture indicates a solid surface, whereas untextured light usually indicates air or water. Gradual changes in texture show whether a surface is vertical or horizontal or oblique, flat or curved or angular—and therefore indicate whether it can be walked on, walked around or climbed over. Discontinuities in texture mark the edges of objects and abrupt changes in surfaces.

**ADAPTIVE SIGNIFICANCE** of form perception was indicated by the preference that infants showed for a "real" face (*a*) over a scrambled face (*b*), and for both over a control (*c*). The results charted here show the average time scores for infants at various ages when presented with the three face-shaped objects paired in all the possible combinations.

From these few examples there can be no question of the importance of visual pattern in everyday life. It is therefore reasonable to suppose that the early interest of infants in form and pattern in general, as well as in particular kinds of pattern, play an important role in the development of behavior by focusing attention on stimuli that will later have adaptive significance.

Further research is necessary to pin down this and other implications more concretely, but the results to date do require the rejection of the view that the newborn infant or animal must start from scratch to learn to see and to organize patterned stimulation. Lowly chicks as well as lofty primates perceive and respond to form without experience if given the opportunity at the appropriate stage of development. Innate knowledge of the environment is demonstrated by the preference of newly hatched chicks for forms likely to be edible and by the interest of young infants in kinds of form that will later aid in object recognition, social responsiveness and spatial orientation. This primitive knowledge provides a foundation for the vast accumulation of knowledge through experience.

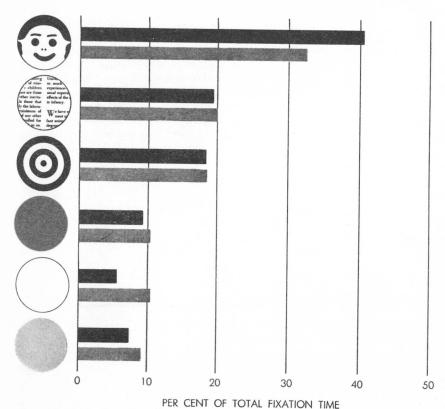

**IMPORTANCE OF PATTERN** rather than color or brightness was illustrated by the response of infants to a face, a piece of printed matter, a bull's-eye and plain red, white and yellow disks. Even the youngest infants preferred patterns. Black bars show the results for infants from two to three months old; gray bars, for infants more than three months old.

# 39

# STABILIZED IMAGES ON THE RETINA

ROY M. PRITCHARD                                                   June 1961

In normal vision the eye is constantly in motion. Small involuntary movements persist even when the eye is "fixed" on a stationary object. As a result the image of the object on the retina of the eye is kept in constant motion. One movement of the eyeball makes the image drift slowly away from the center of the fovea, the region of maximum visual acuity in which the cone receptor cells are most densely concentrated. The drifting motion terminates in a flick that brings the image back toward the center of the fovea. Superimposed on the drift motion is a tremor with frequencies up to 150 cycles per second and an amplitude of about half the diameter of a single cone receptor.

These three involuntary movements of the eyeball, all much smaller than the voluntary movements involved in looking at the visual world or in reading, have been known to physiologists for many years. During the past decade Lorrin A. Riggs of Brown University and R. W. Ditchburn of the University of Reading in England succeeded in measuring them with great accuracy. Though the movements cannot be stopped without incapacitating the subject or endangering the eye, Ditchburn and Riggs found ways to circumvent them and so make an image stand still on the retina. They were thereby able to show that the motion of the image plays a significant role in the sensory function of the eye. When an image is stabilized on the retina by one means or another, it soon fades and disappears. Just how this happens is not yet completely understood.

It was also observed, however, that the stabilized image regenerates after a time and again becomes visible to the subject in whole or in part. The image— or fragments of it—alternately fades and regenerates over prolonged periods of observation. This finding has attracted the attention of psychologists interested in the perceptual aspects of vision, those aspects which involve the functioning of the brain as well as the cells of the retina. At McGill University, D. O. Hebb, Woodburn Heron and I have been investigating the stabilized visual image as a source of data for the formulation of a comprehensive theory of visual perception. We have found that the fragmentation, or the alternate partial fading and partial regeneration, of the image is related to the character and content of the image itself.

Our evidence supports to some extent the "cell assembly" idea that experience is needed to develop the innate potential of perception: a pattern is perceived through the combination in the brain of separate neural impressions that have been established there and correspond to various learned elements. But the evidence also sustains the Gestalt, or holistic, theory, which holds that perception is innately determined: a pattern is perceived directly as a whole and without synthesis of parts, a product of unlearned capacity to perceive "form," "wholeness" and "organization." It is becoming apparent that the complete explanation of perception must be sought in a resolution of these opposing views.

We stabilize the image by attaching the target to be viewed to the eyeball itself. The device we use for this purpose consists of a tight-fitting contact lens on which is mounted a tiny, self-contained optical projector [see *illustration on the next page*]. With the subject lying on a couch, the device is set in place on the cornea and focused to project an image on the retina. The experimenter changes the tar-get film from time to time, and he keeps a continuous record of the subject's report of what he sees.

What the subject sees, before fading sets in, is an image located at apparent infinity and subtending a visual angle of two degrees in a patch of light that subtends an angle of five degrees in the surrounding darkness. Provided that the contact lens does not slip on the cornea, the image remains fixed on the retina and does not move with movement of the eyeball.

After a few seconds of viewing, the image disappears progressively and bit by bit, leaving a structureless gray field of light. Later this gray field may darken, and with complete loss of sensation of light the field becomes intensely black. When the image disappears or reappears the uninitiated subject at first rotates his eyes in an effort to bring the image or a center of interest in the image back to the center of the fovea. These movements are, of course, futile because they cannot change the geometrical relationship between the target, the lens of the eye and the retina. Soon the subject learns to view the image passively and discovers that he can still transfer his attention from point to point over the limited visual field.

In general we have found that the image of a simple figure, such as a single line, vanishes rapidly and then reappears as a complete image. A more complex target, such as the profile of a face or a pattern of curlicues, may similarly disappear and reappear as a whole; on the other hand, it may vanish in fragments, with one or more of its parts fading independently. We have found in addition that the length of time an image persists is also a function of its complexity. A single line may be visible for only 10 per cent of the aggregate view-

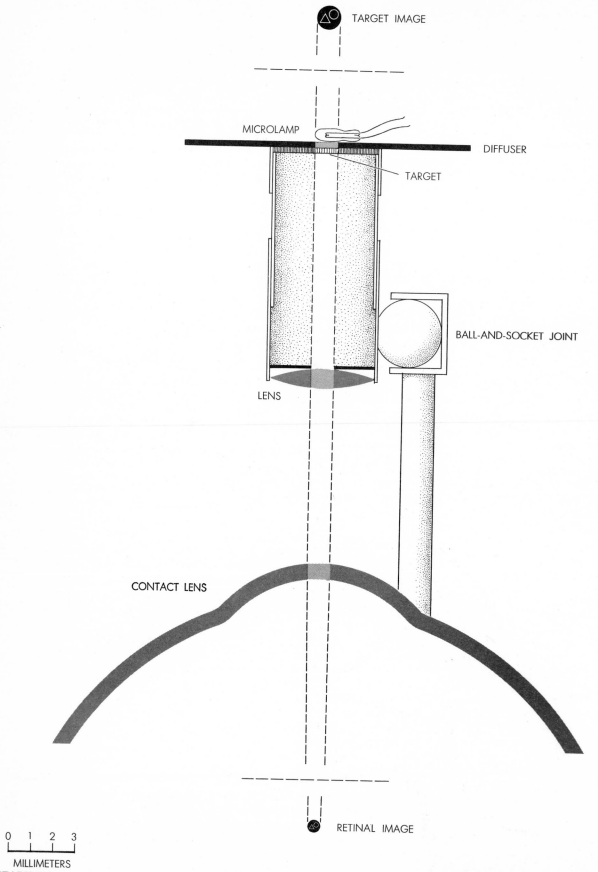

TARGET IMAGE

MICROLAMP

DIFFUSER

TARGET

BALL-AND-SOCKET JOINT

LENS

CONTACT LENS

RETINAL IMAGE

0  1  2  3
MILLIMETERS

**STABILIZED-IMAGE DEVICE** is a tiny projector mounted on a contact lens worn by the subject. The contact lens moves with every movement of the eyeball; so, therefore, does the projector, and as a result the target image (*at top of illustration*) is kept fixed at one point on the retina (*as suggested at bottom of illustration*). The convex lens focuses parallel rays of light on the retina, so the target is viewed by the subject as if it were at an infinite distance. The entire optical system weighs only .25 gram.

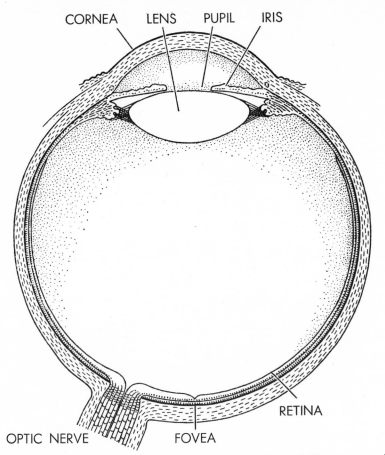

HUMAN EYE, seen here in horizontal cross section, works much like a camera. Light entering through the pupil is focused by the lens upon the retina's light-sensitive receptor cells, from which impulses travel via the optic nerve to the brain. The fovea, the area of most acute vision, is 1.5 millimeters in diameter and subtends a visual angle of five degrees.

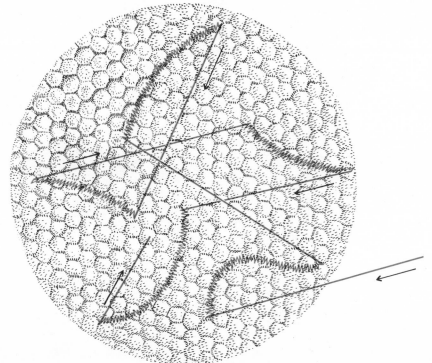

EYE MOVEMENTS that are halted in stabilized vision normally carry an image across the receptors of the retina as shown here. The three movements are a drift (*curved lines*) away from the center of vision, a faster flick (*straight lines*) back toward the center and a high-frequency tremor superimposed on the drift. The magnitude of all these movements is very small; the diameter of the patch of the fovea shown above is only .05 millimeter.

ing time, whereas a more complex figure may remain visible in whole or in part for as much as 80 per cent of the time.

The contrasting manner in which complex images fade and regenerate lends support to the role of learning in perception. For example, the figure of the human profile invariably fades and regenerates in meaningful units. The front of the face, the top of the head, the eye and the ear come and go as recognizable entities, separately and in various combinations. In contrast, on first presentation a meaningless pattern of curlicues is described as extremely "active"; the individual elements fade and regenerate rapidly, and the subject sees almost every configuration that can be derived from the original figure. After prolonged viewing, however, certain combinations of curlicues become dominant and these then disappear and reappear as units. The newly formed groupings persist for longer periods than other combinations, and the figure can no longer be considered unorganized and meaningless.

In the cell-assembly approach to a theory of perception these observations are explained in terms of "perceptual elements," as opposed to purely sensory elements. The "organized," "meaningful" or "recognizable" parts of the image correspond to perceptual elements previously learned or established by experience. The parts of the human profile would thus function as perceptual elements at the outset in the behavior of the stabilized image. Given time for learning, parts of the originally meaningless curlicue pattern become recognizable in turn and operate as perceptual elements. These elements may be excited, it is argued, by the minimum retinal stimulation provided by the stabilized image. To evoke and maintain the image of the entire figure would require the additional information normally supplied by the movement of the image across the retinal receptors.

This interpretation gains additional support from what subjects report about the stabilized images of monograms that combine such symbols as the letters *H* and *B*. One or the other letter, or a fragment such as *P*, constitutes the unit that is perceived from one period to the next, with periods of complete fade-out intervening. When entire words are presented, the partial fragmentation of letters can cause different words to be perceived [*see bottom illustration on the next page*]. In a figure that presents a meaningful symbol such as *B* obscured by hatching lines, the subject sees either the intact *B* or the hatching lines independently. He may also on occasion see the two elements together, but then the *B* appears to float in a plane in front of the one containing the hatching lines. There is nothing haphazard about the fading of such figures, and these effects cannot be attributed to random fluctuation of threshold in various parts of the retina. Even if such fluctuation is thought to occur in the retinal system, the organized or meaningful unit remains visible longer than the unorganized one, in keeping with the presumed importance of learning in visual perception.

But the Gestalt psychologist can argue that it is unnecessary to bring learning and experience into the explanation of these effects. The same effects show up in experiments with meaningless or only semimeaningful figures and can be explained in terms of the Gestalt concept of perception as a process that works by "the whole." If an irregular shape, like that of an amoeba, is obscured by hatching lines, for example, the subject may report the same unitary and separate fading of the amoeba shape and of the hatching lines that he reports in the case of a letter of the alphabet. The two parts of the complete figure may also appear separated in different planes. More commonly in this case, however, parts of both the amoeba shape and the obscuring lines disappear together, and the remaining elements amalgamate to form a new composite figure. The hybrid is a more compact, tidy figure, with fewer disrupting elements.

When the amoeba shape is presented alone, parts of the figure tend to disappear. One or more of the bulges in the figure fade from view, and a line or lines are hallucinated to seal off the gaps produced by their disappearance. The limb or limbs that fade are invariably the grosser or more distorted features of the figure, and their disappearance, together with the closures, produces a "better" or more rounded figure. Any other comparatively irregular or jagged figure similarly appears unstable on first

**STABILIZED IMAGES** typically fade as in the illustrations on this and the following two pages. The parts of a profile drawing that stay visible are invariably specific features or groups of features, such as the front of the face or the top of the head.

**MEANINGLESS CURLICUES** first come and go in random sequence. But after a while small groups of curlicues organized in recognizable patterns start to behave as units. This suggests that they have themselves become meaningful perceptual elements.

**HB H B 3 4**

**MONOGRAM** formed of the letters *H* and *B* also seems to illustrate the importance of elements that are meaningful because of past experience. When the monogram breaks up it is the recognizable letters and numbers within it that come successively into view.

**BEER    PEER    PEEP    BEE    BE**

**WORDS** containing other words behave in much the same manner as the monogram. Here, for example, the subject sees new words made up of letters and parts of letters in the original. He is far less likely to report seeing meaningless groups of letters such as *EER*.

viewing. Its individual elements come and go until the holistic "editing" process reduces it to a more rounded configuration. A smooth, rounded figure, in contrast, appears more stable at the outset and tends to operate more as a whole in the alternate process of fading and regeneration.

As Gestalt theory would predict, contiguity and similarity strongly determine the functioning of the groups as entities isolated from the total figure. A target consisting of rows of small squares usually fades to leave one whole row—horizontal, diagonal or vertical—visible. Similarly a random collection of dots will fade to leave only those dots which lie approximately in a line, and it is the disappearance of the remainder that reveals this linear association. At the same time it must be emphasized that the original figure as well as each configuration that can be derived from it may function as a single unit, disappearing and reappearing as a whole.

Our experiments with stabilized images have thus produced evidence to sustain both of the major theoretical approaches to visual perception, which have for so long been considered mutually exclusive. It may be, however, that the two concepts are really complementary. As in the historic clash of the wave and the particle concepts in physics, the apparent opposition may arise solely from a difference in approach to the same problem. We have performed a number of experiments that conform equally well to both interpretations. This supports our expectation that a modern theory of perception will eventually result from a mating of the two systems.

In experiments with simple straight-line figures the cell-assembly approach is supported by the observation that the line is the apparent unit of perception just as the line is the unit of structure in the figure. It is always the whole line that fades or reappears, independently or in association with others, and the breaking, when fading occurs, is always at the intersection of lines. In fact, the overwhelmingly independent action of

OBSCURING LINES drawn over a figure act in various ways. In the case of the B, the lines often drop into a plane behind the meaningful letter. But lines over a less meaningful amoeba shape usually combine with the amoeba to form a more compact figure.

AMOEBA SHAPE standing alone usually fades by losing one or more bulges. What fades, as in this case, is always the most distorted feature, and it is replaced by a new closure "ghosted" by the subject and tending to form a more symmetrical and rounded figure.

LINES act independently in stabilized vision, with breakage in the fading figure always at an intersection of lines. Adjacent or parallel lines may operate as units. This independent action of lines tends to support the cell-assembly theory of perception.

PLANES operate as units in three-dimensional figures. In this Necker cube (which gives an illusion of reversing in stabilized as well as in normal vision) a line may act alone. But usually lines defining a plane operate together, leaving parallel planes.

lines makes inevitable the inclusion of some cell-assembly concepts in any complete theory of perception.

In a figure composed of a circle and a triangle, either the circle or the triangle may fade to leave the other visible. One could take this independent action of meaningful figures as evidence for the role of learning in perception. On the other hand, the Gestalt psychologist can just as readily explain the unitary action of the circle or triangle as evidence of the behavior of wholes.

But the fading process may also dissect the figure in other ways—for example, it may leave only one side of the triangle and the segment of the circle closest or most nearly parallel to it in view. Gestalt theory explains this report by the so-called field effect. The minimal sensory stimulus provided by the stabilized image is said to excite a perceptual response that goes well beyond the region of actual stimulation. In straight-line figures, furthermore, there is a tendency for noncontiguous parallel lines to operate together, and lines of the Necker cube [*see bottom illustration on preceding page*] usually vanish to leave parallel planes visible in space, with one of the planes in advance of the other. These observations can also be advanced as evidence of a field effect.

Most figures are seen as three-dimensional when viewed as a stabilized image. Most line drawings appear at some stage as "wires" suspended in space. The small squares in a repetitive pattern are perceived as protrusions or depressions. And a simple hexagon has been reported to be the outline of a cube in three dimensions that "reverses" in the same manner as the Necker cube.

In the case of figures drawn in solid tones as distinguished from those drawn in outline, the behavior of the stabilized image seems more consistent with cell-assembly theory. The corner now replaces the line as the unit of independent action. A solid square will fade from its center, and the fading will obliterate first one and then another corner, leaving the remaining corners sharply outlined and isolated in space. Regeneration

**LINEAR ORGANIZATION** is emphasized by the fading of this target composed of rows of squares. The figure usually fades to leave one whole row visible: horizontal, diagonal or vertical. In some cases a three-dimensional "waffle" effect is also noted.

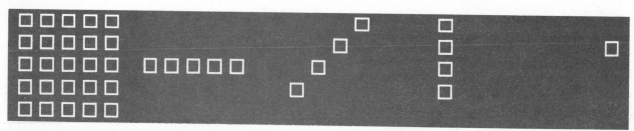

**CIRCLE AND TRIANGLE** may fade as units, leaving one or the other in view. When there is partial fading, a side of the triangle may remain in view along with a parallel segment of the circle, suggesting the "field effect" postulated in Gestalt visual theory.

**CORNERS** are the basic units when solid-tone figures are used. The fading starts in the center and the sharply defined corners disappear one by one. This target, like the others in the series, was presented to subjects both in white-on-black and black-on-white.

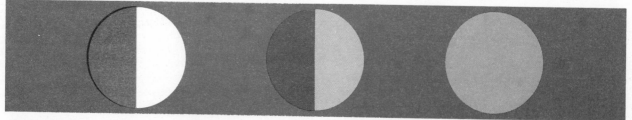

**SENSE OF COLOR** is lost with particular speed. A two-color field like this fades almost immediately when stabilized, to leave two values of gray; then the brightness difference disappears. The stabilized technique promises to be useful for studying color vision.

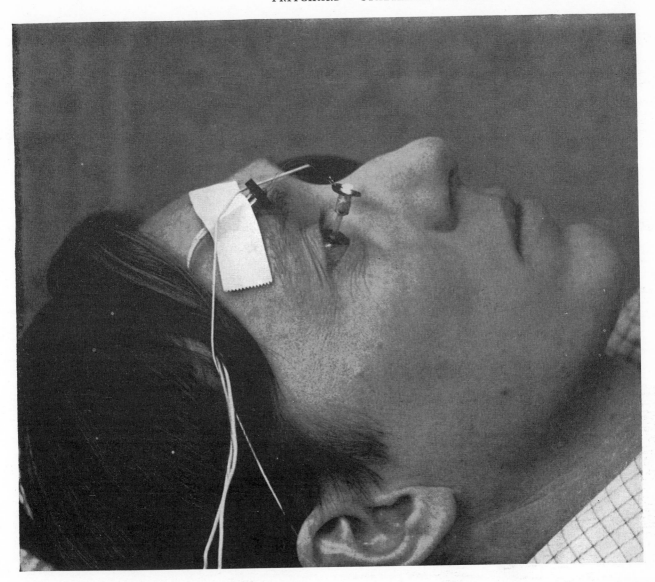

**TAKING TURN AS SUBJECT** in a stabilized-vision experiment, the author wears on his right eye a contact lens on which the projector is mounted. The other eye is occluded by a patch. Wires lead from the small projector lamp to a battery through a connecting jack taped to his forehead. The experimenter inserts a target film under the diffuser. At first the image is clear to the subject, but it soon fades and then regenerates. The subject makes a continuous report of what he sees, and the experimenter records his comments.

correspondingly begins with the reappearance of first one and then another corner, yielding a complete or partial figure with the corners again sharply outlined.

The basic concepts of Gestalt theory receive strong support in our experiments from the observed importance of field effects, from the dominance of "good" figures and from the action of whole figures and of groups of design elements as perceptual entities. But it is the independent action of the parts and not the whole of a figure that is paramount in stabilized vision. This observation agrees with cell-assembly theory and the perceptual elements it postulates. On the other hand, the perceptual elements themselves appear as organized entities and so conform to Gestalt concepts. Perhaps the Gestalt perception-by-the-whole theory can best be used in interpreting perception in a broad sense, while the cell-assembly idea of perception by parts may turn out to be most useful for analysis of perception in detail.

Meanwhile stabilized images have opened up a promising approach to another significant problem in the field of perception: color vision. Color disappears quickly in the stabilized image of a colored figure. In a field composed of the three primary colors, the red, green and blue hues disappear to leave a colorless field of three different brightnesses. These brightness differences also disappear with time, but it is the color that goes first. This supports the suggestion that the hue of a color is produced by radiation of a given wavelength on the retina and that the perception of hue is maintained by continuous changes in the luminosity of the radiation falling on a receptor cell or cells. Movement of the edges of a patch of color across the retina, produced by normal eye movements, would therefore be necessary for continuous perception of color. We are now making an investigation of the amplitude, frequency and form of movement necessary to sustain or regenerate a particular color.

# 40

# PLASTICITY IN SENSORY-MOTOR SYSTEMS

RICHARD HELD                                            November 1965

Anyone who has worn eyeglasses is likely to have experienced distorted vision the first time he put them on. The distortion may have been severe enough to cause him trouble in motor coordination, as in reaching out to touch something or in being sure of where he stepped. Such a person will also recall, however, that in a day or two the distortion disappeared. Evidently his central nervous system had made some adjustment so that the things he saw through the glasses looked normal again and he could have renewed confidence in his touch and step.

This process of adjustment, particularly as it operates in recovery from radical transformations of vision (as when the world is made to appear upside down or greatly shifted to one side by special goggles), has attracted the attention of scientists at least since the time of the great 19th-century investigator Hermann von Helmholtz. What has intrigued us all is the finding that correct perception of space and accurate visually guided action in space are in the long run not dependent on unique and permanently fixed optical properties of the paths taken by light rays traveling from object to eye. This finding, however, must be squared with the normally high order of precision in spatial vision and its stability over a period of time. How can the visual control of spatially coordinated action be stable under normal circumstances and yet sufficiently modifiable to allow recovery from transformation? Recovery takes time and renewed contact with the environment. Adaptation must result from information drawn from this contact with the environment. If the end product of adaptation is recovery of the former stability of perception, then the information on which that recovery is

based must be as reliable and unvarying as its end product. The investigations my colleagues and I have undertaken (first at Brandeis University and more recently at the Massachusetts Institute of Technology) have been directed toward discovering this source of information and elucidating the mechanism of its use by the perceiving organism. A useful tool in our work has been deliberate distortion of visual and auditory signals, a technique we call rearrangement.

Visual rearrangement can be produced experimentally with prisms [see "Experiments with Goggles," by Ivo Kohler, currently available as Offprint #465]. Similarly, the apparent direction of sounds can be distorted in the laboratory by suitable apparatus. We have used such devices to show that in many cases the viewer or the listener subjected to these distortions soon adapts to them, provided that during the experiment he has been allowed to make voluntary use of his muscles in a more or less normal way.

The proviso suggests that there is more to the mechanism of perceptual adaptation than a change in the way the sensory parts of the central nervous system process data from the eyes and ears. The muscles and motor parts of the nervous system are evidently involved in the adaptation too—a revelation that has been very important in our efforts to discover the responsible source of information. The concept of a relation between sensory and motor activities in the adaptive process is reinforced by what happens when humans and certain other mammals undergo sensory deprivation through prolonged isolation in monotonous environments, or motor deprivation through prolonged immobilization. Their performance on perceptual

and motor tasks declines. By the same token, the young of higher mammals fail to develop normal behavior if they undergo sensory or motor deprivation.

Taken together, these findings by various experimenters suggested to us that a single mechanism is involved in three processes: (1) the development of normal sensory-motor control in the young, (2) the maintenance of that control once it has developed and (3) the adaptation to changes or apparent changes in the data reported by the senses of sight and hearing. A demonstration that such a mechanism exists would be of value in understanding these processes. Moreover, it would help to explain a phenomenon that otherwise could be accounted for only by the existence of enormous amounts of genetically coded information. That phenomenon is the adjustment of the central nervous system to the growth of the body—on the sensory side to the fact that the afferent, or input, signals must change with the increasing separation between the eyes and between the ears, and on the motor side to the fact that the growth of bone and muscle must call for a gradual modification of the efferent, or output, signals required to accomplish a particular movement. This problem is especially critical for animals that grow slowly and have many jointed bones. The possibility that the need for genetically coded information has been reduced by some such mechanism is of course contingent on the assumption that the animal's environment is fairly stable. For these reasons it is not surprising that clear evidence for adaptation to rearrangement and for dependence of the young on environmental contact in developing coordination has been found only in primates and in cats.

Such, in brief, is the background of

our effort to discover the operating conditions of the suspected mechanism. Our conclusion has been that a key to its operation is the availability of "reafference." This word was coined by the German physiologists Erich von Holst and Horst Mittelstädt to describe neural excitation following sensory stimulation that is systematically dependent on movements initiated by the sensing animal; von Holst and Mittelstädt also used the word "exafference" to describe the result of stimulation that is inde-

pendent of self-produced movement. "Afference" alone refers to any excitation of afferent nerves. These concepts should become clearer to the reader from the remainder of this article.

Among the contributions von Helmholtz made to science were many that were later incorporated into psychology. His experiments included work on the displacement of visual images by prisms. He was the first to report that the misreaching caused by such a dis-

placement is progressively reduced during repeated efforts and that on removal of the prism the subject who has succeeded in adapting to this displacement will at first misreach in the opposite direction.

Helmholtz' findings and those of similar experiments by many other workers have often been interpreted as resulting from recognition of error and consequent correction. We doubted this interpretation because of our conviction that a single mechanism underlies both

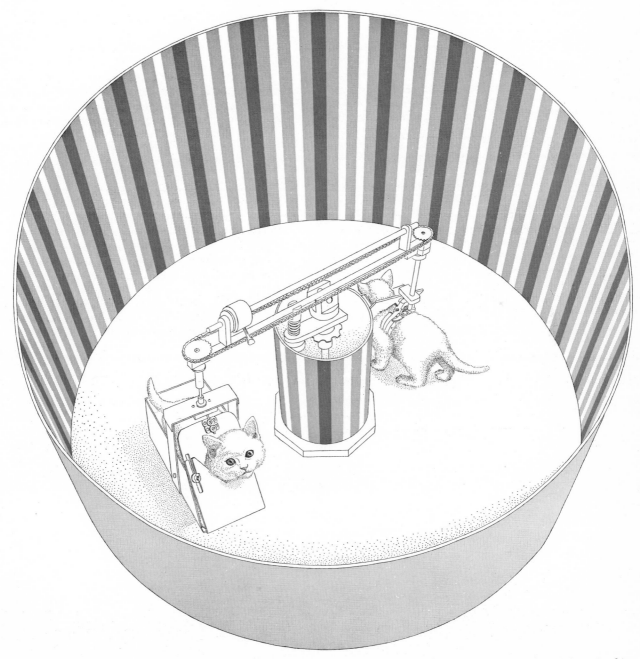

**ACTIVE AND PASSIVE MOVEMENTS** of kittens were compared in this apparatus. The active kitten walked about more or less freely; its gross movements were transmitted to the passive kitten by the chain and bar. The passive kitten, carried in a gondola, received essentially the same visual stimulation as the active kitten because of the unvarying pattern on the wall and on the center post. Active kittens developed normal sensory-motor coordination; passive kittens failed to do so until after being freed for several days.

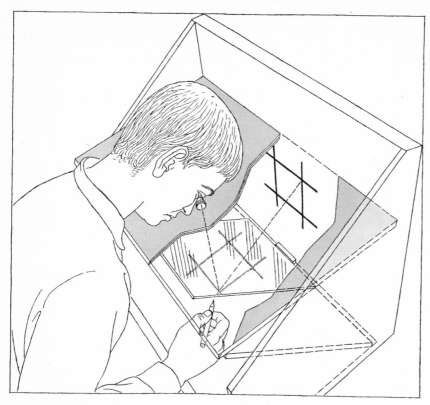

**MIRROR APPARATUS** tests subject's ability to guide his unseen hand to a visible target. Subject first marks under the mirror the apparent location of the corners of the square as he sees them in the mirror. He then looks through a prism, as depicted in the illustration below, after which he makes more marks. They show his adaptation to the prism effect.

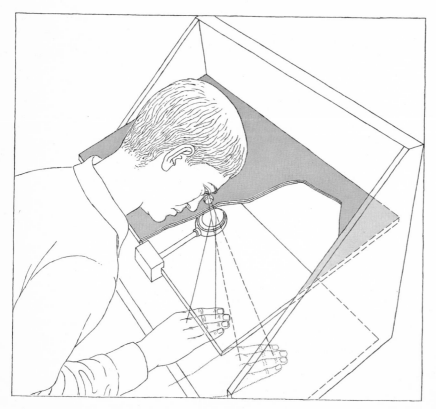

**VIEW THROUGH PRISM** displaces a visual image. Some subjects looked at their motionless hand, some moved the arm back and forth in a left-right arc, and some had the arm moved passively in a similar arc. They then made marks under the mirror as shown in the illustration at the top of the page. Typical results appear in illustrations on opposite page.

adaptation to rearrangement in the adult and the development of the young. An error-correcting process could hardly explain the original acquisition of coordination. If an infant initially has no sense of the spatial relation between his efforts to move his hand and their visual consequences, he cannot recognize a visible error in reaching. Yet infants do acquire eye-hand coordination in their earliest months. Hence we suspected that error recognition was no more necessary for adaptation in the adult than it was in the development of the infant's coordination. To test this assumption we designed an experiment that prevented the subject from recognizing his error. If he still managed to correct his reach to allow for a displaced image, it would be evident that there was more to the matter of adaptation than the simple fact that the subject could see his error directly.

With this objective in mind we designed the apparatus shown in the top illustration at the left. In this apparatus the subject saw the image of a square target reflected by a mirror and was asked to mark on a piece of paper under the mirror the apparent position of the corners of the square. Because of the mirror, he could see neither the marks nor his hand. After he had marked each point 10 times, withdrawing his hand between markings so that he would have to position it anew each time, the mirror and marking sheet were removed and a prism was substituted. Looking through the prism, the subject then spent several minutes moving his hand in various ways, none of which involved deliberate reaching for a target. Thereafter the original situation was restored and the subject made more marks under the mirror. These marks revealed that each of the subjects was making some correction for the displacement of image that had been caused by the prism.

Having thus established that at least partial adaptation can occur in the absence of direct recognition of error, we used the apparatus to test the role of motor-sensory feedback in adaptation. Our main purpose was to see what degree of adaptation would occur under the respective conditions of active and passive movement—in other words, under conditions of reafference and exafference in which the afference was equivalent. In these experiments the subject's writing arm was strapped to a board pivoted at his elbow to allow left and right movement. He then looked at his hand through a prism under three conditions: (1) no movement, (2) active movement, in which he moved the arm back and forth himself, and (3) passive movement, in which he kept his arm limp and it was moved back and forth by the experimenter. In each case he marked the apparent location of points under the mirror before and after looking through the prism.

Comparison of these marks showed that a few minutes of active movement produced substantial compensatory shifts [see illustrations at right]. Indeed, many of the subjects showed full adaptation, meaning exact compensation for the displacement caused by the prism, within half an hour. In contrast, the subjects in the condition of passive movement showed no adaptation. Even though the eye received the same information from both active and passive conditions, the evidently crucial connection between motor output and sensory input was lacking in the passive condition. These experiments showed that movement alone, in the absence of the opportunity for recognition of error, does not suffice to produce adaptation; it must be self-produced movement. From the point of view of our approach this kind of movement, with its contingent reafferent stimulation, is the critical factor in compensating for displaced visual images.

What about an adaptive situation involving movements of the entire body rather than just the arm and hand? We explored this situation in two ways, using an apparatus in which the subject judged the direction of a target only in reference to himself and not to other visible objects [see top illustration on next page]. This kind of direction-finding is sometimes called egocentric localization.

The apparatus consisted initially of a drum that could be rotated by the experimenter, after which the subject, sitting in a chair that he could rotate, was asked to position himself so that a target appeared directly in front of him. Later we dispensed with the drum and merely put the subject in a rotatable chair in a small room. After the experimenter had randomly positioned the target, which was a dimly illuminated slit, the subject rotated himself to find the target.

The first of the two ways in which we tested the role of reafferent stimulation involving movement of the whole body was an experiment in adaptation to short-term exposure to prisms. After several trials at locating the target, the subject put on prism goggles. He then

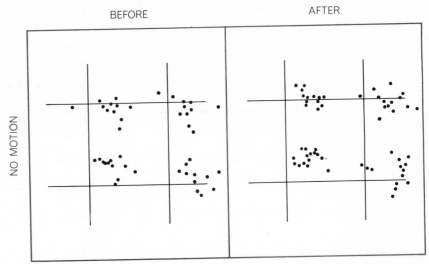

**BEFORE**    **AFTER**    NO MOTION

**MARKINGS** made by a subject before and after looking through a prism as described in illustrations on opposite page are shown. He kept hand still while viewing it through prism.

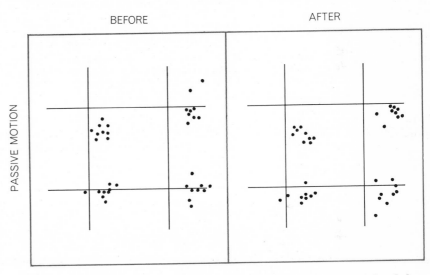

**BEFORE**    **AFTER**    PASSIVE MOTION

**PASSIVE MOVEMENT** of subject's hand as he viewed it through prism produced these marks. They show no adaptation to horizontal displacement of images caused by the prism.

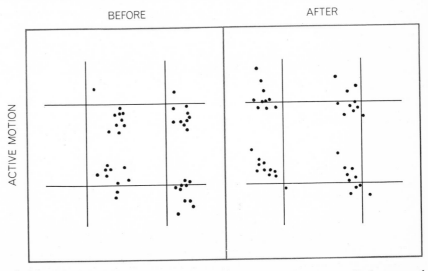

**BEFORE**    **AFTER**    ACTIVE MOTION

**ACTIVE MOVEMENT** of subject's hand produced a clear adaptation to displacement of images by prism. Tests showed importance of such movement in sensorimotor coordination.

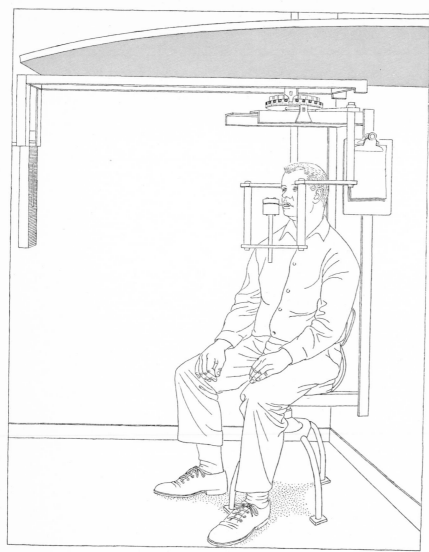

**DIRECTION-FINDING** by egocentric localization, in which a subject judges the direction of a target only in relation to himself and not to other visual cues, uses this apparatus. Target is randomly positioned at subject's eye level; he then rotates himself so that the target is directly in front of him. He does this before and after wearing prism goggles with which he either walks on an outdoor path or is pushed along the same path in a wheelchair. Change in direction-finding after wearing prisms measures adaptation to the prisms.

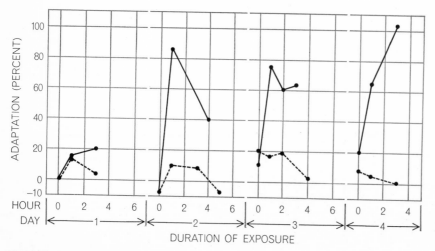

**PROLONGED EXPOSURE** to prisms produced varying degrees of adaptation to them depending on whether a subject's movement was active (*solid lines*) or passive (*broken lines*).

walked for an hour along an outdoor path or sat in a wheelchair that was pushed along the same path for the same length of time. Thereupon he removed the goggles and went back to the target-finding apparatus for more tests. Any error in target-finding after wearing the prism goggles would be a measure of the adaptation the subject had made to the visual displacements produced by the prisms.

Again the degree of adaptation achieved by the subjects who had been involved in active movement was far greater than that of the subjects who had been carried in the wheelchair. This was true both when one subject had been exposed to the active condition and another to the passive and when a single subject had been exposed successively to each condition. Even more striking contrasts appeared in our second test, which involved wearing prisms for several hours at a time under conditions of active and passive movement. In these circumstances several of the subjects who were able to move voluntarily achieved full adaptation, whereas subjects whose movements were passive achieved virtually no adaptation.

In this connection it will be useful to mention an experiment we conducted on directional hearing. The sound emanating from a localized source reaches the listener's nearer ear a fraction of a second sooner than it reaches his farther ear. This small difference in the time of arrival of the sound at the two ears is the first stage in ascertaining the direction from which the sound comes. If, then, a subject's ears could be in effect displaced around the vertical axis of his head by a small angle, he would err by an equivalent angle in his location of the sound. This effect can be produced artificially by a device called the pseudophone, in which microphones substitute for the external ears. Subjects who have worn a pseudophone for several hours in a normally noisy environment show compensatory shifts in locating sounds, provided that they have been able to move voluntarily. In addition they occasionally report that they hear two sources of sound when only one is present. When measurements are made of the two apparent directions of the source, they differ by approximately the angle at which the ears were displaced around the center of the head during the exposure period. I have called the effect diplophonia. The reports of doubled localization following adaptation suggest that compensation for rearrangement consists in the acquisition of a new mode of coordination that is objectively accurate for the condition of rearrangement but that coexists along with the older and more habitual mode. If this is true, the

gradual and progressive course of adaptation usually found in experiments must be considered the result of a slow shift by the subject from the older direction of localization to the newer direction.

All these experiments strongly suggested the role in adaptation of the

close correlation between signals from the motor nervous system, producing active physical movement, and the consequent sensory feedback. This correlation results from the fact that the feedback signals are causally related to movement and that in a stable environ-

PASSIVE TRANSPORT of a subject wearing prism goggles while viewing a random scene is depicted. Purpose of the apparatus was to test the hypothesis that subjects moving actively through such a scene, which looks the same with or without prisms, would show a

degree of adaptation to the prisms whereas subjects moved passively would not. That is what happened. Tests showed a link between visual and motor processes in the central nervous system by altering the correlation between motor outflow and visual feedback.

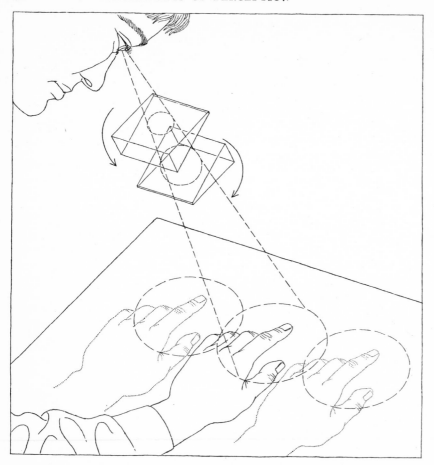

**VERIFICATION EXPERIMENT** sought to show role of correlation of sensory feedback and active physical movement by impairing it. Means of decorrelation was the rotating-prism apparatus shown here. It produces apparently continuous movement of subject's hand in one dimension, thus breaking the link between actual movement and visual feedback.

|  | VERTICAL DISPLACEMENT | | HORIZONTAL DISPLACEMENT | |
|---|---|---|---|---|
| BEFORE EXPOSURE | | | | |
| AFTER EXPOSURE | | | | |

**RESULTS OF DECORRELATION** are shown in markings made by a subject before and after looking through rotating prism. In one condition (*left*) prisms displaced images vertically; in another (*right*), horizontally. Markings after long exposure are spread out in the direction of displacement, showing a loss of precision in visual-motor coordination.

ment there is a unique feedback signal for any particular movement. The correlation is reduced by environmental instability: the presence either of objects that themselves move or of passive movements of the body that are produced by external forces. Under these conditions more than one feedback signal may accompany any particular movement.

From a theoretical point of view the importance of body movement and particularly of self-produced movement derives from the fact that only an organism that can take account of the output signals to its own musculature is in a position to detect and factor out the decorrelating effects of both moving objects and externally imposed body movement. One way to verify the importance of the correlation would be to set up an experimental situation in which the correlation was impaired or deliberately decorrelated. If the consequence was a loss of coordination, evidence for the role of normally correlated reafference in maintaining normal coordination would be strengthened.

We conducted such an experiment in visual perception by means of an apparatus that provided a prism effect of continually varying power [*see top illustration at left*]. In such an apparatus an object such as the hand seems to move constantly, and the movement perceived is wholly independent of whatever actual motion may be taking place. The same arm movement made at different times will produce different retinal feedbacks. Since the subject does not control the continual changes in his visual input that are produced by the prism, his nervous system has no means of distinguishing these changes in the input from those that are self-initiated.

With this apparatus we conducted various experiments, again including active and passive arm movements of the type described previously. We found that the coordination between eye and hand was significantly degraded under conditions of active movement but not under conditions of passive movement. Similar results appeared in tests made by Sanford Freedman of Tufts University of the effect of decorrelation on hearing. Again the performance of subjects who were allowed to move actively during decorrelation deteriorated badly, whereas the performance of subjects whose bodily movements were restricted did not deteriorate. Both the visual and the auditory experiments confirmed the importance of the correlation between movement and sensory feedback in maintaining accurate coordination.

In another test of our hypothesis about reafference we undertook to see what would happen when subjects looked through prisms at a random scene, lacking in the lines and curves that provide normal visual cues. The straight lines characteristic of normal scenes look curved when viewed through a prism. When the prism is removed, such lines seem to curve in the opposite direction. What if straight lines looked curved after a subject had removed prism goggles through which he had viewed a random scene?

Our hypothesis was that such an effect would be produced in subjects who moved actively while viewing the random field but not in those whose movements were passive. If such a result occurred, we would have shown that the subjective geometry of the visual field can be altered by reafference. This finding would have the surprising implication that a motor factor is involved in a process traditionally regarded as purely visual. We would have demonstrated in another way the close, one-to-one correlation between movement and visual feedback and would have further evidence of a link between motor and visual mechanisms in the central nervous system.

Our apparatus for testing this hypothesis consisted of a large drum that had on its inside surface an irregular array of small spots [see illustration on page 327]. These spots looked the same whether viewed with a prism or not. Each subject, before putting on prism goggles and entering the drum, was tested for his perception of a vertical line; we did this by having him indicate when a grating of bars given varying curvatures by prisms appeared straight. Thereafter, entering the drum with the goggles on, the subject either walked around in the drum or was transported on a cart. He stayed in the drum for half an hour and then, after removing the goggles, again took the test with the grating of bars. Without exception the active subjects perceived curvature when looking at lines that were actually straight, whereas the passive subjects perceived little or none.

Having established by these various means the role of reafference in adaptation to changed sensory inputs, we decided to examine its role in the development of visually controlled coordination in the newborn. The contribution of experience to the development of perceived space and of spatially oriented behavior has been debated for some centuries. During the past few decades a number of experimental approaches to the issue have been made. The technique most often used involves depriving very young animals of sensory contact with the environment. It has been hoped that the procedure would decide whether or not sensory experience, as opposed to maturation alone in the absence of such experience, is required for the development of spatial discrimination.

In certain species of higher mammals, including man, various forms of visual deprivation ranging from total absence of light to mere absence of gross movement in a normally illuminated environment have all resulted in deficiencies in visually guided behavior. Unfortunately these deficiencies are not easily interpreted. They can be attributed, at least in part, to several alternative causes, including pathological changes in the anatomy of the retina and its projections to the brain. Since our findings implicated movement-produced stimulation, they enabled us to test this factor without depriving animals of normal visual stimulation.

The experiments my colleague Alan Hein and I have performed to study the earliest development of vision originated from observations made by Austin H. Riesen of the University of California at Riverside and his collaborators. Riesen's research demonstrated that kittens restrained from walking from the time of their earliest exposure to light develop marked deficiencies in the visual control of behavior compared with unrestrained animals reared normally. The deficiencies of Riesen's animals may have resulted either from the lack of variation in visual stimulation, which was the explanation he preferred, or from the lack of visual stimulation correlated with movement, which was our own hypothesis.

To decide between these alternatives we devised an apparatus in which the gross movements of a kitten moving more or less normally were transmitted to a second kitten that was carried in a gondola [see illustration on page 323]. These gross movements included turns to left and right, circular progress around the center post of the apparatus and any up-and-down motions made by the first kitten. The second kitten was allowed to move its head, since prior experimenters had reported that head movement alone was not sufficient to produce normal behavior in kittens, and it could also move its legs inside the gondola. Both kittens received essentially the same visual stimulation because the pattern on the walls and the center post of the apparatus was unvarying.

Eight pairs of kittens were reared in darkness until the active member of each pair had enough strength and coordination to move the other kitten in the apparatus; the ages at which that state was attained ranged from eight to 12 weeks. Two other pairs were exposed to patterned light for three hours a day between the ages of two and 10 weeks; during exposure they were in a holder that prevented locomotion. Thereafter all 10 pairs spent three hours a day in the apparatus under the experimental condition; when they were not in the apparatus, they were kept with their mothers and littermates in unlighted cages.

After an average of about 30 hours in the apparatus the active member of each pair showed normal behavior in several visually guided tasks. It blinked at an approaching object; it put out its forepaws as if to ward off collision when gently carried downward toward a surface, and it avoided the deep side of a visual cliff—an apparatus in which two depths, one shallow and the other a sharp drop, appear beneath a sheet of glass [see "The 'Visual Cliff,'" by Eleanor J. Gibson and Richard D. Walk, Offprint #402, for a full description]. After the same period of exposure each of the passive kittens failed to show these types of behavior. The passive kittens did, however, develop such types of behavior within days after they were allowed to run about in a normal environment.

In sum, the experiments I have described have led us to conclude that the correlation entailed in the sensory feedback accompanying movement—reafference—plays a vital role in perceptual adaptation. It helps the newborn to develop motor coordination; it figures in the adjustment to the changed relation between afferent and efferent signals resulting from growth; it operates in the maintenance of normal coordination, and it is of major importance in coping with altered visual and auditory inputs. The importance of the correlation in all these functions has been revealed by experiments that tamper with its normal operation. In the process these experiments have uncovered a fundamental role of the motor-sensory feedback loop.

# 41

# EXPERIMENTS IN PERCEPTION

W. H. ITTELSON AND F. P. KILPATRICK          August 1951

WHAT is perception? Why do we see what we see, feel what we feel, hear what we hear? We act in terms of what we perceive; our acts lead to new perceptions; these lead to new acts, and so on in the incredibly complex process that constitutes life. Clearly, then, an understanding of the process by which man becomes aware of himself and his world is basic to any adequate understanding of human behavior. But the problem of explaining how and why we perceive in the way we do is one of the most controversial fields in psychology. We shall describe here some recent experimental work which sheds new light on the problem and points the way to a new theory of perception.

The fact that we see a chair and are then able to go to the place at which we localize it and rest our bodies on a substantial object does not seem particularly amazing or difficult to explain—until we try to explain it. If we accept the prevailing current view that we can never be aware of the world as such, but only of the nervous impulses arising from the impingement of physical forces on sensory receptors, we immediately face the necessity of explaining the correspondence between what we perceive and whatever it is that is there.

An extremely logical, unbeatable—and scientifically useless—answer is simply to say there is no real world, that everything exists in the mind alone. Another approach is to postulate the existence of an external world, to grant that there is some general correspondence between that world and what we perceive and to seek some understandable and useful explanation of why that should be. Most of the prominent theories about perception have grown out of the latter approach. These theories generally agree that even though much of the correspondence may be due to learning, at some basic level there exists an absolute correspondence between what is "out there" and what is in the "mind." But there is a great deal of disagreement concerning the level at which

such innately determined correspondence occurs. At one extreme are theorists who believe that the correspondence occurs at the level of simple sensations, such as color, brightness, weight, hardness, and so on, and that out of these sensations are compounded more complex awarenesses, such as the recognition of a pencil or a book. At the other extreme are Gestalt psychologists who feel that complex perceptions such as the form of an object are the result of an inherent relationship between the properties of the thing perceived and the properties of the brain. All these schools seem to agree, however, that there is some perceptual level at which exists absolute objectivity; that is, a one-to-one correspondence between experience and reality.

This belief is basic to current thinking in many fields. It underlies most theorizing concerning the nature of science, including Percy W. Bridgman's attempt to reach final scientific objectivity in the "observable operation." In psychology one is hard put to find an approach to human behavior which departs from this basic premise. But it leads to dichotomies such as organism v. environment, subjective v. objective. Stimuli or stimulus patterns are treated as though they exist apart from the perceiving organism. Psychologists seek to find mechanical relationships or interactions between the organism and an "objectively defined" environment. They often rule out purposes and values as not belonging in a strictly scientific psychology.

THE experiments to be described here arose from a widespread and growing feeling that such dichotomies are false, and that in practice it is impossible to leave values and purposes out of consideration in scientific observation. The experiments were designed to re-examine some of the basic ideas from which these problems stem.

During the past few years Adelbert Ames, Jr., of the Institute for Associated

Research in Hanover, N. H., has designed some new ways of studying visual perception. They have resulted in a new conception of the nature of knowing and of observation. This theory neither denies the existence of objects nor proposes that they exist in a given form independently, that is, apart from the perceiving organism. Instead, it suggests that the world each of us knows is a world created in large measure from our experience in dealing with the environment.

Let us illustrate this in specific terms through some of the demonstrations. In one of them the subject sits in a dark room in which he can see only two star points of light. Both are equidistant from the observer, but one is brighter than the other. If the observer closes one eye and keeps his head still, the brighter point of light looks nearer than the dimmer one. Such apparent differences are related not only to brightness but also to direction from the observer. If two points of light of equal brightness are situated near the floor, one about a foot above the other, the upper one will generally be perceived as farther away than the lower one; if they are near the ceiling, the lower one will appear farther away.

A somewhat more complex experiment uses two partly inflated balloons illuminated from a concealed source. The balloons are in fixed positions about one foot apart. Their relative sizes can be varied by means of a lever control connected to a bellows, and another lever controls their relative brightness. When the size and brightness of both balloons are the same, an observer looking at them with one eye from 10 feet or more sees them as two glowing spheres at equal distances from him. If the brightnesses are left the same and the relative sizes are changed, the larger balloon appears to nearly all observers somewhat nearer. If the size lever is moved continuously, causing continuous variation in the relative size of the balloons, they appear to move dramatically

**FIGURES ARE DISTORTED** when they are placed in a specially constructed room. The woman at left appears much smaller than the one at right because the mind "bets" that the opposite surfaces of the room are parallel.

**HEADS ARE DISTORTED** by the same process. The head of the man at the left appears to be much smaller than the head of the man at the right because the mind assumes that all the windows are the same height.

**LEFT BALLOON APPEARS CLOSER** because it is larger and brighter than the balloon at the right. Both balloons, however, are at same distance.

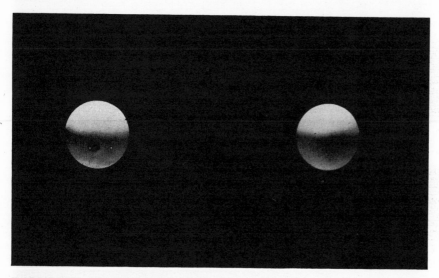

**BALLOONS APPEAR EQUIDISTANT** when they are the same size and brightness. The qualities are manipulated with levers in the demonstration.

**RIGHT BALLOON APPEARS CLOSER** when it is larger and brighter. The demonstration shows that size and brightness are cues for distance.

back and forth through space, even when the observer watches with both eyes open. The result is similar when the sizes are kept equal and the relative brightness is varied.

With the same apparatus the effects of size and brightness may be combined so that they supplement or conflict with each other. When they supplement each other, the variation in apparent distance is much greater than when either size or brightness alone is varied. When conflict is introduced by varying size and brightness in opposition to each other, the relative change in distance is considerably less than when they act in combination or alone. Most people, however, give more weight to relative size than they give to brightness in judging distance.

THESE phenomena cannot be explained by referring to "reality," because "reality" and perception do not correspond. They cannot be explained by reference to the pattern in the retina of the eye, because for any given retinal pattern there are an infinite number of brightness-size-distance combinations to which that pattern might be related. When faced with such a situation, in which an unlimited number of possibilities can be related to a given retinal pattern, the organism apparently calls upon its previous experiences and assumes that what has been most probable in the past is most probable in the immediate occasion. When presented with two star-points of different brightness, a person unconsciously "bets" or "assumes" that the two points, being similar, are probably identical (i. e., of equal brightness), and therefore that the one which seems brighter must be nearer. Similarly the observed facts in the case of two star-points placed vertically one above the other suggest that when we look down we assume, on the basis of past experience, that objects in the lower part of the visual field are nearer than objects in the upper part; when we look up, we assume the opposite to be true. An analogous explanation can be made of the role of relative size as an indication of relative distance.

Why do the differences in distance seem so much greater when the relative size of two objects is varied continuously than when the size difference is fixed? This phenomenon, too, apparently is based on experience. It is a fairly common experience, though not usual, to find that two similar objects of different sizes are actually the same distance away from us. But it is rare indeed to see two stationary objects at the same distance, one growing larger and the other smaller; almost always in everyday life when we see two identical or nearly identical objects change relative size they are in motion in relation to each other. Hence under the experimental conditions we are much more likely to assume distance differences in the objects of changing size than in those of fixed size. In other words, apparently we make use of a weighted average of our past experience in interpreting what we see. It seems that the subject relates to the stimulus pattern a complex, probability-like integration of his past experience with such patterns. Were it not for such integrations, which have been labeled assumptions, the particular perceptual phenomenon would not occur. It follows from this that the resulting perceptions are not absolute revelations of "what is out there" but are in the nature of probabilities or predictions based on past experience. These predictions are not always reliable, as the demonstrations make clear.

VISUAL perception involves an impression not only of *where* an object is but of *what* it is. From the demonstrations already described we may guess that there is a very strong relationship between localization in space ("thereness") and the assignment of objective properties ("thatness"). This relationship can be demonstrated by a cube experiment.

Two solid white cubes are suspended on wires that are painted black so as to be invisible against a black background. One cube is about 3 feet from the observer and the other about 12 feet. The observer's head is in a headrest so positioned that the cubes are almost in line with each other but he can see both, the nearer cube being slightly to the right. A tiny metal shield is then placed a few inches in front of the left eye. It is just big enough to cut off the view of the far cube from the left eye. The result is that the near cube is seen with both eyes and the far cube with just the right eye. Under these conditions the observer can fix the position of the near cube very well, because he has available all the cues that come from the use of the two eyes. But in the case of the far cube seen with only one eye, localization is much more difficult and uncertain.

Now since the two cubes are almost in line visually, a slight movement of the head to the right will cause the inside vertical edges of the cubes to coincide. Such coincidence of edge is strongly related to an assumption of "togetherness." Hence when the subject moves his head in this way, the uncertainly located distant cube appears to have moved forward to a position even with the nearer cube. Under these conditions not only does the mislocated cube appear smaller, but it appears different in shape, that is, no longer cubical, even though the pattern cast by the cube on the retina of the eye has not changed at all.

The same point can be illustrated most dramatically by experiments in which the subject wears a pair of glasses

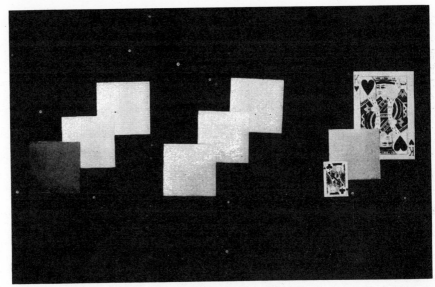

**LEFT CARDS APPEAR CLOSER** than those at the center and right in each of the three rows in this picture. The illusion is revealed below.

**RIGHT CARDS ARE CLOSER** in the rows at the center and right. Here the cues are size and the fact that the cards appear to overlap.

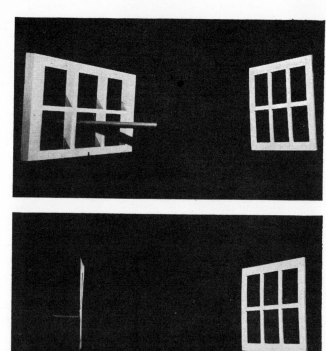

**PERCEPTION OF MOVING OBJECTS** was investigated with a rotating window. At the right in each of the eight pictures on these two pages is a rectangular window; at the left in each picture is a trapezoid painted to

fitted with so-called aniseikonic lenses, which are ground in such a way that they give images of different size and shape to the two retinas. This produces very marked distortions of any objects which the subject visualizes mainly through the use of two-eyed stereoscopic vision. In an ordinary environment there are generally enough one-eye cues, such as shadow, overlay, familiar objects of known size, and so on, to suppress the binocular cues and hold the visual world "in shape." But in an environment poor in one-eye cues the observer is forced to rely on binocular cues, and under these circumstances the distortion is enhanced for anyone wearing such glasses. It has been found that if an ordinary square room is lined with tree leaves, which reduce monocular cues to a minimum by covering the flat wall spaces, most observers looking through aniseikonic lenses perceive a great deal of distortion of the room and the leaves. To an observer looking at the room as a whole through certain glasses of this type the walls appear to slant inward from floor to ceiling, the ceiling seems much lower than it is and its leaves look very small. The floor, which is the object of interest in this particular analysis, appears to be much farther away than its true position, and the leaves covering it look huge. Now, if the observer wearing the same glasses looks at just the floor instead of the room in general, the floor changes markedly in appearance. It appears to be much nearer than before, and instead of being level it

seems to rise from front to back at a pitch of about 45 degrees. The leaves, however, now look more nearly normal in size.

THESE perceptions can be explained in terms of the geometry of stereoscopic vision. The stimulus patterns on the retinas of the eyes are the geometric projections of an external surface. But identical projections may be produced by surfaces of different kinds. In this case a distant surface that is nearly horizontal, a closer surface that is slightly tipped and a very near surface that is sharply tipped all produce the same stereoscopic stimulus patterns. When the observer looks at the whole room, he "chooses" the nearly horizontal faraway floor surface as the focus of perception, probably because he cannot make a room out of the pattern if the floor is sharply tipped up. When he limits his gaze to the floor, he no longer needs to make a room of what he is looking at, and he sees the floor sharply tipped, perhaps because the leaves now appear more nearly the size he assumes them to be.

In the everyday environment outside the laboratory the wearing of these glasses produces similarly interesting illusions. For example, a large body of water such as a lake appears horizontal and farther away than its real position, but a large expanse of level lawn looks tipped and nearer than its real position. Presumably this happens because the observer brings to these occasions the assumptions, based on past experience,

that the probability of a lake surface being other than horizontal is almost zero, while the probability of a grass surface being a slope is fairly high.

The most reasonable explanation of these visual phenomena seems to be that an observer unconsciously relates to the stimulus pattern some sort of weighted average of the past consequences of acting with respect to that pattern. The particular perception "chosen" is the one that has the best predictive value, on the basis of previous experience, for action in carrying out the purposes of the organism. From this one may make two rather crucial deductions: 1) an unfamiliar external configuration which yields the same retinal pattern as one the observer is accustomed to deal with will be perceived as the familiar configuration; 2) when the observer acts on his interpretation of the unfamiliar configuration and finds that he is wrong, his perception will change even though the retinal pattern is unchanged.

Let us illustrate with some actual demonstrations. If an observer in a dark room looks with one eye at two lines of light which are at the same distance and elevation but of different lengths, the longer line will look nearer than the shorter one. Apparently he assumes that the lines are identical and translates the difference in length into a difference in position. If the observer takes a wand with a luminous tip and tries to touch first one line and then the other, he will be unable to do so at first. After repeated practice, however, he can learn to touch

look like a rectangular window seen in perspective. When the trapezoid rotates, the assumption that it is rectangular causes a straight tube to do strange things. The sequence reads horizontally across the two pages.

the two lines quickly and accurately. At this point he no longer sees the lines as at different distances; they now look, as they are, the same distance from him. He originally assumed that the two lines were the same length because that seemed the best bet under the circumstances. After he had tested this assumption by purposive action, he shifted to the assumption, less probable in terms of past experience but still possible, that the lines were at the same distance but of different lengths. As his assumption changed, perception did also.

THERE is another experiment that demonstrates these points even more convincingly. It uses a distorted room in which the floor slopes up to the right of the observer, the rear wall recedes from right to left and the windows are of different sizes and trapezoidal in shape. When an observer looks at this room with one eye from a certain point, the room appears completely normal, as if the floor were level, the rear wall at right angles to the line of sight and the windows rectangular and of the same size. Presumably the observer chooses this particular appearance instead of some other because of the assumptions he brings to the occasion. If he now takes a long stick and tries to touch the various parts of the room, he will be unsuccessful, even though he has gone into the situation knowing the true shape of the room. With practice, however, he becomes more and more successful in touching what he wants to touch with

the stick. More important, he sees the room more and more in its true shape, even though the stimulus pattern on his retina has remained unchanged.

By means of a piece of apparatus called the "rotating trapezoidal window" it has been possible to extend the investigation to complex perceptual situations involving movement. This device consists of a trapezoidal surface with panes cut in it and shadows painted on it to give the appearance of a window. It is mounted on a rod connected to a motor so that it rotates at a slow constant speed in an upright position about its own axis. When an observer views the rotating surface with one eye from about 10 feet or more or with both eyes from about 25 feet or more, he sees not a rotating trapezoid but an oscillating rectangle. Its speed of movement and its shape appear to vary markedly as it turns. If a small cube is attached by a short rod to the upper part of the short side of the trapezoid, it seems to become detached, sail freely around the front of the trapezoid and attach itself again as the apparatus rotates.

ALL these experiments, and many more that have been made, suggest strongly that perception is never a sure thing, never an absolute revelation of "what is." Rather, what we see is a prediction—our own personal construction designed to give us the best possible bet for carrying out our purposes in action. We make these bets on the basis of our past experience. When we have

a great deal of relevant and consistent experience to relate to stimulus patterns, the probability of success of our prediction (perception) as a guide to action is extremely high, and we tend to have a feeling of surety. When our experience is limited or inconsistent, the reverse holds true. According to the new theory of perception developed from the demonstrations we have described, perception is a functional affair based on action, experience and probability. The thing perceived is an inseparable part of the function of perceiving, which in turn includes all aspects of the total process of living. This view differs from the old rival theories: the thing perceived is neither just a figment of the mind nor an innately determined absolute revelation of a reality postulated to exist apart from the perceiving organism. Object and percept are part and parcel of the same thing.

This conclusion of course has far-reaching implications for many areas of study, for some assumption as to what perception is must underly any philosophy or comprehensive theory of psychology, of science or of knowledge in general. Although the particular investigations involved here are restricted to visual perception, this is only a vehicle which carries us into a basic inquiry of much wider significance.

*W. H. Ittelson and F. P. Kilpatrick are instructors in the department of psychology at Princeton University.*

# Part X

## DRUGS AND BEHAVIOR

# X

## DRUGS AND BEHAVIOR

*Introduction*  Most of us are consumers of drugs. Although some commonly used drugs are designed to combat specific diseases, many—if not most of the drugs we use—are selected because of their sensory and behavioral effects. We use readily available drugs to relieve pain, to improve alertness, to aid sleep, to produce mild euphoria, to relieve depressed states, and to tranquilize agitated individuals.

Many of the most commonly used drugs have been used for centuries. Scientific interest in the nature and bases of drug effects on experience and behavior has developed, however, only in the last few decades. Drugs are now used extensively in psychobiological experiments. There are several reasons for this. First, drugs are useful as research tools in studies of mechanisms underlying behavior (see the articles by Fischer, pages 66–74, Hess, pages 107–111, and Olds, pages 183–188). Second, drugs have been found to be useful in the treatments of individuals with behavior disorders. There is some reason to believe that a knowledge of the mechanisms of action of the effective drugs might lead to an understanding of the biological bases of mental disease. Third, many drugs—barbiturates, alcohol, amphetamines, and narcotics—are used excessively and the users become dependent upon them. There is need to gain an understanding of the bases of drug dependency. Finally, some drugs such as mescaline and LSD 25 have profound and bizarre effects on experience and behavior. The problem of understanding the biochemical bases of the effects is extremely challenging. And the answers will undoubtedly provide an increased understanding of the biochemical and neurophysiological basis of behavior.

The articles in this section illustrate some of the ways in which drug effects on experience and behavior have been investigated in recent years. H. E. Himwich, "The New Psychiatric Drugs" (page 340), reviews some of the behavioral, biochemical, and neuropharmacological studies of several drugs commonly referred to as tranquilizers. The bases of the behavioral effects of these drugs are not yet well understood but the effectiveness of these compounds has markedly stimulated research concerning the biochemical bases of behavior disorders. In " 'Truth' Drugs" (page 345) L. Z. Freedman discusses the use of drugs in psychiatric interviewing and interrogation and points out that there is no evidence that individuals tell only the "truth" while under the drug's influence. Subjects are apparently more communicative while drugged, but what they communicate depends upon a variety of conditions. In the third article, "Experimental Narcotic Addiction" (page 351), J. R. Weeks discusses the theories of experimental studies of addiction in laboratory animals. The studies have provided extremely useful information concerning the nature of the process of drug addiction.

In the last article, Barron, Jarvik, and Bunnell examine in some detail available information concerning the sources, the pharmacology, the subjective and behavioral effects, and the uses of several of "The Hallucinogenic Drugs" (page 358). There is no doubt that these drugs have profound psychological effects. Perceptual, hallucinatory, and emotional effects are routinely reported. The authors point out that—as is the case with other drugs such as alcohol—the drugs do not work "alone." The specific effects depend to a considerable extent upon where and by whom the drug is taken. There is some evidence that these drugs are therapeutically useful. The bases of the varied and striking effects need to be understood. As research tools these drugs are potentially extremely useful. For these reasons it is hoped that the increasing abuse of these drugs will not constrain research that may lead to an understanding of the bases of their effects.

# 42

# THE NEW PSYCHIATRIC DRUGS

HAROLD E. HIMWICH                    October 1955

We seem to be entering a new era in the study and treatment of mental illness—a biochemical era. Research on the chemistry of mental disease has recently brought forth several exciting new discoveries. One is the new information on the emotional effects of adrenalin and nor-adrenalin [see "The Physiology of Fear and Anger," by Daniel H. Funkenstein, on page 193 of this volume]. Another is the finding that a psychotic state can be induced artificially by injections of lysergic acid

["Experimental Psychoses," by Six Staff Members of Boston Psychopathic Hospital; June 1955]. This article reviews a third major development: the so-called "tranquilizing" drugs which psychiatrists are using with remarkable effect in treating psychotic patients. These drugs are chlorpromazine (trade name: Thorazine), reserpine (Serpasil) and azacyclonol (Frenquel).

It is well known that in dealing with a psychotic individual the psychiatrist's greatest problem is to make some kind

of effective contact with the patient. This is particularly true of schizophrenia. The patient may be aloof and apathetic; he may be living in a world of hallucinations and grandiose delusions; he may fancy that the radio on the ward is directing insults to him personally. Some schizophrenics are so out of touch with their surroundings that even their speech is completely incomprehensible to others (doctors call it "word salad"). Naturally it is of no avail to attempt to argue or reason with such a

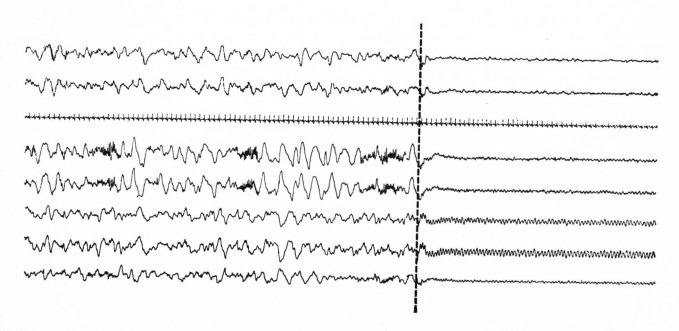

ELECTROENCEPHALOGRAMS are used to show the effect of a drug on the brain's activity. In the two patterns shown here each wavy line represents the electrical impulses recorded from distinct areas of a rabbit's brain. In the first record the wave pattern at

patient. When he becomes violent, the hospital physicians usually have no recourse but to apply a drastic treatment such as electroshock or to quiet the patient temporarily with barbiturates.

The new tranquilizing drugs have introduced a new regime in the management of patients in mental hospitals. The drugs calm the patients without putting them to sleep. Their effects last longer than sedatives. They make it possible to keep severely disturbed patients in an open ward instead of locking them up. And most important, they make even "hopeless" patients accessible to psychotherapy by reducing their anxiety and removing some of the barriers between the patient and the psychiatrist.

The new drugs promise to reduce the cost of caring for the nation's mentally ill, to decrease the number who must be kept in hospitals and to make mental hospitals more attractive places to work. Moreover, the drugs are becoming popular outside of hospitals. Physicians are prescribing them for mildly psychotic patients whom they now treat in their offices, for neurotic patients and even for entirely normal individuals who become tense under some temporary stress or crisis. A dose of one of these drugs relaxes an anxious person and enables him to deal with a trying situation more objectively.

How do the drugs produce their effects? Before we review the research on their mode of action in the body, let us look at the psychological effects in more detail.

At the Galesburg State Research Hospital in Illinois we have found that the drugs produce the most dramatic results in the most disturbed patients. They are particularly effective in quieting elderly psychotics who are apprehensive, irritable and aggressive. Most surprisingly, they show good results on many chronic psychotics who have been ill and hospitalized for a long time.

The three drugs differ in activity. Chlorpromazine seems to be most effective in suppressing the delusions of paranoid patients and in quieting patients who are restless, hyperactive and over-elated. Reserpine is most successful in helping hebephrenic patients (those whose speech is unintelligible) and catatonic ones (e.g., patients who keep a peculiar posture for long periods or turn only at right angles when they walk). Frenquel moderates various kinds of schizophrenic behavior, but its effect is less marked than those of chlorpromazine and reserpine. However, no one drug is uniformly successful against a given type of disorder, and it may be desirable to try another drug or a combination of the drugs in some cases.

There are drawbacks, unfortunately, to the use of some of the drugs. Substantial doses of chlorpromazine or reserpine may produce large reductions of blood pressure, tremors, gastric disturbances, skin eruptions and jaundice. These drugs therefore have to be administered with care. Frenquel has not shown any such undesirable side reactions so far.

The tranquilizing drugs temporarily banish symptoms of mental illness, relieve anxiety and make a psychotic patient more nearly normal. Thus they are a great boon to psychiatric medicine. And in addition the drugs afford a new instrument for exploring how the machinery of the body breaks down when a person has mental or emotional aberrations.

One obviously important site to investigate is the hypothalamus, a structure at the base of the brain which, as Walter B. Cannon showed, plays a key part in mobilizing reactions to an emergency. When an animal is threatened or under stress, it responds with a number of physiological changes which

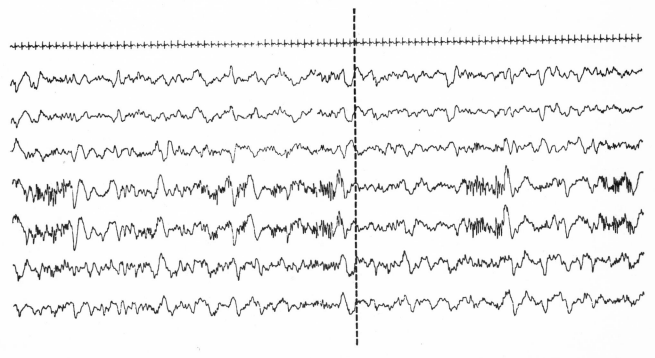

the left is the resting pattern. When a painful stimulus is applied, it changes the brain-wave pattern to that on the right side of the dashed line. The second record shows the effect of chlorpromazine: the pattern remains essentially unchanged after the stimulus.

are triggered by mechanisms in the hypothalamus, particularly in its posterior part. In this portion of the brain are centers which correlate breathing and the heart rate with the individual's emotional state, raise the blood pressure, control basal metabolism and the body temperature, rouse the body and put it to sleep.

Now experiments on animals indicate that chlorpromazine and reserpine inhibit the activities of the hypothalamus. Reserpine is an alkaloid extract from the snakeroot plant (named Rauwolfia for a 16th-century German physician), which has been used in India for centuries as a sedative and a treatment for epilepsy,

snake bite and various other ailments. Chlorpromazine is a synthetic. Both of the drugs act on the hypothalamus to lower the rate of basal metabolism and the body temperature, reduce blood pressure and quiet agitated emotions. Chlorpromazine also seems to affect the nerve system outside the brain, causing the nerves to relax and dilate the small blood vessels.

The hypothalamus is not the only part of the brain influenced by the two drugs. My colleague F. Rinaldi and I have detected effects of the drugs on other brain centers. Our method of research was to analyze electroencephalo-

grams of brain waves.

When the body is touched or stimulated in some way, nerve impulses go from the site of stimulation by pathways called the lemnisci to the thalamus in the center of the brain [see drawing below]. From there the impulses are relayed to parts of the cerebral cortex which interpret the sensation—touch, pain, heat, cold or the like. But there is also a parallel mental system, so to speak, which is affected by the stimulus. In the central core of the brain is a structure known as the activating system; it is located in the "reticular formation." When stimulated, the activating

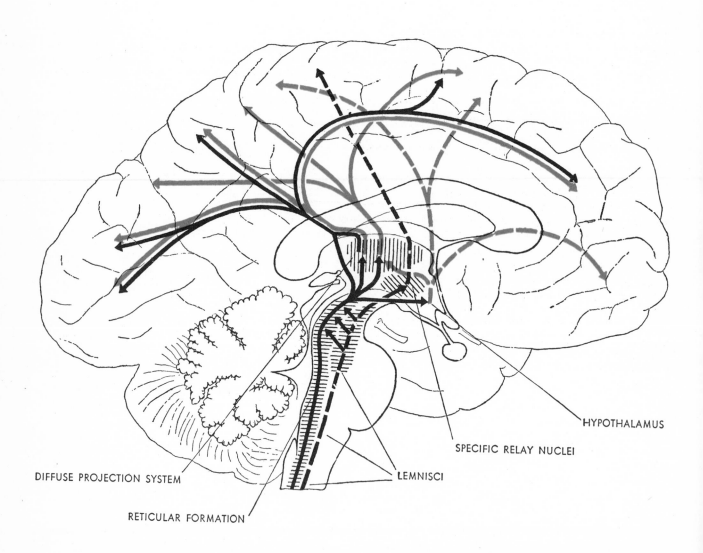

HYPOTHALAMUS

SPECIFIC RELAY NUCLEI

LEMNISCI

DIFFUSE PROJECTION SYSTEM

RETICULAR FORMATION

TWO PATHWAYS of stimulation in the human brain are shown in this diagram. Sensory impulses pass through the lemnisci to the specific relay nuclei of the thalamus in the center of the brain. From there they are relayed to the parts of the cerebral cortex concerned with the analysis of specific sensations. This system is shown by the dashed black arrows. The other set of pathways, called the activating system, begins with branches from the lemnisci. They carry impulses to the midbrain reticular formation, which in turn relays these impulses to the thalamus. From there the activating impulses are carried to the cerebral cortex by way of the diffuse projection system. These paths are indicated by black lines. The reticular formation also sends impulses to the hypothalamus. Secondary impulses from hypothalamus are suggested by dashed colored lines, from thalamus, by solid colored lines paralleling the black.

system produces an arousal reaction. This reaction is clearly shown in an electroencephalogram by a sharp change in the brain-wave pattern [*see illustration on page 340*].

Chlorpromazine in small doses blocks the arousal reaction. If it is given in advance to an experimental animal, even a painful stimulus will not produce the brain-wave change indicating arousal [*see the pattern illustrated on page 341*]. From this we deduce that in a human patient chlorpromazine inhibits the activating system, preventing some stimuli from rising to the level of the cerebral cortex. It thereby places a block between the environment and its influence on the mind. The individual is rendered more aloof from his surroundings. A psychotic is insulated against the terrifying creations of his imagination. A normal person is made less sensitive to troublesome situations which would ordinarily arouse a strongly emotional response, and he can be more objective in evaluating the situation.

On the other hand, small doses of reserpine (or large doses of chlorpromazine) stimulate the activating system. The drug still has a calming effect upon a patient, because it depresses the hypothalamus, but it does not make him sleepy. Unlike a barbiturate, reserpine keeps the sedated patient wide-awake and at full efficiency.

It is clear that the action of the tranquilizing drugs is far from simple. The mystery of their action is deepened when we come to the third of the drugs. Frenquel does not depress the hypothalamus nor interfere with the usual functions of the activating system. How, then, does it calm a psychotic patient? A hint came from some observations by Howard D. J. Fabing of Cincinnati. Dr. Fabing demonstrated that Frenquel could prevent the psychotic symptoms, including hallucinations, which are usually produced by the drugs lysergic acid and mescaline. We returned to our animal experiments to investigate this finding further. Experiments showed that lysergic acid and mescaline would induce the arousal reaction in animals, and that Frenquel would quench this experimentally induced reaction. In other words, Frenquel has an antagonistic effect against these drugs. But just how does it act on a psychotic patient?

The problem has been approached from another angle: the chemistry of the brain. Chlorpromazine and reserpine cause fundamental changes in the brain's chemistry; this has been es-

RESERPINE

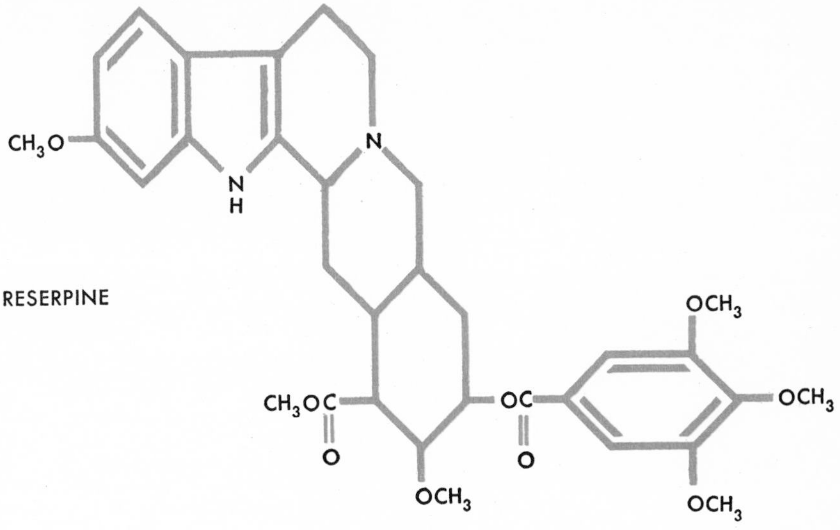

CHLORPROMAZINE

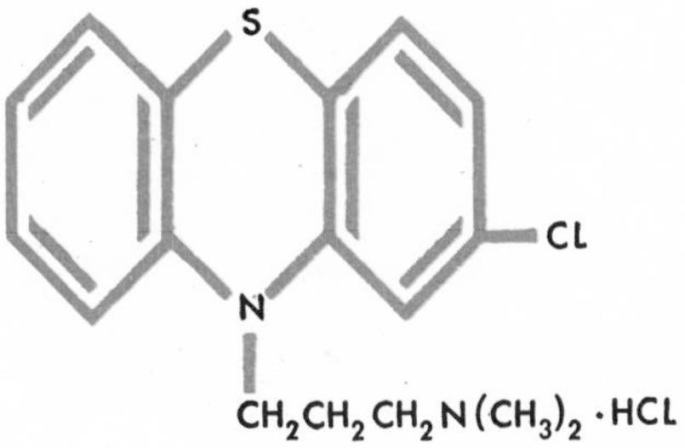

AZACYCLONOL HYDROCHLORIDE

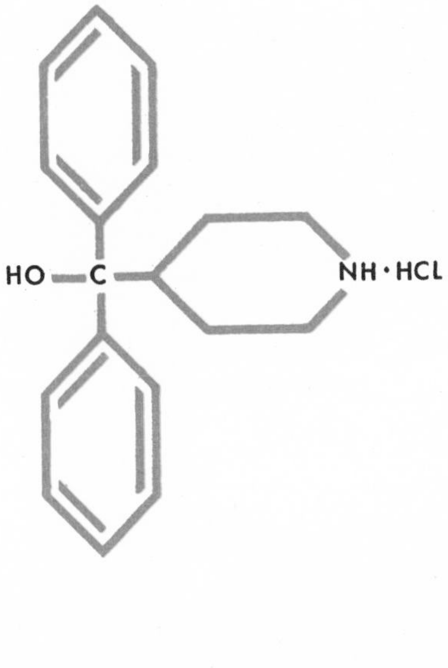

STRUCTURAL FORMULAS of three tranquilizing drugs are represented here. The chemical name of Frenquel is alpha-4-piperidyl benzhydrol hydrochloride. Both it and chlorpromazine (Thorazine) are synthetics. Reserpine (Serpasil) is extracted from Rauwolfia.

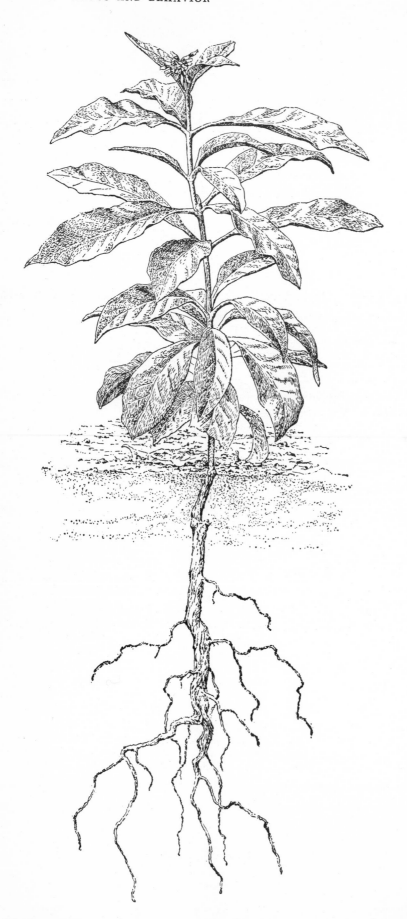

tablished by experiments of Robert G. Grenell and his co-workers at the University of Maryland and by my wife Williamina A. Himwich, in our laboratory. And it now appears that an important role is played in these changes by a brain hormone called serotonin.

Serotonin, a neurohormone, acts as a sedative when given in large doses. Bernard B. Brodie and his co-workers at the National Institutes of Health in Bethesda showed in experiments on animals that the hormone's depressant action is blocked by chlorpromazine and Frenquel, and it is blocked still more strongly by lysergic acid. In our own laboratory Erminio Costa studied the action of serotonin in the uterus of the rat (the hormone is found in certain internal muscles). Serotonin causes the uterus to contract. Costa found that the tranquilizing drugs could prevent this contracting action of the hormone. On the other hand, lysergic acid and mescaline increased the contraction, intensifying the effect of serotonin. If these effects on muscle turn out to apply to the brain as well, we may be able to say that lysergic acid evokes abnormal mental states because it increases the effects of serotonin, while the tranquilizing drugs help mental patients because they diminish the effects of the hormone. An exciting investigation is being conducted into this question.

Physicians who have tested the tranquilizing drugs are convinced that they are a great step forward. Their effects have been corroborated widely in the U. S. and in Europe. Psychiatrists at last have at their command drugs which stop symptoms of psychosis just as insulin stops symptoms of diabetes. Moreover, the drugs may be used generally as sedatives in place of the barbiturates now commonly prescribed.

But chlorpromazine, reserpine and Frenquel are only a beginning. The first two produce undesirable side reactions which must somehow be avoided. None of the three drugs is effective in relieving melancholia (a profound, passive depression) or certain long-standing neuroses and psychosomatic troubles. Nor do the drugs help all schizophrenics. Yet they represent a beachhead which should be steadily extended during the coming years. We have a valuable basic clue in the fact that the drugs seem to influence the action of the hormone serotonin. Future progress seems to lie in the direction of finding other drugs which can act on the neurohormones of the brain to counteract disturbances and suppress mental illness.

**RAUWOLFIA SERPENTINA** is the species of the snakeroot plant from which the pure alkaloid, reserpine, is extracted. For centuries the root has been used in India for many ills.

# 43

# "TRUTH" DRUGS

LAWRENCE ZELIC FREEDMAN March 1960

In his diagnosis and treatment of mental illness the psychiatrist relies heavily upon what the patient says about himself and the things that trouble him. On occasion the psychiatrist has employed drugs with sedative or hypnotic effects in order to stimulate the patient's talk. The technique, sometimes called narcoanalysis, proved useful to physicians charged with the care of large numbers of emotional casualties in the armed forces of the U. S. during World War II and the Korean War. In the semisomnolent state induced by sodium pentothal and other drugs, even the usually noncommunicative patient could talk uninhibitedly. The drugs thus helped to speed treatment, supplying the therapist in a comparatively short time with diagnostic material that might not otherwise have been forthcoming in hours of interrogation.

Even before it became established in the psychiatric interview, such use of drugs excited the interest of people involved in another arena of human difficulty—crime. Police investigators were attracted by the possibility that drugs might facilitate the interrogation of a suspect and of witnesses. Persons accused, reaching desperately for corroboration of their testimony, have been tempted to submit to being questioned under drugs. The subjection of any individual to involuntary examination under drugs is of course as repugnant as torture; evidence secured by such methods is inadmissible in the courts. But the technique has been employed in pretrial investigations of crime, and persons charged with offenses are sometimes challenged to submit voluntarily to examination in a drugged condition. Underlying the willingness of the prosecution, the accused and the public to tolerate this procedure is the idea that the drugs, by stripping away the conscious controls of behavior, will lay bare the "truth."

The technique raises serious ethical questions. This use of drugs plainly lays a threat to the individual's right of privacy and of self-determination. But perhaps the most fruitful way to consider the questions it raises is on practical grounds. Can the drugs in fact elicit the truth? If they do not, then what function may they effectively and legitimately serve in the management of antisocial behavior?

The modern "truth" drug has antecedents going back to earliest times. Indeed, some of the drugs employed in narcoanalysis come from the same plants that awed primitive man with their power to alter his perception, ideas and emotions. Mandrake root, nightshade, belladonna, henbane and Jimson weed all belong to the family *Solanaceae*, various species of which contain the narcotic alkaloids scopolamine, hyoscyamine, atropine and polandrene. These plants have been used in religious and magical rites in all parts of the world: in ancient Europe, in the Orient and in pre-Columbian America. The Pythian priestesses of Delphos made their revelations and prophecies under the influence of narcotic plant drugs. In Aztec Mexico it was believed that the peyote cactus, which contains mescaline, conferred the power of second sight, which could be relied upon to discover the identity of a thief, to recover lost or stolen property and to provide insight into other more arcane matters. Peyote is still consumed in a kind of communion service by the members of the Native American Church, which integrates ancient Indian ritual with Christianity; in the vivid hallucinations and strange psychic state induced by peyote the communicant believes he experiences union with God.

A profound change in man's thinking about himself and the universe had to occur before the revelations produced under narcotics and pharmaceutical hypnotics could appear to be psychological rather than supernatural manifestations. At the close of the 18th century the then young Humphry Davy came close to the notion of the stream of consciousness in his investigation of the effects of nitrous oxide upon himself and a number of his contemporaries. He persuaded Samuel Taylor Coleridge, Robert Southey and Peter Roget, among others, to record their sensations after breathing bags full of "laughing gas," which was a fashionable parlor pastime of that period. Davy wrote: "I gradually began to lose the perception of external things, and a vivid and intense recollection of some former experiences passed through my mind, so that I called out 'What an amazing concatenation of ideas!'" Roget, later known for his thesaurus but then a young physician, said: "My ideas succeeded one another with extreme rapidity, thoughts rushed like a torrent through my mind, as if their velocity had been suddenly accelerated by the bursting of a barrier which had before retained them in their natural and equable course."

Davy noted that the physical and mental effects of the gas varied among individuals, their temperament and mood, and found that in himself breathing nitrous oxide could alleviate anxiety. Looking back, it seems remarkable that no one picked up Davy's suggestive remarks about the anesthetic possibilities of nitrous oxide for surgery or his observations of the psychic changes it produces.

The next illumination of the subject

comes from William James, the propounder of the idea of the stream of consciousness. He was indebted to the "anesthetic revelations" of nitrous oxide recorded by Benjamin Paul Blood, a gentleman farmer of Amsterdam, N. Y. "I think," wrote Blood, "most persons who shall have tested it will accept this as the central point of illumination: that sanity is not the basic quality of intelligence, but is a mere condition which is variable, and like the humming of a wheel, goes up or down the musical gamut according to a physical activity; and that only in sanity is formal or contrasting thought, while the naked life is realized outside of sanity altogether."

This was, James said, a "stepping-stone of my thinking," though he could not share his friend's mystical views. From his own experiments with nitrous-oxide inhalation James drew the conviction that "our normal waking consciousness, rational consciousness as we call it, is but one special type of consciousness, whilst all about it, parted from it by the filmiest of screens, there

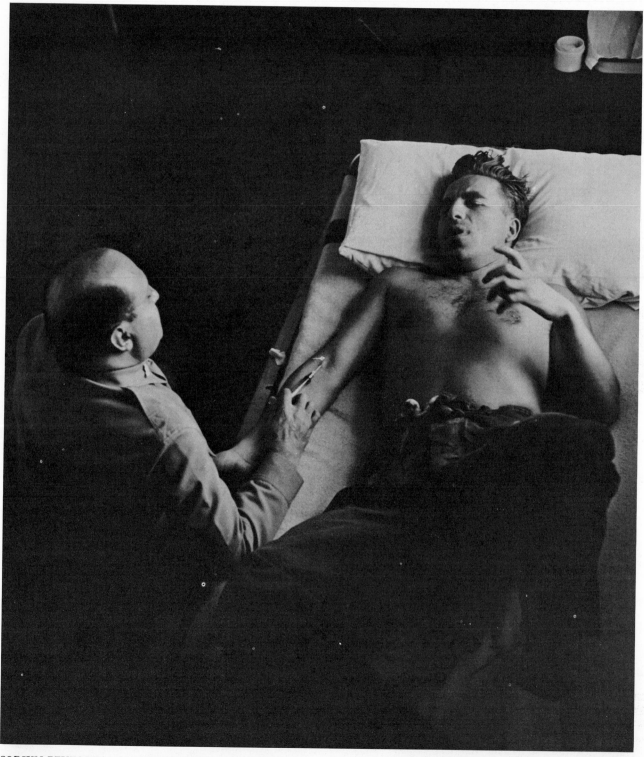

**SODIUM PENTOTHAL IS ADMINISTERED** to a veteran by an Army psychiatrist at the end of World War II. At that time physi- cians found that the use of such drugs during the psychiatric inter- view would aid the patient's recollection of traumatic experiences.

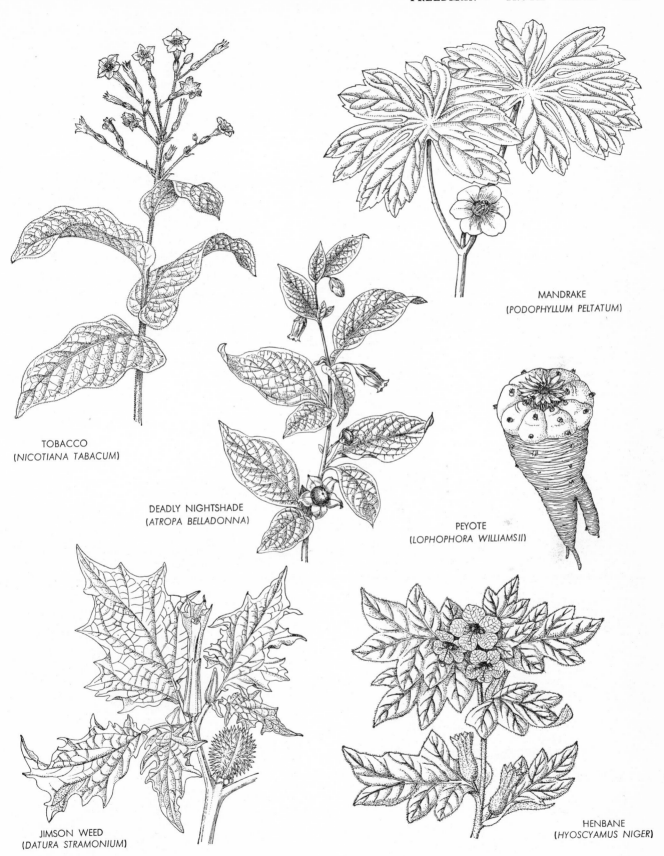

TOBACCO
(NICOTIANA TABACUM)

MANDRAKE
(PODOPHYLLUM PELTATUM)

DEADLY NIGHTSHADE
(ATROPA BELLADONNA)

PEYOTE
(LOPHOPHORA WILLIAMSII)

JIMSON WEED
(DATURA STRAMONIUM)

HENBANE
(HYOSCYAMUS NIGER)

**PLANT SOURCES** of alkaloid "truth" drugs have been known since ancient times. Tobacco, mandrake, deadly nightshade, Jimson weed and henbane belong to the family *Solanaceae*, from various species of which can be extracted the drugs scopolamine, hyoscyamine, atropine and polandrene. From the peyote cactus (*middle right*) can be obtained mescaline, which causes hallucinations.

lie potential forms of consciousness entirely different. We may go through life without suspecting their existence; but apply the requisite stimulus, and at a touch they are there."

The first suggestion that drugs might be employed to facilitate communication with the emotionally disturbed patient came quite by accident in 1916. Arthur S. Loevenhart and his associates at the University of Wisconsin were experimenting with respiratory stimulants; they found that catatonic patients were good subjects because their stuporous condition made it easy to record their breathing. One such patient, who had long been mute and rigid, surprised his observers by relaxing and opening his eyes after an intravenous injection of sodium cyanide; he even answered a few questions. The experience was duplicated with other patients and by other investigators.

By the early 1930's a number of psychiatrists were experimenting with drugs as an adjunct to established methods of therapy. They were in doubt and disagreement, however, as to how the drugs brought change in the behavior of the patients. Some argued that the relaxation and sleep induced by drugs was the decisive factor. They accordingly administered sufficient doses to put the patients in deep sleep and were able to report that even severely catatonic patients seemed to resume normal behavior and experience periods of mental clarity lasting several hours upon awakening.

Then it was discovered that the drugs have more selective and specific effects upon mental activity. Erich Lindemann of the Massachusetts General Hospital found that doses far smaller than those necessary to produce sleep facilitated the patients' responses and their interaction with the therapist. From resistive, seclusive states they could swing into friendly, warm, communicative attitudes. When Lindemann tested the same drugs in the same doses on emotionally healthy persons, they reported a general sense of euphoria, ease and confidence, and they exhibited a marked increase in talkativeness and communicability. Their only cause for concern was a feeling that they had talked too much, though usually they had revealed less than they thought they had. None of them reported any gross distortion of perception, any hallucination or dreamlike experience. The general neurophysiological effect of the drugs was reflected in marked thickening of speech, a moderate decrease in blood pressure, a decrease in heart rate, dilation of the pupils and double vision, some loss of muscular coordination and a marked increase in the pain threshold.

From these observations Lindemann postulated that the drugs removed certain psychic inhibitions and thus brought about verbal release. This is consistent with present views that are based upon closer study of the pharmacological action of the drugs. The drugs affect the higher brain centers generally. Those regions of the cerebral cortex that are usually thought to be of the most recent evolutionary development and that are engaged in the higher associative and behavior-organizing functions seem to be the first to yield to the diminution in brain-tissue metabolism brought about by the drugs. Larger doses in turn depress the function of the next lower cen-

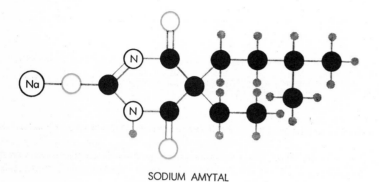

SODIUM AMYTAL

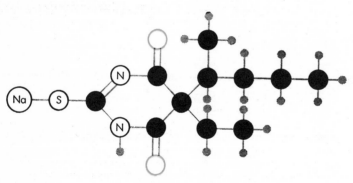

SODIUM PENTOTHAL

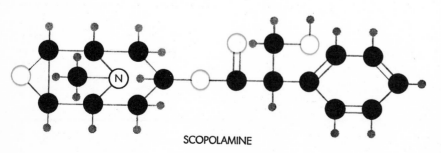

SCOPOLAMINE

**MOLECULES OF THREE TRUTH DRUGS** are diagrammed. Sodium amytal and sodium pentothal are synthetic substances. Atoms in structures are hydrogen (*gray balls*), carbon (*black balls*), oxygen (*open colored circles*), nitrogen (N), sodium (Na) and sulfur (S).

ters. But the pharmacological action of the drugs does not explain or help predict the effect they will have on the behavior of a particular patient. That is the result of at least three factors: the personality structure of the subject, his physiological tolerance for the drug and equally important, the environmental stimuli acting upon him at the time.

The key role that the anticipation, or "set," of the subject may play in his responses was dramatized for me several years ago when I conducted an experiment at the Yale Medical School on sleep. I injected sodium amytal very slowly into a large number of volunteer medical students, having previously attached electrodes to their heads and chests in order to take measurements related to sleep cycles. Since I was concerned with getting them to sleep, I simply informed them of my intention, but the method and rate of injection were otherwise identical with the technique I had used for psychiatric interviews. In only one instance was there any talking, and the subject revealed no "truths" about himself spontaneously. This observation suggests that the role of sodium amytal in an interview involves far more than a "release mechanism."

Unfortunately the whole picture was still quite unclear when the idea of using drugs to "get at the truth" in criminal proceedings first captured the public imagination. Early in this century physicians had begun to employ scopolamine, along with morphine and chloroform, to induce the state of "twilight sleep" during childbirth. They were impressed to note that women in this condition were able to answer questions accurately and often volunteered exceedingly candid remarks. In 1922 it occurred to Robert House, a physician in Dallas, Tex., that scopolamine might be employed in the interrogation of suspected criminals. At the Dallas County Jail he interviewed two prisoners who had received injections of scopolamine. Both men denied the charges on which they were held; both, upon trial, were found not guilty. In his enthusiasm House concluded that the patient under the influence of scopolamine "cannot create a lie . . . and there is no power to think or reason." His experiment and conclusion attracted wide interest, and the truth drug was launched upon the popular consciousness.

Upon closer acquaintance, however, scopolamine was disqualified for service as a truth drug. It proved to have several toxic effects, among which the most disabling is the production of hallucinations. Scopolamine therefore saw only brief service in narcoanalysis before it was abandoned.

The drugs now most frequently used in psychiatric interviews are sodium amytal and sodium pentothal. They are the most easily administered, have the least toxicity and unfavorable side effects and give the most predictable results. The behavior of the subject, especially if he is a psychiatric patient in anxious tension, is dramatic. His features slacken; his body relaxes. Some people are momentarily excited; a few become silly and giggly. This usually passes, and most subjects fall into a state that may be compared to that of a person who has just awakened from a deep sleep.

To form a judgment of what drugs may contribute to establishing the truth, it is necessary to consider what it is that drugs help to elicit from the patient in the psychiatric interview. The psychiatrist is not interested in establishing the truth in any probative sense. In the development of "psychological reality," which is the object of the interview, the patient's account of his fantasies and delusions is as significant as his reliable recollection of past events. Drugs may be helpful to the extent that they provide a "psychological analgesic," a relief from the inhibition of anxiety and guilt that blocks communication with the physician. Under narcosis the patient may achieve, in the words of the psychoanalyst Lawrence Kubie, "a more direct recovery of early traumatic experience than is possible by circuitous pathways of free association in the fully awaking state." It was the resulting acceleration of diagnosis especially that made the drugs so helpful to the military psychiatrists of the U. S. armed forces. But the two medical officers who perhaps made the most extensive use of the technique, Roy R. Grinker and John C. Spiegel, concluded that in almost all cases they could obtain essentially the same material and emotional release in the course of therapy without the use of drugs, providing they had sufficient time.

During the postwar period, with the work of psychiatry proceeding at a more normal rate, narcoanalysis is far less frequently employed. The pressures of time and the stress of reality are rarely paralleled in civilian life—except in the case of individuals who are threatened by legal action and ostracism for criminal or socially offensive acts. Here a psychiatric interview under drugs sometimes offers an avenue of communication urgently needed for proper diagnosis and treatment. But the information thus obtained should never be mistaken for evidence or presented as such in court. Except under such special conditions psychiatrists prefer to deal with a fully conscious patient.

I have employed sodium amytal in investigating the personalities of men accused of various civilian and military antisocial acts. The subjects ranged diagnostically from those with character disorders and neuroses to psychotics. The offenses charged to them included mild delinquency as well as murder. Out of all the information I obtained from them during hours of interrogation under the influence of the drug there was little that could be interpreted directly in the light of its manifest content. These interviews were helpful to me as a psychiatrist and to the subject as my patient. Rarely, however, was my view of objective reality improved as a result of these revelations. I could not, on the basis of a patient's statements, testify in a court that I knew that a given act had or had not occurred. Guilt-ridden subjects under sedation were prone to confess to offenses they had imagined in fantasy but had not in fact committed. Psychopathic individuals could, to the point of unconsciousness, deny crimes that every objective sign indicated they had committed.

At times sedation may diminish self-protective censorship of speech, and the demand of an overburdened conscience may dominate the subject's responses. But these seemingly uninhibited outpourings are vulnerable to distortion resulting from fears, needs and wishes at the deepest levels of his personality. What is more, the cognitive or reasoning functions of the subject's nervous system are to a greater or lesser degree impaired. Even with the best will he may be inaccurate in his observations and recollections. Throughout the interview the psychological processes of repression and resistance and the subtle manifestations of the patients' relationship to the physician continue to operate. Where the role of the interrogator is that of a police investigator or prosecutor, it is hardly likely that the subject would be motivated toward cooperation. "Confessions" obtained with the use of drugs cannot be relied upon, therefore, as testimony or evidence under the standards that are observed by our courts.

In an adversary proceeding, at least one experiment has shown, subjects are capable of maintaining a lie despite injections of a drug. Investigators from the department of psychiatry at Yale University, Frederick C. Redlich and Leonard J. Ravitz, Jr., working with the late George H. Dession of the Yale Law School, conducted the experiment with the aid of volunteers. They administered sodium amytal after the subjects had revealed shameful and guilt-producing episodes of their past and had then invented false self-protective stories about these episodes. Thereafter, under the influence of the drug, they were subjected to cross-examination on their cover story by a second investigator. The results, though not definitive, showed that normal individuals, with good defenses and no overtly pathological traits, could stick to their invented stories and not yield confessions. On the other hand, neurotic individuals, with strong unconscious self-punitive tendencies, not only tended to confess more easily but also to substitute fantasy for the truth, confessing to offenses never actually committed.

In sum, experimental and clinical findings indicate that only individuals who have conscious and unconscious reasons for doing so are inclined to confess and yield to interrogation under the influence of drugs. On the other hand, some are able to withhold information and some, especially character neurotics, are able to lie. Others are so suggestible or so impelled by unconscious guilt that they will describe, perhaps in response to suggestive questioning, behavior that never in fact occurred. The material produced is not "truth" in any sense of conforming with empirical fact.

Serious wrong can be done both to the embryonic science of criminology and to the administration of justice if this procedure is employed as a fact-finding instrument. As the psychoanalyst Theodor Reik pointed out 20 years ago, "fact-finding is still in the province of the police investigator." Moreover, in view of the emphasis upon confessions in this discussion, it should be observed that the extraction of confessions is not the only kind of fact-finding expected of the police.

It is precisely because drugs may facilitate access to psychological reality, as opposed to empirically factual data, that narcoanalysis may have importance for the psychiatrist. The procedure can be helpful in obtaining keener insights into the motivation and psychogenesis of antisocial behavior. Through such studies the psychiatrist may make the best use of drugs in the area of violent criminal behavior. Understanding of the genesis of crime is the rational precursor to the discovery and implementation of preventive measures.

# 44

# EXPERIMENTAL NARCOTIC ADDICTION

JAMES R. WEEKS                                          March 1964

Drug addiction is a complex disease in both the medical and the social sense. The typical addict suffers from an underlying psychiatric disturbance that is often aggravated by economic and social pressures and the censure of the law; his illness does not look the same to the pharmacologist, the practicing physician or psychiatrist, the social worker and the policeman. An investigator who attempts to learn about drug addiction in humans by studying it in animals therefore runs a serious risk of oversimplification. Nevertheless, there are physical aspects of addiction that can be reproduced in rats or monkeys, and over the years much information on these effects has been obtained in laboratory studies. One thing was missing: the essential behavioral aspect of addiction, the voluntary self-administration of a drug by the addicted individual. A few years ago I worked out a method whereby rats addicted to morphine can give themselves injections at will, and subsequent experiments have yielded some interesting data on drug-seeking behavior in these animals.

The World Health Organization describes drug addiction as a state of periodic or chronic intoxication detrimental to the individual and to society, produced by the repeated consumption of a drug and characterized by an overpowering desire or need to take the drug, by a tendency to increase the dose and by psychic and sometimes physical dependence on the effects of the drug. U.S. law specifies the drugs of addiction as opium and its derivatives (such as morphine, codeine, heroin and Demerol), cocaine and marijuana. Opium and its derivatives are narcotics —they depress the activity of the central nervous system and are used in medicine to relieve severe pain; cocaine

is a powerful stimulant (its medical application as a local anesthetic is unrelated to its stimulating effect on the brain); marijuana is a mild intoxicant without medical value. The official list is arbitrary, of course, since many other substances can be addictive, including the barbiturates, amphetamine (Benzedrine) and alcohol.

The characteristics of addiction vary widely with the drug. On repeated administration of an opiate such as morphine two remarkable changes take place in an individual. First of all, he develops a tolerance for the drug, more and more of which must be taken to produce the same effect. A tolerant addict can take 20 or 30 times the usual dose of morphine without becoming drowsy or sleepy. If he can secure enough morphine, the addict remains in apparent good health and is quite able to do productive work; he is outwardly normal and difficult to identify as an addict. Physiologically, however, he is not normal. The second change in opiate addiction, and the most fascinating phenomenon to the pharmacologist, is the development of physical dependence. Once this is established the addict must receive the drug continually for his body to function normally. Deprived of morphine, the addict develops an "abstinence syndrome": he yawns, his eyes and nose water and he suffers "goose flesh," tremor, muscle twitches, restlessness, hot and cold flashes, fever, nausea, vomiting and diarrhea. He is acutely ill—and all for lack of morphine, which he craves intensely. An injection of the drug relieves his symptoms immediately.

These two elements of narcotic addiction, tolerance and physical dependence, can both be induced in animals by the repeated administration of morphine. One experimental application of

such addiction is exemplified in a laboratory at the University of Michigan, where Maurice H. Seevers and Gerald A. Deneau keep a colony of some 100 rhesus monkeys on morphine in order to test new drugs for addictive properties. Dependent monkeys are deprived of morphine and allowed to develop an abstinence syndrome. Then the test drug is injected; the degree to which it relieves the syndrome is a measure of its ability to be itself addictive.

Such experiments do not bear directly on the nature of addiction in animals. Do they, for example, "desire" morphine? More than 25 years ago S. D. Shirley Spragg of the Yale University School of Medicine demonstrated that animals do indeed exhibit morphine-seeking behavior. He addicted chimpanzees by giving them repeated injections of morphine. The apes had been trained to open a box with a stick to get food. Presented with two boxes, one containing food and the other a hypodermic syringe, addicted chimpanzees chose food if they had already received their regular injection; those that were past due for an injection chose the syringe even when they were hungry. (They did not, of course, give themselves an injection.)

A better experimental model would be one in which the animal voluntarily took its own drug. John R. Nichols of Southeastern Louisiana College carried out experiments of this type by adding morphine to the drinking water of rats. Because morphine has an intensely bitter taste the rats had to be forced to drink the drugged water by being deprived of any other supply. Once addicted, they selected morphine water in preference to plain water in spite of the taste. In other words, they sought morphine; they associated its ingestion with the relief of abstinence symptoms.

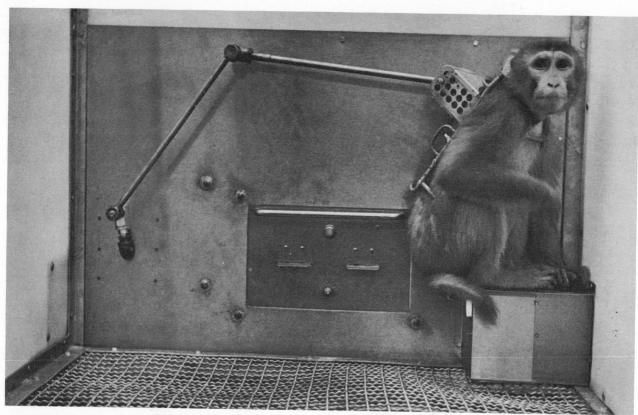

**SELF-INJECTION SYSTEM** developed by the author for rats was adapted for monkeys by Gerald A. Deneau and Tomoji Yanagita at the University of Michigan. The addicted monkey gets an intravenous injection of a drug by pressing one of the two pedals on the wall behind it. The tube that carries the drug solution is protected by lengths of steel pipe that swivel to allow the monkey some freedom of movement, and by the box on the animal's back. From the box the tube passes under skin into jugular vein.

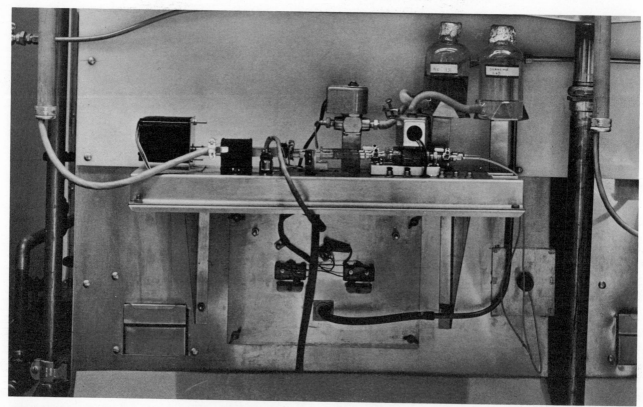

**INJECTION APPARATUS** is on the outside of the cage, on the reverse side of the back wall seen in the top photograph. The two pedals, each with a microswitch above it, are in the center foreground. On the shelf above them are two syringes containing drugs from the two bottles (*top right*). Signals from a pedal activate the electric motor (*left*), and one of the syringes delivers a drug solution to the rubber tubes that are seen (*bottom right*) entering the system of jointed pipes that leads to the animal.

**ALBINO RAT** is prepared for experiments on addiction. A plastic tube is passed under the skin from behind the ears to the front of the neck, where it is connected to a silicone-rubber cannula that is inserted into the animal's jugular vein and leads to the heart.

For a better parallel to human addiction, however, an animal should be able to take the drug at will, by injection—preferably intravenous—and over a long period of time. Self-administration by injection would avoid the complicating effects of thirst and the unpleasant taste of the drugged water. When the way to do this occurred to me it seemed so simple that I wondered why no one had ever tried it. My idea was to put some kind of tube into a vein of the animal and connect the tube to an injection machine the animal could operate itself. To receive an injection the animal would have only to press on a pedal in its cage, thus activating a syringe driver that would inject a metered amount of morphine into the vein. This is essentially the "operant conditioning" technique developed by B. F. Skinner of Harvard University and other workers. In a typical experiment of this type an animal is trained to respond to some stimulus—to press a pedal, for example—by receiving a "reinforcement," usually a reward of food or water, as soon as it responds correctly. Morphine would be my reinforcement.

As far as I know the first such self-injection experiments were those I carried out with rats in 1960 at the Upjohn Company Research Laboratories in Kalamazoo, Mich. Working out the details of the apparatus was more difficult than conceiving the idea, the main problem being to keep an injection tube implanted in the vein without restraining the animal. The solution was to run a sprocket chain of the kind found on bicycles to a saddle on the rat's back.

Polyethylene tubing woven down the chain does not twist because the chain flexes only in one plane, and the tubing is connected to the syringe driver by a sealed swivel [*compare illustration on next page*]. From the saddle the tubing runs under the animal's skin to a cannula, or fine tube, of silicone rubber that is passed down the jugular vein to the heart. (The cannula has to be placed in the heart because it would not remain functional in a rat's small veins for more than a few days.)

Before a rat could be expected to inject itself regularly I had to establish tolerance and physical dependence in it. The syringe driver, controlled by a program punched on film, automatically administered a series of gradually increasing doses, beginning with two milligrams per kilogram. (Drug doses are generally stated in terms of the experimental subject's weight. A dose of "two milligrams per kilogram" would be an injection of half a milligram in the case of a quarter-kilogram rat.) The injection was repeated every hour, each time with a dose 2.5 per cent larger than the previous one. After 122 hours the dose had reached 40 milligrams per kilogram, and this dose was repeated every hour for a day or two. Then the automatic injections ceased, a pedal switch was put in the cage and the syringe was set to inject 10 milligrams of morphine per kilogram every time the rat pressed the pedal.

In this situation it was not long before the rat happened to press the lever. Immediately it got a shot of morphine. After a few repetitions of the response (pressing the pedal) and the reinforcement (the injection) the rat began to press the lever at regular intervals—about once every two hours, more or less, depending on the individual. Some of the rats went into a sort of trance immediately on receiving the injection, sometimes resting on the pedal for about a minute. But as soon as they were prodded they would move about normally without any evidence of the depressive effects of morphine.

One might be tempted to assume at this point that the rat "liked" the morphine, but it is important not to read human reactions and emotions into an animal's behavior. Moreover, although human morphine addicts say they "like" the drug, even in humans it is not clear to what extent the drug is a positive pleasure and to what extent it simply brings relief from the rigors of abstinence. The fact is that the rat may not "like" the morphine at all but has learned that pressing the pedal stops the punishment of early abstinence.

Having established addiction and self-injection, I tried decreasing the dose administered with each response on the pedal. When the dose was cut from 10 to 3.2 milligrams per kilogram, the rats responded more frequently in an effort to satisfy their habit [*see top illustration, page 355*]. Then I disconnected the syringe completely so that the rats received no drug at all for their efforts. There was an abrupt increase in the frequency of responses, which then diminished gradually as the rats developed a severe abstinence syndrome. They became nervous and agitated (but never vicious), breathed rapidly, tried to escape from their cages and were sensitive to handling, as if being touched were painful. Gastrointestinal activity increased, the feces became soft and by the next morning the rats had suffered as much as a 20 per cent loss in weight. They were very sick rats, but a single injection put an end to all their symptoms.

In a second experiment the one-to-one relation between response and injection was changed. When a rat had to respond 10 times in order to get one dose, it would press the pedal rapidly until it received an injection and then leave the pedal untouched until it was time for another shot. This seemed to me one of the most intriguing aspects of the study. One might have expected that the motivation for the response was a gradual increase in the severity of the abstinence syndrome, but in that case the rat would at first respond only sporadically—not trying very hard—and then respond more rapidly until it finally got an injection. What seems to happen instead is that at a precise and reasonably predictable moment the rat is motivated to start working for the drug and that it then presses the pedal steadily until it gets the injection, which produces almost immediate satiation. It is probably the onset of abstinence that triggers the first responses, but there are no obvious symptoms at that point.

With R. James Collins I went on to increase the ratio between responses and injections, leaving the dose fixed. First we stabilized the addiction for a few days at a ratio of 10 responses to one injection. Then we increased the ratio each morning, first to a ratio of 20 to one and then in an approximate geometric progression to 32, 50, 75, 120, 180, 270 and 400 [*see illustration on page 356*]. With the change from 10 to 32 the number of injections obtained per day decreased somewhat, but as the ratio went from 32 to 120 there was only a small further drop in injections: the rats nearly compensated for the ratio change by responding more often. The reason they did not compensate completely apparently was that the effects of an injection still lasted about as long as at lower ratios; it took longer and longer to get an injection, but once the shot was administered satiation was complete and the rat did not start re-

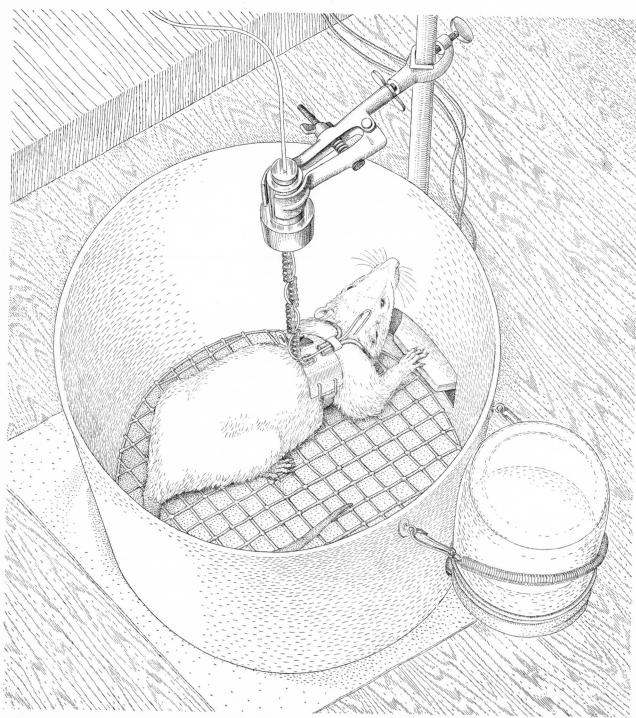

**ADDICTED RAT** takes drug injections at will by pressing the pedal. The drug solution comes down the tube to the clamp, where it passes through a liquid-tight "stuffing box" and a swivel and thence into another tube that is woven along a sprocket chain. The chain prevents the tube from twisting as the animal moves about its cage. The jar at right contains drinking water.

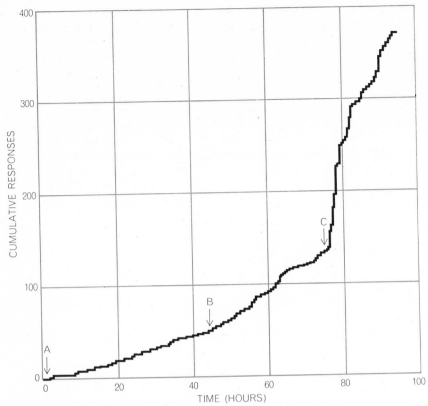

RESPONSE RATE varied with the size of the dose. After addiction the rat began to respond (A), at first receiving 10 milligrams of morphine per kilogram of body weight. When the dose was cut to 3.2 milligrams per kilogram (B), the rate increased. When the drug was then cut off completely (C), the response rate rose sharply again, then slowed.

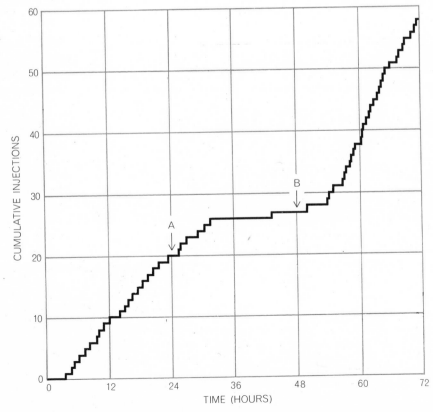

MORPHINE-LIKE DRUG etonitazine was added to the drinking water of an addicted rat at A. After ingesting enough of the new drug the rat stopped taking morphine shots. The etonitazine was removed at B, and after a while the rat resumed its self-injections.

sponding again until it needed more of the drug.

As the ratio passed 120 the number of injections decreased, until at 400 to one the rats were obtaining very little morphine. Whereas responses had been steady at the lower ratios, above 120 the rats would stop pressing the pedal for a few minutes and then begin again, further lengthening the response period. There were some indications that when injections were delayed by the long response periods required, the interval before the next injection was also prolonged. Unlike human addicts, rats do not anticipate their needs!

In the next modification we kept the ratio at one response per injection but decreased the dose every day. We had noticed that in the first experiment a reduction in the dose from 10 to 3.2 milligrams per kilogram had only about doubled the number of doses per day, with the result that the total intake of morphine decreased. There was also a tendency, at the lower dose level, sometimes to take more than one dose at a time. We tentatively interpreted this as an effort by the rat to "titrate" its morphine requirements—to find the exact dose that would satisfy it. To test this hypothesis we began with 10 milligrams per kilogram and reduced the dose each morning in a geometric progression: 10, 3.2, 1, .32 and so on. We expected that the rats would manage to keep their total daily intake about the same for at least two successive dose levels, making up for the reduction in dose by increasing the number of injections. Instead we found that as the dose was cut each day to about a third of what it had been, the number of injections continued merely to double. When the dose went below .32, there was little further increase in the number of injections and the rat was receiving hardly any of the drug. We have no good explanation for this result. It does seem to indicate that the size of the individual injection is a factor in maintaining a high drug intake, possibly because of a "jolt" at the moment of injection or some effect of a momentarily high drug level in the blood.

We were able to use our experimental system to compare the relative potency of various opiate drugs by substituting them for morphine in addicted rats. Dihydromorphinone (Dilaudid) and methadone (Dolophine), both of which are more potent than morphine in human beings, were also more potent in rats. On the other hand, codeine, which is not so potent for human addicts, was

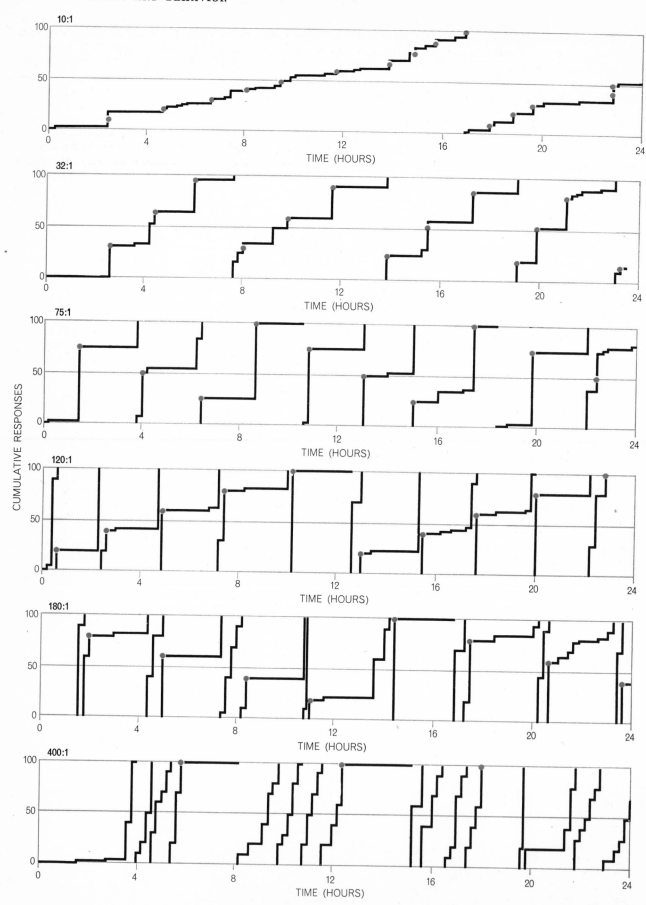

**VARYING THE RATIO** between responses and injections affected the total intake of morphine as shown in these sample records. The dose remained at 10 milligrams per kilogram for each injection, but the rats were made to respond from 10 to 400 times to get each injection (*colored dots*). At low ratios they compensated quite well, working faster to maintain their intake. At higher ratios they responded more sporadically and took longer for each injection, until finally they were receiving very few.

almost as effective as morphine itself in the animals. An attempt to substitute the synthetic drug meperidine (Demerol) was a failure: the rats killed themselves with an overdose. Apparently nothing short of a lethal dose of this drug was able to satisfy the rats' addiction.

In a final series of experiments we investigated the effect on morphine intake of the administration of a second drug. We began by putting into the rats' drinking water five milligrams per liter of etonitazine, a synthetic morphine-like drug that apparently does not taste bad to rats. The drugged water was substituted for plain water at eight o'clock one morning and removed 24 hours later, and it caused a marked decrease in morphine injections [see bottom illustration, page 355]. The decrease was not apparent at first because rats, being nocturnal animals, do most of their drinking (and eating) at night, but late in the day morphine intake practically ceased. The injection-free period lasted for several hours after the drugged water was removed because the animals first had to eliminate the etonitazine consumed in the early-morning hours.

To conduct more precise experiments we connected a constant-rate infusion pump to the intravenous tubing along with the syringe driver in order to administer various drugs by continuous infusion and determine their effect on the voluntary intake of morphine. The test drugs were infused for 24-hour periods alternated with periods in which salt solution was infused as a control. As we had expected, the infusion of morphine or codeine reduced the voluntary injec-tions, and the decrease was related to the rate of infusion. Meperidine, which had killed rats when it was directly substituted for morphine, now simply decreased the morphine intake, because the amount of meperidine administered was less than enough to satisfy the rats' requirements.

The morphine molecule can be modified slightly by substituting an allyl group ($C_3H_5$) for a methyl group ($CH_3$). The resulting molecule is a morphine antagonist called nalorphine. In medicine this drug is used to treat an overdose of morphine and also to detect morphine addiction quickly. Given to an addict, nalorphine temporarily counteracts the morphine in his body and precipitates a short-lived withdrawal reaction. When nalorphine was continuously infused into addict rats, it stepped up their morphine intake. Apparently it nullified the effect of some of the morphine in their bodies and made them feel the need for more of the narcotic.

Monkeys react to addicting drugs more like humans than rats do. It therefore seemed to workers in the University of Michigan group that self-injection experiments with monkeys might provide information with more direct bearing on problems of human addiction, and particularly data on the comparative effects of various drugs. Recently Deneau and Tomoji Yanagita have solved the technical problems involved in designing a saddle-and-swivel arrangement for monkeys—a challenging task in view of the almost uncanny ability of monkeys to undo fastenings and escape from restraint. The Michigan ex-periments are still in a preliminary stage, but they have already demonstrated that monkeys can keep themselves addicted by self-injection for many months; one monkey has maintained its addiction for 21 months.

Intravenous administration of drugs to relatively unrestrained animals has so far been applied only to the study of addiction, but it has many other potential applications. To the behavioral scientist it offers a means of studying the effects of various intravenously administered compounds as reinforcing agents, alone or in combination with conventional reinforcements. Apart from behavioral studies, continuous intravenous administration promises to improve the precision of administration of drugs in long-term experiments. Such investigations usually involve dosing animals two or three times a day, with resulting peaks and valleys in the concentration of the drug in their blood; continuous infusion will maintain a fairly constant level.

It should be emphasized that animal studies of addiction can illuminate only certain phases of the problem of human addiction. These include physical-dependence phenomena in particular and perhaps some of the fundamental aspects of behavior in relation to drugs. Human addiction must, however, be regarded as a combined physical and mental illness, and an understanding of its mechanism and treatment will have to come from research not only by pharmacologists but also by physicians, psychiatrists and social scientists.

# 45

# THE HALLUCINOGENIC DRUGS

FRANK BARRON, MURRAY E. JARVIK AND
STERLING BUNNELL, JR.                    April 1964

Human beings have two powerful needs that are at odds with each other: to keep things the same, and to have something new happen. We like to feel secure, yet at times we like to be surprised. Too much predictability leads to monotony, but too little may lead to anxiety. To establish a balance between continuity and change is a task facing all organisms, individual and social, human and non-human.

Keeping things predictable is generally considered one of the functions of the ego. When a person perceives accurately, thinks clearly, plans wisely and acts appropriately—and represses maladaptive thoughts and emotions—we say that his ego is strong. But the strong ego is also inventive, open to many perceptions that at first may be disorganizing. Research on the personality traits of highly creative individuals has shown that they are particularly alert to the challenge of the contradictory and the unpredictable, and that they may even court the irrational in their own make-up as a source of new and unexpected insight. Indeed, through all recorded history and everywhere in the world men have gone to considerable lengths to seek unpredictability by disrupting the functioning of the ego. A change of scene, a change of heart, a change of mind: these are the popular prescriptions for getting out of a rut.

Among the common ways of changing "mind" must be reckoned the use of intoxicating substances. Alcohol has quite won the day for this purpose in the U.S. and much of the rest of the world. Consumed at a moderate rate and in sensible quantities, it can serve simultaneously as a euphoriant and tranquilizing agent before it finally dulls the faculties and puts one to sleep. In properly disposed individuals it may dissolve sexual inhibitions, relieve fear and anxiety, or stimulate meditation on the meaning of life. In spite of its costliness to individual and social health when it is used immoderately, alcohol retains its rank as first among the substances used by mankind to change mental experience. Its closest rivals in popularity are opium and its derivatives and various preparations of cannabis, such as hashish and marijuana.

This article deals with another group of such consciousness-altering substances: the "hallucinogens." The most important of these are mescaline, which comes from the peyote cactus *Lophophora williamsii;* psilocybin and psilocin, from such mushrooms as *Psilocybe mexicana* and *Stropharia cubensis;* and d-lysergic acid diethylamide (LSD), which is derived from ergot (*Claviceps purpurea*), a fungus that grows on rye and wheat. All are alkaloids more or less related to one another in chemical structure.

Various names have been applied to this class of substances. They produce distinctive changes in perception that are sometimes referred to as hallucinations, although usually the person under the influence of the drug can distinguish his visions from reality, and even when they seem quite compelling he is able to attribute them to the action of the drug. If, therefore, the term "hallucination" is reserved for perceptions that the perceiver himself firmly believes indicate the existence of a corresponding object or event, but for which other observers can find no objective basis, then the "hallucinogens" only rarely produce hallucinations. There are several other names for this class of drugs. They have been called "psychotomimetic" because in some cases the effects seem to mimic psychosis [see "Experimental Psychoses," by Six Staff Members of the Boston Psychopathic Hospital; SCIENTIFIC AMERICAN, June, 1955]. Some observers prefer to use the term "psychedelic" to suggest that unsuspected capacities of the imagination are sometimes revealed in the perceptual changes.

The hallucinogens are currently a subject of intense debate and concern in medical and psychological circles. At issue is the degree of danger they present to the psychological health of the person who uses them. This has become an important question because of a rapidly increasing interest in the drugs among laymen. The recent controversy at Harvard University, stemming at first from methodological disagreements

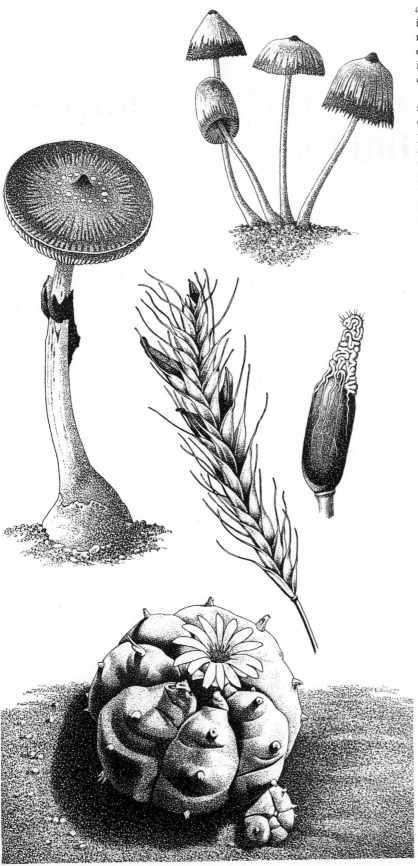

among investigators but subsequently involving the issue of protection of the mental health of the student body, indicated the scope of popular interest in taking the drugs and the consequent public concern over their possible misuse.

There are, on the other hand, constructive uses of the drugs. In spite of obvious differences between the "model psychoses" produced by these drugs and naturally occurring psychoses, there are enough similarities to warrant intensive investigation along these lines. The drugs also provide the only link, however tenuous, between human psychoses and aberrant behavior in animals, in which physiological mechanisms can be studied more readily than in man. Beyond this many therapists feel that there is a specialized role for the hallucinogens in the treatment of psychoneuroses. Other investigators are struck by the possibility of using the drugs to facilitate meditation and aesthetic discrimination and to stimulate the imagination. These possibilities, taken in conjunction with the known hazards, are the bases for the current professional concern and controversy.

In evaluating potential uses and misuses of the hallucinogens, one can draw on a considerable body of knowledge from such disciplines as anthropology, pharmacology, biochemistry, psychology and psychiatry.

In some primitive societies the plants from which the major hallucinogens are derived have been known for millenniums and have been utilized for divination, curing, communion with supernatural powers and meditation to improve self-understanding or social unity; they have also served such mundane purposes as allaying hunger and relieving discomfort or boredom. In the Western Hemisphere the ingestion of hallucinogenic plants in pre-Columbian times was limited to a zone extending from what is now the southwestern U.S. to the northwestern basin of the Amazon. Among the Aztecs there were professional diviners who achieved inspiration by eating either peyote, hallucinogenic mushrooms (which the Aztecs called *teo-nanacatyl*, or "god's flesh") or other hallucinogenic plants. *Teo-nanacatyl* was said to have been distributed at the coronation of Montezuma to make the ceremony seem more spectacular. In the years following the conquest of Mexico there were reports of communal mushroom rites among the Aztecs and other Indians of southern Mexico. The communal use has almost died out today, but in several

**NATURAL SOURCES** of the main hallucinogens are depicted. Psilocybin comes from the mushrooms *Stropharia cubensis* (*top left*) and *Psilocybe mexicana* (*top right*). LSD is synthesized from an alkaloid in ergot (*Claviceps purpurea*), a fungus that grows on cereal grains; an ergot-infested rye seed head is shown (*center*) together with a larger-scale drawing of the ergot fungus. Mescaline is from the peyote cactus *Lophophora williamsii* (*bottom*).

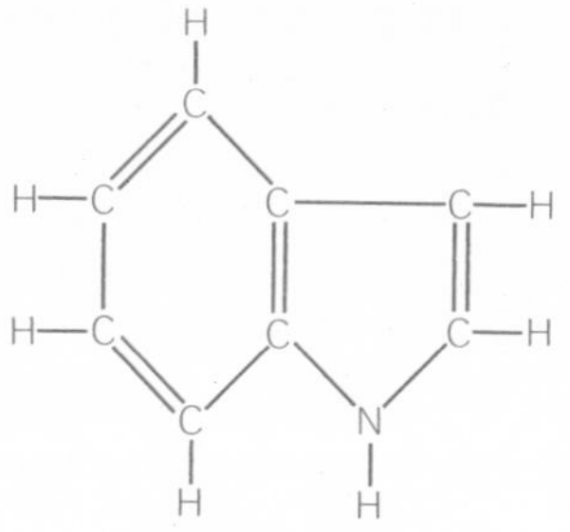

INDOLE RING

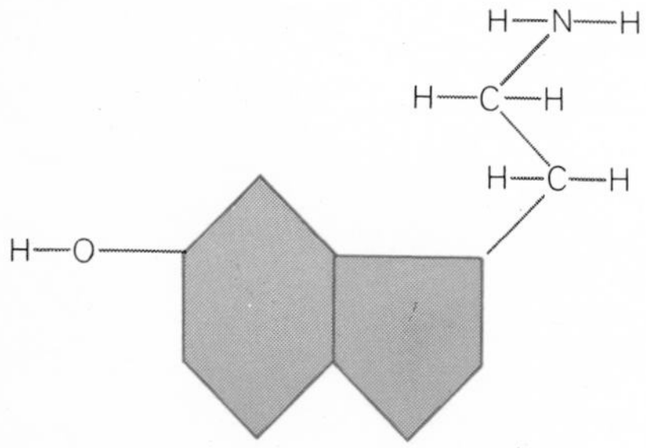

SEROTONIN

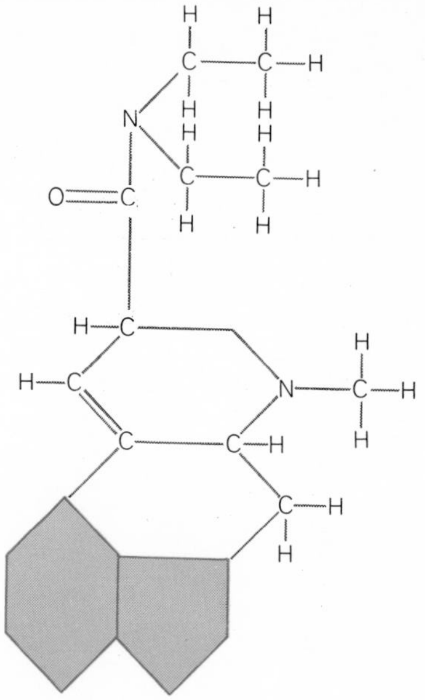

LSD

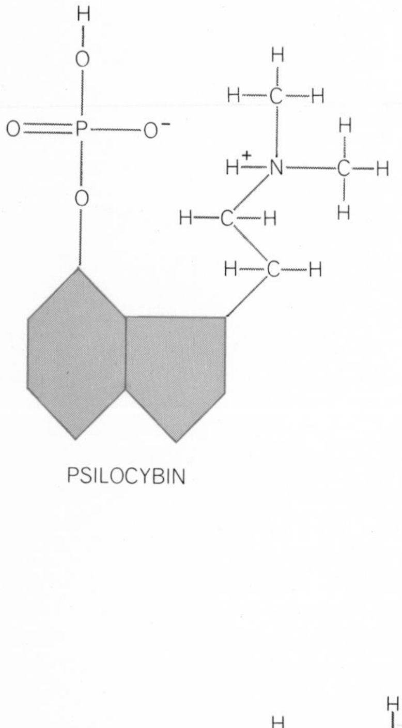

PSILOCYBIN

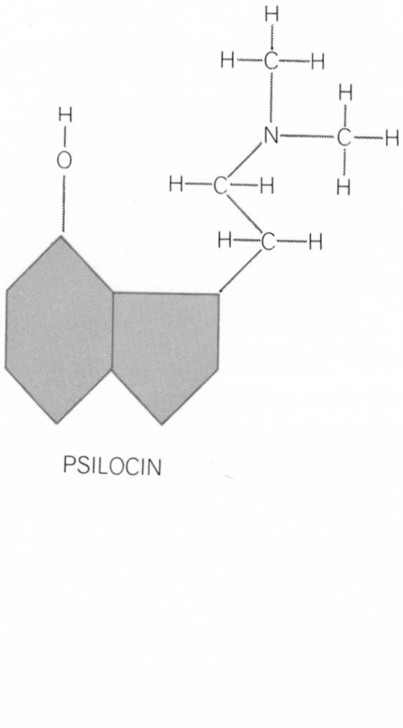

PSILOCIN

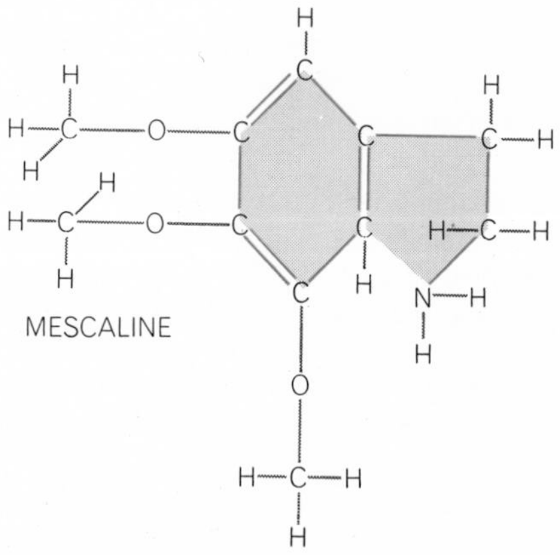

MESCALINE

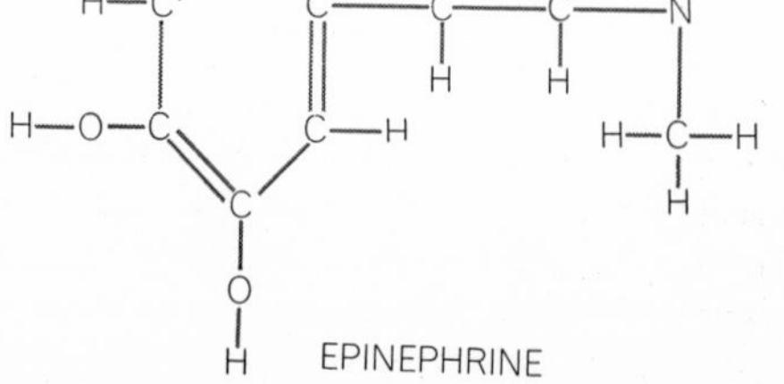

EPINEPHRINE

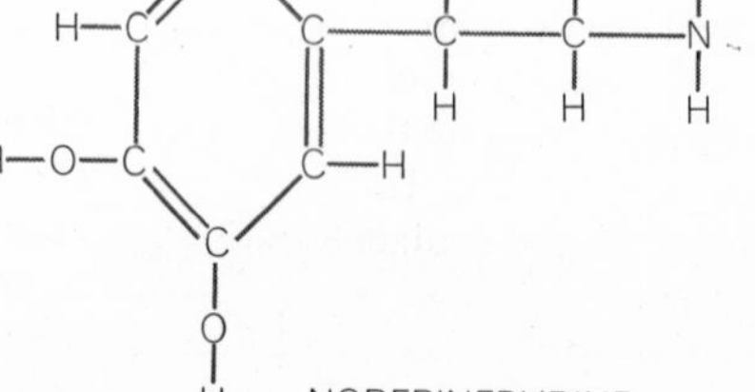

NOREPINEPHRINE

CHEMICAL RELATIONS among several of the hallucinogens and neurohumors are indicated by these structural diagrams. The indole ring (in color at top) is a basic structural unit; it appears, as indicated by the colored shapes, in serotonin, LSD, psilocybin and psilocin. Mescaline does not have an indole ring but, as shown by the light color, can be represented so as to suggest its relation to the ring. The close relation between mescaline and the two catechol amines epinephrine and norepinephrine is also apparent here.

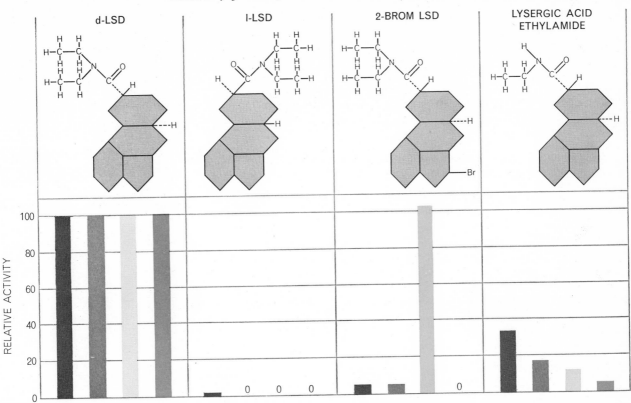

**SLIGHT CHANGES** in LSD molecule produce large changes in its properties. Here LSD (*left*) is used as a standard, with a "relative activity" of 100 in toxicity (*dark gray bar*), fever-producing effect (*light gray*), ability to antagonize serotonin (*light color*) and typical psychotomimetic effects (*dark color*). The stereoisomer of LSD (*second from left*) in which the positions of the side chains are reversed, shows almost no activity; the substitution of a bromine atom (*third from left*) reduces the psychotomimetic effect but not the serotonin antagonism; the removal of one of the two ethyl groups (*right*) sharply reduces activity in each of the areas.

tribes the medicine men or women (*curanderos*) still partake of *Psilocybe* and *Stropharia* in their rituals.

In the arid region between the Rio Grande and central Mexico, where the peyote cactus grows, the dried tops of the plants ("peyote buttons") were eaten by Indian shamans, or medicine men, and figured in tribal rituals. During the 19th century the Mescalero Apaches acquired the plant and developed a peyote rite. The peyotism of the Mescaleros (whence the name mescaline) spread to the Comanches and Kiowas, who transformed it into a religion with a doctrine and ethic as well as ritual. Peyotism, which spread rapidly through the Plains tribes, became fused with Christianity. Today its adherents worship God as the great spirit who controls the universe and put some of his power into peyote, and Jesus as the man who gave the plant to the Indians in a time of need. Saturday-night meetings, usually held in a traditional tepee, begin with the eating of the sacramental peyote; then the night is spent in prayer, ritual singing and introspective contemplation, and in the morning there is a communion breakfast of corn, game and fruit.

Recognizing the need for an effective organization to protect their form of worship, several peyote churches joined in 1918 to form the Native American Church, which now has about 225,000 members in tribes from Nevada to the East Coast and from the Mexican border to Saskatchewan. It preaches brotherly love, care of the family, self-reliance and abstinence from alcohol. The church has been able to defeat attempts, chiefly by the missionaries of other churches, to outlaw peyote by Federal legislation, and it has recently brought about the repeal of antipeyote legislation in several states.

The hallucinogens began to attract scholarly interest in the last decade of the 19th century, when the investigations and conceptions of such men as Francis Galton, J. M. Charcot, Sigmund Freud and William James introduced a new spirit of serious inquiry into such subjects as hallucination, mystical experience and other "paranormal" psychic phenomena. Havelock Ellis and the psychiatrist Silas Weir Mitchell wrote accounts of the subjective effects of peyote, or Anhalonium, as it was then called. Such essays in turn stimulated

the interest of pharmacologists. The active principle of peyote, the alkaloid called mescaline, was isolated in 1896; in 1919 it was recognized that the molecular structure of mescaline was related to the structure of the adrenal hormone epinephrine.

This was an important turning point, because the interest in the hallucinogens as a possible key to naturally occurring psychoses is based on the chemical relations between the drugs and the neurohumors: substances that chemically transmit impulses across synapses between two neurons, or nerve cells, or between a neuron and an effector such as a muscle cell. Acetylcholine and the catechol amines epinephrine and norepinephrine have been shown to act in this manner in the peripheral nervous system of vertebrates; serotonin has the same effect in some invertebrates. It is frequently assumed that these substances also act as neurohumors in the central nervous system; at least they are present there, and injecting them into various parts of the brain seems to affect nervous activity.

The structural resemblance of mescaline and epinephrine suggested a possible link between the drug and mental illness: Might the early, excited stage of schizophrenia be produced or at least triggered by an error in metabolism that produced a mescaline-like substance? Techniques for gathering evidence on this question were not available, however, and the speculation on an "M-substance" did not lead to serious experimental work.

When LSD was discovered in 1943, its extraordinary potency again aroused interest in the possibility of finding a natural chemical activator of the schizophrenic process. The M-substance hypothesis was revived on the basis of reports that hallucinogenic effects were produced by adrenochrome and other breakdown products of epinephrine, and the hypothesis appeared to be strengthened by the isolation from human urine of some close analogues of hallucinogens. Adrenochrome has not, however, been detected in significant amounts in the human body, and it seems unlikely that the analogues could be produced in sufficient quantity to effect mental changes.

The relation between LSD and serotonin has given rise to the hypothesis that schizophrenia is caused by an imbalance in the metabolism of serotonin, with excitement and hallucinations resulting from an excess of serotonin in certain regions of the brain, and depressive and catatonic states resulting from a deficiency of serotonin. The idea arose in part from the observation that in some laboratory physiological preparations LSD acts rather like serotonin but in other preparations it is a powerful antagonist of serotonin; thus LSD might facilitate or block some neurohumoral action of serotonin in the brain.

The broad objection to the serotonin theory of schizophrenia is that it requires an oversimplified view of the disease's pattern of symptoms. Moreover, many congeners, or close analogues, of LSD, such as 2-brom lysergic acid, are equally effective or more effective antagonists of serotonin without being significantly active psychologically in man. This does not disprove the hypothesis, however. In man 2-brom LSD blocks the mental effects of a subsequent dose of LSD, and in the heart of a clam it blocks the action of both LSD and serotonin. Perhaps there are "keyholes" at the sites where neurohumors act; in the case of those for serotonin it may be that LSD fits the hole and opens the lock, whereas the psychologically inactive analogues merely occupy the keyhole, blocking the action of serotonin or LSD without mimicking their effects. Certainly the re-

semblance of most of the hallucinogens to serotonin is marked, and the correlations between chemical structure and pharmacological action deserve intensive investigation. The serotonin theory of schizophrenia is far from proved, but there is strong evidence for an organic factor of some kind in the disease; it may yet turn out to involve either a specific neurohumor or an imbalance among several neurohumors.

The ingestion of LSD, mescaline or psilocybin can produce a wide range of subjective and objective effects. The subjective effects apparently depend on at least three kinds of variable: the properties and potency of the drug itself; the basic personality traits and current mood of the person ingesting it, and the social and psychological context, including the meaning to the individual of his act in taking the drug and his interpretation of the motives of those who made it available. The discussion of subjective effects that follows is compiled from many different accounts of the drug experience; it should be considered an inventory of possible effects rather than a description of a typical episode.

One subjective experience that is frequently reported is a change in visual perception. When the eyes are open, the perception of light and space is affected: colors become more vivid and seem to glow; the space between objects becomes more apparent, as though space itself had become "real," and surface details appear to be more sharply defined. Many people feel a new awareness of the physical beauty of the world, particularly of visual harmonies, colors, the play of light and the exquisiteness of detail.

The visual effects are even more striking when the eyes are closed. A constantly changing display appears, its content ranging from abstract forms to dramatic scenes involving imagined people or animals, sometimes in exotic lands or ancient times. Different individuals have recalled seeing wavy lines, cobweb or chessboard designs, gratings, mosaics, carpets, floral designs, gems, windmills, mausoleums, landscapes, "arabesques spiraling into eternity," statuesque men of the past, chariots, sequences of dramatic action, the face of Buddha, the face of Christ, the Crucifixion, "the mythical dwelling places of the gods," the immensity and blackness of space. After taking peyote Silas Weir Mitchell wrote: "To give the faintest idea of the perfectly satisfying intensity and purity of these gorgeous color fruits

WATER COLORS were done, while under the influence of a relatively large dose of a hallucinogenic drug, by a person with no art training. Originals are bright yellow, purple, green and red as well as black.

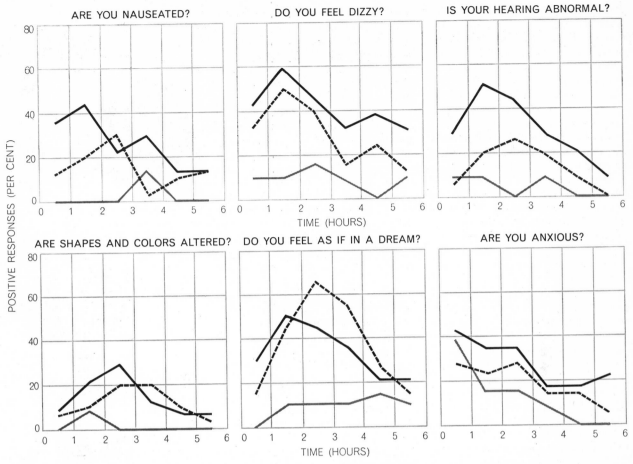

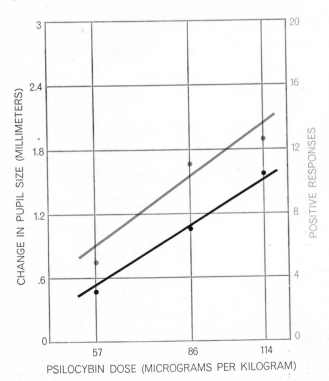

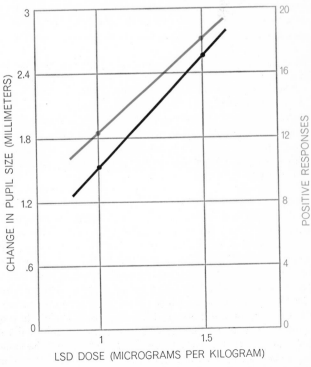

SUBJECTIVE REPORT on physiological and perceptual effects of LSD was obtained by means of a questionnaire containing 47 items, the results for six of which are presented. Volunteers were questioned at one-hour intervals beginning half an hour after they took the drug. The curves show the per cent of the group giving positive answers at each time. The gray curves are for those given an inactive substance, the broken black curves for between 25 and 75 micrograms and the solid black curves for between 100 and 225.

OBJECTIVE AND SUBJECTIVE effects vary with dosage as shown here. The data plotted in black are for the increase in size of pupil; the number of positive responses to questions like the ones at the top of the page are shown in color. The objective and subjective measures vary in a similar manner. The data are from an experiment done by Harris Isbell of the University of Kentucky.

is quite beyond my power." A painter described the waning hours of the effects of psilocybin as follows: "As the afternoon wore on I felt very content to simply sit and stare out of the window at the snow and the trees, and at that time I recall feeling that the snow, the fire in the fireplace, the darkened and book-lined room were so perfect as to seem almost unreal."

The changes in visual perception are not always pleasant. Aldous Huxley called one of his books about mescaline *Heaven and Hell* in recognition of the contradictory sensations induced by the drug. The "hellish" experiences include an impression of blackness accompanied by feelings of gloom and isolation, a garish modification of the glowing colors observed in the "heavenly" phase, a sense of sickly greens and ugly dark reds. The subject's perception of his own body may become unpleasant: his limbs may seem to be distorted or his flesh to be decaying; in a mirror his face may appear to be a mask, his smile a meaningless grimace. Sometimes all human movements appear to be mere puppetry, or everyone seems to be dead. These experiences can be so disturbing that a residue of fear and depression persists long after the effects of the drug have worn off.

Often there are complex auditory hallucinations as well as visual ones: lengthy conversations between imaginary people, perfectly orchestrated musical compositions the subject has never heard before, voices speaking foreign languages unknown to the subject. There have also been reports of hallucinatory odors and tastes and of visceral and other bodily sensations. Frequently patterns of association normally confined to a single sense will cross over to other senses: the sound of music evokes the visual impression of jets of colored light, a "cold" human voice makes the subject shiver, pricking the skin with a pin produces the visual impression of a circle, light glinting on a Christmas tree ornament seems to shatter and to evoke the sound of sleigh bells. The time sense is altered too. The passage of time may seem to be a slow and pleasant flow or to be intolerably tedious. A "sense of timelessness" is often reported; the subject feels outside of or beyond time, or time and space seem infinite.

In some individuals one of the most basic constancies in perception is affected: the distinction between subject and object. A firm sense of personal identity depends on knowing accurately the borders of the self and on being able to distinguish what is inside from what is outside. Paranoia is the most vivid pathological instance of the breakdown of this discrimination; the paranoiac attributes to personal and impersonal forces outside himself the impulses that actually are inside him. Mystical and transcendental experiences are marked by the loss of this same basic constancy. "All is one" is the prototype of a mystical utterance. In the mystical state the distinction between subject and object disappears; the subject is seen to be one with the object. The experience is usually one of rapture or ecstasy and in religious terms is described as "holy." When the subject thus achieves complete identification with the object, the experience seems beyond words.

Some people who have taken a large dose of a hallucinogenic drug report feelings of "emptiness" or "silence," pertaining either to the interior of the self or to an "interior" of the universe—or to both as one. Such individuals have a sense of being completely undifferentiated, as though it were their personal consciousness that had been "emptied," leaving none of the usual discriminations on which the functioning of the ego depends. One man who had this experience thought later that it had been an anticipation of death, and that the regaining of the basic discriminations was like a remembrance of the very first days of life after birth.

The effect of the hallucinogens on sexual experience is not well documented. One experiment that is often quoted seemed to provide evidence that mescaline is an anaphrodisiac, an inhibitor of sexual appetite; this conclusion seemed plausible because the drugs have so often been associated with rituals emphasizing asceticism and prayer. The fact is, however, that the drugs are probably neither anaphrodisiacs nor aphrodisiacs—if indeed any drug is. There is reason to believe that if the drug-taking situation is one in which sexual relations seem appropriate, the hallucinogens simply bring to the sexual experience the same kind of change in perception that occurs in other areas of experience.

The point is that in all the hallucinogen-produced experiences it is never the drug alone that is at work. As in the case of alcohol, the effects vary widely depending on when the drug is taken, where, in the presence of whom, in what dosage and—perhaps most important of all—by whom. What happens to the individual after he takes the drug, and his changing relations to the setting and the people in it during the episode, will further influence his experience.

Since the setting is so influential in these experiments, it sometimes happens that a person who is present when someone else is taking a hallucinogenic drug, but who does not take the drug himself, behaves as though he were under the influence of a hallucinogen. In view of this effect one might expect that a person given an inactive substance he thought was a drug would respond as though he had actually received the drug. Indeed, such responses have sometimes been noted. In controlled experiments, however, subjects given an inactive substance are readily distinguishable from those who take a drug; the difference is apparent in their appearance and behavior, their answers to questionnaires and their physiological responses. Such behavioral similarities as are observed can be explained largely by a certain apprehension felt by a person who receives an inactive substance he thinks is a drug, or by anticipation on the part of someone who has taken the drug before.

In addition to the various subjective effects of the hallucinogens there are a number of observable changes in physiological function and in performance that one can measure or at least describe objectively. The basic physiological effects are those typical of a mild excitement of the sympathetic nervous system. The hallucinogens usually dilate the pupils, constrict the peripheral arterioles and raise the systolic blood pressure; they may also increase the excitability of such spinal reflexes as the knee jerk. Electroencephalograms show that the effect on electrical brain waves is usually of a fairly nonspecific "arousal" nature: the pattern is similar to that of a normally alert, attentive and problem-oriented subject, and if rhythms characteristic of drowsiness or sleep have been present, they disappear when the drug is administered. (Insomnia is common the first night after one of the drugs has been taken.) Animal experiments suggest that LSD produces these effects by stimulating the reticular formation of the midbrain, not directly but by stepping up the sensory input.

Under the influence of one of the hallucinogens there is usually some reduction in performance on standard tests of reasoning, memory, arithmetic, spelling and drawing. These findings may not indicate an inability to perform well; after taking a drug many people simply refuse to co-operate with the tester. The very fact that someone should want to

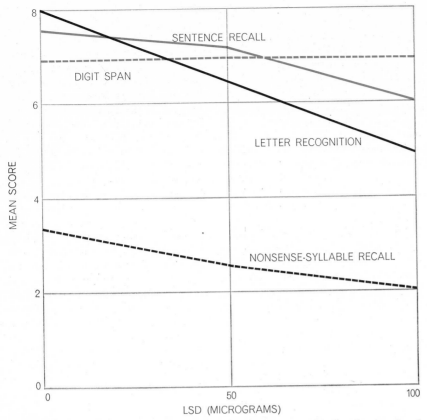

EFFECT OF LSD on memory was determined with standard tests. Curves show results of four tests for subjects given an inactive substance, 50 micrograms of the drug and 100 micrograms respectively. Effect of LSD was to decrease scores except in a test of digit-recall ability.

of psilocybin and two milligrams of LSD. No permanent effects were noted in these cases, but obviously no decisive studies of the upper limits of dosage have been undertaken.

There are also differences among the hallucinogens in the time of onset of effects and the duration of intoxication. When mescaline is given orally, the effects appear in two or three hours and last for 12 hours or more. LSD acts in less than an hour; some of its effects persist for eight or nine hours, and insomnia can last as long as 16 hours. Psilocybin usually acts within 20 or 30 minutes, and its full effect is felt for about five hours. All these estimates are for the standard dose administered orally; when any of the drugs is given intravenously, the first effects appear within minutes.

At the present time LSD and psilocybin are treated by the U.S. Food and Drug Administration like any other "experimental drug," which means that they can be legally distributed only to qualified investigators who will administer them in the course of an approved program of experimentation. In practice the drugs are legally available only to investigators working under a Government grant or for a state or Federal agency.

Nevertheless, there has probably been an increase during the past two or three years in the uncontrolled use of the drugs to satisfy personal curiosity or to experience novel sensations. This has led a number of responsible people in government, law, medicine and psychology to urge the imposition of stricter controls that would make the drugs more difficult to obtain even for basic research. These people emphasize the harmful possibilities of the drugs; citing the known cases of adverse reactions, they conclude that the prudent course is to curtail experimentation with hallucinogens.

Others—primarily those who have worked with the drugs—emphasize the constructive possibilities, insist that the hallucinogens have already opened up important leads in research and conclude that it would be shortsighted as well as contrary to the spirit of free scientific inquiry to restrict the activities of qualified investigators. Some go further, questioning whether citizens should be denied the opportunity of trying the drugs even without medical or psychological supervision and arguing that anyone who is mentally competent should have the right to explore the varieties

test them may seem absurd and may arouse either hostility or amusement. Studies by one of the authors in which tests of attention and concentration were administered to subjects who had been given different doses of LSD indicated that motivation was perhaps as important in determining scores as the subject's intellectual capacity.

The hallucinogenic drugs are not addictive—if one means by addiction that physiological dependence is established and the drug becomes necessary, usually in increasing amounts, for satisfactory physiological functioning. Some individuals become psychologically dependent on the drugs, however, and develop a "habit" in that sense; indeed, there is a tendency for those who ingest hallucinogens habitually to make the drug experience the center of all their activities. LSD, mescaline and psilocybin do produce physiological tolerance. If the same quantity of LSD is administered on three successive days, for example, it will not suffice by the third day to produce the same subjective or physiological effects; tolerance develops more slowly and less completely with mescaline and psilocybin. When an individual becomes tolerant to a given dos-

age of LSD, the ordinarily equivalent dose of psilocybin produces reduced effects. This phenomenon of cross-tolerance suggests that the two drugs have common pathways of action. Any tolerance established by daily administration of the drugs wears off rather rapidly, generally being dissipated within a few days if the drug is not taken.

The three major hallucinogens differ markedly in potency. The standard human doses—those that will cause the average adult male weighing about 150 pounds to show the full clinical effects—are 500 milligrams of mescaline, 20 milligrams of psilocybin and .1 milligram of LSD. It is assumed that in a large enough dose any of the hallucinogens would be lethal, but there are no documented cases of human deaths from the drugs alone. Death has been brought on in sensitive laboratory animals such as rabbits by LSD doses equivalent to 120 times the standard human dose. Some animals are much less susceptible; white rats have been given doses 1,000 times larger than the standard human dose without lasting harm. The maximum doses known by the authors to have been taken by human beings are 900 milligrams of mescaline, 70 milligrams

of conscious experience if he can do so without harming himself or others.

The most systematic survey of the incidence of serious adverse reactions to hallucinogens covered nearly 5,000 cases, in which LSD was administered on more than 25,000 occasions. Psychotic reactions lasting more than 48 hours were observed in fewer than two-tenths of 1 per cent of the cases. The rate of attempted suicides was slightly over a tenth of 1 per cent, and these involved psychiatric patients with histories of instability. Among those who took the drug simply as subjects in experiments there were no attempted suicides and the psychotic reactions occurred in fewer than a tenth of 1 per cent of the cases.

Recent reports do indicate that the incidence of bad reactions has been increasing, perhaps because more individuals have been taking the hallucinogens in settings that emphasize sensation-seeking or even deliberate social delinquency. Since under such circumstances there is usually no one in attendance who knows how to avert dangerous developments, a person in this situation may find himself facing an extremely frightening hallucination with no one present who can help him to recognize where the hallucination ends and reality begins. Yet the question of what is a proper setting is not a simple one. One of the criticisms of the Harvard experiments was that some were conducted in private homes rather than in a laboratory or clinical setting. The experimenters defended this as an attempt to provide a feeling of naturalness and "psychological safety." Such a setting, they hypothesized, should reduce the likelihood of negative reactions such as fear and hostility and increase the positive experiences. Controlled studies of this hypothesis have not been carried out, however.

Many psychiatrists and psychologists who have administered hallucinogens in a therapeutic setting claim specific benefits in the treatment of psychoneuroses, alcoholism and social delinquency. The published studies are difficult to evaluate because almost none have employed control groups. One summary of the available statistics on the treatment of alcoholism does indicate that about 50 per cent of the patients treated with a combination of psychotherapy and LSD abstained from alcohol for at least a year, compared with 30 per cent of the patients treated by psychotherapy alone.

In another recent study the results of psychological testing before and after

LSD therapy were comparable in most respects to the results obtained when conventional brief psychotherapy was employed. Single-treatment LSD therapy was significantly more effective, however, in relieving neurotic depression. If replicated, these results may provide an important basis for more directed study of the treatment of specific psychopathological conditions.

If the hallucinogens do have psychotherapeutic merit, it seems possible that they work by producing a shift in personal values. William James long ago noted that "the best cure for dipsomania is religiomania." There appear to be religious aspects of the drug experience that may bring about a change in behavior by causing a "change of heart." If this is so, one might be able to apply the hallucinogens in the service of moral regeneration while relying on more conventional techniques to give the patient insight into his habitual behavior patterns and motives.

In the light of the information now available about the uses and possible abuses of the hallucinogens, common sense surely decrees some form of social

control. In considering such control it should always be emphasized that the reaction to these drugs depends not only on their chemical properties and biological activity but also on the context in which they are taken, the meaning of the act and the personality and mood of the individual who takes them. If taking the drug is defined by the group or individual, or by society, as immoral or criminal, one can expect guilt and aggression and further social delinquency to result; if the aim is to help or to be helped, the experience may be therapeutic and strengthening; if the subject fears psychosis, the drug could induce psychosis. The hallucinogens, like so many other discoveries of man, are analogous to fire, which can burn down the house or spread through the house life-sustaining warmth. Purpose, planning and constructive control make the difference. The immediate research challenge presented by the hallucinogens is a practical question: Can ways be found to minimize or eliminate the hazards, and to identify and develop further the constructive potentialities, of these powerful drugs?

**NATIVE AMERICAN CHURCH** members take part in a peyote ceremony in Saskatchewan, Canada. Under the influence of the drug, they gaze into the fire as they pray and meditate.

# BIOGRAPHIES AND BIBLIOGRAPHIES

*The biographical and bibliographical data are those that were*
*available at the time the articles appeared in* SCIENTIFIC AMERICAN.

## PART I. ANIMAL BEHAVIOR

### 1. The Curious Behavior of the Stickleback

#### The Author

N. TINBERGEN is Reader in Animal Behaviour at the University of Oxford and a Fellow of Merton College. Born and raised in the Netherlands, he took his doctorate at the University of Leiden in 1932, and later went to the University of Vienna, where he worked with the noted student of animal behavior Konrad Z. Lorenz. At the end of World War II, Tinbergen, already famous for his lectures at Leiden, was invited to pursue his career at Oxford. He has written several articles for SCIENTIFIC AMERICAN.

#### Bibliography

THE STUDY OF INSTINCT. N. Tinbergen. Oxford University Press, 1951.

### 2. The Social Life of Baboons

#### The Authors

S. L. WASHBURN and IRVEN DEVORE are respectively professor and acting assistant professor of anthropology at the University of California. Washburn, a past president of the American Association of Physical Anthropologists and editor of the association's journal since 1955, was educated at Harvard University. He received his Ph.D. from Harvard in 1940, taught anatomy at Columbia University from 1939 to 1942 and then joined the department of anthropology at the University of Chicago. Washburn became a member of the California faculty in 1959. De-Vore, who is currently completing his Ph.D. degree at Chicago, received a B.A. from the University of Texas in 1956 and an M.A. from Chicago in 1959. The study described in the article by Washburn and DeVore was made possible by a grant from the Ford Foundation.

#### Bibliography

BEHAVIOR AND EVOLUTION. Edited by Anne Roe and George Gaylord Simpson. Yale University Press, 1958.

A STUDY OF BEHAVIOUR OF THE CHACMA BABOON, PAPIO URSINUS. Niels Bolwig in *Behaviour*, Vol. 14, No. 1–2, pages 136–163; 1959.

### 3. The Homing Salmon

#### The Authors

ARTHUR D. HASLER and JAMES A. LARSEN are both at the University of Wisconsin. Hasler is head of Wisconsin's Lake Laboratory and professor of zoology. Born in Utah, he studied in Germany, graduated in 1932 from Brigham Young University, worked for two years as an aquatic biologist for the U.S. Fish and Wildlife Service in Chesapeake Bay and in 1937 took his Ph.D. in zoology at the University of Wisconsin, where he has taught ever since. He spent a couple of summers as director of the Lake Geneva Institute of Natural Science before the war, and in 1945 the War Department sent him to Germany in its Strategic Bombing Survey. Hasler is a former vice president of the Society of Limnology and Oceanography. He is currently in Munich working with Karl von Frisch at the Zoological Institute. Larsen is the science editor of the University of Wisconsin News Service. He has done some research in animal and plant ecology, but his only part in the article here was as a collaborator with Hasler in writing it.

### 4. Sound Communication in Honeybees

#### The Author

ADRIAN M. WENNER is assistant professor of biology at the University of California at Santa Barbara. A native of Minnesota, Wenner received a B.S. in mathematics from Gustavus Adolphus College in 1951. He also acquired an M.S. in biology from Chico State College in California in 1955 and a Ph.D. in zoology from the University of Michigan in 1961. He joined the Santa Barbara faculty in 1960.

#### Bibliography

COMMUNICATION AMONG SOCIAL BEES. Martin Lindauer. Harvard University Press, 1961.

COMMUNICATION WITH QUEEN HONEY BEES BY SUBSTRATE SOUND. Adrian M. Wenner in *Science*, Vol. 138, No. 3538, pages 446–447; October, 1962.

SOUND PRODUCTION DURING THE WAGGLE DANCE OF THE HONEY BEE. A. M. Wenner in *Animal Behaviour*, Vol. 10, No. 1/2, pages 79–95; 1962.

ÜBER DIE SCHALLERZEUGUNG BEIM WERBETANZ DER HONIGBIENE. Harald Esch in *Zeitschrift für Vergleichende Physiologie*, Vol. 45, No. 1, pages 1–11; October, 1961.

## 5. The Evolution of Behavior

### The Author

KONRAD Z. LORENZ is perhaps best known in the U.S. as the author of two entertaining works on animal psychology: *King Solomon's Ring* and *Man Meets Dog*. Born in Vienna, he is a son of Adolf Lorenz, a well-known orthopedic surgeon. Lorenz followed in his father's footsteps by acquiring an M.D. degree from the University of Vienna. In 1928 he became an assistant in the University's anatomical institute and four years later acquired a second doctorate, this time in zoology. After several years as lecturer in comparative anatomy and animal behavior, Lorenz left Vienna in 1950 to head the department of psychology at the University of Königsberg. He now serves on the scientific council of the Max Planck Society for the Advancement of Science and is vice-director of the Max Planck Institute of Comparative Ethology.

### Bibliography

THE STUDY OF INSTINCT. N. Tinbergen. Clarendon Press, 1952.

## 6. The Behavior of Lovebirds

### The Author

WILLIAM C. DILGER is assistant director of the Laboratory of Ornithology at Cornell University and head of the laboratory's research program. Dilger began his undergraduate studies at Cornell following the end of World War II, in which he had served as a combat and reconnaissance photographer with the Second Air Command Group in the Southeast Asia theater. He received his B.S. from Cornell in 1949, became curator of birds the same year and acquired his Ph.D. in 1955. Though trained primarily in evolutionary biology and vertebrate zoology, Dilger notes that he has "always been interested in living, whole animals." Dilger taught comparative anatomy and general zoology at St. Lawrence University for a year and then returned to Cornell in 1956.

### Bibliography

THE COMPARATIVE ETHOLOGY OF THE AFRICAN PARROT GENUS AGAPORNIS. William C. Dilger in *Zeitschrift für Tierpsychologie*, Vol. 17, No. 6, pages 649–685; 1960.

THE EVOLUTION OF BEHAVIOR IN GULLS. N. Tinbergen in *Scientific American*, Vol. 203, No. 6, pages 118–130; December, 1960.

SOME RECENT TRENDS IN ETHOLOGY. R. A. Hinde in *Psychology: A Study of a Science*, Vol. 2, edited by Sigmund Koch, pages 561–610. McGraw-Hill Book Company, Inc., 1959.

THE STUDY OF INSTINCT. N. Tinbergen. Oxford University Press, 1951.

# PART II. PHYSIOLOGICAL DETERMINANTS OF INSTINCTIVE BEHAVIOR

## 7. Electrically Controlled Behavior

### The Authors

ERICH VON HOLST and URSULA VON SAINT PAUL are respectively director of the Max Planck Institute for the Physiology of Behavior and a staff member of the institute. Von Holst, who was born in Riga, Latvia, studied at the universities of Kiel, Vienna and Berlin, obtaining his Ph.D. from the last institution. From 1939 to 1947 he was a lecturer at the University of Göttingen, taught for two years at the University of Heidelberg, and in 1949 he became director of the Max Planck Institute for Marine Biology. He has held his present post since 1954. Miss von Saint Paul studied at the universities of Innsbruck, Heidelberg and Münster. She took her doctorate at Münster in 1950. From 1950 to 1957, when she went to von Holst's laboratory, Miss von Saint Paul worked in the laboratory of Gustav Kramer at the Max Planck Institute for Marine Biology.

### Bibliography

FERNREIZUNG FREIBEVEGLCHER TIERE. W. Jechorek and E. von Holst in *Die Naturwissenschaften*, Vol. 43, Part 19, page 455; 1956.

PLEASURE CENTERS IN THE BRAIN. James Olds in *Scientific American*, Vol. 195, No. 4, pages 105–116; October, 1956.

VOM WIRKUNGSGEFÜGE DER TRIEBE. Erich von Holst and Ursula von Saint Paul in *Die Naturwissenschaften*, Vol. 47, Part 18, pages 409–422; 1960.

WIRKUNGEN DER REIZUNGEN UND KOAGULATIONEN IN DEN STAMMGANGLEIN BEI STEREOTAKTISCHEN HIRNOPERATIONEN. R. Hassler and T. Riechert in *Der Nervenarzt*, Vol. 32, No. 3, pages 97–109; March, 1961.

ZENTRALNERVENSYSTEM. Erich von Holst in *Fortschritte der Zoologie*, Vol. 11, pages 245–275; 1958.

## 8. Chemical Stimulation of the Brain

### The Author

ALAN E. FISHER is associate professor of psychology at the University of Pittsburgh. Fisher was graduated from Pennsylvania State University in 1949 and received an M.S. and a Ph.D. in psychology there in 1952 and 1955 respectively. He was a U.S. Public

Health Service Fellow at McGill University from 1954 to 1955 and at the University of Wisconsin from 1955 to 1957. He joined the Pittsburgh faculty in 1957.

### Bibliography

CHEMICAL TRACING OF NEURAL PATHWAYS MEDIATING THE THIRST DRIVE. Alan E. Fisher and John N. Coury in *Thirst: Proceedings of the First International Symposium on Thirst in the Regulation of Body Water,* edited by Matthew J. Wayner. Pergamon Press, 1964.

MATERNAL AND SEXUAL BEHAVIOR INDUCED BY INTRACRANIAL CHEMICAL STIMULATION. Alan E. Fisher in *Science,* Vol. 124, No. 3214, pages 228–229; August, 1956.

## 9. Sex Differences in the Brain

### The Author

SEYMOUR LEVINE is associate professor of psychology in the department of psychiatry at the Stanford University School of Medicine. A native of Brooklyn, N.Y., he obtained a bachelor's de-

gree at the University of Denver in 1948 and a Ph.D. at New York University in 1952. From 1953 to 1956 he was a postdoctoral fellow and research associate at the Institute for Psychosomatic and Psychiatric Research of the Michael Reese Hospital in Chicago. He then spent four years as assistant professor of psychiatry at Ohio State University and two years as a fellow of the Foundations' Fund for Research in Psychiatry and an associate of Geoffrey W. Harris at the Institute of Psychiatry of the University of London. He took his present position in 1962.

### Bibliography

HORMONES AND SEXUAL BEHAVIOR. William C. Young, Robert W. Goy and Charles H. Phoenix in *Science,* Vol. 143, No. 3603, pages 212–218; January 17, 1964.

SEX HORMONES, BRAIN DEVELOPMENT AND BRAIN FUNCTION. Geoffrey W. Harris in *Endocrinology,* Vol. 75, No. 4, pages 627–651; October, 1964.

SEXUAL DIFFERENTIATION OF THE BRAIN AND ITS EXPERIMENTAL CONTROL. G. W. Harris and S. Levine in *The Journal of Physiology,* Vol. 181, No. 2, pages 379–400; November, 1965.

## 10. The Reproductive Behavior of Ring Doves

### The Author

DANIEL S. LEHRMAN is professor of psychology and director of the Institute of Animal Behavior at Rutgers University. Lehrman was graduated from the City College of the City of New York in 1947 and obtained a Ph.D. in psychology from New York University in 1954. He has been a member of the Rutgers faculty since 1950.

### Bibliography

CONTROL OF BEHAVIOR CYCLES IN REPRODUCTION. Daniel S. Lehrman in *Social Behavior and Organization among Vertebrates,* edited by William Etkin. The University of Chicago Press, 1964.

HORMONAL REGULATION OF PARENTAL BEHAVIOR IN BIRDS AND INFRAHUMAN MAMMALS. Daniel S. Lehrman in *Sex and Internal Secretions.* Edited by William C. Young. Williams & Wilkins Company, 1961.

INTERACTION OF HORMONAL AND EXPERIMENTAL INFLUENCES ON DEVELOPMENT OF BEHAVIOR. Daniel S. Lehrman in *Roots of Behavior,* edited by E. L. Bliss. Harper & Row, Publishers, 1962.

# PART III. EXPERIENTIAL DETERMINANTS OF ANIMAL BEHAVIOR

## 11. Stimulation in Infancy

### The Author
(See article number 9.)

### Bibliography

DIFFERENTIAL MATURATION OF AN ADRENAL RESPONSE TO COLD STRESS IN RATS MANIPULATED IN INFANCY. Seymour Levine, Morton Alpert and George W. Lewis in *The Journal of Comparative and Physiological Psychology,* Vol. 51, No. 6, pages 774–777; December, 1958.

EFFECTS OF EARLY EXPERIENCE UPON THE BEHAVIOR OF ANIMALS. Frank A. Beach and Julian Jaynes in *Psychological Bulletin,* Vol. 51, No. 3, pages 239–263; May, 1954.

A FURTHER STUDY OF INFANTILE HANDLING AND ADULT AVOIDANCE LEARNING. Seymour Levine in *Journal of Personality,* Vol. 25, No. 1, pages 70–80; September, 1956.

INFANTILE EXPERIENCE AND RESISTANCE TO PHYSIOLOGICAL STRESS. Seymour Levine in *Science,* Vol. 126, No. 3,270, page 405; August 30, 1957.

## 12. Love in Infant Monkeys

### The Author

HARRY F. HARLOW is George Cary Comstock Professor of Psychology and head of the Primate Laboratory at the

University of Wisconsin. He received his A.B. from Stanford University in 1927 and his Ph.D. from the same institution in 1930, the year in which he joined the Wisconsin faculty. Harlow is currently president of the American Psychological Association.

### Bibliography

THE DEVELOPMENT OF AFFECTIONAL RESPONSES IN INFANT MONKEYS. Harry F. Harlow and Robert R. Zimmermann in *Proceedings of the American Philosophical Society,* Vol. 102, pages 501–509; 1958.

THE NATURE OF LOVE. Harry F. Harlow in *American Psychologist,* Vol. 12, No. 13, pages 673–685; 1958.

### 13. "Imprinting" in Animals

*The Author*

ECKHARD H. HESS is associate professor of psychology at the University of Chicago. The work on imprinting which he carries on there is a part of his larger campaign of research on the experience of infant animals and how it affects their behavior. Hess was born in Germany, graduated from Blue Ridge College and acquired M.A. and Ph.D. degrees from the Carnegie Institution of Washington's Department of Embryology, located in Balimore.

*Bibliography*

EFFECTS OF MEPROBAMATE ON IMPRINTING IN WATERFOWL. Eckhard H. Hess in *Annals of The New York Academy of Sciences*, Vol. 67, Article 10, pages 724–733; May 9, 1957.
KING SOLOMON'S RING: NEW LIGHT ON ANIMAL WAYS. Konrad Z. Lorenz. Thomas Y. Crowell, 1952.
LEARNING AND INSTINCT IN ANIMALS. William Homan Thorpe. Harvard University Press, 1956.

### 14. The Social Order of Chickens

*The Author*

A. M. GUHL is a Kansas State College zoologist who has specialized in the behavior of chickens. He attended North Central College in Illinois, taught school for several years, then went to the University of Chicago, where he took a Ph.D. in 1943. He was interested in the endocrine glands of birds and was studying the comparative anatomy of hawks and owls. At about that time the University of Chicago zoologist W. C. Allee and his students began working on the social behavior of chickens and other vertebrates, and "for some unexplainable reason," Guhl says, "this field fascinated me." He joined the Kansas State faculty in 1943 and was appointed professor in 1950.

*Bibliography*

AGGRESSIVE BEHAVIOR AMONG VERTEBRATES, N. E. Collias in *Physiological Zoology*, Vol. 17, No. 1, pages 83–123; January, 1944.
SOCIAL BEHAVIOR OF THE DOMESTIC FOWL. A. M. Guhl. Kansas Agricultural Experiment Station, 1953.
SOME MEASURABLE EFFECTS OF SOCIAL ORGANIZATION IN FLOCKS OF HENS. A. M. Guhl and W. C. Allee in *Physiological Zoology*, Vol. 17, No. 3, pages 320–347; July, 1944.

## PART IV. LEARNING AND MEMORY

### 15. Place-Learning

*The Author*

HENRY GLEITMAN is professor of psychology at Cornell University. Born in Leipzig, Germany, in 1925, Gleitman received a B.S. from the College of the City of New York in 1946 and a Ph.D. in psychology from the University of California at Berkeley in 1949. Shortly thereafter he joined the faculty of Swarthmore College, where he conducted the experiments described in this article. In July of this year he was appointed professor of psychology at Cornell, where he is currently studying memory and forgetting in various laboratory animals.

*Bibliography*

PLACE LEARNING WITHOUT PRIOR PERFORMANCE. Henry Gleitman in *Journal of Comparative and Physiological Psychology*, Vol. 48, No. 2, pages 77–79; April, 1955.
STUDIES IN SPATIAL LEARNING: PART I, ORIENTATION AND THE SHORT-CUT. E. C. Tolman, B. F. Ritchie and D. Kalish in *Journal of Experimental Psychology*, Vol. 36, No. 1, pages 13–24; February, 1946.
STUDIES IN SPATIAL LEARNING: PART II, PLACE LEARNING VERSUS RESPONSE LEARNING. E. C. Tolman, B. F. Ritchie and D. Kalish in *Journal of Experimental Psychology*, Vol. 36, No. 3, pages 221–229; June, 1946.

### 16. What Is Memory?

*The Author*

RALPH W. GERARD is professor of neurophysiology at the Mental Health Research Institute of the University of Michigan. He was born in Harvey, Ill., in 1900. He studied at the University of Chicago, taking his Ph.D. in 1921, and then got an M.D. at the Rush Medical College in 1925. After his internship he spent two years in London and Berlin as a National Research Fellow, returning in 1928 to the University of Chicago, where he later became professor of physiology. Gerard has worked chiefly in the field of neurophysiology, investigating the chemical and electrical characteristics of the nerves and brain during activity, growth and injury. During the war he was director of the physiological section at Edgewood Arsenal, where he did research on the effects of phosgene.

*Bibliography*

THE ELECTRICAL ACTIVITY OF THE NERVOUS SYSTEM. Mary A. Brazier. The Macmillan Company, 1951.
PSYCHOLOGY OF HUMAN LEARNING. John Alexander McGeogh. Longmans Green, 1951.
HANDBOOK OF EXPERIMENTAL PSYCHOLOGY. S. S. Stevens. John Wiley & Sons, Inc., 1951.

### 17. Learning in the Octopus

*The Author*

BRIAN B. BOYCOTT is reader in zoology at University College London. He is a graduate of Birkbeck College London, which he attended while employed as a laboratory technician at the National Institute for Medical Research. After a short time lecturing in zoology at University College he spent five years as a research assistant in the anatomy department, returning to the zoology department in 1952. Boycott writes that in addition to his investigations of the octopus he is "currently working on the vertebrate retina and changes in the structure of the brain of hibernating mammals." Although he bears a surname that has entered the language as both a common noun and a verb, he is not related to the Captain Charles Boycott whose activities were responsible for the origin of the word.

*Bibliography*

BRAIN AND BEHAVIOR IN CEPHALOPODS. M. J. Wells. Stanford University Press, 1962.

THE FUNCTIONAL ORGANIZATION OF THE BRAIN OF THE CUTTLEFISH SEPIA OFFICINALIS. B. B. Boycott in *Proceedings of the Royal Society of London*, Series B, Vol. 153, No. 953, pages 503–534; February, 1961.

IN SEARCH OF THE ENGRAM. K. S. Lashley in *Physiological Mechanisms in Animal Behaviour*. Symposia of the Society for Experimental Biology, No. 4, 1950.

A MODEL OF THE BRAIN. J. Z. Young. Oxford University Press, 1964.

SOME ESSENTIALS OF NEURAL MEMORY SYSTEMS: PAIRED CENTRES THAT REGULATE AND ADDRESS THE SIGNALS OF THE RESULTS OF ACTION. J. Z. Young in *Nature*, Vol. 198, No. 4881, pages 626–632; May, 1963.

## 18. Short-Term Memory

### The Author

LLOYD R. PETERSON is professor of psychology at Indiana University. He is a native of Minneapolis and was graduated from Gustavus Adolphus College in St. Peter, Minn., in 1944. He obtained master's and doctor's degrees from the University of Minnesota in 1951 and 1954 respectively. Peterson has been at Indiana University since 1954 except for the academic year 1964–1965, when he was visiting professor at the University of California at Berkeley and a research psychologist at the Institute of Human Learning there. His research interests include not only short-term memory but also the processes involved in learning and thinking. In some of his work Peterson has had the assistance of his wife, Margaret Jean Peterson, who received a Ph.D. in psychology at the University of Minnesota in 1955.

*Bibliography*

IMMEDIATE MEMORY IN SEQUENTIAL TASKS. Michael I. Posner in *Psychological Bulletin*, Vol. 60, No. 4, pages 333–349; July, 1963.

IMPLICATIONS OF SHORT-TERM MEMORY FOR A GENERAL THEORY OF MEMORY. Arthur W. Melton in *Journal of Verbal Learning and Verbal Behavior*, Vol. 2, No. 1, pages 1–21; July, 1963.

SHORT-TERM MEMORY AND INCIDENTAL LEARNING. Leo Postman in *Categories of Human Learning*, edited by Arthur W. Melton. Academic Press Inc., 1964.

SHORT-TERM MEMORY AND PAIRED-ASSOCIATE LEARNING. Bennet B. Murdock, Jr., in *Journal of Verbal Learning and Verbal Behavior*, Vol. 2, No. 4, pages 320–328; November, 1963.

SHORT-TERM VERBAL MEMORY AND LEARNING. Lloyd R. Peterson in *Psychological Review*, Vol. 73, No. 3, pages 193–207; May, 1966.

# PART V. COMPARATIVE ASPECTS OF LEARNING

## 19. The Evolution of Intelligence

### The Author

M. E. BITTERMAN is professor of psychology and chairman of the department of psychology at Bryn Mawr College. He is a native New Yorker who was graduated from New York University in 1941; the following year he obtained an M.A. from Columbia University and in 1945 he received a Ph.D. at Cornell University. During World War II he was involved in the training of specialized military personnel. Subsequently he taught at Cornell and the University of Texas. He spent a year as a visiting professor at the University of California at Berkeley and two years as a member of the Institute for Advanced Study before going to Bryn Mawr in 1957. Since 1955 he has been coeditor of the *American Journal of Psychology*. He conceived the general plan of his present work in the comparative intelligence of animals as an undergraduate but has pursued it intensively only in the past few years.

*Bibliography*

ANIMAL INTELLIGENCE. E. I. Thorndike. The Macmillan Company, 1911.

SOME COMPARATIVE PSYCHOLOGY. M. E. Bitterman, Jerome Wodinsky and Douglas K. Candland in *American Journal of Psychology*, Vol. 71, No. 1, pages 94–110; March, 1958.

TOWARD A COMPARATIVE PSYCHOLOGY OF LEARNING. M. E. Bitterman in *American Psychologist*, Vol. 15, No. 11, pages 704–712; November, 1960.

## 20. The Intelligence of Elephants

### The Author

B. RENSCH is professor of zoology and director of the Zoological Institute of the University of Münster in Germany, where he conducted the psychological experiments described in his article. After graduating from the University of Halle, he spent 11 years at the University of Berlin's Zoological Museum as head of the mollusk department. In 1937 he went to Münster to direct the Biological Museum there. He recently participated in scientific symposia in New York and in Brisbane, Australia.

## 21. Learning to Think

### The Authors

HARRY F. HARLOW is George Cary Comstock Professor of Psychology and head of the Primate Laboratory at the University of Wisconsin. He received his A.B. from Stanford University in 1927 and his Ph.D. from the same institution in 1930, the year in which he joined the Wisconsin faculty. He is currently president of the American Psychological Association. The Harlows, co-authors of this article, have four children.

### Bibliography

THE NATURE OF LEARNING SETS. H. F. Harlow in *Psychological Review*, Vol. 56, No. 1, pages 51–65; 1949.
THE MENTALITY OF APES. W. Köhler. Harcourt, Brace & Co., 1925.

# PART VI. SENSORY STIMULATION, MOTIVATION, AND EMOTION

## 22. Curiosity in Monkeys

### The Author

ROBERT A. BUTLER is a research psychologist at the Audiology and Speech Correction Center of the Walter Reed Army Hospital. He took up the study of psychology after the last war, receiving his Ph.D. from the University of Chicago in 1951. Before going to his present position he taught at the University of Wisconsin, where he began his work on curiosity in the Primate Laboratory. He is continuing the research at Walter Reed.

## 23. The Pathology of Boredom

### The Author

WOODBURN HERON is assistant professor of psychology at McGill University. He was born in Jamaica, B.W.I., in 1926 and received his undergraduate and graduate training at McGill, where at the suggestion of the psychologist D. O. Hebb he became one of the first to work on the problem of perceptual isolation.

### Bibliography

EFFECTS OF DECREASED VARIATION IN THE SENSORY ENVIRONMENT. W. H. Bexton, W. Heron and T. H. Scott in *Canadian Journal of Psychology*, Vol. 8, No. 2, pages 70–76; June, 1954.
THE MAMMAL AND HIS ENVIRONMENT. D. O. Hebb in *The American Journal of Psychiatry*, Vol. 111, No. 11, pages 826–831; May, 1955.

VISUAL DISTURBANCES AFTER PROLONGED PERCEPTUAL ISOLATION. Woodburn Heron, B. K. Doane and T. H. Scott in *Canadian Journal of Psychology*, Vol. 10, No. 1, pages 13–18; March, 1956.

## 24. Pleasure Centers in the Brain

### The Author

JAMES OLDS is engaged in physiological and behavioral studies at the University of California at Los Angeles. He was born in Chicago in 1922, attended the University of Wisconsin, St. Johns College at Annapolis, and Amherst College, with three years out for the U. S. Army, and went to Harvard for his Ph.D. in social psychology. His wife received a doctorate in philosophy at Radcliffe in the same year. Olds later studied physiological psychology for two years with D. O. Hebb at McGill University. There he began the series of experiments discussed in his article.

### Bibliography

THE BEHAVIOR OF ORGANISMS: AN EXPERIMENTAL ANALYSIS. B. F. Skinner. Appleton-Century-Crofts, Inc., 1938.
DIENCEPHALON. Walter Rudolf Hess. Grune & Stratton, Inc., 1954.
PSYCHOSOMATIC DISEASE AND THE "VISCERAL BRAIN": RECENT DEVELOPMENTS BEARING ON THE PAPEZ THEORY OF EMOTION. Paul D. MacLean in *Psychosomatic Medicine*, Vol. 11, pages 338–353; 1949.

## 25. Ulcers in "Executive" Monkeys

### The Author

JOSEPH V. BRADY is head of the department of experimental psychology in the Neuropsychiatry Division of the Walter Reed Army Institute of Research, Washington, D.C. Born in Brooklyn in 1922, he received his B.S. from Fordham University in 1943. While still an undergraduate, Brady had joined the R.O.T.C.; in 1945 he was sent overseas and commanded an infantry platoon in Europe. He remained in the Army after the war, and spent two years in Germany as Chief Clinical Psychologist in the European Command. The Army then sent him to the University of Chicago, where his interest soon shifted from clinical to experimental psychology. He received his Ph.D. in 1951; his thesis concerned emotional behavior in rats. Now a major in the Army's Medical Department, Brady presently works on the experimental analysis of behavior, with special reference to its physical concomitants.

### Bibliography

EVIDENCE ON THE GENESIS OF PEPTIC ULCER IN MAN. Stewart Wolf and Harold Wolff in *The Journal of the American Medical Association*, Vol. 120, No. 9, pages 670–675; October 31, 1942.
AN EXPERIMENTAL METHOD OF PRODUCING GASTRIC ULCERS. William L. Sawrey and John D. Weisz in *Journal of Comparative and Physiological Psychology*, Vol. 49, No. 3, pages 269–270; June, 1956.

## 26. The Physiology of Fear and Anger

### The Author

DANIEL H. FUNKENSTEIN is director of clinical psychiatry at Boston Psychopathic Hospital and an associate in psychiatry at the Harvard Medical School. After taking his M.D. at the Medical College of Louisiana in 1934, he trained in surgery at Barnes Hospital and Washington University in Saint Louis, but his work in the Air Force in World War II turned him from sur-gery to psychiatry. On his return to civilian life he obtained psychiatric training and began to investigate stress reactions in the laboratory. Most of the research he reports in his article was financed by grants from the 33rd-degree Scottish Rite in the U. S. Northern Masonic Jurisdiction through the National Association of Mental Health.

### Bibliography

THE DIRECTION OF ANGER DURING A LABORATORY STRESS-INDUCING SITUATION. Daniel H. Funkenstein, Stanley H. King and Margaret Drolette in *Psychosomatic Medicine*, Vol. 16, No. 5, pages 404–413; September-October, 1954.

NOR-EPINEPHRINE-LIKE AND EPINEPHRINE-LIKE SUBSTANCES IN PSYCHOTIC AND PSYCHONEUROTIC PATIENTS. Daniel H. Funkenstein, Milton Greenblatt and Harry C. Solomon in *The American Journal of Psychiatry*, Vol. 108, No. 9, pages 652–662; March, 1952.

THE WISDOM OF THE BODY. Walter B. Cannon. W. W. Norton & Company, Inc., 1932.

# PART VII. NEURAL SYSTEMS AND BEHAVIOR

## 27. How Cells Receive Stimuli

### The Authors

WILLIAM H. MILLER, FLOYD RATLIFF and H. K. HARTLINE have collaborated in studies of visual receptors and neural interaction at the Rockefeller Institute since 1955. Miller, assistant professor of biophysics, is a graduate of Haverford College and received his M.D. degree from Johns Hopkins University in 1954. He first began doing research on the eyes of invertebrates in Hartline's laboratory at Johns Hopkins. After an internship at Baltimore City Hospital, Miller joined the Rockefeller Institute in 1955. Ratliff, associate professor of biophysics, took a B.A. at Colorado College in 1947 and a Ph.D. in psychology at Brown University in 1950. He went to Johns Hopkins the following year on a National Research Council fellowship to study retinal interaction with Hartline. Before going to the Rockefeller Institute in 1954, Ratliff was assistant professor of psychology at Harvard University. Hartline joined the Rockefeller Institute as Member and professor in 1953. A graduate of Lafayette College, he took his M.D. degree at Johns Hopkins in 1927, did graduate work in physics at the same institution and from 1931 to 1949 was a staff member of the Johnson Research Foundation at the University of Pennsylvania. He went to Johns Hopkins in 1949 as professor and chairman of the newly established Jenkins Department of Biophysics.

### Bibliography

INITIATION OF IMPULSES AT RECEPTORS. J. A. B. Gray in *Handbook of Physiology, Vol. I, Section I: Neurophysiology*, pages 123–145. American Physiological Society, 1959.

THE NEURAL MECHANISMS OF VISION. H. K. Hartline in *The Harvey Lectures, 1941–1942*, Series 37, pages 39–68; 1942.

RECEPTORS AND SENSORY PERCEPTION. R. Granit. Yale University Press, 1955.

SENSORY COMMUNICATION. Edited by Walter A. Rosenblith. John Wiley & Sons, Inc., 1961.

## 28. How Cells Communicate

### The Author

BERNHARD KATZ is professor and head of the biophysics department of University College London. Born in Leipzig, Germany, in 1911, Katz acquired an M.D. degree at the University of Leipzig in 1934. From 1935 to 1939 he worked under the direction of A. V. Hill at University College, where he received a Ph.D. in 1938. Katz served with the Royal Air Force in the Pacific from 1942 to 1945 and then returned to University College. A Fellow of the Royal Society since 1952, Katz was Herter Lecturer at Johns Hopkins University in 1958 and Dunham Lecturer at Harvard University this past year.

### Bibliography

BIOPHYSICAL ASPECTS OF NEURO-MUSCULAR TRANSMISSION. J. del Castillo and B. Katz in *Progress in Biophysics and Biophysical Chemistry*, Vol. 6, pages 121–170; 1956.

IONIC MOVEMENT AND ELECTRICAL ACTIVITY IN GIANT NERVE FIBRES. A. L. Hodgkin in *Proceedings of the Royal Society*, Series B, Vol. 148, No. 930, pages, 1–37; January 1, 1958.

MICROPHYSIOLOGY OF THE NEURO-MUSCULAR JUNCTION, A PHYSIOLOGICAL "QUANTUM OF ACTION" AT THE MYONEURAL JUNCTION. Bernhard Katz in *Bulletin of the Johns Hopkins Hospital*, Vol. 102, No. 6, pages 275–312; June, 1958.

THE PHYSIOLOGY OF NERVE CELLS. John Carew Eccles. The Johns Hopkins Press, 1957.

## 29. Patterns of Dreaming

### The Author

NATHANIEL KLEITMAN retired this year as professor of physiology at the University of Chicago. Born and raised in Russia, he came to the U. S. in 1915 to study at the College of the City of New York, receiving his B.S. in 1919. After acquiring his M.A. at Columbia University in 1920 and his Ph.D. at the University of Chicago in 1923, he went abroad to study at the universities of Utrecht and Paris, returning in

1925 to join the faculty at Chicago, where he has taught for the past 35 years. Kleitman has been "thinking of going to Bali, whose inhabitants," he says, "have strange sleeping habits. I devote my free time to writing up data gathered many years ago and to the preparation of a revised edition of my 21-year-old monograph *Sleep and Wakefulness*."

## Bibliography

A COMPARISON OF "DREAMERS" AND "NONDREAMERS": EYE MOVEMENTS, ELECTROENCEPHALOGRAMS AND THE RECALL OF DREAMS. Donald R. Goodenough, Arthur Shapiro, Melvin Holden and Leonard Steinschriber in *The Journal of Abnormal and Social Psychology*, Vol. 59, No. 3, pages 295–302; November, 1959.

CYCLIC VARIATIONS IN EEG DURING SLEEP AND THEIR RELATION TO EYE MOVEMENTS, BODY MOTILITY, AND DREAMING. William Dement and Nathaniel Kleitman in *Electroencephalography and Clinical Neurophysiology*, Vol. 9, No. 4, pages 673–690; November, 1957.

THE RELATION OF EYE MOVEMENTS DURING SLEEP TO DREAM ACTIVITY: AN OBJECTIVE METHOD FOR THE STUDY OF DREAMING. W. Dement and N. Kleitman in *Journal of Experimental Psychology*, Vol. 53, No. 5, pages 339–346; May, 1957.

STUDIES IN PSYCHOPHYSIOLOGY OF DREAMS. I: EXPERIMENTAL EVOCATION OF SEQUENTIAL DREAM EPISODES. Edward A. Wolpert and Harry Trosman in *A.M.A. Archives of Neurology and Psychiatry*, Vol. 79, No. 4, pages 603–606; April, 1958.

TWO TYPES OF OCULAR MOTILITY OCCURRING IN SLEEP. E. Aserinsky and N. Kleitman in *Journal of Applied Physiology*, Vol. 18, No. 1, pages 1–10; July, 1955.

## 30. The Reticular Formation

### The Author

J. D. FRENCH followed his father's example in becoming a brain surgeon. He is director of research at the Veterans Administration Hospital in Long Beach, Calif., as well as professor of surgery at the University of California School of Medicine at Los Angeles. After taking an M.D. at the University of Southern California School of Medicine, he served as intern and resident at Strong Memorial Hospital in Rochester, N.Y., and joined the teaching staff of the University of Rochester School of Medicine in 1943. In 1948 he returned to California to become head of neurosurgery at the Long Beach veterans' hospital.

### Bibliography

BRAIN MECHANISMS AND CONSCIOUSNESS. J. F. Delafresnaye. Blackwell Scientific Publications, 1954.

BRAIN STEM RETICULAR FORMATION AND ACTIVATION OF THE EEG. G. Moruzzi and H. W. Magoun in *Electroencephalography and Clinical Neurophysiology*, Vol. 1, No. 4, pages 455–473; November, 1949.

PATTERNS OF ORGANIZATION IN THE CENTRAL NERVOUS SYSTEM. Edited by Philip Bard. The Williams & Wilkins Company, 1952.

SPASTICITY: THE STRETCH-REFLEX AND EXTRAPYRAMIDAL SYSTEMS. H. W. Magoun and Ruth Rhines. Charles C Thomas, 1947.

## 31. The Great Cerebral Commissure

### The Author

R. W. SPERRY is Hixon Professor of Psychobiology at the California Institute of Technology. Sperry received an A.B. and an M.A. in psychology from Oberlin College in 1935 and 1937 respectively and a Ph.D. in zoology from the University of Chicago in 1941. He did research at Harvard University and at the Yerkes Laboratories of Primate Biology before joining the Chicago faculty in 1946. From 1952 to 1954 he was chief of developmental neurology for the National Institutes of Health. He has been at Cal Tech since 1954. Sperry's work has covered various aspects of the central nervous system, including the mechanisms involved in perception, learning and memory.

### Bibliography

CEREBRAL ORGANIZATION AND BEHAVIOR. R. W. Sperry in *Science*, Vol. 133, No. 3466, pages 1749–1757; June, 1961.

CONFERENCE ON INTERHEMISPHERIC RELATIONS AND CEREBRAL DOMINANCE, edited by Vernon B. Mountcastle. The Johns Hopkins Press, Baltimore, 1962.

CORPUS CALLOSUM AND VISUAL GNOSIS. R. E. Myers in *Brain Mechanisms and Learning*, a symposium edited by J. F. Delafresnaye. Blackwell Scientific Publications, 1961.

SOME FUNCTIONAL EFFECTS OF SECTIONING THE CEREBRAL COMMISSURES IN MAN. M. S. Gazzaniga, J. E. Bogen and R. W. Sperry in *Proceedings of the National Academy of Sciences*, Vol. 48, No. 10, pages 1765–1769; October, 1962.

# PART VIII. PHYSIOLOGICAL BASES OF SENSATION AND PERCEPTION

## 32. The Ear

### The Author

GEORG VON BÉKÉSY, winner of the 1961 Nobel Prize in medicine for the work described in this article, is a senior research fellow in psychophysics at Harvard University. Born in Hungary in 1899, he studied at the universities of Berne and Budapest and received a Ph.D. from the latter in 1923. Besides the teaching posts which he held at the University of Budapest, von Békésy was for many years a research scientist with the Hungarian telephone system. His work on adapting telephone receivers to the mechanics of the ear led eventually to a revision of the theory of hearing. After leaving Hungary in 1947 he was for several years a research professor at the Karolinska Institute in Stockholm as well as a fellow at Harvard. In 1955 he received the Howard Crosby Warren Medal of the Society of Experimental Psychologists.

### Bibliography

THE EARLY HISTORY OF HEARING— OBSERVATIONS AND THEORIES. Georg v. Békésy and Walter A. Rosenblith in *The Journal of the Acoustical Society of America*, Vol. 20, No. 6, pages 727–748; November, 1948.

HEARING: ITS PSYCHOLOGY AND PHYSIOLOGY. Stanley Smith Stevens and Hallowell Davis. John Wiley & Sons, Inc., 1938.

PHYSIOLOGICAL ACOUSTICS. Ernest Glen Wever and Merle Lawrence. Princeton University Press, 1954.

## 33. Auditory Localization

### The Author

MARK R. ROSENZWEIG is professor of psychology at the University of California. He received B.A. and M.A. degrees from the University of Rochester in 1943 and 1944 respectively. He spent the next two years in the Navy before continuing his work in the Psycho-acoustic Laboratory at Harvard University, where he acquired a Ph.D. in 1949. Joining the faculty of California as a physiological psychologist in 1950, Rosenzweig continued the research on the physiological mechanisms of auditory localization he had begun earlier at Harvard. His original interest in auditory perception has since led him to study various problems in speech, communication and the psychology of language. At the present time he is investigating the relationships between learning behavior and brain chemistry, a field of research he first entered in 1953.

### Bibliography

CORTICAL CORRELATES OF AUDITORY LOCALIZATION AND OF RELATED PERCEPTUAL PHENOMENA. Mark R. Rosenzweig in *The Journal of Comparative and Physiological Psychology*. Vol. 47, No. 4, pages 269–276; August, 1954.

## 34. The Visual Cortex of the Brain

### The Author

DAVID H. HUBEL is associate professor of neurophysiology and neuropharmacology at the Harvard Medical School. Born in Windsor, Ontario, in 1926, Hubel received a B.Sc. and an M.D. from McGill University in 1947 and 1951 respectively. He studied clinical neurology for three years at the Montreal Neurological Institute before coming to this country in 1954 to spend a year's residency in neurology at the Johns Hopkins Hospital. In 1955 he began neurophysiological research at the Walter Reed Army Institute of Research in Washington, and in 1960 he joined the Harvard faculty.

### Bibliography

DISCHARGE PATTERNS AND FUNCTIONAL ORGANIZATION OF MAMMALIAN RETINA. Stephen W. Kuffler in *Journal of Neurophysiology*, Vol. 16, No. 1, pages 37–68; January, 1953.

INTEGRATIVE PROCESS IN CENTRAL VISUAL PATHWAYS OF THE CAT. David H. Hubel in *Journal of the Optical Society of America*, Vol. 53, No. 1, pages 58–66; January, 1963.

RECEPTIVE FIELDS, BINOCULAR INTERACTION AND FUNCTIONAL ARCHITECTURE IN THE CAT'S VISUAL CORTEX. D. H. Hubel and T. N. Wiesel in *Journal of Physiology*, Vol. 160, No. 1, pages 196–154; January, 1962.

THE VISUAL PATHWAY, Ragnar Granit in *The Eye, Volume II: The Visual Process,* edited by Hugh Davson. Academic Press, 1962.

## 35. Vision in Frogs

### The Author

W. R. A. MUNTZ is a research fellow at St. Catherine's College of the University of Oxford. He also works at the Institute of Experimental Psychology at Oxford. A native of New Zealand, Muntz acquired a B.A. and a D.Phil. from Oxford in 1958 and 1962 respectively. His summers as a student were spent mostly at the Zoological Station in Naples doing research on the behavior of the octopus; he received his doctorate on the basis of this work. In 1961 he spent six months at the Research Laboratory of Electronics at the Massachusetts Institute of Technology, where he first became interested in frog vision. His research at Oxford on the development of vision in various amphibians is supported in part by the Nuffield Foundation and also by the U.S. Office of Naval Research.

### Bibliography

THE BIOLOGY OF THE AMPHIBIA. G. Kingsley Noble. Dover Publications, Inc., 1954.

EFFECTIVENESS OF DIFFERENT COLORS OF LIGHT IN RELEASING POSITIVE PHOTOTACTIC BEHAVIOR OF FROGS AND A POSSIBLE FUNCTION OF THE RETINAL PROJECTION TO THE DIENCEPHALON. W. R. A. Muntz in *Journal of Neurophysi-*

*ology*, Vol. 25, No. 6, pages 712–720; November, 1962.

SUMMATION AND INHIBITION IN THE FROG'S RETINA. H. B. Barlow in *The Journal of Physiology*, Vol. 119, No. 1, pages 69–88; January, 1953.

## 36. Taste Receptors

### The Author

EDWARD S. HODGSON is professor of zoology at Columbia University. He was born in Wilmington, Del., in 1928 and received his B.S. from Allegheny College at the age of 18. He did graduate work in sensory physiology under V. G. Dethier at Johns Hopkins University, acquired a Ph.D. in biology at that institution in 1951 and joined the faculty of Columbia later the same year. The research discussed in the present article was begun at Tufts University, where Hodgson worked for a year in the laboratory of Kenneth D. Roeder.

### Bibliography

CHEMORECEPTOR MECHANISMS. V. G. Dethier in *Molecular Structure and Functional Activity of Nerve Cells*, edited by R. G. Grenell and L. J. Mullins, pages 1–30. American Institute of Biological Sciences, 1956.

ELECTROPHYSIOLOGICAL STUDIES OF ARTHROPOD CHEMORECEPTION. III: CHEMORECEPTORS OF TERRESTRIAL AND FRESH-WATER ARTHROPODS. Edward S. Hodgson in *Biological Bulletin*, Vol. 115, No. 1, pages 114–125; August, 1958.

PROBLEMS IN INVERTEBRATE CHEMORECEPTION. Edward S. Hodgson in *The Quarterly Review of Biology*, Vol. 30, No. 4, pages 331–347; December, 1955.

# PART IX. DETERMINANTS OF PERCEPTION

## 37. The Perception of Pain

### The Author

RONALD MELZACK is assistant professor of psychology at the Massachusetts Institute of Technology and a member of the Research Laboratory of Electronics at that institution. He was born and raised in Montreal and received his B.S. and M.S. from McGill University in 1950 and 1951 respectively. After a year of research at the University of Chicago he returned to McGill, obtaining his Ph.D. in 1954. In the preceding year Melzack had read an article in SCIENTIFIC AMERICAN called "What Is Pain?" This led to correspondence with the author, W. K. Livingston, and to a fellowship in Livingston's laboratory at the University of Oregon Medical School. "My fellowship," Melzack writes, "was extended to permit me to spend three very happy years" at the laboratory. "They were years that had a profound influence on my thinking about pain, and about sensory perception in general." Melzack taught and studied abroad during the next two years, first as a visiting lecturer at University College London and then as a research fellow at the Institute of Physiology of the University of Pisa. He joined the faculty of M.I.T. in 1959.

### Bibliography

ANATOMIES OF PAIN. K. D. Keele. Blackwell Scientific Publications, 1957.

CORD CELLS RESPONDING TO TOUCH, DAMAGE AND TEMPERATURE OF SKIN. Patrick D. Wall in *Journal of Neurophysiology*, Vol. 23, No. 2, pages 197–210; March, 1960.

EFFECTS OF DISCRETE BRAIN STEM LESIONS IN CATS ON PERCEPTION OF NOXIOUS STIMULATION. Ronald Melzack, W. A. Stotler and W. K. Livingston in *Journal of Neurophysiology*, Vol. XXI, No. 4, pages 352–367; July, 1958.

MEASUREMENT OF SUBJECTIVE RESPONSES. Henry K. Beecher, Oxford University Press, 1959.

PAIN MECHANISMS. W. K. Livingston. The Macmillan Company, 1943.

RESPONSES EVOKED IN THE BRAIN STEM BY TOOTH STIMULATION. D. I. B. Kerr, F. P. Haugen and R. Melzack in *American Journal of Physiology*, Vol. 183, No. 2, pages 253–258; November, 1955.

## 38. The Origin of Form Perception

### The Author

ROBERT L. FANTZ is assistant clinical professor of psychology at Western Reserve University. Born in Muncie, Ind., in 1925. Fantz took two degrees at the University of Chicago, receiving his Ph.D. in 1954. As a graduate student he did research with Eckhard H. Hess, Austin H. Riesen and L. L. Thurstone and became particularly interested in the early development of vision in animals and humans. This interest, he says, "began perhaps with the study of D. O. Hebb's theory of perceptual development through learning, representing the culmination of the experimental-psychological approach in this area, and the work of Konrad Lorenz, N. Tinbergen and W. H. Thorpe, showing a high degree of innate perceptual organization in the instinctive behavior of animals."

### Bibliography

EFFECTS OF EARLY EXPERIENCE UPON THE BEHAVIOR OF ANIMALS. Frank A. Beach and Julian Jaynes in *Psychological Bulletin*, Vol. 51, No. 3, pages 239–263; May, 1954.

FORM PREFERENCES IN NEWLY HATCHED CHICKS. Robert L. Fantz in *The Journal of Comparative and Physiological Psychology*, Vol. 50, No. 5, pages 422–430; October, 1957.

ON THE STIMULUS SITUATION RELEASING THE BEGGING RESPONSE IN THE NEWLY HATCHED HERRING GULL CHICK. N. Tibergen and A. C. Perdeck in *Behavior*, Vol. 3, Part 1, pages 1–39; 1950.

PATTERN VISION IN YOUNG INFANTS. Robert L. Fantz in *The Psychological Record*, Vol. 8, pages 43–47; 1958.

THE PERCEPTION OF THE VISUAL WORLD. James J. Gibson. Houghton Mifflin Company, 1950.

## 39. Stabilized Images on the Retina

### The Author

ROY M. PRITCHARD is a research associate at McGill University in Montreal, where he is an investigator in the departments of psychology and physiology. Pritchard served with the Royal Air Force from 1950 to 1952; then he entered the University of Reading to study physics. At Reading he collaborated with R. W. Ditchburn in the development of the first system to compensate completely for all eye movements in stabilizing images on the retina. He taught at Reading Technical College from 1955 to 1957 and received his Ph.D. in physics the following year. After developing the stabilizing system discussed in his article, Pritchard became interested in applying it to problems of perception theory. He joined the staff of McGill in 1959.

### Bibliography

THE ORGANIZATION OF BEHAVIOR. D. O. Hebb. John Wiley & Sons, Inc., 1949.

VISUAL EFFECTS OF VARYING THE EXTENT OF COMPENSATION FOR EYE MOVEMENTS. Lorrin A. Riggs and S. Ülker Tulunay in *Journal of the Optical Society of America*, Vol. 9, No. 8, pages 741-745; August, 1959.

VISUAL PERCEPTION APPROACHED BY THE METHOD OF STABILIZED IMAGES. R. M. Pritchard, W. Heron and D. O. Hebb in *Canadian Journal of Psychology*, Vol. 14, No. 2, pages 67–77; 1960.

## 40. Plasticity in Sensory-Motor Systems

### The Author

RICHARD HELD is professor of experimental and developmental psychology at the Massachusetts Institute of Technology. As an undergraduate at Columbia University, from which he was graduated in 1943, he majored in science and engineering. Becoming interested in the work of the psychologist Wolfgang Köhler, he joined Köhler at Swarthmore College and obtained a master's degree in psychology there in 1948. Four years later he received a Ph.D. in experimental psychology from Harvard University. Held taught at Harvard and at Brandeis University before going to M.I.T. in 1962; he also spent a year at the Institute for Advanced Study in Princeton, N.J. He has been interested in questions of space perception for many years; his work with Köhler at Swarthmore was on electrical responses of the brain to visual stimulation.

### Bibliography

MOVEMENT-PRODUCED STIMULATION IN THE DEVELOPMENT OF VISUALLY GUIDED BEHAVIOR. Richard Held and Alan Hein in *Journal of Comparative & Physiological Psychol-ogy*, Vol. 56, No. 5, pages 872–876; October, 1963.

NEONATAL DEPRIVATION AND ADULT REARRANGEMENT: COMPLEMENTARY TECHNIQUES FOR ANALYZING PLASTIC SENSORY-MOTOR COORDINATIONS. Richard Held and Joseph Bossom in *The Journal of Comparative and Physiological Psychology*, Vol. 54, No. 1, pages 33–37; February, 1961.

PLASTICITY IN HUMAN SENSORIMOTOR CONTROL. Richard Held and Sanford J. Freedman in *Science*, Vol. 142, No. 3591, pages 455–462; October 25, 1963.

## 41. Experiments in Perception

### The Authors

WILLIAM H. ITTELSON and F. P. KILPATRICK were instructors in psychology at Princeton University when they wrote this article. Professor Hadley Cantril, their senior in the department, had revived interest in the work of Adelbert Ames, Jr., and had established a laboratory at Princeton to carry on his pioneering investigation into the psychology of perception. Ittelson is now profesor of psychology at Brooklyn College, and Kilpatrick is working in research and development at National Analysts, Inc. in Philadelphia.

### Bibliography

THE "WHY" OF MAN'S EXPERIENCE. Hadley Cantril. The Macmillan Company, 1950.

# PART X. DRUGS AND BEHAVIOR

## 42. The New Psychiatric Drugs

### The Author

HAROLD E. HIMWICH is director of research at the Thudichum Psychiatric Research Laboratory in the Galesburg State Research Hospital in Illinois. He grew up in New York, where both his parents were physicians, and was graduated from the College of the City of New York in 1915. After taking his M.D. at Cornell University in 1919, he interned at the Bellevue Hospital in New York City. From 1926 to 1946 he taught physiology and pharmacology at the Albany Medical College in New York State, then became chief of the Clinical Research Division of the Army Chemical Corps Laboratories in Maryland. His current research program ranges from basic studies of drugs to clinical evaluation of their effects.

## 43. "Truth" Drugs

### The Author

LAWRENCE ZELIC FREEDMAN is a research associate in psychiatry at the Yale University School of Medicine, but is presently on leave at the Center for Advanced Study in the Behavioral Sciences in Stanford, Calif. Born in 1919 in Gardner, Mass., he is a graduate of Tufts College, and acquired his M.D. there in 1944. After service in the Navy he became a resident in psychiatry at Yale and remained there to become an associate professor in 1957. He has also been a cooperating faculty member of the Yale Law School and chairman of the Yale Study Unit in Psychiatry and Law. He is a permanent nongovernmental delegate to the United Nations from the International Society of Criminology.

### Bibliography

DRUG-INDUCED REVELATION AND CRIMINAL INVESTIGATION. George H. Dession, Lawrence Z. Freedman, Richard G. Donnelly and Frederick C. Redlich in *Yale Law Journal*, Vol. 62, No. 3, Page 315–347; February, 1953.

EXPERIMENTAL INVESTIGATION INTO THE VALIDITY OF CONFESSIONS OBTAINED UNDER SODIUM AMYTAL NARCOSIS. Martin J. Gerson and Victor M. Victoroff in *Journal of Clinical Psychopathology*, Vol. 9, No. 3, pages 359–375; July, 1948.

MEN UNDER STRESS. Roy R. Grinker and John P. Spiegel. Blakiston, 1945.

NARCOANALYSIS AND TRUTH. Frederick C. Redlich, Leonard J. Ravitz, Jr., and George H. Dession in *The American Journal of Psychiatry*, Vol. 107, No. 8, pages 586–593; February, 1951.

## 44. Experimental Narcotic Addiction

### The Author

JAMES R. WEEKS works in the Pharmacology Research Laboratories of the Upjohn Company in Kalamazoo, Mich. After obtaining a BSc. in pharmacy from the University of Nebraska in 1941, Weeks served for four years as an officer of the Army Chemical Warfare Service. He returned to the University of Nebraska after the war and received an M.S. in pharmacology there in 1946. He acquired a Ph.D. in pharmacology from the University of Michigan in 1952. Weeks joined the faculty of the College of Pharmacy at Drake University in 1950 and was professor of pharmacology at that institution when he left to become a research associate at Upjohn in 1957. In addition to his work on narcotic addiction, Weeks does research mainly on hypertension and artificial heart stimulants.

### Bibliography

EXPERIMENTAL MORPHINE ADDICTION: METHOD FOR AUTOMATIC INTRAVENOUS INJECTIONS IN UNRESTRAINED RATS. James R. Weeks in *Science*, Vol. 138, No. 3537, pages 143–144; October, 1962.

OPIATE ADDICTION: PSYCHOLOGICAL AND NEUROPHYSIOLOGICAL ASPECTS IN RELATION TO CLINICAL PROBLEMS. Abraham Wikler. Charles C Thomas, Publisher, 1952.

## 45. Hallucinogenic Drugs

### The Authors

FRANK BARRON, MURRAY E. JARVIK and STERLING BUNNELL, JR. do research on this subject in New York and California. Barron is a research psychologist at the University of California's Institute of Personality Assessment and Research in Berkeley. A graduate of La Salle College in Philadelphia, he received an M.A. from the University of Minnesota in 1948 and a Ph.D. from the University of California at Berkeley in 1950. He has taught at Bryn Mawr College, Harvard University, Wesleyan University and the University of California. Jarvik is associate professor of pharmacology at the Albert Einstein College of Medicine and attending physician at Bellevue Hospital in New York. He was graduated from the City College of the City of New York in 1944 and subsequently acquired an M.A. in psychology from the University of California at Los Angeles in 1945, an M.D. from the University of California School of Medicine in 1951 and a Ph.D. in psychology from the University of California at Berkeley in 1952. He has taught and done research in the fields of pharmacology, psychology and neurophysiology at various institutions. Bunnell is a resident in psychiatry at the Mount Zion Medical Center in San Francisco. He received an M.D. from the University of California School of Medicine in 1958 and is currently working on a Ph.D. in neurophysiology at the University of California at Berkeley.

### Bibliography

THE CLINICAL PHARMACOLOGY OF THE HALLUCINOGENS. Erik Jacobsen in *Clinical Pharmacology and Therapeutics*, Vol. 4, No. 4, pages 480–504; July–August, 1963.

LYSERGIC ACID DIETHYLAMIDE (LSD-25) AND EGO FUNCTIONS. G. D. Klee in *Archives of General Psychiatry*, Vol. 8, No. 5, pages 461–474; May, 1963.

PROLONGED ADVERSE REACTIONS TO LYSERGIC ACID DIETHYLAMIDE. S. Cohen and K. S. Ditman in *Archives of General Psychiatry*, Vol. 8, No. 5, pages 475–480; May, 1963.

THE PSYCHOTOMIMETIC DRUGS: AN OVERVIEW. Jonathan O. Cole and Martin M. Katz in *The Journal of the American Medical Association*, Vol. 187, No. 10, pages 758–761; March, 1964.

# INDEX